D1285490

# PHILOSOPHY

## and the

# SCIENCE of BEHAVIOR

# THE CENTURY PSYCHOLOGY SERIES AWARD

# 1965

Each year Appleton-Century-Crofts gives an award for a distinguished manuscript in psychology selected by the Editors of the Century Psychology Series.
Considered will be works of two hundred typed pages or longer, which provide
a significant contribution to the field of psychology.

*Editors*
RICHARD M. ELLIOTT
GARDNER LINDZEY
KENNETH MacCORQUODALE

1962   BERNARD RIMLAND
*Infantile Autism: The Syndrome and its Implications for a
Neural Theory of Behavior*

1963   EDWARD E. JONES
*Ingratiation: A Social Psychological Analysis*

1964   JACK BLOCK
*The Challenge of Response Sets: Unconfounding Meaning,
Acquiescence, and Social Desirability in the MMPI*

MERLE B. TURNER

SAN DIEGO STATE COLLEGE

# PHILOSOPHY

## and the

# SCIENCE of BEHAVIOR

New York

APPLETON-CENTURY-CROFTS

DIVISION OF THE MEREDITH PUBLISHING COMPANY

Copyright © 1967 by MEREDITH PUBLISHING COMPANY

617–1

Library of Congress Card Number: 66–25267

PRINTED IN THE UNITED STATES OF AMERICA

E88878

## ACKNOWLEDGMENTS

Acknowledgments are made to the following sources for quotations and figures used in this book.

Page 8    Quote from AN INTRODUCTION TO PSYCHOLOGY by William McDougall by permission of Methuen & Co. Ltd., London.

Page 10    Quote from A. Comte, *The Positive Philosophy of Comte*. London: G. Bell & Sons Ltd., 1896.

Page 17    Quote from E. A. Burtt, *The Metaphysical Foundations of Science*. By permission of Routledge and Kegan Paul Ltd., London, and Humanities Press Inc., New York.

Pages 21, 22, 24, 25    Quotes from J. Locke, *An Essay Concerning Human Understanding,* edited by A. S. Pringle-Pattison. London: Oxford University Press, 1924.

Page 39    Quote from H. H. Joachim, *Descartes's Rules for the Direction of the Mind*. London: George Allen & Unwin Ltd., 1957.

Page 39    Quote from L. Roth, *Descartes' Discourse on Method*. London: Oxford University Press, 1937.

Page 40    Quote from B. Russell, *A Critical Exposition of the Philosophy of Leibnitz*. London: George Allen & Unwin Ltd., 1949.

Page 52    Quote from THE NATURE OF PHYSICAL REALITY by H. Margenau. Copyright 1950. McGraw-Hill Book Company. Used by permission.

Pages 54, 69    Quotes from E. Mach, *The Analysis of Sensations*. La Salle, Illinois: The Open Court Publishing Company, 1914.

Page 55    Quote from E. Mach, *The Science of Mechanics*. La Salle, Illinois: The Open Court Publishing Company, 1960.

Page 63    Quotes from E. Husserl, "Phenomenology and Anthropology," in *Philosophy and Phenomenological Research*, 1941, Vol. 1, pp. 1–14.

Pages 75, 76, 103    Quotes from B. Russell, *Mysticism and Logic*. London: George Allen & Unwin Ltd., 1917.

Page 78    Quote from *Realism and the Background of Phenomenology,* edited by R. Chisholm. New York: The Free Press, 1960.

Pages 87, 88, 125–126    Quotes from L. Wittgenstein, *Tractatus Logico-Philosophicus*. London: Routledge and Kegan Paul Ltd., 1922.

Pages 88–89, 90, 100    Quotes from B. Russell, *Logic and Knowledge*. London: George Allen & Unwin Ltd., 1956.

Page 101    Quotes from A MODERN INTRODUCTION TO LOGIC by L. S. Stebbing by permission of Methuen & Co. Ltd., London.

iv

Page 110     Quote from W. T. Stace, "Metaphysics and Meaning," in *Mind*, 1935, Vol. 44, pp. 417–438.

Pages 110, 111, 124–125     Quotes from A. J. Ayer, "Demonstration of the Impossibility of Metaphysics," in *Mind*, 1934, Vol. 43, pp. 335–345.

Page 114     Quote from M. Schlick, "Positivism and Realism" in *Logical Positivism*, edited by A. J. Ayer. New York: The Free Press, 1959.

Pages 114, 116, 126     Quotes from M. Schlick, "Meaning and Verification," in *Philosophical Review*, 1936, Vol. 45, pp. 339–369.

Pages 117, 118     Quotes from *Language, Truth and Logic* by Alfred J. Ayer, Dover Publications, Inc., New York.

Pages 119, 120     Quotes from A. J. Ayer, *The Problem of Knowledge*. Harmondsworth, England: Penguin Books, Ltd., 1956.

Pages 131, 132, 134     Quotes from R. Carnap, *The Logical Syntax of Knowledge*. London: Routledge and Kegan Paul Ltd., 1937.

Pages 135, 136, 137     Quotes from C. Hempel, "On the Logical Positivist's Theory of Truth," in *Analysis*, 1935, Vol. 2, pp. 49–59.

Page 139     Quote from N. R. Hanson, *Patterns of Discovery*. New York: Cambridge University Press, 1958.

Pages 141–142     Quote from R. Carnap, *Philosophy and Logical Syntax*. London: Routledge and Kegan Paul Ltd., 1935.

Page 160     Quote from M. Schlick, "Facts and Propositions," in *Analysis*, 1935, Vol. 2, pp. 65–70.

Page 160     Quote from B. von Juhos, "Empiricism and Physicalism," in *Analysis*, 1935, Vol. 2, pp. 79–92.

Pages 163, 271–272     Quotes from K. Popper, *The Logic of Scientific Discovery*. London: Hutchison Publishing Group Ltd., 1959.

Page 165     Quote from A. Kaplan, *The New World of Philosophy*. New York: Random House, 1961.

Page 180     Quotes from *The Value of Science* by Henri Poincaré, Dover Publications, Inc., New York.

Page 180     Quote from *Science and Hypothesis* by Henri Poincaré, Dover Publications, Inc., New York.

Pages 184–185     Quotes from P. A. M. Dirac, *Quantum Mechanics* (3rd ed.). London: Oxford University Press, 1947.

Pages 187, 188, 245, 264–265     Quotes from P. Duhem, *The Aim and Structure of Physical Theory*. Princeton, N.J.: Princeton University Press, 1954.

Page 198     Quote from MODERN LEARNING THEORY by William K. Estes *et al.*, Copyright 1954, by Appleton-Century-Crofts, Inc. Reprinted by permission of Appleton-Century-Crofts.

Pages 200, 201, 202     Quotes from PSYCHOLOGY: A STUDY OF A SCIENCE, Vol. II by S. Koch. Copyright 1959. McGraw-Hill Book Company. Used by permission.

Pages 211, 212     Quotes from P. K. Feyerabend, "Explanation, Reduction and Empiricism," in *Minnesota Studies in the Philosophy of Science*, Vol. III, edited by H. Feigl and J. J. Maxwell. Minneapolis, Minnesota: University of Minnesota Press, 1962.

Pages 214–215     Quote from C. I. Lewis, "A Pragmatic Conception of *a priori*," in *Journal of Philosophy*, 1923, Vol. 20, pp. 169–177.

Page 215     Quote from *Mind and the World Order* by C. I. Lewis, Dover Publications, Inc., New York.

Page 216     Quote from K. Koffka, *Principles of Gestalt Psychology*. New York, Harcourt, Brace & World, 1935.

Page 217     Quote from F. Hayek, *The Sensory Order*. Chicago: Chicago University Press, 1952; London: Routledge and Kegan Paul Ltd., 1952.

Page 228     Quote from *Foundations of Science* by Norman R. Campbell, Dover Publications, Inc., New York.

Pages 256, 324     Quotes from: PRINCIPLES OF BEHAVIOR by Clark L. Hull. Copyright 1943, by D. Appleton-Century Company, Inc. Reprinted by permission of Appleton-Century-Crofts.

Page 264     Quote from Suppes and Atkinson, *Markov Learning Models for Multiperson Interaction* (Stanford, Stanford University Press, 1960), p. 279.

Pages 275, 278     Quotes from C. Hempel and P. Oppenheim, "Studies in the Logic of Explanation," in *Philosophy of Science,* 1948, Vol. 15, pp. 135–175.

Page 277     Quote from M. Scriven, "Explanation, Prediction and Laws," in *Minnesota Studies in the Philosophy of Science,* Vol. III, edited by H. Feigl and J. C. Maxwell. Minneapolis, Minnesota: University of Minnesota Press, 1962.

Page 283     Quotes from C. D. Broad, *Mind and its Place in Nature*. London: Routledge and Kegan Paul Ltd., 1925.

Page 284     Quote from E. Nagel, *The Structure of Science*. New York: Harcourt, Brace & World, 1961.

Page 290     Quote from PRINCIPLES OF TOPOLOGICAL PSYCHOLOGY by K. Lewin. Copyright 1936. McGraw-Hill Book Company. Used by permission.

Pages 297, 298     Quotes from Henri Bergson: AN INTRODUCTION TO METAPHYSICS, copyright © 1949, 1955 by The Liberal Arts Press, Inc., reprinted by permission of the Liberal Arts Press Division of the Bobbs-Merrill Company, Inc.

Page 317     Quote from: THE BEHAVIOR OF ORGANISMS by B. F. Skinner. Copyright 1938, by D. Appleton-Century Company, Inc. Reprinted by permission of Appleton-Century-Crofts.

Page 320     Quote from P. Bridgman, "Remarks on the Present State of Operationism," in *Scientific Monthly,* 1954, Vol. 79, pp. 224–226.

Pages 320–321     Quote from A. Eddington, *Space, Time and Gravitation*. New York: Cambridge University Press, 1920.

Pages 323, 324     Quote from J. H. Woodger, *Language and Biology*. New York: Cambridge University Press, 1952.

Page 324     Quote from C. L. Hull, *Essentials of Behavior*. New Haven, Conn.: Yale University Press, 1951.

Pages 329–330     Quotes reprinted and illustration redrawn from *The Structural Basis of Behavior* by J. A. Deutsch by permission of the University of Chicago Press. © 1960 by the University of Chicago.

Pages 356–357     Quote from K. Spence, *Behavior and Conditioning*. New Haven, Conn.: Yale University Press, 1956.

Page 358     Illustration redrawn from Richard T. Weidner, Robert L. Sells, ELEMENTARY MODERN PHYSICS, © Copyright 1960, Allyn and Bacon, Inc., Boston. Reprinted with permission.

Page 368     Quotes from G. Ryle, *The Concept of Mind*. New York: Barnes & Noble, 1949; London: Hutchison Publishing Group Ltd., 1949.

Pages 382, 416     Quotes from *A Philosophical Essay on Probabilities* by Pierre Simon de Laplace, Dover Publications, Inc., New York.

Pages 402-403, 404     Quotes from B. Russell, *Human Knowledge*. London: George Allen and Unwin, Ltd., 1948; New York; Simon and Schuster, 1948.

Pages 409–410     Quotes from A. N. Kolmogorov, *Foundation of the Theory of Probability*. Copyright © 1950 and 1956, by CHELSEA PUBLISHING COMPANY, New York.

Pages 461, 462    Quotes from R. A. Fisher "Statistical Methods and Scientific Induction," in *Journal of the Royal Statistical Society,* Ser. B., 1955, Vol. 17, pp. 69–78.

Page 463    This material is taken from R. A. Fisher: *Statistical Methods and Scientific Inference,* published by Oliver & Boyd Ltd., Edinburgh, and by permission of the literary executor and publishers.

Page 471    Quote from M. Black, *Problems of Analysis.* Copyright 1954 by Cornell University. Used by permission of Cornell University Press.

Pages 475, 481, 482    Quotes from H. Reichenbach, *Theory of Probability.* Berkeley, Calif.: University of California Press, 1949.

# PREFACE

THE PRESENT BOOK examines certain aspects of behavioristic psychology in the context of the philosophy of science. Quite obviously the treatment must be limited. The subject matter of experimental and theoretical psychology is much too diversified to be subjected to extensive critical analysis. Here the argument is necessarily a restricted one, concentrating as it does on stimulus–response paradigms and on learning where psychologists have presumed to a theory worthy of the name.

As a science, psychology presents neither the formal maturity nor yet the quandary that has characterized modern physics. As a result, one hears the claim that psychology is not ready for its philosophy. Or, more often, one hears that philosophical analysis has little to contribute to the skills that the behavioral scientist must bring to his experimental problems. Such reactions are reasonable ones only if the psychologist has little to question concerning first principles or concerning the basics of his language. Frequently, however, the behaviorist overlooks the fact that his scientific credo was born in philosophical ferment, that whenever he defends the data of behavior as being the proper subject matter for the language of his science, he is making a commitment which itself is to be defended not as a subject of science but as one of philosophy in its technical sense. The logical positivists learned long ago that antimetaphysics, and all the protestations, lead nowhere if not to metaphysics. And the behaviorist who restricts the data language of his science to public observation, and does so out of his commitment to clarity, to communicability, and to systemic efficiency, shows his own philosophical hand as surely as the philosopher who often waits until his major work is done before he pens his prolegomena.

Perhaps an apology should be in order for undertaking such an extensive review of empiricistic philosophers as we find in Part I of this essay. It is not just that background is important. Experience and the data and language of experience are where the problems begin for the psychologist

ix

who would look critically at his own science. The contemporary behaviorist frequently vacillates between a radical, naïve empiricism and a facile operationism. Having disdained philosophy he has to a large degree forgotten how difficult has been the chore of analyzing the language of experience itself. Nothing short of a comprehensive review of empiricism will do. It is primarily through an examination of the English empiricists, of Kant, the phenomenalists, and especially the logical empiricists, that one is prepared to recognize how unobvious and how debatable is so simple a thing as a fact. One cannot divest the fact of its theoretic attribute, one cannot divorce theory from its apperceptive function.

In brief, a theme of this book is that theory is integral with all behavioral science, that, more explicitly, scientific fact cannot be rendered independent of theory. Furthermore, it is maintained that theory is not wholly the subject of an arbitrary option as befits the taste of the practitioner. Nor is one open to just any kind of operational license. To the criteria of parsimony and comprehensiveness in selecting from among our theoretical languages, we must add and emphasize that of reduction. The questions of alternative theoretical conceptions will be resolved by reducing the terms of one science to those of a more basic science. In some such sense there is a real convergence in scientific endeavor. It is in the reduction that one finds whatever sense of scientific realism is philosophically defensible.

The best summary accounts of the subject matters of this book are to be found in Chapters 1 and 7. Contemporary empiricism is covered in considerable detail in Chapters 4, 5, and 6. Part II of the book is devoted to the classical topics in the philosophy of science. Chapters 11 and 12 undertake the discussion, criticism, and defense of reductionism in psychology, a subject matter about which there is some contention.

Hardly any work in the philosophy of science would be complete without a discussion of inductive inference. Part III is therefore added in the way of an addendum. With the revival of the ideas of subjective probability and Bayesian inference among philosophers, statisticians, and scientists, the whole subject of inductive decision has become so extensive as to warrant a survey work in itself. Nevertheless, I have tried to include as much of the subject as is feasible to indicate that the Humean struggles to define and defend inductive decisions continue unabated.

Acknowledgments are due many people who contributed directly or indirectly to this work. I am indebted to Miss Mary Dowse, Mrs. Helen Ledbetter, and Mrs. Lynn White for the travails of typescript.

I am especially indebted to David Hawkins for the sense of realism that is invasive of pragmatism, to R. B. Braithwaite for the formal analysis of scientific thinking, to Norwood R. Hanson for the conceptual prescription of fact and theory, and to the late Charles L. Sherman, my first mentor in philosophy, for the Kantian critique of empiricism. I wish to express my appreciation to Stanley Weissman for his critical reading of selected parts of the manuscript.

I am indebted to the Literary Executor of the late Sir Ronald A. Fisher, F.R.S. Cambridge, Dr. Frank Yates, F.R.S. Rothamsted, and to Messrs. Oliver & Boyd Ltd., Edinburgh, for permission to reprint from their book *Statistical Methods and Inference.*

I am grateful to the Department of Psychology, the Moral Sciences Faculty, and the trustees of the University of Cambridge, for the use of library resources during the writing of parts of this book.

M. B. T.

# CONTENTS

# PART II    PSYCHOLOGY AND THE
# PHILOSOPHY OF SCIENCE

# PART III   PROBABILITY AND INFERENCE

PART I

# Backgrounds
## in Empiricism

# CHAPTER 1

# *Introduction*

THE PROBLEMS of psychology are the problems of other sciences. Systematically treated, they follow the resumé of the philosophy of science. They are the problems of data, of method, of theory, and of inference. Where solutions to the problems are not immediately forth-coming, procedural agreements and rules may arise which permit either the inspired novitiate or the drudging veteran to get on with his work. In a word, most of us become uncritical positivists, with little inclination to consider the matter further. Still, problems of meaning, of construction, of explanation remain obtrusive. On occasion each one of us slips into his own armchair, if only to rest. The positive moments become less positive, and we wonder what kind of science, what knowledge, can be built on a critical empiricism.

There was a time not too long ago when psychology was the maid-servant of philosophy. Its major function was to tidy up the household of epistemology. But that was changed by the irascible behaviorists. They emancipated us from philosophy. They freed us once, but not for all, from the skeins of mentalism, from the tangles of volition, feeling, and imageless thought. Thus by taking behavior, and only behavior, as the source of its data, psychology was to become a science like physiology, or even physics. It would have no need of metaphysics. It could renounce its grandparentage, as indeed it did, and turn to positivism and operationism for familial support. But unfortunately, they, the sciences and positivism, were siblings, and boasts of allegiance came just at a time when positivism itself was temporizing its proprietary claims on dogmatic objectivity.

It is difficult to date the inceptions of behaviorism and logical positivism; but if we turn to their respective manifestoes, published within a decade or so of one another, we might suspect that one was the progeny of the other, or that they had a common ancestry. No doubt there is

1

something here for the genealogist, but it is rather a teasing fact that the two movements, representing diverse disciplinary trends, arose for quite different reasons (cf. N1.1). Be that as it may, the critical functions of the two movements were the same. Methods of analysis were prescribed which would enable scientist and philosopher alike to distinguish that which was clearly meaningful from that which was not.

Watson's early writings on behaviorism (1913, 1914, 1919) proved provocative because of the impact they had on a confrerie grown confused and weary over the subtleties of introspection. How could one talk sense about images in thought, about the dimensions and attributes of consciousness, about the temporal relations of feeling to action, when, indeed, in each case the controversialists could not concur on first principles? When men agree as to the subject matter of their science but disagree as to its data, then the discipline is ripe for critical analysis.

Behaviorism, of course, undertook that analysis. It changed both the subject matter and the data of psychology, but not so much so that people trained in the older ways of introspectionism and structuralism could not be enticed to embrace the newer gospel of public observation. In performing its critical function, early behaviorism had not been particularly sophisticated about what that function was. But at the turn of the century, positivism was in the air, both in physics and in philosophy. And finally, when behaviorism needed doctrinaire support, it found a ready ally in the positivism of the Vienna Circle. An alignment was secured which proved mutually supportive to both parties.

Philosophically speaking, the critical issues were epistemic ones. What, for example, constitutes meaningful discourse? Whereof may we speak sense? What are the boundaries of defensible knowledge? These proved to be rather tiresome questions. However, the success of the physical sciences had led to a vigorous reaffirmation of the logico-empirical foundations of knowledge. A meaningful statement is one that is amenable to truth analysis. It must be capable of a truth evaluation. If what a statement asserts can be known to be true, and what it asserts is true, then the statement is unequivocally meaningful. Likewise, if what a statement asserts can be known to be false, and what it asserts is false, then that statement is meaningful by virtue of its falsification. Thus the function of philosophy is critical. Critical philosophy should enable us to determine whether our statements are subject either to verification or to falsification. Should a statement prove to be neither verifiable, nor falsifiable, nor true by its purely logical status, then it is meaningless. Thus all statements stand as judged in the court of critical analysis.

Although our analogy of a court of linguistic judgment does not fully represent the actual situation, it is perhaps a useful one. The judges, of course, are ourselves—all sophisticated people, presumably, who would take communication seriously. The admissible evidence is that which the rules of the court prescribe. Thus the crux of meaning rests in what constitutes admissible evidence. Positivists and empiricists generally have admitted two types of evidence. One, there is evidence in the usual sense, the evidence of perception, observation, data, reports, etc. And two, there is "evidence" that derives from the legitimate use of language according to the rules of the particular grammar. Thus a statement can be meaningful if it correctly reports some empirical state of affairs (e.g., pointer readings on our instruments). Or, a statement can be meaningful if it is true in a logical sense; that is, given certain definitions and rules of manipulation, then certain valid conclusions follow upon application of the rules.

The prescription for meaning is thus clear-cut. If a statement asserts an empirical state of affairs and there is the possibility of data such that all communicants can reach agreement as to whether that state of affairs obtains, then that statement is subject to verification (or falsification) and is thereby meaningful. But statements or sets of statements may also be meaningful if they follow an orderly argument within some set of prescribed rules, even though the specific referents of such statements are unknown. Thus, for example, if for two statements $A$ and $B$ we assume the rule that $A$ materially implies $B$, and $A$ is assumed to be true, we may then conclude that $B$ is true. Given $A$ implies $B$, then from $A$ we conclude $B$, regardless of whether there is anything in the world of experience for which either $A$ or $B$ stand.

Thus two classes of statements are meaningful: empirical ones which are meaningful by virtue of their being empirically true or false, and logical ones which are meaningful by virtue of their following prescribed rules of construction and inference. At first glance these positivistic criteria of meaning are straightforward. Though a programmatic formulation of the verification theory of meaning had to wait for the efforts of the logical positivists, as such, the ideas and restrictions implicit within the criteria were as old as empiricism itself. To ask for the meaning status of a statement one need only apply the straightforward criteria of meaning. If the statement expresses a proposition (i.e., makes an assertion) which is either a matter of empirical reference or of logic, it is meaningful; otherwise, it is not (cf. N1.2). Observation statements, reports of evidence, pointer readings, descriptions of apparatus and physical stimulus conditions are meaningful as are the arguments of mathematics and logic. But statements that are not directly reducible to data or to a purely logical rubric are not meaningful. It was clear from this that speculative metaphysics which germinated such terms as "substance," "essence," "the absolute," "the soul," etc., was largely spawning nonsense. But how about the language of introspective psychology, the language of "images," "awareness," and "conscious content"? Are the terms of introspective analysis meaningful?

With varying degrees of sophistication the early behaviorists pronounced their negative judgments (cf. N1.3). The language of introspection does not satisfy the criterion of empirical reference. Reports on the contents and processes of consciousness are private affairs; they are not subject to public verification. To be sure, the argument at that time was not very sophisticated. Neither psychologist nor philosopher had as yet learned to torture himself with the subtleties of the arguments about "other minds." Doubtless, it was just as well for the behavioral psychologist. His new freedom to concentrate upon learning and comparative behavior enabled him to bring "man" back into the purview of life science. However, in the long run, a science needs more than the security of dogmatic proscription; it needs a philosophy. As behaviorism matured, it turned more and more to a systematic positivism.

The more systematic presentation of the positivistic philosophies is made in the chapters that follow. However, for the present, the argument of logical positivism can be stated as follows. The focal problem of philosophy is meaning. Language, the instrument of meaning, has both syntactic and semantic structure. The syntax of a language is the set of rules for forming and manipulating word symbols; in short, it is the grammar of the language. On the other hand, the semantics of the language concerns matters of meaning, of how we assign meaning to symbols and to sentences. For efficient communication, we need a consistent and comprehensive set of rules for manipulating symbols and statements. But given a syntactically rigorous language, then the problem of meaning devolves upon the signification that we give to individual terms and sentences. It then becomes the critical task for philosophy to ascertain which sentences and arguments are meaningful and which are not.

So far as meaning is concerned, some words of the language are not at all problematic, for example, conventional definitions and utility words such as connectives and articles. However, words, phrases, sentences, which purport to signify some thing in the world, or some process, or some state of affairs, can be problematic if unequivocal rules for designating their referents are not forthcoming. Turning to the language of psychology, for example, we see at a glance that some words are unambiguous. Words which symbolize the state of an experimenter's apparatus or the minutiae of a subject's conduct are not problematic. Words like "turning," "pausing," and "striking" are clearly understood. They symbolize phenomena which all of us can witness. If the question of correct usage arises, we can literally present the suspect case to a panel of judges for a decision. The judges, of course, have a dictionary of usage, and each judge is capable of experiencing that phenomenon to which the word in question is to refer. Now suppose the phenomena to be verbalized are those which arise in the context of a simple discrimination experiment. We expose cards of different hues to a subject and ask him to respond with the appropriate color name. Thus when we expose a blue card, the subject says "blue," when we expose a green card, he says "green," and so on. What could be simpler? The results are straightforward. The subject names all the cards correctly. If we repeat this experiment with other subjects, and presuming none are color blind or are liars, we get unanimous agreement in naming the stimulus cards. We may then conclude by way of generalization that our subjects under these conditions perceive the colors correctly. But here I have changed from "name" to "perceive," and deliberately, so as to introduce an ambiguity. By our concentrating on naming as the response, our experiment is a purely behavioral one. But by introducing perceiving as the response, I have introduced a semantic complication. If the phenomena we are reporting are those of naming, then there is no ambiguity. We can correlate the exposure of the card and the name that is uttered in response to the card, and the scientific community concurs in what is meant by our description. On the other hand, if we report that when S says "blue" to the presentation of a blue card he is *seeing* blue, we have an ambiguity. On the one hand, our description is of his discriminating colors without specific reference to the content of seeing. On the other hand, our description is of what he sees—but not having access to what he sees, we do not know if he has used the phrase "seeing blue" according to a dictionary (cf. N1.4).

No doubt this is wearisome argument. The tedium of it may give ballast to philosophical journals but it is hardly the kind of thing to bestir the psychologist still marching to the echoes of Watson's trumpet. But this is indeed a serious argument, and it is on this argument that the promise of an introspective psychology stands or falls. Our subject, for example, reports a "sharp pain," and then again a "dull pain," or perhaps again a "tingling pain." What is it, precisely, that is here reported? In dealing with the young child, the parent well knows the counsel of semantic despair. He sends the child to the doctor who looks for external symptoms. We shall meet this argument again in a later chapter. For the present, the point is that correct usage of the phenomenal vocabulary depends upon the availability of an explicit dictionary. Thus, the catch. There are no private dictionaries, and as Wittgenstein concluded, no private languages (1953).

If confining oneself to matters of public fact and to matters of logic were all there is to science, then perhaps scientists and philosophers could remain as sanguine and as dogmatic as some of their early pronouncements made them out to be. For example, if it were only a question of prescribing the limits for admissible data, then, indeed, behavioral data are acceptable for the psychologist whereas reports taken to signify introspected states of consciousness are not. Few scientists, however, are content merely to collect data. They also feel the need to interpret the data. They seek explanations. They construct theories.

Now theories are more than summaries of data and more than mere calculating devices. Invariably they contain statements which are neither purely logical nor purely empirical. They embody hypothetical terms which are only indirectly related to data. There is, as we shall see, a very large critical literature attending to this issue; but regardless of the outcome, there is no question but that the dogmatic shell of empiricism is cracked. The task of adjudicating meaning has become complicated. There is at least one class of scientific statements, namely statements about hypothetical entities, which is problematic. No easy decision as to the semantic status of such statements can be reached, for they are neither purely logical nor strictly empirical.

Almost as soon as the groups of sympathetic English and continental empiricists coalesced into the positivistic movement, the doubts and misgivings concerning a dogmatic logical empiricism were raised and aired. Some types of sentences proved refractory to the judgment of linguistic analysis; e.g., statements of hypothetical constructs as suggested above. Another problem immediately arose with respect to universal statements. From antiquity, scientists had placed faith in lawlike descriptions of natural phenomena, trusting largely to induction to discover such natural laws. How are any lawlike statements to be accepted as meaningful if an empiricistic criterion of meaning requires that such statements be reduced to signifying a finite set of empirical events? Here again the element of hypothesis intrudes. Even in the field of logic, the security system of formal argument was challenged by our inability to establish consistency and completeness in logical systems. The matter of completeness is complicated, but simply stated it is this: within any logical system, such as that upon which we base arithmetic, it is desirable that any statement expressible in the system should be capable of either proof or disproof. Thus, we should know whether any statement that is a legitimate construction within the system and that expresses a possible theorem of the system is capable of proof. If this strong criterion of completeness cannot be met, then there must be some subclass of strictly logical statements (theorems) to which we cannot assign meaning by virtue of our criteria. Kurt Gödel (1931), one of the original members of the Vienna Circle, proved by ingenious indirection that is is impossible to establish completeness for logical systems. It is possible in a logical system, such as arithmetic, to formulate true theorems for which no formal proof can be found. Such theorems cannot be dismissed as nonsensical, since they would follow the rules of the logical system for forming meaningful sentences (cf. N1.5).

Almost from its beginning then, the logico-empiricistic theory of meaning upon which logical positivism was built was subject to attack, and by the members of the movement themselves. The literature of positivism burgeoned—in England, on the Continent, and in the United States. Almost every paper that survived to become a classic announced some new retreat from positivism. Logic and science became the paradigms of meaningful discourse—of truth, if you will. Yet the critical examination of the paradigmatic arguments rendered them suspect, and by the very criteria which recruited the philosopher and scientist alike to the positivism of their respective disciplines.

It is always a bit ironical when a house which professes to virtue topples under censure by its own precept. This is to some extent the history of empiricism. Yet in the review that follows, we shall find that self-imposed criticism is also the strength of modern empiricism. Problems of meaning remain beclouded. Scientific truth may in the end be as "nonsensical" and as "metaphysical" as other brands of truth. And the senses sprinkled with dosages of logic may still not be a very direct route to systematic knowledge. However, the retreat from dogmatism has itself been systematic. The goal of seeking publicly meaningful descriptions is still a worthy one. We may have to use the language of uncertainty, of hypothesis, even of fiction, but the criteria of testability remain the touchstone of usable truth. Empiricism itself is culpable, yet we have found no reliable substitute for a knowledge supported by the fact of its public communicability.

For the empiricist, the alternative to absolute skepticism is the wistful embrace of a principle of convergence. Truth is something beyond our reach, but it ever teases us on to better approximations. We would, of course, rest more assured if that convergence had a mathematical pedigree, wherein each new speculation solidified to take its place within the asymptote. But this is not the case. Could we know otherwise, there would be no occasion for skepticism. Rather we must take comfort in the fables for empiricists—like that of Olive Schreiner (1883) whose stranger describes truth as a great white bird on wing, which lures us on and on and on, and which molts a feather now and then to settle on the breast of some expiring aspirant. Touching? Yes, and allegorical. But there are seasoned defenses of the time-bound epoch. Each new advance emits a spark of certainty, and then the certainty is gone.

But for those less given to musing, for those hard at work, and for those, like myself, who talk of the work of others, there are slogans, such as

"The meaning of a proposition is to be found in its uses," or
"The meaning of a proposition is the method of its verification."

No doubt such slogans lack the intoxication of certainty. Perhaps we shall get used to that. We should, for the philosophy of science is largely a matter of choosing from among alternative conceptions and alternative explanations without the benefit of proof.

# NOTES

## NOTE 1.1

On a paradoxical note it can be said that the behaviorist revolt as popularized by John B. Watson arose because of the paucity of scientific contributions made by the traditional structural psychology of the time, whereas logical positivism arose to a large extent because of the diversity of puzzling results coming out of the mathematical and physical sciences. Sympathetic bonds between the two movements were established after each was well under way on its own internal momentum. Neurath's paper on physicalism as applied specifically to the problems of psychology was published in 1931. Stevens' article bringing logical positivism specifically to the attention of psychologists was published in 1939.

The feeling that structuralism had become entangled in sterile controversy and that insoluble problems had arisen with respect to introspection was rather widespread prior to Watson's 1913 publication of "Psychology as the Behaviorist Views It" (Diserens, 1925; Dunlap, 1912; James, 1904; Holt, 1914; Thorndike and Herrick, 1915). For example, William McDougall, hardly a crusader for Watsonian behaviorism (cf. Watson and McDougall, 1928), could write in the 1908 edition of his *Introduction to Social Psychology:*

> Psychologists must cease to be content with the sterile and narrow conception of their science as the science of consciousness, and must boldly assert its claim to be the positive science of mind in all its aspects and modes of functioning, or, as I would prefer to say, the positive science of conduct or behavior (p. 15).

On the other hand, the circle of philosophers, mathematicians, and physicists who joined together to found the Vienna Circle turned to philosophy in despair over the inconsistencies and the paradoxes that were found in the new mathematics and physics of the early twentieth century.

With respect to behaviorism, one should also note that some people leaned that way simply because they were interested in animal behavior or physiology as such (Loeb, Jennings, Pavlov, Bethe, v. Uexkill, Morgan) while others felt more specifically that the inadequacy of introspection was the focal issue (Dunlap, 1912; Lashley, 1923; Tolman, 1922, 1923; F. Allport, 1924). The spokesmen for behaviorism came primarily from the latter group.

## NOTE 1.2

As a manifesto of early positivism we might well take David Hume's often quoted benediction to *An Enquiry Concerning Human Understanding:*

> When we run over libraries, persuaded of these principles, what havoc must we make? If we take in our hand any volume; of divinity or school

metaphysics, for instance; let us ask, *Does it contain any abstract reasoning concerning quantity or number?* No. *Does it contain any experimental reasoning concerning matter of fact and existence?* No. Commit it then to the flames; for it can contain nothing but sophistry and illusion (Hume, Selby-Bigge edition, p. 165).

## NOTE 1.3

John B. Watson's attack on introspectionism represented a mixture of positivistic critique and pragmatic distaste. In his classic pronouncement of behaviorism (1913) he argues: (1) introspectionists cannot duplicate one another's work as concerns their data; (2) there is little agreement as to the attributes of sensation (i.e., as to what the data are); (3) inference by analogy as to the data of other minds is a dubious procedure; (4) traditional psychology (structuralism) has had little practical impact in behavioral control and public affairs; and (5) psychologies concerning any variant of the mind–body problem cannot qualify as a functionally oriented science. Pertaining to this latter point, he wrote:

> I feel that *behaviorism* is the only consistent logical functionalism. In it one avoids both the Scylla of parallelism and Charybdis of interaction. These time-honored relics of philosophical speculation need trouble the student of behavior as little as they trouble the student of physics. The consideration of the mind–body problem affects neither the type of problem selected nor the formulation of the solution of that problem. I can state my position here no better than by saying that I should like to bring my students up in ignorance of such hypotheses as one finds among other branches of science (1913, p. 166).

Watson was not alone at the helm in taking the foundering ship of psychology through its Homeric straits. Although Watson did not deny consciousness outright, he came close to it when in the footnote to his *Psychological Review* article (1913) he questioned the existence of Galtonian imagery. Other behaviorists were more cautious. Most embraced some variant of methodological behaviorism (Calkins, 1921; Dunlap, 1912; A. P. Weiss, 1917, 1925; Bode, 1914; Tolman, 1922) as meticulously formulated in Lashley's classic papers (1923). Lashley took great pains to show that attributions of consciousness arise only in the presence of physiological and behavioral processes. Since at best conscious descriptions are ambiguous, we should attend only to behavioral observation. There is no need to deny or even proscribe introspective data, but the latter do not enjoy the objective status of the data appropriate to behavioral analysis. Therefore, as a methodological commitment, one should avoid the data of introspection.

It would be misleading, however, to attribute the positivistic revolt against introspectionism to Watson or to any of his contemporaries. In a review of psychological objectivism published in 1925, Diserens cautions that behaviorism is as old as mentalism itself.

Mention here can be made of only a few of Watson's more immediate predecessors who are distinguished for their positivistic points of view. It is well known that David Hume found introspection inadequate to support many of the ideas that had been useful to science. As a result, such ideas were either rejected or were qualified as habit processes, e.g., structured categories of thinking and concepts such as causation and ego. His conclusions were those of skepticism, although he did not refrain from using either a causal or an ego-predicated language. The implications of his analysis, however, are clear for the scientist. Neither cause nor the ego are introspectible. Therefore, the psychologist who makes the structure and content of consciousness the subject of his psychology should look critically upon what are givens (the sense data, the impressions) and what are cognitive constructions (ideas). However, this skepticism is not an attack upon introspective psychology as such. Looking at psychology and introspection, it was Kant who drew the inevitable conclusion. One cannot introspect the subject matter of psychology—that is to say, one cannot introspect the introspective acts themselves. Thus Kant denied to psychology the aspirations of scientific status. That is, he denied to introspectionists (i.e., to structuralists) their pretensions to science. He did not deny, nor would he have denied, scientific pretensions to a behavioristically restricted psychology. Historians of psychology have overstated the case of Kant's skepticism concerning a scientific psychology.

This issue was brought into sharp focus by August Comte. In fact the overall issues were hardly stated more clearly and more comprehensively by any of the early behaviorists than they are in the following free quotation of Comte.

> . . . the mind may observe all phenomena but its own. It may be said that a man's intellect may observe his passions, the seat of reason being somewhat apart from that of the emotions in the brain; but there can be nothing like scientific observation of the passions, except from without, as the stir of the emotions disturbs the observing facilities more or less. It is yet more out of the question to make an intellectual observation of intellectual processes. The observing and observed organ are here the same, and its action cannot be pure and natural. In order to observe, your intellect must pause from activity; yet it is this very activity that you want to observe. If you cannot effect that pause, you cannot observe; if you do effect it, there is nothing to observe. The results of such method are in proportion to its absurdity. After two thousand years of psychological pursuit, no one proposition is established to the satisfaction of its followers. They are divided, to this day, into a multitude of schools, still disputing about the very elements of their doctrine. This interior observation gives birth to almost as many theories as there are observers. We ask in vain for any one discovery, great or small, which has been made under this method (1896, vol. I, p. 9).

Even in his most limpid polemics, Watson could hardly have improved on this indictment against introspectionism. In his own program for psychology, Comte calls for a behavioro-contextual definition of the ego and would thereby endow animals as well as human beings with egos. Comte would also stress neuroanatomy and physiology as supportive of behavioral studies.

Henry Maudsley, in *The Physiology and Pathology of the Mind* (1867), presents as sharp an indictment of introspectionism as the writer has found in a brief search of the literature. Maudsley was one of the early writers in the field of psychopathology. He argues for humane methods of treatment of the insane, and for sane methods of study of the problems of psychopathology. His style is a delight to read, and his opening chapter on methods should be compulsory reading for all those who would endow twentieth century behaviorism with any of the conceits of precedence. To get the flavor of his style, consider two brief passages wherein he chronicles man's progression from the futility of superstition and fear to that of metaphysics.

> As was natural, man, who thus imposed his laws on nature, soon lost all his former humility, and from one erroneous extreme passed to the opposite: as once he fell abjectly down in an agony of fear, so now he rose proudly up in an ecstasy of conceit (1876, p. 4).

And,

> Fruitful of empty ideas and wild fancies, philosophy has not been unlike those barren women who would fain have the rumbling of wind to be the motion of offspring (p. 5).

However, the poignance of his critique of introspection does not alone rest on the felicities of rhetoric. He makes the following points.

1.   By its focusing upon itself, by its rendering the introspective state static, introspection falsifies its own subject matter. As explicitly stated by Kant and Comte, one cannot introspect the act of introspection.

2.   There is little agreement among introspectionists.

3.   Where agreement does occur, it can be attributed to the fact that introspectionists must be meticulously trained, and thereby have a bias built into their observations.

4.   A body of knowledge based on introspection cannot be inductive; no discovery is possible from those who are trained specifically on what to observe.

5.   Due to the extent of the pathology of mind, self-report is hardly to be trusted.

6.   Introspective knowledge cannot have the generality we expect of science. It must be restricted to the class of sophisticated, trained adult subjects.

7.   Much of behavior (habit and performance) occurs without conscious correlates.

8.   Mind and consciousness are not coextensive.

9.   Introspection and consciousness cannot give an adequate explanation of memory ("the static state of the mind").

10. The arousal of a conscious image is not itself introspectible.

11. The brain records unconsciously; its response is a function of organic states which themselves are not introspectible.

12. Emphasis upon introspection minimizes attention given to physiological processes without which there would be no mental states.

The indictment is complete. All that is missing are the formal details of a positivistic theory of meaning. Maudsley rounds out his indictment with this admonition: ". . . he who thinks to illuminate the whole range of mental action by the light of his own consciousness is not unlike one who should go about to illuminate the universe with a rushlight."

As a final addendum to this item, it should be noted that introspection-ists, or rather those who would use introspectionist methods, are not without apologies for treating their own methods as objective by virtue of reasonable, if not positivistic, grounds. Boring has on different occasions presented many of the introspectionist's counterarguments (1929, 1933, 1953). How-ever, the critical response to behaviorism runs from outright re-jections of the behavioristic thesis by Titchener (1914) and Morton Prince (1928) to that admonition of Margaret Washburn (1922) which counseled the continuance of introspection as a key to the analysis of mediating variables in behavioral processes. McDougall, in debate and writing (1928a, 1928b) dis-claimed any originality for Watsonian behaviorism and held that eliminating introspection from behavioral description was meaninglessly restrictive. One senses therefore that behaviorism did not burst like a rocket upon the scene; the positivistic inclinations of a behavior-oriented psychology were pretty gen-eral from the beginning of the century. The contentiousness of behaviorism and its public appeal derived mostly from the popularization of its doctrines (e.g., Watson, 1925). In his 1931 discussion of behaviorism, Woodworth could write[1]:

> Exactly where the bogey of subjectivism hides himself nowadays I cannot guess. It seems to me I have not seen him rear his head in psychologi-cal circles for lo! these thirty years or more. But he must be somewhere about, for do we not see the behaviorists charging all over the field and jousting at him? (p. 84)

## NOTE 1.4

There shall be other occasions to refer to the "other minds" controversy. Analy-sis of the problem represents one of the more infectious maladies of analytical philosophy (Wisdom, 1952; Austin, 1946; Ryle, 1949; and Ayer, 1946, 1954); even in psychology the issue will not stay interred (Burt, 1962).

In the present context what should be stressed is the dictionary. A dic-tionary is a set of rules by which the body of communicants assigns meanings to the vocabulary of its language. In a psychophysical experiment, in which we attempt to correlate physical stimulus variables with verbal reports of the subjects, there is no problem; the language we use to describe the relevant events refers to behavior and to other physical variables. The subject may be discriminating among different levels of loudness, say, and he judges one physi-cal stimulus to be noticeably louder than another. A loudness judgment is thereby correlated with a stimulus intensity measure. Loudness under these terms can be adequately defined in terms of verbal response under a set of experimental instructions. Thus loudness judgment is the variable as measured by verbal response. (Discrimination experiments using conditioning techniques would be even less problematic so far as their description is concerned.) In or-

---

[1] Robert S. Woodworth—CONTEMPORARY SCHOOLS OF PSYCHOLOGY, Copyright 1931, The Ronald Press Company.

der to avoid ambiguity, one must avoid implying that the verbal response is one in which the words of the response symbolize the intrinsic loudness that is heard in the privacy of the subject's sensorium. This in substance is Stevens' operational defense of psychophysical experiments (1939, 1959). See also Bergmann and Spence (1944).

The semantic difficulty that philosophers of the problem of other minds focus upon involves the two-subject situation. $S_1$ and $S_2$ simultaneously say "blue" to a blue card. Can we say that they both had the same experience? We can, of course, say they made the same response. No problem there. *Our* language describing *their* response is unambiguous. But how can we say that they both had the same experience when the experience is the seeing of blue, or rather perhaps, the occurrence of a blue sense-datum in the consciousness of a given observer? In other words, if the phenomenon to be verbalized is the occurrence of a phenomenon of consciousness and not the verbal response itself, we do indeed have a semantic problem for which no dictionary is written. How can we tell that our subjects have used the word "blue" correctly? By inference? By analogy? These have been stock suggestions. But they will not do. They beg the question. How can we check the analogy? And how can we bring $S_1$ and $S_2$ together to compare responses? The phenomena, the thingnesses to which their words "blue" apply are different and are not in any way comparable.

It has often been asked: "But what if we could plug into one another's sensoriums? What if conscious impressions were like slides that we could somehow interchange?" But even with the questionable "somehow," this will not do. I leave it to the reader to puzzle out this enigma.


## NOTE 1.5

Of Gödel's 1931 paper, Braithwaite writes: "Gödel's discovery of this incompleteness, presented in this paper, is one of the greatest and most surprising of the intellectual achievements of this century" (Gödel, 1962, p. 32).

The issues of the argument are too complex to go into in any detail. In general, proof of the essential incompleteness of formal systems such as arithmetic came as a fatefully astonishing result to those logicians and mathematicians who wished to establish the sufficiency of axiomatic method. For an axiomatic system to be sufficient, it should possess two properties: consistency and completeness. An axiomatic or formal system is *consistent* if, and only if, no well-formed formula or proposition in the system can be both proved and disproved from the given set of postulates. This in turn assures us that contradictory propositions cannot be proved within that system. An axiomatic or formal system is *complete* if, and only if, from the set of axioms and proved theorems it is possible either to prove or to disprove any and all well-formed formulae or propositions expressible in the system. Hilbert and his students, for example, had attempted to prove the sufficiency of deductive systems by an astringent formalization of their contents and procedures. He succeeded to the extent of demonstrating that one system, geometry, is consistent only if another system, arithmetic, is consistent. But this left the proof of consistency open. In effect Gödel put an end to the quest.

By largely inventing and perfecting a powerful device for mapping logical arguments onto arithmetic (of unique Gödel numbers) Gödel was able to prove the following (paraphrased) propositions.

1.   As treated by Gödel, proof is a matter of the method of recursive definition (i.e., mathematical induction). His Proposition VI states in effect that if a formal system, P, is consistent, then for the recursive class of formulae there is at least one subclass of theorems such that neither the theorem nor its negation are provable in P. Thus the undecidability of at least one theorem signifies the incompleteness of P.

2.   Since from an inconsistent set of axioms any theorem can be inferred, it must be assumed that a formal system P is consistent. Gödel's Proposition XI then asserts that if P is consistent, as it is assumed to be, then the propositional formula which asserts that P is consistent is not provable in P.

This is what Nagel and Newman (1958) allude to as the "melancholy conclusion that the axiomatic method has certain inherent limitations . . ." (1958, p. 6). For example, if arithmetic or the formal system of *Principia Mathematica* is consistent, it is necessarily incomplete. There are some propositions, possibly known to be true by virtue of metamathematical considerations, which cannot be proven true within the formal system (for example, this might be the case for Goldbach's theorem that any even number other than 2 is a composite of two primes, or for Fermat's theorem which states that for $x^n + y^n = z^n$, solutions for the values for $x$, $y$, $z$ can be found for $n = 1$ and $n = 2$, but for no higher integer values of $n$). But equally melancholic is the realization that no proof for the consistency of the formal system can be found in the system itself.

The significant point here is that if an ideal deductive system requires that its calculus must be both consistent and complete then no such ideal system exists. Moreover, to this "melancholy" state of affairs was added the result of Church (1936) that within any formal system P there exists no effective method, no algorithm, for determining which propositions in P are provable. What constitutes "effective method"? Rosser (1939) has proposed that an effective method for determining provable propositions in P exists if a machine can be built to solve any problem of a set of possible problems, without the solution involving human intervention other than the initial input of the problem and the subsequent read-out.

The questions of completeness and computability are of significance concerning the capabilities and limitations of possible automata. The theorems of Gödel and Church seem to place certain limitations on the function of any conceivable machine. But whether Gödel's proof signifies that human ratiocination is nonsimulable, as Nagel and Newman (1958) appear to suggest, has been questioned (Putnam, 1960; Scriven, 1960). The predicament is this: whereas the human computer can establish the truth of an undecidable proposition in P by carrying out a proof in some meta-system of its invention, the machine is bound, as it were, by the formal system incorporated into its design (see Putnam, 1960a, 1960b; Nagel and Newman, 1961) (cf. N12.8).

An English translation of Gödel's paper (1962) is now available, but requires a competence in mathematical logic. However, this edition is accompanied by an excellent expository introduction by Braithwaite. Relatively non-
technical discussions of Gödel's theorems can be found in Nagel and Newman
(1958), Rosser (1939), Findlay (1942), and Quine (1950).

# CHAPTER 2

# The Empiricists

TO DISCUSS modern empiricism properly one should first pay homage to a host of its ancestors. Empiricism did not erupt full bloom at the advent of the scientific enlightenment. From antiquity on, each new epoch brought forth contributions to the history of science and empirical philosophy. Even the middle ages were not silent. Yet in scanning history for the viable seeds of empiricism we pass quickly over whole families of brilliant and observant people until we come inevitably to focus upon the figures of Locke, Berkeley, and Hume. Why is this? The answer is in their singleness of outlook. With them philosophy is equated with epistemology in which empiricistic skepticism undertakes to define the limits of knowledge.

One should note that the observational disposition was not original with the later empiricists. The Milesian philosophers, Thales, Anaximander, Anaximines, Anaxagoras, resorted to observation as much as they did to intuition and logic in formulating their doctrines of substance and process, of unchanging basic stuffs and mechanism. And the atomists and the Pythagoreans, in spite of their reliance on reason, keyed their descriptions to the structures and harmonies of the external world.

If the Greeks failed in their efforts to build a lasting experimental science, it was because they trusted reason too much. At most, the world of fact provided momentary cues to the truths of geometry. Believing in a rational universe, the Greeks had little need for experiment. Through reason, and reason alone, they felt they could decipher the structure of the universe. Pythagoras, Euclid, and the expository skills of Plato were sufficient to establish the authority of reason (cf. N2.1).

For the most part that authority, augmented by the logical rubrics of Aristotle, carried through into the scientific enlightenment. Of course, reason did not stand alone; with the invention of instrumental aids, observation and experiment became increasingly important. But the motive was that of discovery, of revelation, where the world to be revealed was regarded as the embodiment of rational principles. The new scientists, culminating in the genius of Galileo, let observations guide their speculations; but even for them, there was always the expectation and the confidence that fact would support some pervasive mathematical structure of the world.

Galileo is an exemplary figure of the scientific revolution. Contrary to his popular image, he was more rationalist and theoretician than experimentalist. And it was not just because he antedated the age of technology and instrumentation. He believed in a rational world, ideally simple in its structure, and lawful. It was for him to discover that structure, by observation, by experiment if need be, but always by seeking to unfold the enduring mathematical plan. Thus, typically, he writes:

> Philosophy is written in that great book which ever lies before our eyes— I mean the universe—but we cannot understand it if we do not first learn the language and grasp the symbols, in which it is written. This book is written in the mathematical language, and the symbols are triangles, circles, and other geometrical figures, without whose help it is impossible to comprehend a single word of it; without which one wanders in vain through a dark labyrinth (*Il Saggiatore,* quoted by Burtt, 1955, p. 75).

It was true that mathematics now became the instrument of reason to supplant the logic of the syllogism. But the element of rationalistic faith remained. Right reason, prompted as it might be by experiment, was the road to truth. Nor was Galileo alone. There were other giants in his time who played upon mathematics as the instrument of truth: Gassendi, Copernicus, Bruno, Kepler, Boyle. For those who looked outward to the heavens (Bruno, Galileo, Copernicus, Brahe, Kepler), geometry was regarded as the key to knowledge; for those who focused upon the earth (Gilbert, Boyle, Harvey), experiment and hypothesis became more important. Trusting reason, the scientists of that age did not as yet surrender to sense data. This was the period in which distinctions between primary and secondary qualities of experience were being emphasized (Galileo, Boyle, and later, Descartes) not in the effort to found a psychology of perception but in order to separate the essential qualities of substance from what was thought to be the inessential and evanescent contributions of the observer.

# THE RATIONALISTS

In an age of Copernicus, Galileo, Kepler, Boyle, and, finally, Newton, it is not surprising that philosophical rationalism also reached its highest development. The great rationalists were also men conversant in science. They differed not so much in their beliefs about the ultimate nature of the world as they did in their methods of insight and investigation. Men of scientific temperament looked to the world to decipher the order they were convinced was there. The rationalists, being convinced of the order, sought to work within a realm of reason itself; thus, logic and reason alone were thought sufficient to answer significant questions. There was an important sense in which scientists and philosophers were alike. Reason supervened over the senses. Perception could be illusory. It was the responsibility of the observer to separate the capricious qualities of observation from what was essential to the object.

The great rationalists were Descartes, Spinoza, and Leibniz. With the possible exception of Descartes, none would qualify as scientists. Descartes and Leibniz were mathematicians, Spinoza was a moralist, Leibniz an original logician. Temperamentally different, these people had this in common: the rationalistic method. One begins with first principles, which either by intuition or systematic query are found to be given and indubitable. From these principles and the methods of logic, one deduces valid conclusions. Since some premises express significant propositions either about the world or about man's relation to the world, then significant knowledge follows from the application of reason alone. Mathematics and logic prove sufficient to derive important physical truths. They should prove equally sufficient in the field of metaphysics. The only difference would be that inherent principles of belief would replace the initial fund of physical data.

Only the briefest account of the methods of these great rationalists can be given here. This is intended only to afford a backdrop for the empiricists that follow.

### Descartes (1596–1650)

Of all the philosophers of the age of reason, Descartes was perhaps the most closely attuned to the scientific revolution. He wrote essays in the fields of optics and physical cosmology. His description of method was the most explicit of all the rationalists. In the *Discourse on Method* (1637) he took pains to plot, step by step, the rules for thinking to correct conclusions. Briefly, they are as follows: (1) to proceed by means of doubt, to take nothing for granted, to avoid bias and prejudgment; (2) to divide the substance of the argument into the simplest parts; (3) to proceed step by step from the simple to the more complex; (4) to "enumerate" and review so as to make sure nothing is missed in the argument, and that as many sources for the correct conclusion as possible may be collated. The tools for step by step thinking are, of course, logical tools. The simples from which the argument proceeds are indubitable propositions arrived at either by intuition or through the fruits of systematic doubt. Thus true knowledge comes from combining *intuition* and *deduction* within the method. The true science is that of mathematics. However, Descartes was contemptuous of pure mathematics, of arithmetic and geometry, which are inapplicable as descriptions of the world. Thus he perfected his analytical geometry as the means to a true physical science. With spatial intuition providing the simples, man could proceed deductively to true knowledge by means of the new geometry (cf. N2.2).

## Spinoza *(1632–1677)*

Spinoza is in many respects the most intensely rationalistic of all the philosophers. He was not so scientifically committed as Descartes, nor so logically oriented as Leibniz; yet in the sheer exaltation of pure reason, he had no peer. Still Spinoza was not devoid of mathematical and scientific interests. He was considered an authority on optics; the only work of his published in his lifetime (*Metaphysical Thoughts*) was an exposition of Descartes' geometrical philosophy. However, in his most important work, the *Ethics,* logical and mathematical reasoning are taken for granted; there is little emphasis on method, *per se,* as the means of truth. Rather, the task is to know the world, and, in knowing it, to know that one has a true idea. One can achieve this state of knowing only by a kind of personal disengagement, by attending not to sense perception, nor to the signs signifying the world, but only to a reflective identification with the world itself. It is a strange doctrine, and few empiricists can testify to finding sense in the argument.[1] However, it is very much a rationalistic philosophy. What Spinoza proposes is this. The event as truly seen cannot be false: it simply is. The stuff of the world is partly represented by body, partly by mind, where mind and body are but attributes of true nature. This nature, however, has an ethereal quality; it transcends both of its attributes. Its rational aspect is imbedded in the fluid and dynamic character of nature. Access to this nature is by virtue of the contemplative attitude commended to us by intuition and by logic and mathematics.

What distinguishes Spinoza from the other rationalists is a more profound distrust of language and perception. There is a true science in which all events in the natural process are strictly determined, just as a logical chain is strictly determined. However, the customary means to knowledge will not suffice. Neither sense perception nor linguistic habits are trustworthy. Intuition, pure reason, and contemplation alone help man to the transcendent state of *being-in* the nature of the thing he studies. In spite of Spinoza's uncompromising determinism, his doctrine has had little attraction for the empiricist (cf. N2.3).

[1] For a sympathetic account by a person conversant in modern skepticism, see R. L. Saw: *The Vindication of Metaphysics* (1951).

### Leibniz (1646–1716)

In matters of logic Leibniz was the most creative of the rationalists. He carried the analysis of propositions further than it had ever been carried before. He anticipated the economies and refinements of symbolic logic. He shared with Newton the distinction of inventing the infinitesimal calculus. And then, to counterpoise these accomplishments, he created one of the most fantastic metaphysical systems ever to be espoused by a philosopher: the doctrine of pure autonomy, with its windowless monads and pre-established harmony. But even in fantasy, it seems, Leibniz was systematic. After an examination of the Leibnizian monadology, Bertrand Russell declared that all of the conclusions of his metaphysics followed logically from a minimal set of premises (cf. N2.4).

The monadology represents the culmination of Leibnizian doctrine. Monads are the atoms of substance, each being independent of another. Interaction between monads, such as we perceive as causal relations, are illusory. According to the principle of sufficient reason, whereby every event must have a cause, no physical description of a concatenation of events is a sufficient explanation of a causal relation. Therefore, God, the agent of pure cause, must effect that relation. God does so supraphysically; i.e., he does so by means of harmony programmed from the moment of creation. Monads, thus, do not transmit their effects one to another, but take each moment in time as the occasion for manifesting their own preprogrammed destinies. Perception is of a real world; and, in its illusionless purity, it is to be trusted. Each monad, within its own opaque windowless cell, perceives at the precise moment and time that which is occasioned by God in the world external to it.

This is strange metaphysics, but, as is noted by Russell, it is one suggestive of the kind of skepticism which was later exposited by the empiricists. The significant factor is that Leibniz arrived at his monadology by means of logical analysis and by means of an analysis of the limits of empirical knowledge. He was not antiempirical (his doctrine of the windowless monads gainsays that we will ever be empirically deceived by God), yet the ultimate truths are to be gained through the rationalistic examination of the structure of propositions and the rules of inference. The success of the Leibnizian method rests in asking "meaningful" questions that empiricism cannot answer.

## THE EMPIRICISTS

The philosophy and science of the early seventeenth century were rationalistic. Theologians aside, there was no conflict between the scientists and the great rationalists of the time. Knowledge in the domain of physics and metaphysics seemed secure. That is why it is perhaps surprising that a man like Locke should rise to effect a revolution in thinking whose impetus carries through even to this day.

## John Locke (1632–1704)

Locke's life span coincided with that of Spinoza and Leibniz. He was a personal friend of Newton and Boyle. Disdaining the academic philosophy of the time, he became a philosopher by virtue of the inclinations of his middle age. (*An Essay Concerning Human Understanding* was not published until he was fifty-seven.) He was neither mathematician nor scientist. His comments upon traditional logic were mostly critical. By temperament he was conservative, and on religious matters he was orthodox (he would not deny the possibility of miracles but preferred to think God talked to us in the language of empirics). He made no dramatic pronouncements, declared no slogans, anticipated no great reactions to his work. He passes "into thy hands what has been the diversion of some of my idle and heavy hours." In the "Epistle to the Reader" which introduces the *Essay,* Locke writes:

> The commonwealth of learning is not at this time without master-builders, whose mighty designs in advancing the sciences will leave lasting monuments to the admiration of posterity; but every one must not hope to be a Boyle or a Sydenham; and in the age that produces such masters as the great Huygenius, and the incomparable Mr. Newton, with some other of that strain, it is ambition enough to be employed as an under-labourer in clearing the ground a little, and removing some of the rubbish that lies in the way to knowledge . . . (Pringle-Pattison edition, p. 6).

Some of the rubbish indeed! He sowed the seeds of epistemic criticism, and with the fruits, his immediate heirs brought down the house of metaphysics and thereby left more rubbish than even he could have swept away.

Locke's theory of knowledge is to be found in *An Essay Concerning Human Understanding.* We shall confine ourselves to this prolix but rewarding work. Following Locke, but not necessarily in his order, we shall address ourselves to the following questions: What is the structure of knowledge? What are its limitations? What is the nature of the real world? What are the roles of experience and logic in the theory of knowledge? What is the role of language?

Briefly, the thesis of Lockean empiricism is this. The mind is devoid of preconceptions of any kind (*tabula rasa*). What it can know comes by way of the senses in the form of ideas. These ideas are constructions from the sense data. Some of these data are of properties inherent in the substantial world, and some reflect the unique contribution of the sensing organism. Some ideas are simple, some are complex. By a process of reflection, the mind can abstract universals from particulars. Thus mind is capable of abstract reasoning, yet it is bound by experience. All ideas must be reducible to sensory input. Therefore, concepts which purport to represent some object state but which in fact do not reduce to particular data or cannot be abstracted from them are by the limitations of knowledge declared suspect. We see then that in Locke's attempts at defining the primary givens of knowledge we are compelled to attend as much to what we cannot know as to what we can.

Locke foresees that he may lose his readers on the first pages of his argument. Therefore, in the "Epistle," he begs the reader to see him through. The issue at first is that of the origins of ideas, an idea "being that term which, I think, serves best to stand for whatsoever is the object of the understanding when a man thinks" (I. 1.8).[2] No ideas are innate: there are no inherent conceptions of morals, God, or substance. All ideas are derived from perception. "To ask at what *time* a man has first any idea is to ask when he begins to perceive; having ideas, and perception, being the same thing" (II. 1.9).

This is not the entire story, for not only are ideas passively received through perception, but they can also be called up through reflection. Such ideas, however, are mnemonic, their origin being in sensing. The limits of knowledge are prescribed by experience: "All those sublime thoughts which tower above the clouds, and reach as high as heaven itself, take their rise and footing here: in all that great extent wherein the mind wanders in those remote speculations it may seem to be elevated with, it stirs not one jot beyond those ideas which *sense* or *reflection* have offered for its contemplation" (II. 1.24).

Locke distinguished between simple and complex ideas somewhat in the fashion that was to become popular with the logical atomists of the twentieth century. The *simple* ideas are the basic elements of experience. It is out of them that phenomena are constructed. Some simple ideas are singular in their sensory modality, e.g., ideas of color, tactual solidity and extension, pleasure and pain; some of these ideas are more constructual, such as existence and unity. Locke is not clear how such ideas emerge. Sensory inputs are, of course, immediately given. But ideas of succession, of power inherent within objects, are clearly more complicated and were later to be held suspect by Berkeley and Hume. However, to Locke such ideas are given through the impact of sensing and reflection upon understanding. *Complex* ideas are abstractions from simple ideas. But as abstractions they are inseparable from their anchorings in simple ideas. Nowadays we might regard them as belonging to the classes of predicates by which we assign either properties or relations to particulars; the

[2] All references are to Locke's book, chapter, and section headings.

Lockean modes, substances, and relations may be treated as classifications of the predicates we assign to perceivable things. In matters of abstraction, a complex idea can only arise from collating the data of many simples and discarding all qualities and properties which are not held in common by the set of simple ideas.

Perhaps the most renowned of all Lockean distinctions is one which was not at all original with him; namely, the distinction between primary and secondary qualities of perceived objects.[3] This distinction need hardly be labored. Quality is indirectly defined: "the power to produce any idea in our mind, I call the quality of the subject wherein the power is" (II. 8.8). Such powers are said to rest in the material objects ("the subject"). They evoke the qualitative subjective experience. Thus some qualities are independent of particular objects, but derive solely from the fact that they are resident in objects (solidity, extension, figure, motion or rest, number). Some qualities are produced in the perceiver by the objects. As such they represent the perceiver's unique contributions to ideas. Berkeley later was to challenge both the distinction and the notion of evocative "power."

Much of the *Essay* is spent in Locke's defense of his classification of types of ideas. Let us skip over most of this material and turn our attention to the status of substantive ideas. What can we know of the world? Specifically, what is the status of substance, of universals, of causal relations? Do we have any access to sure knowledge?

The Lockean notions of substance and universals have frequently been misunderstood as having meaning in an existential sense. Consider *substance*. According to Locke, substance is a poorly defined something which is capable of supporting "such qualities which are capable of producing simple ideas in us" (II. 23.2). Substance is therefore the thingness, the particularity to which we assign predicates. It is that which produces sense data in us. It is the residence of the Lockean power. But as such, it is not something we can talk about in the way the child talks about things in his pocket. Yet substance is the basis of our notions of subsistence and of a real world. The idea of substance permits Locke to avoid retreating into a complete phenomenalistic skepticism.

The notion of abstract ideas is always problematic for the empiricist. However, it plays an important role in Locke's theory of knowledge; and for this, Locke was criticized by Berkeley. What is the problem? If all knowledge is perceptual (i.e., factual knowledge), how can ideas of universals arise when there is no fact to support the universal? Locke answers this by attributing to the mind and its understanding the capacity to enter-

[3] In his examination of Locke's theory of knowledge, Gibson (1917) carries the source of the distinction back to the Greek atomists. The terminology for the distinction Locke himself borrows from his friend Boyle.

tain many facts and to classify them according to a schedule of common properties: "It is plain that *general* and *universal* belong not to the real existence of things; but are the inventions and creatures of the understanding, made by it for its own use, and concern only signs, whether words or ideas" (III. 3.11).

The rejection of rationalism could hardly be stated more blatantly. But in this context, Locke speaks of essences as being implicit within general or universal ideas. This is unfortunate, for it then implies some kind of existence. The nominal essence of a thing is that by which we give a thing its classification. As such, however, this essence is not something which inheres in an object. Unfortunately, Locke (with some reluctance) also speaks of real essences, with no clear differentiation between abstraction according to convention and abstraction in honor of some Platonic substratum in which the particular specimen participates. At any rate, Locke's treatment of abstraction is the source of a later critique which served forthrightly to commit the empiricist to a radically nominalistic position (cf. N2.5).

Finally, let us consider the idea of causality. As Berkeley was to attend to Locke's notion of primary and abstract ideas, Hume was to attend to that of cause. Do we have an idea of a causal relation? Locke, strangely, has little to say about causation. But his answer seems unequivocally affirmative (however awkwardly stated):

> That which produces any simple or complex idea, we denote by the general name *cause;* and that which is produced, *effect*. Thus finding in that substance which we call wax fluidity, which is a simple idea that was not in it before, is constantly produced by the application of a certain degree of heat, we call the simple idea of heat, in relation to fluidity in wax, *the cause* of it, and fluidity *the effect* (II. 26.1).

Examination shows that "cause" signifying productive power is a concept much like that of the power which produces the qualities of sensing and is inherent within the substance. Power and substance are very imprecise concepts—they are abstract ideas, yet any given instance of a succession of events is not itself sufficient to promote the idea of a causal relation or of a power effecting that relation. This quite obviously is troublesome to the empiricist.[4] But at no place does Locke reply that we have direct perceptual access to causal ideas. And in this he is laying the groundwork for the later skepticism.

The foregoing presents a bare outline of Locke's theory of knowledge, but from it a summary statement is possible. The seeds of all empiricistic skepticism can be found within Locke's doctrines. Experience is both the

---

[4] For example, "Should anyone . . . pretend to define a cause by saying that it is something productive of another, 'tis evident he would say nothing" (Hume, *Treatise;* I: III:II).

source and the limitation of all knowledge. One begins with the ideas as instrumented through experience; he also ends with it. Even the processes of observation are completely bound by experience. The doubtful ideas, such as those of power and substance, are the inferred substrata of experience. Nevertheless, they are to be freed of both their metaphysical and their existential overtones. There is intuitive knowledge of the agreement and disagreement among facts; there is rational demonstration. Such knowledge is certain. But there is also the knowledge of sensing, of perceiving what we, in our naïveté, construe to be the nature of things. Of this Locke writes:

> There is, indeed, another perception of the mind employed about the *particular existence of finite beings* without us; which, going beyond bare probability, and yet not reaching perfectly to either of the foregoing degrees of certainty, passes under the name of knowledge. There can be nothing more certain, than that the idea we receive from an external object is in our minds; this is intuitive knowledge. But whether there be anything more than barely that idea in our minds, whether we can thence certainly infer the existence of anything without us which corresponds to that idea, is that whereof some men think there may be a question made; because men may have such ideas in their minds when no such thing exists, no such object affects their senses (IV. 2.14) (cf. N2.6).

## Bishop George Berkeley (1685–1753)

George Berkeley is among the most stimulating of philosophers. Few philosophers have provided so much entertainment for undergraduates, nor provoked so much lively exegesis among academicians. Why? Undoubtedly this popularity of his is due to his denial of the existence of matter and to his unrelenting attack on the doctrine of abstract ideas. He is more empirical than any of his scientific contemporaries, and more skeptical than any of his predecessors. If the reader searches his works in epistemology, he will find prevision to nearly every question that has been raised in present-day empiricism.

Berkeley fashioned the tenets of his philosophy in two remarkable essays, *A New Theory of Vision* and *The Principles of Human Knowledge,* both of which were published by the time he was twenty-six. In these formative years, he also kept the notebooks of the *Commonplace Book,* not published until 1871. Here in the form of queries and aphorisms, Berkeley laid out what was to be his program of philosophical inquiry. Finally, these works were to be followed immediately by what has proved to be one of the most popular works of all philosophical literature, the *Three Dialogues Between Hylas and Philonous.*

What is Berkeley's philosophy, or rather, for this is where his fame resides, what is his theory of knowledge? We shall briefly examine the following: first we shall look to the theory of vision for the roots of Berkeley's empiricism; then we shall examine the theory of knowledge as laid out in the *Principles* and *Dialogues;* and finally we shall look at his critique of the Newtonian science, the most explicit statement of which is to be found in the *Analyst.*

In his theory of vision, Berkeley adopts the rubric of the empiricistic theory of vision as reported by Malebranche (*Recherche de la Vérité*). But to it, he adds the important principle of tactual mediation. Malebranche's theory (held generally by the contemporaries and friends of Descartes) accounted for spatial vision in terms of sensory and kinesthetic cues appropriate to vision alone.[5] However, Berkeley was to contend that the cues of vision alone are not sufficient for the construction of an idea of space. Nor is the addition of optic muscular cues sufficient. Only by coordinating visual cues with the data of tactual exploration is one able to endow these visual cues with the dimension of depth. As Berkeley was to argue later, there are no properties common to two senses (i.e., something does not look like it feels); therefore, the experience of depth as we know it emerges as an associative achievement (cf. N2.6). Furthermore, the experience of depth does not refer to any physical property existentially external to the experience. As in all material things, the essence of depth and physical space is in perception. Thus, *esse est percipi.* To be is to be perceived. This is the slogan by which Berkeley calls us to our senses.

The essence of a thing is in its being perceived. This slogan is not unlike the positivist's principle of verification; it carries with it that potential for skepticism and disbelief which Locke had fostered. In the *Principles of Human Knowledge,* Berkeley introduces his treatise on epistemology with a plea to the reader to see the essay through before tossing it aside as an exasperating attack on common sense. He is to argue that vulgar common sense is in error. It is only through skepticism that one can be brought to true common sense.[6] The argument begins with the problem of existence.

For a thing to be is for it to be perceived. All formulations of the existence of a thing must be in terms of ideas which derive from experience. The source of all ideas, either immediate or mnemonic, is in perception. Consider any thing, any concept, and it becomes meaningful to

[5] Angle of subtension, muscular sensation, clearness of retinal image, relative size of retinal image, number and kind of intervening objects in visual field, and light intensity from object of vision.

[6] Thus, at the conclusion of the *Dialogues* Berkeley has Philonous say: "You see, Hylas, the water of yonder fountain, how it is forced upwards, in a round column, to a certain height; at which it breaks, and falls back into the basin from whence it rose: its ascent, as well as descent, proceeding from he same uniform law or principle of gravitation. Just so, the same principles which, at first view, lead to Skepticism, pursued to a certain point, bring men back to Common Sense."

us only in so far as we can secure it to a perceptual context. Thus the world is a world of ideas, not of independent essences, substances, or abstact reals. This doctrine has two explicit consequences for ontology. One, it calls into question the Lockean distinction between primary and secondary qualities; and two, it bids rejection of all abstract ideas.

First, consider the matter of qualities. Locke found primary qualities to be inherent within the material world. True, he asserted that we cannot penetrate to the substratum in which qualities such as extension and motion inhere, but, nevertheless, that material substratum (substance) has a kind of enduring existence. Berkeley, on the other hand, rejects both the notion of primary qualities and that of substances. Any description of primary qualities necessitates our resorting to predicates designating a perceptual state of affairs. Thus primary qualities are no freer of an indispensable perceptual endowment than are the secondary qualities. This being the case, there is no need for Lockean substance, nor any other notion of substance. Any description of substance, if it is to be meaningful, is to be reduced to the qualities of sensory-perceptual experience.

Berkeley also objects strongly to the notion of abstract ideas. Locke implied that an abstract idea is constructed out of a set of particular ideas by an activity of the understanding. Once derived, this abstract idea has general signification, applying to a set of many similar particulars rather than singularly to any one of them. These abstract ideas are constructed experientially without any intuitive content. However, Berkeley counters that abstraction can be, at best, no more than the selection or isolation of components of particular ideas. One cannot think of an abstract idea such as a scalene triangle, say, without his having an idea of a particular triangle of such and such dimensions. Confused thinking about abstraction has led to bad science and bad metaphysics. It is the subject of Berkeley's attack on Newtonian science and mathematics.

Berkeley is renowned for his declamations against the language of existence. What kind of existence does he deny? What is the sense of his intimating that a world of existence flicks on and off as we blink our eyes? First hear what Philonous has to say in the *Dialogues:*

> I see this *cherry,* I feel it, I taste it: and I am sure *nothing* cannot be seen, or felt, or tasted: it is therefore *real.* Take away the sensations of softness, moisture, redness, tartness, and you take away the *cherry.* Since it is not a being distinct from sensations; a *cherry,* I say, is nothing but a congeries of sensible impressions, or ideas perceived by various senses: which ideas are united into one thing (or have one name given them) by the mind; because they are observed to attend each other. Thus, when the palate is affected with such a particular taste, the sight is affected with a red colour, the touch with roundness, softness, &c. Hence, when I see, and feel, and taste, in sundry certain manners, I am sure the *cherry* exists, or is real; its reality being in my opinion nothing ab-

stracted from those sensations. But if, by the word *cherry,* you mean an unknown nature, distinct from all those sensible qualities, and by its *existence* something distinct from its being perceived; then, indeed, I own, neither you or I, nor anyone else, can be sure it exists. (*Dialogues,* p. 117)

Thus, the meaning of existence. But in *The Principles,* Berkeley takes the issue into the realm of definition: ". . . what is meant by the *absolute existence of sensible objects in themselves,* or *without the mind.* To me it is evident those words make out either a direct contradiction, or else nothing at all." And in the same paragraph: "It is on this therefore that I insist, to wit, that the *absolute existence of unthinking things* are words without a meaning, or which include a contradiction" (*Principles,* ¶ 24).

It is clear from this that Berkeley treats as axiomatic the equivalence of sensory reports and predications of existence. A more precise treatment of existence propositions must wait for Russell's theory of descriptions (cf. N4.6); however, the germ of the critique is clear. It is contradictory to assert existence without at the same time translating statements of that existence into the ideas of Berkelian perception.

Next we turn to the notion of causation. Hume is frequently given credit for being the great skeptic concerning the principle of causality, but Berkeley spells out the details of the critique. (The character of the skepticism itself had been anticipated by Malebranche, Geulincx, Descartes, and Leibniz.) The thesis of skepticism is as simple as it is straightforward. Look as carefully as we may, we do not anywhere discover the percept of a causal relation. As for Berkeley, he does not deny that we have some general idea of causality. Rather, in affirming causal relations, he asserts that causal descriptions signify only a concatenation of events in which one event prior in time is the sign for an expectancy, in the mind of the perceiver, of another event posterior in time. Look as one may, however, he shall find no perceptual evidence of a causal connection as such:

> . . . the connection of ideas does not imply the relation of *cause* and *effect,* but only of a mark or a *sign* with the *thing signified.* The fire which I see is not the cause of the pain I suffer upon my approaching it, but the mark that forewarns me of it (*Principles,* ¶ 65).

And again Berkeley writes:

> Hence, it is evident that those things which, under the notion of a cause co-operating or concurring to the production of effects, are altogether inexplicable and run us into great absurdities, may be very naturally explained, and have a proper and obvious use assigned to them, when they are considered only as marks or signs for *our* information (*Principles,* ¶ 66).

Thus a causal relation is an expectancy relation leading to an inductive inference. But why should such inferences be trustworthy? If a causal relation is no more than a set of contiguous events, how can we be sure that our inferences are to be trusted? Berkeley gives one answer, only to qualify it later. To follow the argument we need to call attention to the role of Spirit (or God) in the scheme. There are no "corporeal causes," only spiritual causes. That is to say, God is both the repository and the source of ideas. The rules and methods by which the Spirit effects the ideas are simply the *laws of nature*. However, such laws of nature are not ontologically tied to existence in a real world. Our only source of assurance in the uniform lawful sequence of events is that such sequences do arise in our experience. Yet we have no idea of universality as such, nor do we have assurance that the laws of nature will not change (*Principles,* ¶ 107).

Here Berkeley has an interesting question to ask of himself. If God or Spirit commands the *idea,* why all the need for the complicated machinery of intermediating events? Why, for example, does a clock not keep time, should it have a face and hands but only a hollow shell in place of its works? God could command such a clock to keep time. It would be a simpler scheme. And it would save the need to probe into the structural detail of things which underlie the surface phenomena. Berkeley's answer is ingenious: ". . . though the fabrication of all those parts and organs be not absolutely necessary to the producing any effect, yet it is necessary to the producing of things in a constant regular way, according to the laws of nature" (*Principles,* ¶ 62). Thus lawfulness of events is contingent upon their complexity.[7]

Berkeley's treatment of *space* and *time* is equally skeptical. There are no ideas of space and time, as such. Time is an abstraction of a succession of ideas in the mind, and space is an abstraction of a set of coexistent ideas. There is no time independent of sequences of perceptually independent events; therefore, there is no abstract time. There is no space independent of the ideas of objects set in a spatial manifold; therefore, there is no absolute space. Consequently, Newton was in error, for he hypostatized an absolute space and an absolute time not *out* of events but *for* events in order that the universe might be seen as lawful. And similarly for absolute motion. To Berkeley the postulate of ideal motion is meaningless, since it is conceived as independent of perceived bodies and perceived relations.

However, the errors of Newton extend beyond his treatment of space, time, and motion. To Berkeley, gravitation is not an empirical law but a tautology. "Newton's harangue amounts to no more than that

---

[7] For a contemporary treatment of a similar idea, see E. Schrödinger, *What is Life?*

gravity is proportionate to gravity" (*Commonplace Book,* No. 361). And even the method of fluxions in the newly invented calculus fell under attack. Here Berkeley is perhaps at his polemical best as he turns the arguments of the antimetaphysical infidels against their own mathematical edifice.

Berkeley's comments upon mathematics can be found in several of his works, but it is in the *Analyst* that he systematically undercuts the methods of infinitesimal calculus. First, he notes that certain "infidels" in mathematics rule out mysteries of metaphysics and religious faith presumably because of their extra-empirical character; and yet, in their own work, they resort to the methods of infinitesimals which are at least equally remote from empirical meaning. Characteristically, differential calculus makes use of the ratio between units of change in two related variables. Thus, for example, velocity is a ratio between $\Delta d$ and $\Delta t$, the latter representing the increments of change in distance and time. When velocity is changing in time, as it is in problems involving acceleration, then the instantaneous velocity can be found only by making $\Delta d$ and $\Delta t$ smaller and smaller. The gist of Berkeley's argument is that it is nonsensical to assert that one can make $\Delta d$ and $\Delta t$ vanishingly small and still end up with a finite value for their ratio. If to be is to be perceived, then matter, space, and time are not infinitely divisible. The infinitely small is not perceivable. Thus, in a classic passage which might conceivably appeal to the beginning student of differential calculus, Berkeley remarks:

> A point, therefore, is considered as a triangle, or a triangle is supposed to be formed in a point. Which to conceive seems quite impossible. Yet to some there are who, though they shrink at all other mysteries, make no difficulty of their own, who strain at a gnat and swallow a camel (*Analyst;* in the *Works,* p. 282).

Berkeley was equally critical of ideas of the infinitely large. There is no space without its being populated by ideas; i.e., the idea of space is constructible only from ideas instrumented by the tactual and other senses. Mathematicians may treat space as they treat lines in geometric optics, but it must be realized that without such abstractions being translated into sense data, they become mere fictions. To Berkeley, then, mathematics has a formal character. One may do what he will with his symbols and his fluxions; the sins of the mathematician stem from his hypostatizing his mathematical entities (cf. N2.7).

A final point concerning the philosophy of Berkeley: if to be is to be perceived and the idea is the perception, then there must be a perceiver. "This perceiving active being is what I call *mind, spirit, soul,* or *myself*" (*Principles,* ¶ 2). And then, Berkeley passes on to other issues. He saw clearly that nothing much could be added to his perceiver, for the act of perceiving cannot itself be the object of perception. However, this willingness to postulate being other than idea kept Berkeley from complete skepticism and did indeed result in his being a subjective idealist, and a somewhat orthodox theist, rather than a committed phenomenalist.[8]

## David Hume (1711–1776)

Critics and historians often succumb to the temptation to classify Hume as the heir of Locke and Berkeley. Indeed, there is good reason to do so. His early critics and expositors (Reid, Beattie, and Green) treated him as such. And the refinements of his skepticism inescapably follow from a theory of knowledge which attributes to perceptual data their crucial pre-eminence. On the other hand, thinkers other than the empiricists left their impression upon his works. The philosopher Hutcheson showed Hume that not all philosophical convictions are supportable by logic or experience alone, that at some point one must resort to sentiment, to taste, or to some other emotionally satisfying commitment. But what is more important to us, Hume was also greatly influenced by the continental rationalists, especially by Descartes. The role of reason and the logic of doubting and contradiction were to play a much more significant role in his skepticism than they ever did in the philosophies of Locke and Berkeley.

*Analysis of causation.*    Consider the notion of causation. Berkeley was a phenomenalist and a skeptic concerning physical causation, as was Locke perhaps by implication. Causal relations were reduced to concatenations of events; and aside from the sequence and juxtaposition of such events; all that remains of the ontological substance of cause is the residue of psychological expectancy. Now this discussion reads very much like that of Hume's justly famed account of causation in which contiguity, habit, and expectation play important roles. Yet, Hume did not arrive at his own analysis by the direct route we would expect of him were he simply to have carried on the radical empirical analysis of his two great predecessors.

Let us consider this matter further. We begin with the simples. Hume, like Locke and Berkeley, derives all ideas from perception. For Hume, the immediate data of experience are impressions; these are the most lively or vivacious of the cognitive events. Ideas are "faint images" of impressions in thinking and reasoning, and although ideas

---

[8] Noting the problems here, Thomas Reid writes:

He [Berkeley] maintains that we have no idea of spirits, and that we can think, and speak, and reason about them, and about their attributes, without having any ideas of them. If this is so, my Lord, what should hinder us from thinking and reasoning about bodies and their qualities, without having ideas of them? The Bishop either did not think of this question, or did not think fit to give any answer to it (Reid, 1810; p. 466).

vary as to their faintness or strength, all are reducible to impressions: *"That all our simple ideas in their first appearance are deriv'd from simple impressions, which are correspondent to them, and which they exactly represent"* (*Treatise*, I: I:I). This is the thesis of phenomenalism. It is also the precept for a theory of meaning. Now, according to Hume, it is a fact that we have notions of "cause" and "causation." The psychological account as to how these ideas arise, however interesting it may be, is of no relevance to the epistemological analysis. Our question is: "Do we have an 'idea' of a casual relation of, say, *A* efficiently causing *B* to move?" This question is loaded now in favor of the answer Berkeley might have given. "No, there is no idea, no impression with which to identify the efficient cause." Yet Hume nowhere discusses Berkeley in this context, nor does he seek to analyze causal impressionism on purely phenomenalistic grounds. Rather he pursues a logical argument. And in this he reveals the influence of the continental rationalists more than that of the empiricists.

In substance, Hume argues that we have no idea of absolute necessity existing as a connection between two ideas (events). Neither experience nor reason will attest to that necessity. But before evaluating the role of experience in generating notions of causality, we must first show that reason alone cannot give rise to ideas of causation.

Hume's more analytic treatment of causality is to be found in *A Treatise of Human Nature*. It is here that he lays out the logical character of the argument (cf. N2.8). Knowledge is composed of relations between ideas. The expression of the relations of the ideas is found in the proposition.[9] The nature of the proposition is determined by the character of the relation. If the proposition expresses a relation between two ideas such that this relation is invariable, then the proposition is indubitable. That is to say, it would be inconceivable that we should deny the truth of such a proposition. For example, "The sum of the angles of a triangle is equal to two right angles" is such a proposition. (It was not until later that such propositions were to be called "analytic.") On the other hand, if the ideas which are components of the proposition are not invariably related but are separable, then the truth of such a proposition is contingent upon the occurrence of the ideas.[10]

With this distinction in mind, Hume then proceeds systematically to show that a causal relation cannot be of the first, or analytic, type. First, the contradiction of any proposition *"A is the cause of B"* is always conceivable. Therefore, no proposition of a causal character is either logi-

---

[9] The language of propositional analysis was adopted in the more popular *Enquiry Concerning Human Understanding*. For convenience that language is adopted here.

[10] This distinction is carried over into the *Enquiry* as that between *Relations of Ideas* and *Matters of Fact* (No. 20).

cally necessary or intuitively certain. The argument from "the productive principle" of a first cause also will not do. Any gambit that one may wish to make concerning the need for a cause to bring some thing, or idea, into existence is always subject to the possibility of contradiction. It is not true necessarily that every effect must have a cause. It is not contradictory to assert that *no* cause may precede a so-called effect, nor to assert that a thing can be its own cause. Nor is it true that the idea of effect logically implies the idea of cause. Thus Hume concludes, "The true state of the question is, whether every object, which begins to exist, must owe its existence to a cause; and this I assert neither to be intuitively nor demonstratively certain . . ." (*Treatise;* I: III:III).

Now it is only after the logical analysis and rejection of causation are completed that Hume turns to the psychological analysis which is to place him within the empiricist camp:

> Since it is not from knowledge or any scientific reasoning, that we derive the opinion of the necessity of a cause to every new production, that opinion must necessarily arise from observation and experience. The next question, then should naturally be, *how experience gives rise to such a principle?* But as I find it will be more convenient to sink this question in the following, *Why we conclude, that such particular causes must necessarily have such particular effects, and why we form an inference from one to another?* we shall make that the subject of our future enquiry. 'Twill, perhaps, be found in the end, that the same answer will serve both questions (*Treatise,* I: III:III).

Thus a problem which has psychological roots resolves itself into the problem of inductive inference.

From the passage quoted above Hume indicates that a purely psychological analysis of our notions of causality will not suffice. To see or know that a particular succession of events occurs habitually, or in constant conjunction, does not tell us how in effect we utilize the emergent notions of causality to make inferences. Such notions are internalized; i.e., they determine expectancies and serve as the basis for our making inferences from one to another state of affairs. Hume says, "There is no object which implies the existence of any other if we consider these objects in themselves, and never look beyond the ideas which we form of them" (*Treatise;* I: III:VI). However, our impressions and ideas are not independent in a purely punctiform sense. In a mnemonic context, they perseverate and overlap one another to form a coherent sequence. Thus according to our experience, events are not seen as disconnected but as overlapping and in such a way that the occurrence of an event we call a "cause" leads us to expect, *but not with certainty,* that another event, the "effect," will follow. This relation of expectancy is to be differentiated from the necessary relations of reason. It is a matter of belief or of "probability." But what kind of probability?

The idea of cause and effect is deriv'd from *experience,* which informs us, that such particular objects, in all past instances, have been constantly conjoin'd with each other: And as an object similar to one of these is suppos'd to be immediately present in its impression, we thence presume on the existence of one similar to its usual attendant. According to this account of things, which is, I think, in every point unquestionable, probability is founded on the presumption of a resemblance betwixt those objects, of which we have had experience, and those of which we have had none; and therefore 'tis impossible this presumption can arise from probability (*Treatise;* I: III:VI).

For our purposes the last sentence in the passage could be italicized. It is plain that we should regard probability not as of logical relation connecting events but as a matter of belief which serves as the basis for inferring one event from another. This, of course, is consistent with the denial of an implicit logical connection between events. And it is important to emphasize that the probability of which Hume writes refers not to events, as such, but rather to the state of mind concerning such events. His relating probability and belief is not unlike the treatment we meet later in the discussions of subjective probability (cf. N2.9). In summary: "The necessary connexion betwixt causes and effects is the foundation of our inference from one to another. The foundation of our experience is in the transition arising from the accustom'd union. These are, therefore, the same" (*Treatise;* I: III:XIV).

*Self.*     We find, then, that *causation, resemblance,* and *contiguity* are the relations by which we associate ideas. As such, these relations have no existential significance; they represent activities of the imagination, and not ideas reducible in any way to impressions. Of these, the first two are instrumental in our deriving notions of the self (ego) and personal identity. Here, too, Hume is skeptical. In a passage well known to psychologists, Hume writes:

> . . . what we call a *mind* is nothing but a heap or collection of different perceptions, united together by certain relations, and supposed, though falsely, to be endowed with a perfect simplicity and identity (*Treatise;* I: IV:II).

As in the treatment of causality, Hume carefully examines the "idea" of the self only to find that it, too, is obfuscated in the flux of perceptual impressions. There is no sharp image of the ego. What there is evaporates as we attempt to bring it into focus:

> For my part, when I enter most intimately into what I call *myself,* I always stumble on some particular impression or other, of heat or cold, light or shade, love or hatred, pain or pleasure. I never catch *myself* at any time without a perception, and never can observe any thing but

the perception. . . . If any one upon serious and unprejudic'd reflexion, thinks he has a different notion of *himself,* I must confess I can reason no longer with him. All I can allow him is, that he may be right as well as I, and that we are essentially different in this particular. He may, perhaps, perceive something simple and continu'd, which he calls *himself,* tho' I am certain there is no such principle in me.

But setting aside some metaphysicians of this kind, I may venture to affirm of the rest of mankind, that they are nothing but a bundle or collection of different perceptions, which succeed each other with an inconceivable rapidity, and are in a perpetual flux and movement (*Treatise;* I: IV:VI).

How then, we may ask, do notions of the self arise? As in the case of causal analysis, Hume turns to memory and to belief based upon the concatenation of events. First, he notes that the idea of identity, itself, is suspect. This notion derives from a succession of related impressions. If we are not cognizant of small changes in the sequence of impressions, then we impute a perseverating identity to the object. And if the object of thought is our own connected flux of perceptions, the identity we affirm is the personal self. Second, the matter of belief operates as it does in cause and effect connections. From any moment of our impression, we make inferences to a succeeding moment. Since we are dealing here with awarenesses of one's own impressions, the locale, as it were, for the succession of these awarenesses appears to be the self.

Again, as in the case of causality, Hume does not deny that we have "ideas" or notions of the self. What he denies, or rather what he brings into the purview of his skepticism, is the fact that one has no direct impression of the self, nor any idea of it which reduces directly, without the aid of imagination, to impressions. It is this reductive analysis which tells Hume that the self is no more than a flux of perceptions.

*Metaphysics.*     A third point concerning Hume's contribution to empiricism is his explicit distrust of metaphysics. He is distinguished from his predecessors by being more explicit than they about this distrust. Metaphysical assertions are questioned on the grounds that the meaning of any metaphysical proposition must be arbitrated by means of what Zabeeh (1960) calls the "principle of the priority of impressions to ideas." Hume agrees with Berkeley's formulation of skepticism. One cannot penetrate behind the shell of impressions to get at the substratum of substance. Space and time are contextual constructions; they derive from the particular occurrences of events and have no reality, no meaning aside from the given context. The idea of existence is bound to the occurrence of impressions. Every impression carries with it the predication of its own existence; the two are inseparable. Therefore, there is no property of existence which does not include the presence of an impression. And, finally, abstract ideas are limited by the conventions of selecting and classifying particulars for the linguistic convenience of the observer.

There is not much which is original here in the substantive aspects of Hume's critique. What sets Hume apart from Locke and Berkeley is the stress he puts on systematic principles for deciding which questions are meaningful. Either our judgments must have the support of reason (i.e., are logically true) or they must be reducible to a set of impressions. In the opening paragraphs of the *Enquiry* Hume writes, "When we entertain, therefore, any suspicion that a philosophical term is employed without any meaning or idea (as is but too frequent), we need but enquire, *from what impression is that* supposed idea derived?" (¶ 17). Hume is fully aware that this principle has serious implications for traditional philosophy. The above quotation is taken from the attack on metaphysics which introduces the *Enquiry*. At most, we can permit the indulgence in metaphysics as a "gratification of an innocent curiosity." But even an innocent indulgence can be misleading. Metaphysical ideas obscure philosophy and science alike, and as to the "gratification," Hume writes:

> . . . yet ought not even this to be despised. . . . The sweetest most inoffensive path of life leads through the avenues of science and learning; and whoever can either remove any obstructions in this way, or open up any new prospect, ought so far to be esteemed a benefactor to mankind (¶ 6).

Just as he opens his *Enquiry* with imputations against metaphysics, so does he close it. In the famous final paragraph, he bids us to "commit . . . then to the flames" our libraries of senseless philosophy (cf. N2.10).

Attention has been given to Hume's treatment of causality, the personal self, and the crude criteria of meaning. With respect to refinements on the latter point we must take note of the important distinction Hume makes between logical truths, or *relations of ideas,* as he calls them, and empirical truths, or *matters of fact*. The distinction is nascent within the writings of Leibniz, although the latter would say that logical truths are not empty of content. It is explicitly made by Locke when he differentiates "trifling propositions" (identities, definitions by class membership) from particular propositions. It is implicit within Berkeley's conventionalistic treatment of mathematics. And it becomes an all important departure for Kant's *Critique of Pure Reason*. Its significance rests in its being prescriptive of what classes of propositions lend themselves to meaningful discourse. It is little wonder then that this, the distinction between *analytic* and *synthetic* propositions, was to become crucial to the positivistic theory of meaning.

In brief, *relations of ideas* refer to propositions of logic "which are discoverable by the mere operation of thought." Hume recognized that mathematical propositions are of this character despite the fact that concepts of number and geometry may have been acquired through experience. But so far as matters of fact are concerned, reason plays no part. The relations by which we build complex ideas of the world are those such as causal connection, contiguity, and resemblance. And, as Hume takes great pains to show, reason is not involved in these associative relations. The truth of logical propositions can be ascertained only by thought; the device for testing the truth of such propositions is the principle of contradiction.

*Matters of fact* are readily distinguishable from purely logical propositions on the basis of the principle of contradiction. The contradictory of a logical proposition is simply nonsense; but for any meaningful empirical proposition, its contradictory is also meaningful. That is to say, it is possible to visualize a situation which renders the empirical proposition false. The truth, then, of a proposition which expresses a matter of fact is contingent upon a perceptual state of affairs. Thus, the truth of any such proposition is reducible to sets of impressions or to ideas which themselves are reducible to these impressions. In the *Enquiry,* Hume applies this distinction between types of propositions as the scalpel of his skepticism. By means of it, he attempts to separate sense from nonsense in philosophy and science. It is here that the positivists' indebtedness to Hume is most conspicuous. The positivists were to adopt a similar rubric of propositions as the basis for a theory of meaning.

## SUMMARY

Our review of the British empiricists is completed. We need not concern ourselves with contributions of the immediate successors of Hume. Nor need we touch on issues other than those relating to the philosophy of science. In many respects the philosophies of Locke, Berkeley, and Hume are quite divergent; and it is often overlooked that each of the three, in his own way, used his skepticism as a means of affirming some kind of knowledge, whether it be scientific, spiritual, or moral. Skepticism, in other words, was not for them an end in itself. But whatever their divergencies, their communalities in the theory of knowledge are what remains significant for scientific empiricism.

Let us summarize as follows. The significant elements of the empirical philosophy are: (1) Knowledge of the world is reducible to perceptual data, to experience; there is no direct access to knowledge except by observation. (2) Complex ideas are derived from simple ideas (percepts); a complex idea is meaningful only if it can be reduced to a set of simple ideas. (3) Pure logic, i.e., argument originating in the manifold of logic itself, cannot yield knowledge of the external world. Events are logically independent of one another. (4) Existence propositions imply a perceptual state of affairs. (5) Arguments both in science and philosophy must conform to a logico-empirical rubric of propositions in order to be considered meaningful. (6) Abstract ideas are conventions for classifying particulars, each of which possesses the appropriate defining properties. No subsistent extra-empirical reals or essences can be isolated as part of, or as underlying, that abstract idea. (Locke, to the contrary, acknowledged substance and essence; but he affirmed that nothing can be known of them.) (7) Physical concepts such as causality, space, time, are to be examined critically. Rather than being observables, or being ontologically primitive, they are schemata which are conventionally derived for the relating and association of events. The statements above outline an empiricist theory of meaning that defines and thereby restricts the limits of knowledge.

Finally, and incidentally to the issues here, it should be added that skepticism such as that of the British empiricists does not necessarily culminate in the rejection of ideas dear to the tender heart or to common sense. It is only that ideas, if we may call them that, of morals and the metaphysics of common sense must be sanctioned by sentiment or by taste rather than by logic or by empirics. If we accept Kemp Smith's analysis of Hume's essays (N. Kemp Smith, 1960), then we are to interpret skepticism as the route to a naturalistic theory of the world, not because experience or logic compels us to take this way, but rather because there is something inherently satisfying about such a theory. One of the little-appreciated ironies of Hume's analysis is that on closer examination he appears to reassert the very ideas he found wanting in the court of his own skepticism.

# NOTES

## NOTE 2.1

As is well known, antiquity is not distinguished for its accomplishments in experimental science. Some writers are disparaging (e.g., Farrington, 1944; Russell, 1946), even going so far as to claim that Greek philosophic preoccupations were a tragedy against the spirit of science. It is doubtless true that the Academy and the Lyceum stressed logic, mathematics, and rational discourse over experimental investigations, yet there can be little question that the Greeks from Thales to Ptolemy had an intense curiosity about the world they lived in. True also, the Greeks were more interested in the cosmos than they were in terrestrial investigations, but they were not the last to attempt to build a theory before they had the facts.

There are many sources for the study of Greek science. I can only mention a few. The mathematical sciences of Babylon and of Greece are covered in O. Neugebauer, *The Exact Sciences in Antiquity*. For general references: M. Clagett, *Greek Science in Antiquity;* S. Sambursky, *The Physical World of the Greeks;* G. de Santillana, *The Origins of Scientific Thought;* and G. Sarton, *A History of Science*. For an appreciative treatment of the achievements of Greek science, see S. Toulmin and J. Goodfield, *The Fabric of the Heavens*.

Historical research on the science of the Renaissance and post-Renaissance periods has been especially productive. Aside from studies of the works of individuals, the following general sources are readily available: E. A. Burtt, *The Metaphysical Foundations of Modern Science;* A. C. Crombie, *Medieval and Early Modern Science*, 2 volumes; H. Butterworth, *The Origins of Modern Science;* A. R. Hall, *The Scientific Revolution;* A. Koyré, *From the Closed to the Infinite Universe*. For accounts which reveal that not all of the Middle Ages was darkness see Crombie (1959), vol. 1, and M. Clagett, *The Science of Mechanics in the Middle Ages*.

## NOTE 2.2

Although Descartes applied his method to the ontological proof of God, he was very much world-oriented. He trusted intuition to give him information about the world. Then by logical amplification of the simple to the complex, he arrived at a mechanistic picture of the material world. He fell out with Blaise Pascal, after the latter's conversion, over issues in support of science and applied mathematics. Moreover, he thought his method general. For example, in a study of Descartes' method, Joachim concludes:

> By method he [Descartes] means certain and easy rules such that anyone who precisely obeys them will never take for truth anything that is false, and will advance step by step, in the correct order without waste of mental energy, to the knowledge of everything he is capable of knowing (1957, p. 63).

Descartes was very skillful in the application of his own method. He was reported to challenge his listeners by deriving a set of simples to support any given conclusion or to show that a given conclusion was false by deriving it from insupportable premises. Of this skill, the mathematician Poisson noted that Descartes:

> . . . would first ask many questions about the definition of the terms, and, after that, the meaning of certain principles received in the schools. He would then ask whether they would not agree on certain known principles which he pretended to accept . . . and, on the basis of the whole would fashion one single argument which it was very difficult to evade (quoted in Roth, 1937; p. 65).

In the procedures for deduction, Descartes stressed what he called "enumeration." This referred to the practice of combing the argumentive skein carefully for any breaks or tangles in logic. Mathematics will be of no help if such abuses in logic occur. And he cautioned against the cavalier postulation and reification of the mathematical variables.

## NOTE 2.3

Spinoza was neither antiscientific nor antiempirical. Rather like some of the absolute idealists to follow, he complained that empiricists are often not empirical enough. In fact, Spinoza anticipates the empiricists concerning the formation of ideas. The idea of, say, "man" is a composite image of all characteristics, acts, relations of which we are perceptually or ideationally aware. But this is a very limited selection of the total predicates we can assign to man in the vast complexity of interacting events. The cognitive activities as described and catalogued by the psychologist are simply insufficient for providing us with adequate general ideas. Such activities are often too selective, too much biased with our own passions, for us to achieve a fair survey of all the predicates appropriate to an idea.

The fact is, however, that in spite of Spinoza's idealization of mathematics and logic, in spite of the fact that he uses a Euclidean format for the arguments in his treatises, he does not have a method of analysis which has proved useful to the philosophy of science. This may be due in large part to our behavioral empiricism, but as we become preoccupied with the "designs for brains," the relevance of some of Spinoza's analyses may emerge (cf. Hawkins, 1962).

## NOTE 2.4

The premises of the Leibnizian argument are as follows:

I.   Every proposition has a subject and a predicate.
II.  A subject may have predicates which are qualities existing at various times. (Such a subject is called *a substance*.)
III. True propositions not asserting existence at particular times are necessary and analytic, but such as assert existence at particular times are contingent and synthetic. The latter depend on final causes.
IV.  The Ego is a substance.
V.   Perception yields knowledge of an external world; i.e., of existents other than myself and my states (Russell; 1949, p. 4).

In addition we have the following distinctions and principles:

1. *A necessary* (analytically true) proposition is one whose predicates are contained in the definitions of the subject. *A contingent* proposition (synthetically, *a posteriori* true) is one whose predicate is not contained in the subject.

2. *Law of contradiction:* Two contradictories cannot be held to be true.

3. *Principle of sufficient reason:* Contingent propositions are such that there must be facts to make them true, all events must have a cause.

4. *Principle of the identity of indiscernibles:* No two substances are completely alike; two substances differ as to the predicates they support.

Derivations of the arguments are too involved to consider here. However, some implications of the logistic system are of interest. One, the idea of substance derives from the fact that all predicates are assignable to a subject; the subject itself is definable by a set of predicates. Therefore, substance is the subject of the predicates which are analytically equivalent to the subject and is thereby subsistent to the subject. Two, a subject is completely implied (i.e., the substance is known) only when all possible predicates are assigned to it. Thus the complete definition of a subject entails an analytically equivalent set of predicates. (This type of analysis has been the source of subsequent concern over the logical distinctions between analytic and synthetic propositions.) And three, regarding the notion of cause, a concatenation of physical events does not constitute an adequate causal explication of those events. This idea is often thought of as being endemic to the causal skepticism of the empiricists; namely, there is no experience of the agencies of causality as such.

One can appreciate the Leibnizian analysis without succumbing to the surface blandishments of the monadology. For example, in his early study of Leibniz, Russell (1900) rejected the subject–predicate structure of all propositions, but he was later to make the independence of monads the fruitful source of his own logical atomism. In fact, Russell was the first in recent times to draw attention to Leibniz's original contributions to logic.


## NOTE 2.5

Nominalism implies that what a thing is is exhaustively describable in terms of the totality of its empirical attributes. Realism implies there are underlying essences, or things in themselves, of which objects partake by means of their attributes. What the latter implies is that there is some real essence whose description is not equivalent to the enumeration and relating of a set of attributes. Since Locke does postulate substance as a binding media for predicates, there may be some justification for attributing belief in real essences to him. However, he makes it clear that the notion of real essences is of little service to us:

> . . . the supposition of essences that cannot be known, and the making them nevertheless to be that which distinguishes the species of things, is so wholly useless and unserviceable to any part of our knowledge, that that alone were sufficient to make us lay it by, and content ourselves with such essences of the sorts or species of things as come within the reach of our knowledge: which, when seriously considered, will be found, as I have said, to be nothing else but those abstract complex ideas to which we have annexed distinct general names (*Essay;* III. 3.17).

Thus in an offhand way Locke does admit real essences, but only as they are to be translated into abstract ideas which in turn derive from the experiencing of particulars having common properties. The whole point of postulating real essences is nullified when Locke tells us: "It is plain, by what has been said, that *general* and *universal* belong not to the real existence of things; but are the inventions and creatures of the understanding, made by it for its own use, and concern only signs, whether words or ideas" (*Essay;* III. 3.11).

And again in passages that follow, he emphasizes that universals do not belong to particular things, but "are only creatures of our own making." It would seem clear from the above, and other passages as well, that Locke is conventionalistic in his treatment of general ideas; that is to say, general ideas are to be regarded as the conventions of the understanding for managing many particulars. Whether this treatment warrants the sustained attack that Berkeley was later to give it is questionable. Locke was careful to endow general ideas with a conventionalistic character and Berkeley does not concentrate on this aspect of such ideas. Rather, he would think of Locke's general ideas as signifying things. And, of course, Berkeley is correct in thinking that things can only be particulars.

## NOTE 2.6

In a letter to Locke, Molyneux proposed a question which has been a source of classroom curiosity ever since. "Suppose," he begins, "a man born blind, and now adult, and taught by his touch to distinguish between a cube and a sphere. . . ." The question goes on to specify standard conditions of the ball and sphere, etc. and then inquires: if the man suddenly were to gain his eyesight would he then be able to distinguish between the two objects by vision alone? The consensus of Locke's contemporaries was "no." The answer was based on the supposition that senses were independent, as if their relationship was assumed to be strictly orthogonal. It was assumed that tactual acquaintance with objects gives no knowledge whatsoever of visual linear perspective. On fairly recent lines, experimental evidence relevant to the question has come forth. Senden (1960), analyzing the visual adjustments of individuals cured by operation of congenital cataract, and Riesen (1947), working with chimpanzees reared in darkness, have found evidence which would, for the most part, support the empiricists.

## NOTE 2.7

The fact is that the Berkelian critique of the calculus continued to plague mathematics until the last century, at which time analysis in terms of limits succeeded in circumventing the problems of infinitesimals. The *Analyst* evoked immediate reaction from mathematicians who were already deifying

Newton in his own lifetime. However, Berkeley's argument was weakened because of its *tu quoque* character. He takes the infidel mathematicians to task for not accepting the "mysteries of religion" on authority or faith, when in turn they embrace the fictions of infinitesimals without misgivings. This, of course, was beside the point. Berkeley was not angling for an entente with the infidels; he was presenting a serious critique of mathematical methods and this on the basis of misgivings which were gestating within his mind at least from the time of his *Commonplace Book*. Berkeley states the argument in the following ways:

> Now, as our Sense is strained and puzzled with the perception of objects extremely minute, even so the imagination, which faculty derives from sense, is very much strained and puzzled to frame clear ideas of the least particles of time or the least increments generated therein; and much more so to comprehend the moments, or those increments of the flowing quantities in *statu nascenti;* in their very first origin or beginning to exist before they become particles. (*Analyst,* No. 4)

And again,

> Now to conceive a quantity infinitely small—that is, infinitely less than any sensible or imaginable quantity, or than the least finite magnitude—is, I confess, above my capacity. (*Analyst,* No. 5)

Then covering both Newtonian and Leibnizian methods of calculus he offers:

> But he who can digest a second or third fluxion or a. second or third difference, need not, methinks, be squeamish about any point in divinity. (*Analyst,* No. 7)

Berkeley did not contest the findings of the methods of calculus ("I have no controversy about your conclusions but only about your logic and method"). He objected only to the defense of doubtful presuppositions on the grounds they lead to reasonable consequences: "I say that in every other science men prove their conclusions by their principles, and not their principles by their conclusions" (*Analyst,* No. 19). In this context, at least, and doubtless in all others, Berkeley goes on record as being opposed to the hypothetico–deductive method.

Berkeley was subjected to vigorous and at times abusive attacks by the mathematicians of his day. He was a skillful polemicist and could return abuse when necessary. In his reply to Dr. Jurins, the *Philalethes Cantabrigiensis* of a series of published attacks upon the *Analyst,* Berkeley writes:

> You represent yourself as a man 'whose highest ambition is in the lowest degree to imitate Sir Isaac Newton.' It might, perhaps, have suited better with your appelation Philalethes, and been altogether as laudable, if your highest ambition had been to discover truth. ("A Defense of Freethinking in Mathematics," *Analyst,* No. 15)

## NOTE 2.8

The textual discussion is drawn primarily from Book I of *A Treatise of Human Nature*. Although published in 1739, this work had been completed in 1736 before Hume had reached the age of twenty-six. It is the work of a brilliant young man. Its style is discursive and at times cumbersome, but it represents a forthright examination of all issues germane at that time to a theory of knowledge: the origin of ideas, the nature of abstract ideas, space and time, cause and effect, the limits of human knowledge, and the range of skepticism. *The Enquiry Concerning Human Understanding* is a more readable but less comprehensive book. Hume himself considered this latter work to be the definitive statement of his philosophy; but in spite of proprietary claims, philosophers are seldom afforded the prerogative of judging their own works. In Hume's case, scholars are inclined to prefer the *Treatise*.

The style of the *Enquiry* is more felicitous than that of the *Treatise*. The work is written by a person conscious of rhetoric. It represents a skillful editorial and rewrite job of the *Treatise*. As Selby-Bigge suggests in the introduction to his edition of the *Enquiry,* Hume edited out those parts of the *Treatise* which would be found "the least generally interesting to the habitués of the coffee houses"—that clientele which like today had discovered reading as an acceptable source of pleasure.

Nevertheless, the *Enquiry* is distinguished for its clarity and for what Selby-Bigge calls its "applied philosophy." That is to say, the *Enquiry,* more than the *Treatise,* draws out the philosophical implications of skepticism. It more clearly reveals the antimetaphysical bias of critical empiricism.

## NOTE 2.9

In both the *Enquiry* and the *Treatise* Hume distinguishes between the probability of chances and "the probability of cause" in a way suggestive of contemporary writers on the subject of probability. The probability of chances relates to denumerable events each of which can be assigned equal chance. This leads directly to the classical treatment of probability according to the premise of equally likely events. On the other hand, the probability of cause relates to a state of subjective expectancy, and nowadays would be referred to as subjective probability. A significant aspect of this distinction is that subjective probability does not serve as the basis for relating classes of objects in the world (as we might expect from the treatments of Venn, Peirce, and other nonsubjectivist students of probable inference). Although, as Hume indicates, the evaluation of chances may determine our subjective expectancies in the probability of causes, it is not necessary that they do. In the absence of a uniform calculus, we can only rely upon the mnemonic repository of positive and negative instances in a given relation.

In this context it is of interest to call attention to the conventionalistic aspect of Hume's philosophy which, according to Kemp Smith, has been seriously underplayed. Hume was influenced by the philosopher Hutcheson perhaps as much as he was by Locke and Berkeley. In a series of essays published in the decade prior to the *Treatise,* Hutcheson had argued that in the face of skepticism and uncertainty one is impelled to reason from premises of taste and preference. This especially is true in the area of moral theory. However, Hume appropriated taste as a means literally for escaping an incapacitating skepticism in the field of epistemology. Lacking any logical basis for causal inference, and lacking any assurance of a universe guided by a principle of the uniformity of nature, man is compelled to resort to judgments whose justification is other than logical. Hume writes as follows:

> Thus all probable reasoning is nothing but a species of sensation. 'Tis not solely in poetry and music, we must follow our taste and sentiment, but likewise in philosophy. When I am convinc'd of any principle, 'tis only an idea, which strikes more strongly upon me. When I give the preference to one set of arguments above another, I do nothing but decide from my feeling concerning the superiority of their influence. Objects have no discoverable connexion together; nor is it from any other principle but custom operating upon the imagination, that we can draw any inference from the appearance of one to the existence of another (*Treatise;* I: III: VIII).

Hume does not argue for necessary connection, that is certain; however, he does affirm that belief is a plausible ground for inference and that in the face of uncertainty he commits himself to the logically and empirically unsupportable conventions of his belief.


## NOTE 2.10

The paragraph is quoted in N1.2.

Despite the brashness of passages such as this in the *Enquiry,* the *Treatise* is perhaps the more skeptical work. Whether the former was an effort to popularize or an effort to bring to Hume "the literary fame" he candidly sought is beside the point. He is aware in the *Treatise* that his analyses are unrelentingly skeptical. Almost every idea he touches is subjected to distinctive critical analysis: the material world, space and time (not extensively covered in the *Enquiry*), causality, the self, religion, and metaphysics in general. It is only in Books II and III that the more affirmative aspects of his philosophy are revealed.

As Hume confesses, living his critical philosophy is a lonely, somewhat insane life. He has attacked mathematicians, metaphysicians, and theologians with equal fervor:

> I am first affrighted and confounded with that forlorn solitude, in which I am plac'd in my philosophy, and fancy myself some strange uncouth monster, who not being able to mingle and unite in society, has been expell'd all human commerce. . . . When I look abroad, I foresee on every side, dispute, contradiction, anger, calumny and detraction. When I turn my eye inward, I find nothing but doubt and ignorance. All the world conspires to oppose and contradict me, tho' such is my weakness, that I feel all my opinions loosen and fall of themselves, when unsupported by the approbation of others (*Treatise;* I. IV:VII).

Presumably, when he later left philosophy for history, Hume was to regain his sanity, and his friends.

# CHAPTER 3

# Kant, Phenomenalism, and Phenomenology

SUBSEQUENT CRITIQUES of empiricistic philosophy served both to draw out and to sharpen the issues upon which a contemporary scientific empiricism was to establish itself as a positivistic philosophy. Here we shall briefly touch upon three such influences. One is the philosophy of Immanuel Kant. The other two are philosophical themes, both of which emphasize the phenomenally contingent character of our knowledge. Phenomenalism stresses sense data as the irreducible and indispensable givens of all knowledge, with those sense data being epistemically prior to perceiver and perceived alike. Phenomenology, on the other hand, stresses the participative role of the perceiver. There is a distinction to be made between the relation of any two or more objects and the relation between a subject and its objects. This distinction implies that no primary givens, such as the sense data of the phenomenalists, can be predicated independently of the unique participative ego. All perception involves the relation of the perceiving subject and its object.

Kant was to claim that knowledge of the world requires of the perceiver prior organizational propensity as well as sensory input. Therefore, no knowledge would be possible under Hume's radical empiricism of sensory impressions. On the other hand, no knowledge transcends the schemata for the organization of sense input. Therefore, *meta*physics is impossible. Phenomenalism rejected the *a priorism* of Kant and took the sense data as the given neutral stuff out of which both subject and object alike were to be constructed. It has proved a popular doctrine; one, because it has emphasized the importance of the idea of the basic data of experience, and two, because it lends itself to systematic empiricism such

46

as that of logical atomism and positivism. And phenomenology, more nearly Kantian, emerged to protest that a person's perceiving and thinking about an object is productive of phenomenal representations quite unlike anything that might defensibly be regarded as the object itself.

Phenomenalism has been a popular though not entirely adequate doctrine for the empiricist. Kant in his way and phenomenology in its ways have been critical of the apparent naïveté of pure empiricism. Empiricists have had to seek counterarguments to these critiques. They have often succeeded, yet it must be noted that Kant did raise significant issues for the empiricist. The modern empiricist has had to contend with the problems of the structure of experience, of hypothesis and presupposition, even after it has no longer been popular to embrace nativism and intuition.

## IMMANUEL KANT (1724–1804)

Kant was as plodding as Hume was precocious. Hume had written the draft of his *Treatise* by the time he was twenty-six. Kant did not publish a major philosophical work until he was over twice that age (cf. N3.1). His great work, the *Critique of Pure Reason* (1781), gestated over a period of eleven years. During that time he compiled his discursive notes, but the denoument of the problems of empiricism came only after reading Hume's *Enquiries*. Then the finished copy of the *Critique* was completed in a matter of a few months. As Bertrand Russell puts it: "Hume, by his criticism of the concept of causality, awakened him [Kant] from his dogmatic slumbers—so at least he says, but the awakening was only temporary, and he soon invented a soporific which enabled him to sleep again" (1947, p. 731).

What is the soporific? It is a difficult philosophy, more circumspectly respected nowadays than read. Acknowledged to be important, it is soon laid aside, for Kant made the mistake of prematurely giving dogmatic answers to the questions raised by the empiricists (cf. N3.2). The dogmatism would not stand up, for the heart of it—the idea of the *a priori* structuring of our knowledge of the physical world—committed science and philosophy alike to the enduring framework of absolute Newtonian space and time. When this imperative for a unique spatio–temporal structure had to yield to alternative relativistic hypotheses, the whole argument for the *a priori* conditions of knowledge seemed to buckle. Kant was in error concerning the nature of the physical world, and *a fortiori* concerning the constructual aspects of the mind. Thus empiricism was to take a less dogmatic turn, keep to its skeptical ways, and, for the psychologist at least, make room for a genuine science of behavior (cf. N3.3).

### Causality and Skepticism

Let us begin at the point at which Kant was to be awakened. We have seen in the previous chapter that Hume could find no rational support for the principle of causality. It could be supported neither by reason nor by empirical impressions. What is causality then? To Hume the answer was psychological. Causal relations derive from the temporal association of ideas, such that the occurrence of one idea leads to a belief in the occurrence of another. Such a principle can express neither a law nor a necessary connection between events. Its entire support is derived from "custom" or "habit," and a habit, moreover, for which there is no epistemic mechanism for its formation. Memory plays a role to be sure, and the concatenation of events is sufficiently fine-grained that continuity is evidenced. Yet the explanation of why one event appears to cause another can only be in terms of habitual expectancies, "being determined by custom to transfer the past to the future."

Kant rejected this analysis of causation:

> If we accept his [Hume's] conclusions, then all we call metaphysics is mere delusion whereby we fancy ourselves to have rational insight into what, in actual fact, is borrowed solely from experience, and under the influence of custom has taken the illusory semblance of necessity. If he had envisaged our problem in all its universality, he would never have been guilty of this statement, so destructive of all pure philosophy (*CPR*, B 20).

From this he proceeds in characteristically tortuous fashion to derive the premises which he found necessary for a reaffirmation of the principle of causal necessity. Had this been his only task, however, he would have been vulnerable; for it is often an innocuous procedure for a person to start with a conclusion and then find a set of premises sufficient to derive that conclusion. Rather what Kant found is that a causal or any other perceptual relation would be impossible without our presupposing certain penchants or predilections for structuring experience (cf. N3.4). Hume resorts to an associationistic, psychological explanation of causal relation. In effect, Kant's reply is to ask how it is possible that association by any principle can take place without the intellect's having the relevant predisposition to associate in just the way it does.

### Role of the a priori

The issue here needs to be labored for it is crucial to the whole Kantian scheme. The naive empiricist might believe in the *tabula rasa* of antiquity: the mind is a blank tablet, or better still, an impressionable tablet of wax, initially naive, without any innate ideas. Sensory impressions from the outside are projected onto the tablet where they are recorded, let us say, for the inspection and later memorization of the individual. A radical associationist, such as Hume, would then maintain that all simple and complex ideas could be constructed from the congeries of inputs that leave their impression upon the wax. In this context experience, and experience alone, would be sufficient to account for the origin of ideas. But is it? Kant says no. He asks in turn how it is possible to build ideas, i.e., to associate ideas, if there is no *a priori* patterning of the impressions from which the associative–perceptual extrapolation is to be made. The only idea a naive observer can get from a flux of impressions is a flux of impressions, without order, and without phenomenal integrity. The associator is bound, and necessarily so, by his innate dispositions of association.

Thus, we may say, Kant enunciated the predicament of necessary presupposition. He may have been in error as to the nature and origin of the *a priori* assumptions essential to the structure of knowledge, but once and for all he dispensed with the myth of the completely naive organism. The wax tablet had to have its peculiarly impressible properties (cf. N3.5).

Kant opens his argument with the question: "How are *a priori* synthetic judgments possible?" First, we must understand what he is asking. Judgments are propositions having the subject–predicate structure. *Analytic* judgments are those in which the predicate follows from the definition of the subject; and because the predicate is contained in the definition of the subject, it would be contradictory to assert the one and not the other (e.g., "All bodies are extended" or "A dead man is not alive"). *Synthetic* judgments are those in which the predicate is extraneous to the definition of the subject (e.g., "The dead man left six children"). In a word they are empirical propositions. There is also a second dimension for classifying propositions (I shall use "proposition" in place of "judgment" hereafter). A proposition may be *a priori*, in which case its truth is not in any way contingent upon experience. Thus all *a priori* propositions are universal and strictly necessary. But a proposition may be *a posteriori*, in which case its truth is made contingent upon the experiential state of affairs of which it is the assertion. We have then four possible combinations: analytic *a priori*, analytic *a posteriori*, synthetic *a priori*, and synthetic *a posteriori*. We will consider only synthetic *a priori* propositions.

If a proposition is *a priori* it is known to be true intuitively; that is, it carries with it apodictic sanction independent of experience. On the other hand, a proposition is *synthetic* if its truth is contingent upon experience. Do synthetic *a priori* propositions then represent a contradiction? According to Kant, the answer is no. A proposition can be known to be true *a priori*, yet the content of what is asserted can only be known through experience. If indeed the combination of the synthetic and the *a priori* is possible, then some propositions which describe empirical states of affairs can be known with certainty. Hence, the scandalous skepticism of Hume is answered.

### Epistemology

Successors of Kant have had misgivings about this answer to Hume. To say that causality is a matter of synthetic *a priori* judgment, and thereby certain and not subject to Hume's skepticism, sounds very much as if the problem of causality is solved by the circular procedure of *a priori* fiat. The argument is more subtle than this, however. In order to answer the original and larger question of the synthetic *a priori*, Kant first asks: how is knowledge possible?

This turns into a much larger question. Its answer occupies fully one-third of the *Critique of Pure Reason*, and I can only present it here in bare outline. We note initially that to distinguish between knowledge and the possibility of knowledge, between experience and the possibility of experience, requires a rather extensive vocabulary. We will follow the argument as Kant himself develops the nomenclature.

1.   *Real and possible worlds: Intuition* is a mode of knowledge whereby objects are given to us by means of perception. *Transcendental* relates to a mode of knowledge "in so far as this mode of knowledge is to be possible *a priori*." Thus the transcendental aspects of knowing are those which relate to the possibility of *a priori* structuring of knowledge. They are therefore to be differentiated from *transcendent* aspects of knowing—which because they are purportedly supraphysical and yet nonanalytic could only pretend to the status of knowledge.

2.   *Transcendental aesthetic:* The Kantian argument starts with space and time. According to Leibniz, space and time are derived from relations between particulars. Thus, they have no existential properties independent of the relations. Newton, on the other hand, maintained that space and time are entities independent of the particular objects and events occurring within their scopes. Thus it would be meaningful to speak of absolute space and time and to treat them as basic entities in the foundations of physical science. Although Kant sided with Newton concerning the absolute character of space and time, he reached what can be regarded for him as the necessary compromise. Space and time are pure forms of intuition. That is to say, the intuition of objects is inconceivable except that they occur in a space–time manifold. Invent what world you will, there is no possible reification of objects except in the space and time manifold. You can strip objects of all their qualities, and replace them with new ones, but you cannot strip away or replace their spatio–temporal dependencies. Thus we see that events are reified in space and time, they are made possible by the pure forms of intuition. Hence events themselves cannot be the means by which we generate the ideas of space and time. For us to build an image of space according to a plan such

as that of Berkeley, we would first have to isolate events in a spatial manifold in order for us to develop the cues for the idea of space.

3.  *Transcendental analytic:* To think meaningfully of objects, to have phenomena emerge as the meaningful objects of perception that we know, requires other transcendental dimensions of intuition. Operating from the vantage of logic, Kant predicates ("deduces") a set of categories which represent the possibilities of experience. An object is perceived as being such and such in a given manifold, this such and such itself being the possibility of structure. And the possibility of structure prescribes both the apodictic nature and the limits of science. As with space and time, events cannot be recorded in the mind for the empirical extrapolation of their characteristics and relations, if first the events are not intuitable in specific ways. Thus the possibility of knowledge requires the postulation of *a priori* dispositions. The categories of thinking belong to the transcendental apparatus of the mind.

Kant's deduction of a specific set of categories is suspect. Whether just these categories (quantity, quality, relation, modality) are necessary or sufficient to account for the possibility of knowledge is beside the point; however, the premise that some such categorical predispositions are necessary for the structuring of experience is not. The argument for deducing the categorical instrumentation of knowledge is difficult. However, it is regarded by Kant to be crucial, and he repeats and rephrases it much as if it were a fugue. The thematic outline of the argument is as follows:

(*a*) The experience of the person displays a phenomenal unity in time and space. It is undeniable that experience displays a synthetic unity; perceptions occur only in the context of a person's experience.

(*b*) The sense of the synthetic unity of experience is *given* in experience, it is not *explained.* A flux of perceptions would remain a flux devoid of any synthetic unity were it not for some transcendental grounds for their coalescence.

(*c*) The *a priori* grounds for conditions of possible experience (i.e., the aesthetic and categorical framework) are at the same time grounds for the unification of perception.

(*d*) By virtue of (*a*), (*b*), and (*c*), we are led to the formulation of the *transcendental unity of apperception.* That is to say, the indispensable condition for the unification of perception into experience, and for the reification of this experience as representations of objects, is that there be some apperceiving, synthesizing ego in which the object-integration takes place. Thus the experienced object requires the transcendental ego.

(*e*) By virtue of (*c*), the synthesis, or unification, of experience takes place according to rules or laws. Thus experience is systematic and reliable.

(*f*) The conclusion follows that the synthesis of experience reflects a systematic universe in conformity with the categories of understanding (indeed, made possible by them). The categorically conformal world is the proper subject of the sciences. Phenomenal representations of this world are lawful. Thus, Hume is answered.

The argument is something of a *tour de force*. It rejects rationalism on the grounds that pure thought without object would provide no means for the derivation of the synthetic unity of experience or of the consistency which makes science possible. On the other hand, it rejects naïve empiricism; for without the transcendental unity of apperception, the associative principles stressed by Hume and others could provide no grounds for the synthetic unity of experience. Not only is Hume answered, but the whole of Kant's transcendental deduction represents a defense of physical science.

We leave the argument at this point, and one at which we have barely covered the first third of the *Critique*. However, this excursion should be sufficient to provide an understanding of the critical philosophy which systematically exploits the postulates of apperceptive structuring as being necessary to the possibility of knowledge. Kant's philosophy is a positive one; at the same time it is a critical one (the major part of the *Critique* presents a systematic demolition of traditional metaphysics). It suffered, and fatefully so, from its premature dogmatizing about a positive science. Yet, there is no question but that it has left its impact upon empiricism. We are no longer comfortable in rejecting the mystique of the *a priori*. We may not particularly like Kant's idea of the prefabricated bias for the synthetic *a priori*, of his aesthetic and his categories; but the idea of some commitment being made *a priori* in the task of knowing has become a precept both in science and philosophy (cf. N3.6). Margenau poignantly summarizes the contribution of Kant to the philosophy of science:

> Metaphysics is an odious word in some scientific quarters. Its meaning has fluctuated widely throughout the history of philosophy. But since Kant it has tended to designate two large branches of thought; ontology and epistemology. We hold with Kant that epistemology must precede ontology and that epistemology denotes the methodology of the cognitive process. The methodology of science involves deliverances of sense as well as rules of correspondence, constructs and principles of regulating constructs. Having learned that the latter are not conveyed by sensory data and yet function in guiding experience, we should call them metaphysical principles in the modern sense of the word. Metaphysical principles, thus understood, are an important part of all procedures which ultimately define reality (1950, p. 80).

# PHENOMENALISM

On initial inspection, phenomenalism appears to epitomize the precept to which Margenau alludes: epistemology must precede ontology. Studies of the origins and structure of knowledge are propaedeutic to the examination of propositions concerning the nature of the real, whatever that may be. Phenomenalism follows the empiricist tradition, i.e., all knowledge of the external world is made contingent upon perception; but it is even more explicit in its reducing knowledge of material objects to sense contents, and to sense contents alone. Thus, for phenomenalism, all ontological statements are reducible to statements whose meanings are assignable only in terms of empirical constituents. What is subsumed here is the empiricistic epistemology of Berkeley and Hume; namely, that our knowledge of the world extends only as far as the range of our impressions. According to phenomenalism, then, we may conclude that: (1) all material objects are reducible to empirical elements; and (2) the meaning of all other statements which are neither material-object statements nor analytic is, by virtue of the implicit theory of meaning, rendered nil.

As we shall see, the phrasing of the thesis of phenomenalism becomes a bit sticky. Thus to avoid any confusion between objects and statements about objects, as one might discern in the preceding paragraph, we confine ourselves to knowledge as expressible in terms of statements about objects and statements about phenomena. Thus by phenomenalism we mean the doctrine which asserts that every statement about material objects, their existence, persistence, structure, behavior, etc., can be reduced to a set of statements about sense data, actual and possible.[1]

Statements about sense data are the primitives in the system of linguistic derivation. Whether one builds from the primitives or reduces to the primitives is immaterial (at most it is a psychological problem); the significant implication is that there should be nothing in our object language which does not have its underpinnings in the sensory language.

This is little more than the familiar thesis of the empiricists. It represents a paraphrase of Berkeley without his idealistic ontology. It is Hume again, offering us an invitation to skepticism. That is to say, phenomenalism concerns itself with the physical world; in enunciating its criteria for significant statements about this world, it takes upon itself the critical function of delineating between sense and nonsense. However, since

---

[1] Many writers have concurred on a definition equivalent to this, with the bare exception being made to the admissibility of "possible" sense data. The present definition is essentially a paraphrase of that given by G. F. Stout (1938). Emphasis upon statements puts the phrasing in the "formal" as opposed to "material" mode of speech.

phenomenalism has traditionally been concerned with the analysis of physical objects, and with the positive aspects of physical science, the skepticism of a radical empiricism (such as that of Hume) becomes problematic to its own affirmative analyses. Just what is the range of knowledge as defined by phenomenalism? There are several troublesome questions to face. What role do hypotheses about the structure of material objects play? What is the status of objects which are not at the moment being perceived? How do we differentiate between permanence and evanescence as applied to perceptual states? How do we distinguish between illusory and nonillusory perceptual states? How, in fact, do we address ourselves to the subject of objectivity in the sciences? These are the questions confronting phenomenalism. They are not mutually exclusive. Not all perhaps are insoluble, or even problematic. However, in order to appreciate fully their troublesome character, it will pay us to look at a significant expression of phenomenalism which has been taken as a basis for positivistic science.

### Ernst Mach (1838–1916)

Whereas Berkeley, Hume, and John Stuart Mill arrived at phenomenalism primarily in the pursuit of philosophy, Mach arrived at it by virtue of a critical examination of the foundations of physics. By his own admission, he was not particularly well-grounded in philosophy. With the possible exception of the works of his contemporary Avenarius, he disdained philosophical writing as being weighted down in personal jargon:

> For constructions of this kind I had neither occasion nor vocation, neither inclination nor talent; I am a scientist and not a philosopher. . . . It is asking rather much of an elderly man that to the labor of learning the languages of the nations he should add that of learning the language of an individual (1897, p. 47).

However, Mach possessed the perceptual acumen of a David Hume; when he looked critically at the foundations of classical physics, he was not at all happy with what he saw. The substance of his argument is this: classical physics frequently uses concepts that are either tautologies or are hypothetical in character and devoid of any reference to sensory experience. In the one case, the concepts should be recognized for what they are, tautologies without ontological significance. In the other case, hypothetical properties of material objects, i.e., properties which are not equivalent to some complex of sense events, should be eliminated from science. Thus, Mach undertook the critique of scientific concepts. Concepts without direct empirical foundations are metaphysical and should be eliminated from scientific description (cf. N3.7).

It is a matter of question whether Mach himself started with ontology or with epistemology. However, he begins with the premise that sense elements are the givens. "Thing, body, matter are nothing apart from the combinations of the elements—the colors, sounds and so forth—nothing apart from their so-called attributes" (1897, p. 6). These sense elements are neither mental nor physical. That is to say, all assertions which imply either that sense elements are mental or physical or that they reduce to mental or to physical descriptions do in themselves obscure the fact that what is designated as mental and what is designated as physical are themselves abstractive constructions of sense elements. These sense elements tend to occur in configurational complexes; the symbolic activities both of perceiving and conceiving then function as economical summaries of such complexes.

> Nature is composed of sensations as its elements. . . . The thing is an abstraction, the name a symbol, for a compound of elements from whose changes we abstract. The reason we assign a single word to a whole compound is that we need to suggest all the constituent sensations at once. When, later we come to remark the changeableness, we cannot at the same time hold fast to the idea of a thing's permanence, unless we have recourse to the conception of a thing in itself, or other such like absurdity. Sensations are not signs of things; but, on the contrary, a thing is a thought-symbol for a compound sensation of related fixedness. Properly speaking the world is not composed of 'things' as its elements, but of colors, tones, pressures, spaces, times, in short what we ordinarily call individual sensations. The whole operation is a mere affair of economy (1883, p. 579).

It is apparent from this that Mach will really have nothing to do with ontology. Sense elements are not things one can talk about—they are the givens, the basic ingredients, without which there is nothing. The rest, that is, the language of science, is a matter of economical description.

How, then, do we distinguish the permanent from the nonpermanent, the complex of elements symbolized as an object from the complex of elements symbolized as the thought of an object? Mach would answer both these questions in terms of differences in the complexes of elements. The elements of a permanent object display a certain fixedness in their relations throughout the context of diverse perspectives, whereas the elements of an object in thought, for example, show no such constancy and occur always within the partisan locale of the observer. In this context it should be noted that Mach agrees with Hume. The "ego" has no phenomenal status; at most it is a construction referring not to some unit complex of ideas, but only to the ambulant focal point of perspectives for sense complexes. Thus the world might be thought of as a set of such focal points with each point representing a kind of vortex of sense complexes. It is from these vortices, then, that we get all complexes, the fixed ones of the material world, the fluid, somewhat capricious ones of the immaterial world. However, no component, no aspect of these complexes suggests an ego; nor to Mach, at least, can it be suggested that "ego" represents an economical conceptualization of any sense complex (cf. N3.8).

But we may ask other questions. How do we treat causal or other lawful relations? How are effects produced? What is the psycho-physical relation? To begin with, there is no mind–body problem. Mental and physical descriptions are examples of the "conceptual shorthand," to use Karl Pearson's phrase. Lawful relations of phenomena are simply functional relations where from one complex of elements we can derive or anticipate in logical manner another complex of ideas. There are no substrata of substances, efficient forces, or conformal principles. Lawful descriptions are descriptions that satisfy the principle of economy. They are the simple and efficient symbolic representations of phenomena.

This is Mach's argument in bare outline. What in brief are its implications? Generally speaking, Mach's phenomenalism is threadbare empiricism; it shows an ascetic disdain for the raiments of the imagination, for the hypothetical, for the concealed, and for anything that suggests fictive entities. But in its nakedness, so to speak, resides its elegance. If all concepts of science are to be simple abstractive descriptions of sense data, then an appropriately constructed science will describe functional relationships between phenomena without theoretical adornment. Metaphysical entities will be eliminated, even those that escaped the critical eyes of a giant like Newton: concepts like force, mass, absolute space and time.

Perhaps the most significant implication of Mach's phenomenalism, then, is its bias against all metaphysical speculation in science. It is critical of hypothetical constructions, of ideal premises, of provisional hypotheses, should any of these presume to be more than temporary aids to the construction of a purely phenomenal science. A second implication derives from the first. Mach's phenomenalism is operationist in all essential details. The meaning of a concept is specified by a set of operations all details of which are, in effect, reducible to sense complexes. Like the operationists to follow (Einstein, Eddington, Bridgman), Mach undertook a critical analysis of time and space. Time, for example, is not something which permeates all physical change. One cannot measure changes in things, process, and the like, by time. Rather time is measured by changes in things. Uniformity is not a property of time but of things, and arbitrarily chosen things at that. If some new clock should show some "standard" clock to be nonuniform, then a different standard may be chosen. For example, if the earth's rotation is not uniform by some arbitrary definition of time, then perhaps the resonating properties of a quartz crystal are. At any rate, change is not a property of time, rather time is a property of change.

In general then, Mach's phenomenalism is uncompromising empiricism. The concepts of science are restricted to complexes of sense elements. Scientific explanation should be confined to descriptions of functional relations between physical events. The principle of economy should be our constructual guide, prompting us always to cut away those descriptive embellishments which resist empirical analysis. In a word, then, phenomenalism is the route to *positive* knowledge.

## Phenomenal Elements

The critique of phenomenalism can be written only after cognizance is taken of subsequent refinements in the language of empirical elements. Slogans in behalf of empiricism seem unequivocal and straightforward. *"Esse est percipi."* "No entities without empirical foundation." "All material objects are logical constructions out of sense data." But what is common to these slogans is that which needs clarification. What precisely is the empirical element? We have previously phrased the thesis of phenomenalism in terms of statements about objects and statements about sense data. Now we have to ask: what are sense data? To what does our term 'sense data' refer?

One suspects from the discussions of people like Hume, Mach, and James that sense data are elements of a phenomenal kaleidoscope into which we look. But this is not enough. We have to know in what relation sense data stand to the physical objects which presumably are constructed from them. Are sense data, then, properties of the objects? Are they surface characteristics, sensorylike sparks coruscated off for us to sense and to utilize in the construction of objects? This suggestion will not do. For objects are obviously more than surface characteristics; that is to say more than the surface characteristics in a perceptual exposure. Objects are inferred or are constructed from only minimal cues, and as constructions they inform as to what we may expect to perceive from vantage other than the given one. "Objects as perceived" must therefore of themselves provide hypotheses for missing data. They must stand as cues to other sense data missing in the sensorium but necessary for the completion of the object. Now this objection to a pure phenomenalism is in itself not insuperable; but there is one problem that is more difficult to resolve. How do we treat hallucination? If one has a false perception, then obviously the sense data of the false perception cannot be the surface characteristics of a real object. Nor can we succumb to the temptation of regarding sense data as the components of energy systems which activate the peripheral nervous system. Such a description presumes a physical world which we have initially to define as a construction of sense data. Thus, if sense data are the irreducible elements out of which objects are constructed, they cannot at the same time be properties of objects.

If, as phenomenalists, we cannot hold that sense data are attributes of objects, can we admit they stand in a sensing relation to the observer? In other words, can we regard sense data as things we perceive? If so, what is their status should the observer be removed from the scene? Do sense data continue to exist when we close our eyes? Now, both Russell (1912, 1927) and G. E. Moore (1922), for somewhat different reasons, attested to the persistent character of sense data, Moore because they were objects of perception and had therefore to be independent of the act of perceiving, and Russell because, for the better part of his philosophy, sense data were thought to require some causal substratum. Both arguments result in our rejecting a subjectivist treatment of sense data. They are neither pure contents of perception nor the ultimate elements in perception to which all phenomena reduce. Rather they are objects *of* perception as distinguished from objects *in* perception. It is difficult, then, to see how we are to avoid our previous dualistic predicament. Should we admit to dualism then, the arguments for phenomenalism and for the primacy of perceptual content fail.

Finally, we may ask what if sense data are autonomous? What if they simply are, ontologically basic and unrelated? That they should appear to occur in the sensorium of a particular observer is due to the fact that the pattern of their constancies and inconstancies yields to the economical construction of a given person's observing a given world. This, in other words, is the point of view held by Mach. But it, too, is subject to serious difficulties. Why does not the flux of sense data just remain a flux? What is the instrument of organization? How can some sense of identity among the ambient and ambulatory perspectives emerge from a flux of sense data? A physical event is a set of perspective complexes of sense data, i.e., a set of sets of sense data each member of which is a perceptual context. But how can we speak in these terms unless physical structure is already subsumed? Once again we are faced with the need for *a priori* structuring, only this time it is structuring from without (there is no transcendental ego), rather than from within as in the fashion of Kant (cf. N3.9).

But now there are formal difficulties as well. Following Marhenke's catalogue of complaints (1950), I mention the following: First, note that in the formal mode of speech (cf. N3.10) phenomenalism asserts that material object statements (M-statements) reduce to a set of sense data statements (S-statements). We may then express the formal difficulties in the following manner: (1) Any reduction of an M-statement to a set of S-statements is circular. The material object is assumed in the argument of reduction. Therefore, by virtue of material implication, a given M-statement can be inferred from any set of S-statements. The only way to escape this trap is to assume the equivalence of the M- and S-statements —which is what one would wish to demonstrate.[2] (2) Phenomenalism is

[2] This argument is due in large measure to Carnap. The logic of implication and equivalence is briefly discussed in the following chapter. Note, however, from the material implication "If S then M" and the assertion of "M" one can infer "S *or* not-S."

committed to an erroneous theory of sense perception. "Seeing M" is reduced to "seeing the sense data of M," wherein these sense data are related to M. But M itself is stated in terms of sense data. (We have previously touched upon the problems of establishing the inferential relation between M-objects and sense data.) (3) In order to make positive identification of M-objects, the reduction of an M-statement would require an infinite set of S-statements. Several commentators have made this point, but one of its most explicit formulations is that given by Braithwaite (1938). In order for us to make a positive assertion about the existence of an M-object, we must not only know all the properties of the object, but must be absolutely sure that we are not being deceived by hallucination, illusion, demons, or what not. Thus every observation requires concurrence on the part of a "normal observer." What is a normal observer? He is one who can be vouched for as being reliable under the given conditions of observation. But how do we ascertain whether he is a "normal observer?" Who is to vouch for him? I suppose we might answer, "The normal-normal observer." And so it goes, to the infinite regress. Braithwaite, it should be mentioned, treats such predicaments as this not as incapacitating, but only as limiting (e.g., 1953). However, the predicament of regressive confidence does signify a retreat from positivism.

In concluding this discussion of phenomenalism, I might add that its length is justified by its relevance to later developments of empiricism. The issues are invariably to be found germane to the development of a systematic empiricism. They are found in logical atomism, in logical empiricism, in pragmatism, and even in phenomenology. Berkeley, Hume, Russell, Ayer, C. I. Lewis, Husserl, across the spectrum of empiricist philosophers, have all had something to say on phenomenalistic reduction. The substance of the manifold argument spells out a retreat from positivism. What emerges, or better, what survives, is a methodological phenomenalism in which by agreement, or convention, we take some set of sense data as being equivalent to a material object. Sense data? Perceptual contents? Not very precise concepts to be sure. However, the empiricist wants to get on with his work; even if he is to find that gentlemanly agreements are hardly ever enduring (cf. N3.11).

## PHENOMENOLOGY

Since philosophical analysts through the past two decades have been trying rather unsuccessfully to surmount the barriers to phenomenalistic reduction, one wonders why they did not follow the lead of the Gestalt psychologists and resort to a configurational, object-given empiricism. The answer is simply that the logical and linguistic problems of perception are not the same as the psychological or, for that matter, the physiological problems. And, even if we were to embrace phenomenology in place of phenomenalism, we would have to face some of the same questions relating to the status of perceptual data. What is the ontological status of the given? What are the contents and conditions of existence? What, if anything, subsists? Note, for example, that both atomistic and configurational analyses of perception would have to deal with the problems of object identity and object constancy. The one approach will no more yield a positivistic science than will the other. Still, one might add, the configurational point of view is closer to describing the everyday world of things. It is closer to home, so to speak, for it talks of objects and events rather than of abstractions such as sense data.

In general terms, phenomenology is that empiricistic philosophy which asserts that the givens of experience are configurational entities having a unique integrity of their own and are, therefore, not reducible to sense contents or to any other elemental structure. Stress is placed on uniqueness of events. Formalized science is suspect because of its abstractive character. To name or to classify an object of experience is to deprive it of its phenomenological purity as a unique event. Thus one must concentrate on the private intuition (Anschauung) of experience, rather than committing oneself to the intellectual and abstractive activities that make experience the subject of public communication.

On first inspection, then, phenomenology would appear to be antiscientific. But that is only because of the bias that we bring to the argument from our backgrounds in the abstractive sciences. However, if physics, chemistry, biology, etc., do not qualify as pure science, what does?

### Brentano

We pick up the story with Franz Brentano. Although he does not qualify as a self-identified phenomenologist, he is important in the movement for having been the teacher of Stumpf, Meinong, and Husserl, all of whom were influential in determining the course phenomenology was to take. In his *Psychologie vom empirischen Standpunkte,* Brentano begins with his celebrated distinction between mental and physical phenomena. Every *mental* phenomenon involves presentation in which acts of sensing, feeling, thinking accompany that which is sensed, felt, thought. Thus hearing a sound, feeling a pain, thinking of a horse, are examples of such presentations. *Physical* phenomena, on the other hand, are independent of the act of presentation. They are color, weight, odor, landscape, as such, and may be described as objects of the presentational act. This distinction is further refined under the thesis of *intentionality*. A mental phenomenon always involves conjoining an act of experiencing *and* the object of the experience. One cannot speak of seeing as a mental event but only of seeing something, a colored surface, or a cloud, for example. No mental phenomenon is complete without this intentional structure. Physical phenomena, on the other hand, are independent. The object can exist independently of any other object and independently of its being perceived. The cloud, as such, is independent of the act of its being perceived. We note, too, that the objects of presentation in mental phenomena need not exist in the way physical objects do. That is, the objects of mental events need not have physical objectivity. Thus it is appropriate to speak of the *intentional inexistence* of an object.

Brentano writes: "This intentional inexistence is exclusively characteristic of mental phenomena. No physical phenomenon manifests anything similar. Consequently, we can define mental phenomena by saying that they are such phenomena as include an object intentionally within themselves" (Chisholm, editor, 1960, p. 50). If one grants this distinction between mental phenomena (sensing, feeling, being conscious of, etc.) and physical objects, then the predicament of intentionality becomes inevitable (cf. N3.12). However, the status of intentionally inexistent objects beclouds the issue, and leads us from the empirical psychology of Brentano into what Russell calls "the Meinongian jungle."

## Meinong

Meinong accepted the thesis of intentionality, but he expanded the theory of objects to give existential status to intentional inexistents. Since the intentional act involves an intended object, then all such objects have some kind of existential status regardless of whether they embody physical existence or not. Thus the full potential of experience involves thinking about ideal objects, which subsist but do not exist in the physical sense. Moreover, the characteristics we assign to an object are independent of the fact of an object's physical existence. Thus Meinong asserts: "There are objects of which it is true that there are no such objects" (Chisholm, editor, 1960, p. 83). Golden mountains, prancing centaurs, bucolic unicorns; all these subsist in the blessed state of intentional inexistence (cf. N3.13). Meinong's philosophy revolves primarily upon his theory of objects, and does not, as in the case of other phenomenologies, rely upon the contributions of the transcendental ego for a systematic development of experience.

## Husserl

Edmund Husserl, another of Brentano's students, is the person perhaps most responsible for promulgating phenomenology as a philosophical movement. He was trained in mathematics as well as in philosophy, and his initial work investigated the nature of logic (*Logische Untersuchungen,* 1900–1901). In this work he rejected both the idea that logic was derived from experience (J. S. Mill) and the idea that logic was purely formal and conventional schema (Schröder). Instead he embraced an intuitionism wherein neither experience nor formal rule of inference was operative; a valid logical argument was simply known to be true. The method of intuitionism is carried over into all cognitive activity. "Psychologism" is anathema. If one seeks the phenomenologically pure description, then causal and genetic analyses tend only to obscure. And so, also, for abstraction. To describe an event in general terms rather than in intuited essences is corruptive. Thus traditional scientific descriptions are vulgarizing; they enshroud the unique event in the anonymous garb of general terms and characteristics; and even more significant, they eliminate the transcendental ego from the true description of events. Thus traditional science is too restrictive, the empiricism of Berkeley and Hume is too limited. What is needed is a pure science and an extended empiricism under the direction of phenomenological method.

What is the method? We have seen already that intuition must play a part. We know, too, that the general, the universal, is admissible only in its purity of being the essence of what a thing is in its intention. First, then, the method prescribes pure description over explanation. Husserl rejects positivistic and naturalistic description. Facts that are filtered into classificatory systems, general principles that are the ground for inference, may have "utility" in the practical sense of the term, but they remove phenomenal events from their state of being unique. Intuition alone can apprehend the uniqueness of the fact. One must approach the act of intuition as if he were, one by one, to strip the event of all its general characteristics, of all its class memberships, thus to leave the event denuded but resplendent in its essential phenomenal being. It is as if we were to proceed by noting that the object of perception is not-A (in which A is a general characteristic), not-B, not-C, etc. What is left when the event is stripped of its putative class memberships is the intuited object.

But the event is not just pure object; intuition also involves the subject. This leads us to the matter of phenomenological reduction, the second important feature of the method. Sartre has said of Husserl that he only elaborated upon the transcendental method of Kant. To a large extent this is true. For Husserl, every act of intuition involves the transcendental ego and the object of intention. The act of knowing not only draws one's attention to an object, but it also entails the awareness of an ego's participation in the act of knowing. It is true, as Kant implied, that one cannot make an object of the ego without its ceasing to be ego; but every intentional act as regards an object implies that the object is known by the apperceiving ego. There is subjective perspective as well as objective reference. But whereas Kant admits the transcendental ego and then rejects it as an essential ingredient of objective description, Husserl would maintain that all objects must be phenomenologically described in such a way that the essence of the object is definable only in terms of the perceiving ego. In such matters, it is better to let Husserl speak for himself.

> Merely empirical, descriptively classificatory (inductive) knowledge is not yet science in the full sense of the word. It merely furnishes relative truth, tied to specific situations. Philosophy, genuine science, aims at absolute, ultimately valid truths, which transcend all relativity. Such truth defines what exists, as it exists in itself. The world of perception and prescientific experience reveals itself, of course, as a really existent world in spite of its relativity, but its properties, true in themselves, transcend naïve experience. Although philosophy, genuine science, can only be approximated gradually, it is reached by appealing to the *eidos*, the pure *a priori* which anybody can grasp in apodictic insight (Chisholm, edition, 1960, p. 131).

And what is a thing in terms of its transcendental subjectivity? It is a "manifold of modes of consciousness" which belong together in the "supposed object."

> For instance, the manifold modes of appearance which compose the perception of a thing and through which we become immanently conscious of the thing belong together by virtue of the synthesis of identity which necessarily occur in the transition. The thing which presents itself unified and perhaps even unchanged to the naïve observer becomes the transcendental guide for the systematic and reflective study of the varieties of consciousness which belong to this one thing. This is true of every single real something and also of the world as a total phenomenon. The existence of these apodictic essential laws of correlation was an entirely new discovery of far-reaching importance (Chisholm, editor, 1960, p. 140).

The discovery was new with Husserl, as perhaps it was with Mach in his own way. But however this "genuine science" may transcend the public antics of positivism, Husserl's promise of new horizons of empiricism has not been realized. Nor has the invitation to develop the new science been seized upon. Rather his influence has been felt among the contemporary existentialists, whom Abraham Kaplan (1961) sympathetically describes as "amateur literary psychologists."

There is a heavy but seductive element in the cumbersome refrains of transcendentalism. Self-awareness, the personal meaning, the I sense, I think, I feel: in all of these, the ego component is always there if we incline to reflect upon it. However, empiricists generally will have none of it. From Locke and Berkeley down through Hume to the present, looking inward, reflecting, and questing for the ego have uncovered nothing but confusion. What one discovers, if it may be called discovery, is a volatile ego, an "I" that evaporates upon inspection. If not that, it becomes a "me" and a "mine" documented by a set of semicohesive particulars.

What Hume and Mach have done in their own straightforward ways is to turn the doctrine of intentionality upon the ego itself. They applied it with vengeance. In the language of intention, thinking always involves an object; thus it is quite unsatisfactory to personalize knowledge as the phenomenologists have done, or to elevate the ego to transcendental status, and then remove it from the arena of intelligible discourse. One might just as well leave the ego in its objective shambles, a concatenation of states, involvements, ownerships, moods. For then, the onerous weight of the transcendental ego, if one would bear it, could be borne in silence.

There can be little question but that the phenomenological recommendations of Husserl may serve as an exhortation about a personal attitude toward experience. Existentialists such as Sartre and Camus have, of course, exploited such attitudes as reflecting upon the inescapable investment one has in the human predicament. However, it is questionable whether intuition can supplant natural science. There is no reason to believe that intuition has proved any more exemplary for man than has science. Unless knowledge is to degenerate into the retreat of transcendental soliloquies (in which case a person is not only confronted by egocenteredness, but also never allows himself to forget it) then we must continue to abstract among particulars, to classify, and to symbolize with selective disregard for the uniqueness of particulars (cf. N3.14).

## ADDENDUM ON PHYSICALISM

Because of its communality with phenomenalism, at least so far as ontology is concerned, the doctrine of physicalism is mentioned here. Physicalism is that doctrine (of logical empiricism) which asserts that sense data statements are to be replaced by object- or thing-statements. This gambit has two advantages: one, it avoids the difficulties of defining sense data; and two, it provides a pool of protocol statements which can be used to form the foundation of empirical science.

This doctrine has difficulties of its own, as we shall see in later discussion. However, it does have the advantage of taking for granted the perception of physical objects. It is presumed that we can distinguish between illusions and veridical perception. Thus the game of inference and scientific construction begins with what is given. Just how we know whether we are using a thing- or object-statement correctly should be a matter of some concern to us. If we assume the semantic task is a common sense kind of procedure, or that objects and things are easily known, or that they can be taken for granted, then we can begin where phenomenalism ends. That is, we can assume the fund of phenomenological entities. The language of science then advances a level in concreteness, for statements in the theoretical language are to be reduced to statements in the thing-language. Since the doctrine of physicalism was proposed by members of the Vienna Circle, further discussion of it is deferred until the exposition of logical empiricism.

# NOTES

## NOTE 3.1

The great *Critique of Pure Reason* was published in 1781 when Kant was the age of fifty-seven. So far as publications are concerned, only Locke contends with him for the honor of late maturing. As A. C. Ewing (1938) has suggested, it is very likely that Kant would be unknown today had he died at an age when the productive lives of most creative people are over. It is almost certain that had he not lived to see the first *Critique* through to publication, he would today have been forgotten in the shadows of his own contemporaries.

Kant published very little of any consequence prior to the first *Critique*. *Dreams of a Spirit Seer* (1766) and his *Inaugural Dissertation* (1770) were his most significant essays during this time, and both contain seeds of the later *Critique of Pure Reason*. There is a chapter in the *Dreams* in which the great spiritualist Swedenborg is subjected to some rather good-natured twitting. The essay is to be recommended to those who read Kant only as the cumbersome author of the *Critiques* and thereby visualize him as the Königsberg peripatetic who was as desiccated as he was punctual. Kant presumed that spiritualists such as Swedenborg might have some private access to knowledge or communication denied to most of us; but then, should they insist on the privacy of their knowledge, they could not expect us to consider it the province of reason. "The possibility of immaterial things can, therefore, be supposed without fear of its being disproved, but also without hope of proving it by reason" (*Dreams*, p. 47). The function of metaphysics is to ascertain the limits of knowledge. Thus:

> [The advantage of metaphysics] . . . consists in recognizing whether the task [of knowing] be within the limits of our knowledge and in stating its relation to the conceptions derived from experience, for these must always be the foundation of all our judgments. In so far, metaphysics is the science of the boundary of human reason (*Dreams*, p. 113).

It is clear from the preface to the second edition of the *Critique of Pure Reason* that Kant saw his philosophy as providing us with the analytical tools for distinguishing sense from nonsense in metaphysics. His philosophy is indeed a critical one, and in many respects it carries criticism further than Hume was able to do.

**NOTE 3.2**

In the preface to the first edition of the *Critique of Pure Reason,* Kant wrote:

> In this enquiry I have made completeness my chief aim, and I venture to assert that there is not a single metaphysical problem which has not been solved, or for the solution of which the key at least has not been supplied. Pure reason is, indeed, so perfect a unity that if its principle were insufficient for the solution of even a single one of all the questions to which it itself gives birth we should have no alternative but to reject the principle, since we should then no longer be able to place implicit reliance upon it in dealing with any one of the other questions. (A, xiii)

Apparently there was no occasion for him to change this sanguine appraisal by the time of the second edition, for the preface to that edition leaves it intact.

Kant was not the first, nor the last, to be so finalistically appreciative of his own work; Berkeley preceded him and Wittgenstein followed him to share the honors. But the last sentence of the above quotation shows that Kant all but deliberately set the trap for his own demise. Part of the *a priori* edifice had to come down; and, nudged on by Kant's own categorical appraisals, most of the rest of the structure came with it. This has been unfortunate, for although Kant may have been wrong in his conception of space and time, the questions concerning the necessity of presuppositions for the structuring of experience remain to be ever puzzled through.

**NOTE 3.3**

For the most part psychologists and historians of psychology pay dutiful respects to Kant and then proceed forthwith to find him anathema to the spirit of modern psychology. For Kant is that person who implied that psychology could not be a science! But what kind of psychology? The psychology of the knowing ego! Kant, I believe, would have had no doubts concerning a science of behavior. In fact Kant's argument would support the behaviorist's definition and restriction of the subject matter of his science, although, to my knowledge, no behaviorist has ever sought to recruit Kant to the methodological fold.

Kant's argument is this. Psychology traditionally deals with the knowing ego. Its subject matter is the "I" of awareness and cognition. Examination of this subject matter shows: (1) the data of awareness or consciousness are schematized only in the dimension of time, whereas the data of the physical sciences are schematized in both time and space and therefore possess locale external to the experiencing person; (2) the mental elements of the knowing ego are, by virtue of (1), not subject to public inspection; and (3) the knowing ego is itself unknowable. All that is known of what purports to be an ego is the retrospective residues of the elements of experiencing. This last point is the crucial one. We run into it again and again as the problem of intentionality. One does not have access to the immanent activity of the knowing ego.

So long as introspection is to be both the method and the subject of psychology, psychology cannot be a science. Neither modern psychophysics nor behaviorism have gainsaid that argument.


## NOTE 3.4

This point is made by R. P. Wolff in one of the more recent commentaries on Kant's theory of knowledge (1963). Regressive analysis (e.g., wherein, from the accepted conclusion, causal necessity is sought for a set of sufficient premises) is never convincing; for by material implication, a true conclusion can be inferred from any set of premises, and a false set of premises will yield any conclusion (see the following chapter). However, as Wolff points out, Kant did not preferentially exploit a logical predicament in rejecting Hume's thesis, but rather he found that Hume was challenging the foundation of all knowledge. That is to say, Kant's analysis of the problem led him to believe that the penchants of *a priori* structuring were *necessary* for any knowledge. Hume, for example, could not even formulate the problem of causation without the intellect's having its cognitive predispositions for structuring experience.


## NOTE 3.5

Much of the debate over nativism in perception reveals, I think, a significant failure to appreciate the Kantian argument. Does a person perceive phenomenal configuration independently of prior experience as the Gestalt psychologists, for example, have maintained? Or does he build these phenomenal configurations out of associative complexes as, say, Senden (1960), Hebb (1949), and Taylor (1962), following the Berkelian tradition, have maintained? The experiments and observations concerning subjects reared in darkness (Riesen, 1947), or congenitally blind subjects gaining their eyesight (Senden, 1960) are not at all decisive. They show only that associative experience is necessary for the emergence of configural perception (i.e., Locke, Berkeley, Molyneux were correct). They do not at all show how that associative experience could effect the emergence of the phenomena, as such. They do not instruct us as to how the synthesis of sense data takes place. Nor, I may add, is the question of organizational penchant answered by referrals to the physics of the nervous system, as both Gestalt psychologists (Köhler, 1938, 1947) and neurophysiologists (Brain, 1951) have sometimes presumed. Whether there are physical systems to support *a priori* structuring is beside the point. The fact is that events cannot be seen as taking place in time and space, as manifesting qualities, relations, etc., unless there is some predisposition to turn a kaleidoscope of impressions into the configural orders we actually perceive. Kant, himself, might argue that physiologists would do well to be Kantians; but the Kantian problem itself is one in which the activities of perception are indispensable to and prior to an understanding of the objects of perception.

**NOTE 3.6**

See, for example, Arthur Pap's *The A Priori in Physical Theory* (1946). Pap dismisses the particulars of the Kantian *a priori* on grounds on which others have been critical. Kant's treatment of space, time, mathematics, and science will not stand up under analysis from modern logic and science. However, under the influence of the pragmatism of C. I. Lewis and Dewey, Pap does see the need for general propositions, *a priori*. These propositions are essential to the task of making inferences such as those from cause to effect. He differs from Kant in that the propositions are not synthetic *a priori* but rather are conventions subject to occasional revision from a broader sampling of experience.

Pap's argument is especially relevant for the discussion and understanding of law. We will have occasion to refer to it later. What is significant here is that nondogmatic pragmatists, appalled as they are at absolute judgments, do find that *a priori* judgments are essential to one's knowledge of the world.

**NOTE 3.7**

Mach's status in philosophy stems largely from the favorable impact he had upon members of the Vienna Circle. Philipp Frank, from nearby Prague and an early associate of the Circle, has written appreciatively of Mach's influence (Frank, 1941). Mach's status in scientific criticism is somewhat mixed. He has been, and was in his time, strongly criticized for his rejection of physical atomism. On the other hand, he has been rather generally lauded for his critical appraisal of early Newtonian mechanics.

It seems strange nowadays, in the age of nuclear particles, that Mach should have been critical of atomic hypotheses. We would hardly know what to do without our fine submicroscopic "entities." However, there is little question that Mach would continue to be appalled at the state of atomic physics were he alive today. There is no direct connection of atomistic concepts with sense complexes. They are pure constructions and, to Mach, devoid of any saving virtues of economy. Mach would not deny to hypotheses a certain heuristic or provisional role, but the goal of scientific endeavor is to arrive at economical descriptions of the observables. One should always seek to substitute more economical, more empirical, constructions for the hypothetical entities. When, for example, we see that fine-grain descriptions of matter have been reduced to the paradoxes of complementarity, wherein the primitives are sometimes wavelike, sometimes particlelike, we can also see the ghost of Mach shaking its finger at us. It should be noted that those who were critical of atomism in the last century, and those who have reservations about atomism today, are critical as they are for reasons similar to those that Mach incorporated into his principle of economy. The constructs have become estranged from the data.

Mach's critique of Newton is generally accepted. In the first place, the definition of mass is circular, and thereby conventional rather than empirical. To define mass as the product of density and volume subsumes a density measured as mass per unit of volume. Secondly, it is tautologous to assert that change in motion is proportional to force when acceleration has previously been defined in terms of applied forces. Mach himself proposed an adequate operational definition of mass to replace the circular one of Newton; but mainly his discussion was clarifying and elucidatory rather than destructive. In his historical review of mechanics (1883), he gives special credit to Lagrange and to Newton for breaking away from the "mechanical mythology" of the past (e.g., of Pascal, von Guericke, Leibniz, and Maupertius). However, when Newton presumed to reify force, he succumbed to the blandishments of metaphysics. Mach writes: "It would appear as though Newton . . . still stood under the influence of the medieval philosophy as though he had grown unfaithful to his resolves to investigate only actual facts" (1883, p. 272).

## NOTE 3.8

The taunt of solipsism is always with the consistent empiricist, just as in chronic tinnitus the ringing of the ears is always there when it occurs to the victim to listen. Mach, however, can deny that there is a problem. If the ego, or any other self-concept, is itself a construction of sense complex, then in behalf of solipsism one would have to argue that a host of sense complexes are contingent upon another complex called the "ego." This would be nonsense. For sense complexes are autonomous. They are the raw, unconstructed givens. To say that the givens are contingent upon the ego is to say that all givens are contingent upon something that is a construction of givens—which, of course, is to deny the significance of "being given."

Both mind and body have to be given up. They are ontological constructions and are thereby metaphysically presumptuous. It is interesting also that Mach found the idea of the "ego" morally suspect.

> The ego must be given up. . . . In this way we shall arrive at a freer and more enlightened view of life, which will preclude the disregard of other egos and the overestimation of our own. The ethical ideal founded on that view of life will be equally far removed from the ideal of the ascetic, which is not biologically tenable for whoever practices it, and vanishes at once with his disappearance, and from the ideal of an overweening Nietzschean "superman," who cannot, and I hope will not be tolerated by his fellow-men. (1897, p. 25)

## NOTE 3.9

Concerning sense data:

(1) There seems to be no adequate solution to the problem of defining sense data. More often than not, empiricists take a commonsense point of view. It is assumed that everyone knows what sense data are; they are the

contents of perceptual experience. However, either they are definable, and ostensively so, or they are given. And in either case, they are problematic. There is, however, another recourse; there is the inevitable retreat into "methodism." That is, by adopting *methodological phenomenalism* we mean to act as if material-object statements are reducible to sense data statements and to exclude any other reduction because of its intractability. For example, "the table is before me" is meaningful because it designates a complex of brown, hard, square sense data; but "my soul" is meaningless because there is no equivalent set of sense data which I may substitute for it. However, methodological qualifications are always accompanied by a tinge of sadness; they invariably signal a retreat from dogmatism. So it is with methodological behaviorism, methodological empiricism, and, I suppose, methodism wherever you find it.

With methodological phenomenalism (E. W. Hobson used the term; cf. Woodger, 1929), we are driven back from a secure ontologic position to one of precept. That is, we propose to act as if all meaningful constructions of the world are reducible to basic perceptual elements. It is not that the perceptual data language is precise or that it is exclusive, yet there is no alternative language which is adequate to designate what is given and what is indubitable. Thus methodological phenomenalism is a commitment entered into by users of the language. It avoids the difficulties of trying to designate things, if such there be, which have no counterpart in the fund of sensible events.

(2) One of the persistent difficulties of the sense data approach to empiricism is imbedded in the privacy of experience. Should one maintain a pure phenomenalism, without the substrata of a persisting real world, he will be driven into the snares of solipsism. He cannot escape the fact that all constructions are out of events (sense data occasions) within his own sensorium. Now, the echoes of solipsism invariably reverberate to tease the empiricist. His solution to the problem is both provisional and peremptory. He may resort to a methodological solution, or to a common sense solution, or to a linguistic solution, or to any one of a number of devices which represent an uneasy truce about "other worlds." Constructual phenomenalism, such as that of Hume and Mach, presents the solution most compatible with an empirical point of view. Egos and selves, like objects in the material world, are constructions out of sense data. Therefore, there is no justification for arguing for the privileged perspective of any one constructed ego. This, it is true, does not deal with the predicament that one has access only to his own families of impressions. But if egos are constructions, meaning for Hume and Mach there are no sensible egos, then the problem dissolves into the classical one of assigning to constructions some kind of ontological status.

(3) There is a rather tantalizing excursus into science fiction which should be of interest in this context. It is the story of the viable brain and the Cerebrofactual Demon. The issue it exploits is that which Russell Brain (1951) describes under the poignant phrase "physiological idealism." Suppose that a brain with its lower activating, intermediating, and processing centers, intact but devoid of any peripheral input elements, is kept viable in the laboratory. Suppose further there is a Cerebrofactual Demon whose omniscience is re-

flected in the capacity to know the effects of all combinatorial excitations of the elements of the cerebral system. Moreover, he can play this brain, as if it is a vast console, wherein the keyboard of his Klavicerb can activate any of the ten billion or so elements of the system or any assemblies of those elements.

Let us first assume that the console is an old brain that already has mnemonic structure. Then the demon can play out any pattern of impressions, perceptions, or ideas. Since all elements are at the control of the demon, he can make the brain think, or wander through familiar gardens, or relive old loves, or hear itself say "good morning" to the postman. He could even make the brain philosophize, or wonder whether the world is an illusion, or whether just such a demon, as the one that is, is playing a "Fugue to Ontology" on the cerebral keyboard. In other words, the well-played brain could generate a living world much like yours or mine.

But now let us assume that the brain is a new one, the naive precipitate of some kind of mother and devoid of any substantive mnemonic structure. It is interesting then to speculate what possibilities are open to the demon. He can improvise. In time he can make the brain think of itself as residing in the body of a winged angel herding unicorns, or sitting among the lilies working on (solving?) Fermat's Last Theorem. We, of course, cannot attest to the extents of the demon's musicianship, but whatever he makes the brain to be, philosopher, poet, centaur, or some unnameable thing, X, it is inconceivable that the brain will come into its own being without the essential thematic materials being developed in its sensory areas, without those phenomenal flashes out of which all things come. To think is not to be; but to think about something offers the innocent, at least, the occasion also to think on the possibility of its own being.

The moral is obvious. Something like what the phenomenalists have been saying has to be said. There is a *sine qua non* concerning that which is the object of our propositions of existence. Whether the essential data are floating in the unpropertied ether, whether they are the emissaries of a subsisting material world, or whether they are the flashes of sentience from within the cerebral console, it is difficult to say clearly and unequivocally. However, the conclusion that we must have data is inescapable. How they get to the sensorium of the console is, I am reluctant to write, immaterial.

## NOTE 3.10

In order to clarify semantic muddles, Carnap (in *Logical Syntax of Language*) proposed a distinction between the *formal mode* of speech in which analysis, explication and reduction of meaning are solely in linguistic terms, and the *material mode* of speech in which words purportedly are about things. Ontological muddles frequently arise from our adopting the material mode of speech where the formal mode of speech is the appropriate one. "Nothing but" statements typically reveal our confusion over modes of speaking. "Phenomena are nothing but sense data." "Thought is nothing but implicit muscular response." "No psychosis without neurosis." All these are statements presuming to say something about reality, about the ontological significance of sense data, response, and neurological events. Actually they are derivability statements, which specify only (or recommend) how statements about phenomena, thought, and mental activity are to be derived from statements about sense data, muscular response, and neurological events. As such, then, the appropriate critique of such statements belongs to the domain of linguistic analysis and logical syntax rather than semantics.

Scientists and philosophers sometimes argue as if some terms are about things and then proceed to argue that queries and debates as to meaning can be properly answered by pointing to the facts. "Awareness is nothing more than discrimination." "Awareness is something more than discrimination." Both statements may be held by partisans with equal ontological fervor. Clarification of the debate comes only when we reach agreement as to how awareness statements are to be used, i.e., what is the range of the class of their equivalence statements.

The issues this distinction touches upon are discussed in Chapter 6. For a good statement of the distinction, and a critical evaluation of the syntactical over the semantical analysis of meaning see J. O. Urmson, *Philosophical Analysis,* Chapter 8 (1956).

## NOTE 3.11

The history of phenomenalism would have to cover realists such as Russell, Moore, Price, as well as the pure phenomenalists such as Berkeley, Hume, and Mach. Whether these realists embrace some kind of dualism is not always clear from their writings. For the most part they are not interested in ontology as such. By their own analyses of knowledge they are driven to a methodological phenomenalism. They are inclined to maintain that although something like the material object world, subsistent and independent of perception, must be predicated, our only knowledge of such a world comes to us by means of sense data.

Mach himself draws attention to the work of the philosopher Richard Avenarius which was being published about the same time as his own. Although he devotes a chapter of his *Analysis of Sensations* to a comparison of his work with that of Avenarius, it is not clear whether the two of them were thinking and writing from convergent points of view, or whether Mach in particular was being influenced by the other's unique contributions. One suspects the former. At any rate, Avenarius' writings have never been made readily available in translation, and the credits attributed to him are, for the most part, due to Mach. Mach is perhaps most taken with Avenarius' treatment of the fallacy of *introjection.* According to this idea, we tend to take unto ourselves the constructions we give of another person's perception of the world wherein it is thought of the other person that his perceptions are copies of an object world. This type of thinking would imply dualism. However, Avenarius maintains that the introjection is fallacious; since as perceiving individuals, we do not perceive the world in any sense of a perception's being a copy of an external world. From this type of critique, Mach then draws support for (1) a psychology based on physiology, and (2) the rejection and avoidance of solipsism. Briefly the argument is this: the "material" and the "mental" refer to constructions which differ only as to reference. That is, when sense data are referred to their sensory source (the eye, ear, nervous system, etc.) they are mental, but when they refer to a physical source they are material. Thus sense data yield both mental and material constructions. It is obvious from this why Mach should maintain that the proper science of psychology is physiological psychology. It is perhaps less obvious, but nevertheless reasonable, that he should conclude solipsism to be a fallacy of introjection and egoism.

The eminent biometrician and statistician Karl Pearson (1857–1936) popularized the doctrine of phenomenalism with his successful book, *The Grammar of Science*. Pearson belongs among the great popularizers of scientific ideas, such as Eddington and Jeans. Consequently, like them, his work suffers at times from a tendency to let analogy replace logic. Pearson adopts a subjectivist position (as, incidentally, do Eddington and Jeans), but then at times he alludes to things in themselves and to the ego's perceiving and projecting the outside world. His telephonic description of perception in terms of the ego's sitting behind the central switchboard of the nervous system where the latter then constructs a picture of the outside world is memorable. But it does subsume something calling in the messages. The implied dualism spoils the argument that science is "a conceptual shorthand."

John Stuart Mill (1806–1873) carried on the traditions of philosophical empiricism against the onslaughts of realists and idealists alike. In *An Examination of Sir William Hamilton's Philosophy*, he states his own theory of perception. Mill rejects both the idea of intuitive knowledge beyond sense data and the notion of a representative theory of perception. He finds ideas of the *tertium quid*, the thing in itself beyond perception, to be dispensable. In support of the hypothesis of the permanence of the object world, he proposes two arguments. One, in the argument from causal consistency, the human mind possesses the capabilities of expectancy such that one set of events or of sense complexes becomes the occasion for expecting some other causally related set of events. Expectancies are the foundation of consistency in the empirical world; they are the source of the inferences which underlie the fund of general knowledge. The mechanism of such expectancy is to be found in the laws of association: similarity, contiguity, and repetition. It is by virtue of these laws that we acquire the impression of the "inseparability" of events in the factual world. The second argument is the one based upon Mill's idea of the permanent possibilities of sensation. The argument is more persuasive than expositors often make it out to be. Ontologically, we can only speak of sensation, this must be granted. However, complexes of sensation have the property of permanence.

> The whole set of sensations as possible, form a permanent background to any one or more of them that are, at a given moment, actual; and the possibilities are conceived as standing to the actual sensations in the relation of a cause to its effects . . . (1878, p. 231).

In the context of this argument he goes on to say that the permanent possibilities of sensation assume a reality different from the sensation itself; they form a background to all sensation and are assumed to be "intrinsically distinct" from sensation. Furthermore, other individuals ground their expectancies on manifolds of permanent possibilities just as do I (or any other given observer), the coincidence of such backgrounds thus forming the common grounds of perception. Since this world of possibilities is experienced by others as well as myself, it is external. Mill then concludes the argument by saying:

> Matter, then, may be defined, a Permanent Possibility of Sensation. If I am asked whether I believe in matter, I ask whether the questioner accepts the definition of it. If he does, I believe in matter; and so do all Berkelians. In any other sense than this, I do not (1878, p. 233).

Needless to say, not everyone accepted Mill's definition of matter; but we do find it cropping up again in perhaps the most singular of all of Bertrand Russell's many bouts with the material world, *Mysticism and Logic*.

G. E. Moore (1922) enjoys the distinction of having made 'sense data' a part of the technical nomenclature of phenomenalism. He, himself, was not a phenomenalist as such. His renown resides in his "common sense" philosophy whose matter of factness belies an undercurrent of incisive and often destructive analysis. Common sense inclined Moore to a dualistic position, but he found it difficult to make an explicit statement of the position. It is perhaps surprising then that a person who could handily dispense with subjective idealism by a matter-of-fact resort to ostensification (1939) should have so much difficulty with the problem of relating sense data to the perceiver and his world. But such is the case, and understandably so. 'Sense data' as a synonym for the class of all experience designates that which has sensible components. Such experiential elements are the indubitable givens: "Nothing should be called a sense datum but what *is* given; so that to talk of a non-given sense datum would be a contradiction in terms" (1922, p. 171). First of all, Moore believes sense data to be in the mind; that is, they are "apprehended" by the mind. Second, they are the communicants of our knowledge of the world. Third, with respect to his own realism, Moore confesses a "strong propensity" to believe that sense data persist independently of the mind. They possess some kind of potentiality for experience; but they are, he believes, independent of experience. What then is their relation to objects? Here Moore critically examines several alternatives and then somewhat reluctantly supports a Lockean view of perception. Objects exist and do resemble sense data, but only in so far as the primary qualities are concerned, not the secondary. That is to say, the act of apprehension itself contributes the secondary qualities of experience. However, this dichotomy of qualities puts the relation of the sense data to the objects in jeopardy. Moore does not, and perhaps cannot, commit himself as to whether sense data are surface characteristics of objects. And for this, his account of sense data is wanting (Ayer, 1947).

Few contemporary philosophers have had as much to say concerning sense data as has Bertrand Russell. His discussions of problems relating to sense data cover a range of at least twenty-five years, with each new essay promoting some modification in his thinking. Only a brief account of that thinking can be given here. However, we will see in the chapter which follows, that sense data are the *sine qua non* of Russell's logical atomism.

Throughout his discussions of sense data and the material world, Russell has maintained the undercurrent of dualism (although in his later writings we find that the idea of a material object subsisting independent of its sensory and conceptual qualities is all but suppressed). However, as he became more subjective concerning sense data, he also admitted to greater abstraction in physics. The ideal of a pure physics of logical constructions, purified of all hypothetical elements not reducible to sense data, had to be abandoned.

In *Problems of Philosophy* (1912), Russell combines dualism with a causal theory of perception. Sense data, as he was later to call the perceptual elements, are caused by physical objects. We cannot know the nature of these objects beyond the reach of the sense data, but the fact that the sense data coalesce in object percepts the way they do and give us the impression that we have of their continuity is sufficient grounds psychologically for our belief in a material world. However, since the material world is restricted to the kind of constructions we can make of sense data, there is a suggestion of subjectivity which seems to override the postulation of an objective world. Therefore, sense data must be given some kind of substantive support that they do not have if they are taken as pure mental contents. Sense data must be *of* things; if not, then there should be some means of distinguishing between the illusory and the factual perceptions.

I shall not attempt to pull together the various threads of the argument Russell has spun over the years. Many of his most explicit statements concerning sense data and phenomenalistic reduction can be found in two of the essays in *Mysticism and Logic* (1917), and comment will be restricted to them. In "The Ultimate Constituents of Matter" Russell writes:

> The persistent particles of mathematical physics I regard as logical constructions, symbolic fictions enabling us to express compendiously very complicated assemblages of facts; and, on the other hand, I believe that the actual data in sensation, the immediate objects of sight or touch or hearing, are extra-mental, purely physical, and among the ultimate constituents of matter (1917, p. 128).

Two features of this passage bear comment. One, the idea of a logical construction is important in the argument of logical atomism. Suffice it to say at this time that by saying physical entities are logical constructions, Russell means that such entities are not immediately apprehended but are constructed, as it were, out of elements with which we are in fact acquainted. Thus logical constructions have a kind of derivative existence; but, nevertheless, in the context of the construction they are real. That existence, however, is contingent upon the set of sense data which comprise the elements of the construction (cf. the following chapter on "Logical Atomism"). The second point is a more curious one, curious because in spite of the mentalistic overtones of the term, Russell maintains that sense data are physical. This is not to deny that the sensed qualities of objects are determined (caused by) the perceptual apparatus and physiology of the mind; what is implied is that sense data, extension, heaviness, color, etc., are part of the physical world. Sense data, then, are just those qualities of the physical world of which we can be aware.

> If we have been right in our contentions, sense data are merely those among the ultimate constituents of the physical world, of which we happen to be immediately aware; they themselves are purely physical, and all that is mental in connection with them is our awareness of them, which is irrelevant to their nature and to their place in physics (1917, p. 143).

Care should be taken here not to confuse "physical" and "material." Material objects are logical constructions out of sense data, whereas physical elements are the ultimate elements of the world.

In the essay "The Relation of Sense Data to Physics," Russell supplements his account of sense data with some useful distinctions: (1) *Sense datum* is the physical datum of which an observer becomes aware. (2) *Sensing* and *sensation* imply a two-term relation, in which an observer becomes acquainted with the sense data. The act of awareness is given, and, therefore, "is inherently incapable of truth or falsehood." (3) *Perception* is expressed in propositional form; i.e., it involves an assertion about an object and is therefore subject to being true or being false. (4) *Sensibilia* are what we might call the subsistent potentialities of sense data. They are not unlike Mill's permanent possibilities of sensation; but Russell is explicit in putting them in a physical world, where, upon the observational relation of acquaintance, they become actualized sense data. With the help of these distinctions, Russell is now able to deal with the persistent problems of phenomenalism: illusion and subsistence.

One might question whether this is phenomenalism. If Russell is a dualist then, indeed, he cannot be a phenomenalist. However, it is clear that he will have no part of a physical world whose physical extension goes beyond sense data. This experienceability of sense data is essential to any description of the world. Leaving the ontological status of sense data aside, then for all practical derivations of existence statements Russell would find himself among the methodological phenomenalists. In Russell's analysis there is much that is suggestive of Mach's phenomenalism. However, Russell himself gives the primary credit in his thinking to his contemporary T. P. Nunn.

The literature on phenomenalism is extensive. A good bibliography is to be found in Pap and Edwards (1957) following the selection on phenomenalism by C. H. Whiteley (1949). Aside from the references mentioned in the text and notes, several other items can be recommended as source materials: A. J. Ayer has written both clearly and critically on the subject. See, for example,

> Ayer, A. J., *Language, Truth and Logic* (1946),
> Ayer, A. J., *Philosophical Essays* (1954),
> Ayer, A. J., *The Problem of Knowledge* (1956),
> Ayer, A. J., *The Foundations of Empirical Knowledge* (1958).

Sooner or later every English analyst comes to wrestle with the subject of sense data and phenomena. In addition to Ayer we can point to relevant passages in

> Price, H. H., *Perception* (1950),
> Ryle, G., *The Concept of Mind* (1949).

A little-referenced but excellent critical discussion of Machian and Pear-sonian phenomenalism can be found in

Woodger, J. H., *Biological Principles* (1929).

In this country phenomenalism has not got the play that it has received in England. However, mention should be made of the following:

Marhenke, P., "Phenomenalism," in M. Black, editor, *Philosophical Analysis* (1950),
Black, M., *Problems of Analysis* (1954),
Goodman, N., *The Structure of Appearance* (1951).

The problems of phenomenalistic reduction are assumed under the logical empiricist's principle of verification. Thus discussions germane to phenomenalism will be found in the vast literature on the verification principle of meaning.

## NOTE 3.12

One can hardly overstress the importance of this thesis. If we grant feeling, consciousness, i.e., the qualia of introspection, then it does follow that mental events have a unique intentionality not possessed by physical events. Thus a behaviorist, if he is to be consistent, must either deny or ignore conscious events. If he chooses the latter alternative and therein attempts physicalistic reduction, then, as Feigl has pointed out on several occasions (1953, 1958, 1959, 1961), he is in the predicament of trying to explain an intentional act by means of physical events which are distinguished by the fact that they do not possess intentionality.

## NOTE 3.13

Thus into the Meinongian jungle—into the world of nonexperience as well as that of experience, and all a part of an expanded empirics.

(1) Brentano was not pleased with his students for their efforts to open up the frontiers of being. He himself had distinguished between presentation and judgment. Not only does an object of mental experience enter into mental phenomena by an act of presentation but it also is an object of affirmation or denial (i.e., judgment). The object can be factual or nonfactual, fictional or nonfictional. However, the status of fictional objects should not be dignified as being existential. Existence is something that obtains only in the act of affirmation. Judgments have objects and they have content (i.e., subject–predicate structure). The object, so-called, of the judgment is its subject and is subject to presentation and affirmation. The content of a judgment is not affirmed, however; only components are affirmed. Thus in order for us to say, for example,

that A is B, A must be affirmed. Any predication of existence (e.g., let B designate "an existent being") is therefore redundant; before we can assign the predicate "existence" to A, A's existence must be affirmed.

(2) Russell cuts his way out of the jungle with the refined theory of descriptions, which is to be discussed in the following chapter. There, Meinong's golden mountains will be found to have little value, cash, subsistent, or otherwise.

(3) Meinong's argument, to which Russell and other British empiricists give serious consideration, is based upon the distinction of Objects and Objectives. As we have seen, Objects subsist independently of the attributes of existence and nonexistence. They are the intentions of perception and thinking. On the other hand, judgments (expressible as propositions) involve not only the object, of which it can be said a proposition is true or false, but also a predicative state of affairs which enables us to ascertain whether the proposition is true or false. Suppose we assert "The golden mountain does not exist." This is a judgment. Not only do we have the pure Object, the golden mountain, but also a different kind of object, the nonexistence of the golden mountain. Meinong called this latter type of objects Objectives. In Meinong's words:

> Thus instead of deriving the being of an Object from the being of an Objective, even on the basis of a questionable analogy where the Objective is an Objective of non-being, it would be better to conclude from the facts with which we are concerned [the being of non-being] that this analogy does not apply to the Objective of non-being—i.e., that the being of the Objective is not by any means universally dependent upon the being of its Object (Chisholm, editor, 1960, p. 85).

Apparently this passage is to be regarded as elucidatory, for Meinong's next sentence is: "This is a position which speaks for itself without any further ado."


## NOTE 3.14

One might question whether phenomenology, with its highly personalistic reference and transcendentalistic language, should be given consideration under a survey of empiricism. There are several reasons that it should be. One, from Brentano to Husserl, at least, there was a genuine concern to improve upon and possibly to expand the reach of experience. Two, the phenomenologists combated the artificial reduction of the objects of experience to sense data. And three, phenomenology had an impact upon scientific psychology. What resulted was a psychology that stressed perceptual activity over perceptual content.

With respect to this last point it is well known that Ehrenfels and the Gestalt psychologists adopted as propaedeutic to their own psychologies the act-oriented analysis of Brentano and his students. But what was more explicit (especially in the writings of Koffka) was the fact that psychological descriptions and psychological environments were describable only in terms of the idiosyncratic individual functioning within a unique cognitive field. Thus phenomenological method in psychology, in MacLeod's definitive language, was regarded as "the systematic attempt to observe and describe in all its essential characteristics the world of phenomena as it is presented to us" (1947, p. 193). MacLeod's elucidation of this definition was both timely and influential. It was followed soon by two very popular textbooks, Snygg and Combs: *Individual Psychology,* and Krech and Crutchfield: *Theory and Problems of Social Psychology,* each of which was written in the phenomenological vein. The authors of the latter book were especially indebted to MacLeod.

However, when one examines the revisions which were made in the second editions of each of these books, he discovers a curious byplay in the sociology of knowledge. In the first edition of their book (1949), Snygg and Combs spoke out bravely for the phenomenological method, indexing "phenomenological" on eleven occasions and including the term in two chapter headings. But by the time of the second edition (1959), the terminological retreat had been sounded: "In this book we will not use the term 'phenomenological,' but we shall occasionally use the term 'phenomenal field' " (p. 21). The case with the Krech and Crutchfield book is even more notable. In the first edition of that book (1948), MacLeod's exposition of phenomenology was to be a salient influence upon the authors' quasi-formal efforts to systematize both the language and the structure of social psychology. But when the second edition of this book appeared (1962) with an additional author and a new title (Krech, Crutchfield, and Ballachey: *Individual and Society*) we find that all references to MacLeod (five are indexed in the first edition) and to phenomenology have, with Orwellesquian efficiency, been expunged from the text.

This should not be surprising. The phenomenology of Husserl is hardly applicable in any way as a methodology of scientific inference. The language of the contemporary phenomenologist tends to be obscurantistic. What is more important, however, is the fact that the intuitive inference upon which phenomenology relies is quite unlike that scientific inference which proceeds on the basis of demonstrating a particular to be a case in instance of a general rule. In fact the two methods of inference are rather in opposition to one another. Nor will those bastardizations of intuition such as empathy (Lipps) and *verstehende* (Dilthey) bridge the gap. The latter are hardly more than psychologically inverted inference rules that are bootlegged as autonomous means to insight. Pure phenomenology and pure intuition are what they are, cognitively ascetic contemplations of what a thing is, independent of every other thing. Thus neither one can be of any help to a scientific psychology which wishes to explain and to predict on the basis of rules and manifest similarities.

As Spiegelberg suggests in his comprehensive review of phenomenology (1960), not all of phenomenology is antiscientific. However, the phenomenological point of view breeds a different type of science. It is idiographic rather than nomothetic science. Be that as it may, Spiegelberg is able to trace the roots of phenomenology to phenomenalists and positivists such as Kirchhoff and Mach, and then more directly to the critiques of atomistic introspectionism by traditionally trained psychologists such as Stumpf and Brentano.

Besides the Chisholm selection of excerpts from the writings of the phenomenologists (1960) and the two-volume exposition by Spiegelberg (1960), the following are recommended.

Husserl, E. *Ideas: General Introduction to Pure Phenomenology* (1913)

Husserl, E. "Phenomenology," *Encyclopedia Britannica,* 14th ed.

Sellars, R. W., McGill, V. J., and Farber, M. *Philosophy for the Future* (1949)

Merleau-Ponty, M. *Phenomenology of Perception* (1963)

Kuenzli, A. *The Phenomenological Problem* (1959)

Walker, K. K. "A Critique of Phenomenological Theory." *Austr. J. Psychol.,* 1957, **9,** 97–104.

# CHAPTER 4

# Logical Atomism

AT FIRST GLANCE the program of logical atomism appears Utopian. It proposes no less than to say perfectly what can be said about the world, and to say nothing else. What we can say about the world is one set of things, what the world is may be another (though it is difficult to say it); but given the tools of an ideal language, then the logical structure of appropriately derived propositions will in some sense reflect the structure of the world. To be sure, logical atomism presents an ambitious program. It promises perfectible descriptions with ingeniously simple logical devices. It is even (or rather has been on occasion) bold enough to venture metaphysical judgment about the nature of the real world. For if language and logic can exhaustively map the structure of experience, then a perfect language may indeed map its conceivable realities.

## PICTURING

The concept of mapping, or picturing, is a basic one. Let us approach logical atomism by means of an informal treatment of picturing, and then proceed to the details of its logical structure.

The metaphor of "picturing" is Wittgenstein's and it is well taken.[1] Pictures are representations; a good picture, therefore, is one which represents faithfully what there is to represent. It says what there is to be said about the world; what it cannot say can only be shown.[2]

Although the medium of picturing in logical atomism is language, we can proceed initially by means of photographic and cartographic ana-

---

[1] L. Wittgenstein, *Tractatus Logico-philosophicus;* 2.1–3; 4.01. The decimal notation here and elsewhere refers to the statements in this epigrammatical work.

[2] Wittgenstein actually writes "What *can* be shown *cannot* be said." See *Tractatus;* 4.116–4.1212.

logues wherein the picturing is the mapping of a terrain. Suppose we have a section of rough mountainous terrain which we wish faithfully to describe. We might build a true-scale, three-dimensional model, or perhaps we might take offset photographs for three-dimensional projection. Such maps are very faithful representations. We are inclined to comment on how very realistic they are. Still they are not the actual mountains, the actual boulders, trees, etc. The difference can only be shown. However, to bring our mapping situation closer to the symbolic mapping of language, let us confine our attention to two-dimensional representations. Consider first the photograph. The clear positive print is presented as a faithful picture of the world. But is it? In a sense, yes. The photograph corresponds more to fact than does, say, a freehand drawing. Yet the photograph is merely a picture. That is to say, the black–white gradients of the emulsion are the symbols for real mountains, real terrain. The correspondence is considerable (although this "correspondence" is by no means easy to explicate), yet there is still some ambiguity. No matter how fine the grain, nor how great the resolving power of the camera, one always finds ambiguities implicit within the symbols of the photograph. Not only that, but a bit of introspection tells us that a photograph does not at all look just like that part of the world of which it is a photograph. Be that as it may, we do read from the photograph a great deal of what there is to know about that world.

Next consider a topographic map. Here the grain of detail is much coarser. The symbols are more outrightly conventional than empiric. For example, elevation is represented by color or by contour lines of equal elevation. The legend of the map gives us the dictionary for transcribing the language of the map into the image of the world.[3] From it we understand that the terrain rises at some relatively definite inclination. We know, for example, the greater the density of contour lines, or the greater the gradient in color, then the steeper the inclination of the terrain. Doubtless such maps are very informative; e.g., they indicate to the pilot of an aircraft at what elevation he should fly. They are representative of the terrain. However, there is more ambiguity here than in the case of the photograph; the grain is coarser, so to speak. For example, conventions have to be adopted for interpolating between any two adjacent isometric lines. Such conventions are the result of surmises. They are based on generalizations that very likely do not hold for the given case. And it may be that no information at all is given concerning the nature of the ground cover, buildings, etc., and almost certainly no information about phenomena perceivable in sensory modalities other than vision.

[3] Here we distinguish between picture and image. 'Picture' designates the map; 'image' here is taken to indicate what is the person's knowledge of the world. As we shall see later, the temptation to treat a dictionary as that book that translates from a symbol to the world, as such, invites serious difficulties.

I have pursued this brief discussion of photographic and cartographic mapping first to indicate in a very loose way what picturing and mapping are, and then to show, (1) that maps and pictures are what they are, symbolic presentations, and (2) that no matter how fine their grain, maps and pictures are subject to ambiguity. Needless to say, when we turn to linguistic mapping, the matter becomes more complicated. At first glance, a major difference between linguistic and cartographic mapping would appear to rest in the isomorphic pretensions of each. We have all seen the cartographer's map. Let us now imagine a linguistic map, in which, say, for a verbalized grid of geographic coordinates we associate statements of altitude, statements of obstructions, etc. Thus the air-pilot would get his map through his earphones rather than his eyes. An important factor that distinguishes this verbal map from the visual one is a lack of visual isomorphism. Although all two-dimensional maps of three-dimensional worlds are subject to distortion, different types of cartographic projections are distinguishable for their degrees of isomorphic fidelity. The cartographer's map itself, if it is a good one, shows the geometric patterning of the world. It is, in an important perceptual sense, conformal to the world. However, one of the important contributions of logical atomism was to point out that so-called conformal descriptions need not be restricted to any kind of perceptual isomorphism. Structure and meaning of the world as projected in verbal statements need not be restricted, say, to geometrized spaces. There are also logical spaces that are amenable to description by means of isomorphic projections. It may very well be that the unexplored terrain of thought and cognition can best be mapped, indeed must be mapped, in logical space and with logical conventions.

Such, in brief, is the substance of the doctrine of linguistic picturing. A perfect language implies perfect picturing. How fine, we may then ask, how perfect can we make the logical map? Perfection is always most readily demonstrable for simple worlds. Let us look then at a very simple world. Suppose we have a display board on which is mounted a ten-by-ten grid of lights where each of the hundred lights can be "on" or "off." Our atomic facts are then the on–off states of the separate lights, and no other facts are to be considered possible. We are not to consider the background, the boundaries, or any other thing extraneous to the states of the lights. We now ask, "What kind of knowledge can we have of this world?"

Initially we may proceed by a simple enumeration of the atomic facts. That is, we can take a census of all facts in our finite universe. For each light, we have a possible fact. Each fact then can be expressed as a proposition; e.g., "this one is 'on,'" "that one is 'off,'" for the one hundred individual lights. Such a census would then represent a faithful map of the state of the universe at some given time. However, it is also characteristic of thinking that we connect or group atomic facts by means of logical connectives. One of the great achievements of Russell and

Whitehead (in *Principia Mathematica*) was to show that even the most complex manipulations and groupings of atomic events can be reduced to a very few logical operations. To be explicit, we can construct and express facts such as this light on (off) *or* that light on (off); facts such as this light on (off) *and* that light on (off); and facts such as if this light on (off) *then* that light on (off). And in addition we may express the negation of a fact; that is, we may express the fact this light is not-on (which, of course, for our world is to say "this light is off"). Thus we have four ways of forming statements; by means disjunction (*or*), conjunction (*and*), implication (*if–then*), and negation (*not*). All meaningful statements about our universe are structured by our utilizing one or more of these logical operations. No matter how complex the patterning of the lights, no matter what orderings, or sequential effects, the world before us is exhaustively describable by means of these few logical operations upon atomic propositions. There are no ambiguities, no obscurities, no inexpressible residuals. The world is completely mappable at any given time. In this we have the program but not all of the tools for perfect mapping.

## TRUTH FUNCTIONS AND THE THESIS OF EXTENSIONALITY

It need not concern us that the world can be more or less complex than the grid example we have just considered. We may entertain a universe of two, three, one hundred possible atomic facts . . . or one of an unlimited number of such facts. Our knowledge of the atomic states along with the logical operations at our disposal allow descriptions of all possible states of the given universe. Here we are using 'descriptions' in a somewhat general sense. To describe the world accurately is to express a sentence or a group of sentences which are in fact true. However, not all sentences need be true. In fact, a false sentence can be informative, or meaningful, if it is known to be false. Even a contradictory sentence is informative if, of course, it is known to be contradictory. Thus for a sentence to be meaningful, it must be either true or false or contradictory. (All contradictories are false.) On the other hand, if the sentence is such that there are no possible means of establishing its truth value, then that sentence is meaningless.

We now proceed more systematically. Conceive of a universe of $n$ possible atomic facts. Let $p, q, r, \ldots$, be sentences expressing possible atomic facts. What $p$ asserts may be so, in which case $p$ is true. What $p$ asserts may not be so, in which case $p$ is false. If $p$ is false then the negation of $p$ (expressed '$\sim p$') is true. According to our code of logical operations, we then have the complex sentences:

(*a*)  *p or q*, expressed '$(p \vee q)$.' This proposition will be regarded as true if either *p* is true, or *q* is true, or if both *p* and *q* are true. The last phrase indicates an *inclusive disjunction*. Sometimes the last phrase is replaced by 'but not both *p* and *q* are true,' in which case we have the *exclusive disjunction*. However, for our purposes all disjunctions will be considered as inclusive unless otherwise stipulated.

(*b*)  *p and q*, expressed '$p \cdot q$.' This proposition is known as the conjunction of *p* and *q* and it is true if, and only if, both *p* and *q* are true.

(*c*)  *not-p*, expressed '$\sim p$' (or '*p* is false'). This is the negation of *p*.

(*d*)  if *p* then *q*, expressed '$p \supset q$.' The material implication (conditional) relation is false only when *p* is true and *q* is false; otherwise it is true. This is true when $\sim (p \cdot \sim q)$ is true.

(*e*)  *q* if, and only if, *p* expressed '$p \equiv q$.' Logical equivalence is a special case of implication and conjunction. Thus $(p \equiv q) \equiv [(p \supset q) \cdot (q \supset p)]$.

Now consider a proposition such as the following:

$$[(p \cdot \sim q) \vee (\sim p \cdot \sim r)] \vee (q \vee r) \qquad (1)$$

Let '*p*' be "it is raining in Portland"; let '*q*' be "it is raining in Quebec"; and let '*r*' be "it is raining in Rochester."

Proposition (1) then reads, "Either it is raining in Portland and not Quebec, or it is not raining in Portland nor in Rochester; or it is raining in Quebec or in Rochester." (The example is taken from DeSua, 1954.) Is this complex proposition a meaningful one? Is it true? or false? or contradictory? What is its truth status?

The *thesis of extensionality* states that the meaning of any proposition is truth functional; that is to say, the truth value of a proposition is a function of the truth values of the atomic propositions constituting the complex proposition. How, then, are we to evaluate proposition (1) above?

In order to proceed systematically, we must first stipulate the conventions for truth functional analysis (cf. N4.1). Since the axioms of arithmetic manipulations (transitivity, association, commutativity) also hold for atomic propositions, any complex proposition can be reduced to a logical treatment of no more than two propositions. For example, (1) above can be reduced say to $S \vee G$ where $S \equiv [(p \cdot \sim q) \vee (\sim p \cdot \sim r)]$ and $G \equiv (q \vee r)$.

The rules of truth functional analysis for propositions *p* and *q* are given in Table 4.1. Note that for each logical connective or logical operation there is a truth table for each set of truth values of the atomic propositions. A set of truth values of the atomic propositions constitutes a possible state of the world (of such propositions). Thus for a world describable by two propositions there are four possible states. Since each proposition can take two values, then for an *n*-propositional world there are $2^n$ possible states.

For our complex proposition (1) we have the analysis in Table 4.2. In this analysis, we first establish, on the far left, the set of all possible states of our world. We then proceed from the analysis of the simpler propositions to the more complex. A convention of bracketing is adopted here so that the truth value of the final propositional construction is found

**Table 4.1**     Truth tables for the set of logical operations.

| *p* | *q* | *p* ∨ *q* | *p* · *q* | *p* ⊃ *q* | ~*p* | *p* ≡ *q* |
|---|---|---|---|---|---|---|
| T | T | T | T | T | F | T |
| T | F | T | F | F | F | F |
| F | T | T | F | T | T | F |
| F | F | F | F | T | T | T |

within the triple brackets. Note (*a*) there are eight possible propositional states of the world and (*b*) that regardless of the propositional state of our world the truth value of the final proposition is true.

This latter fact may at first glance appear odd. However, it suggests a further classification of propositions. Some complex propositions are true for all propositional states. Such propositions are logically true and are called *tautologies*. Thus, for example, the analysis of $(p \equiv q) \equiv$

**Table 4.2**     Truth table for the proposition $[(p \cdot \sim q) \vee (\sim p \cdot \sim r)]$ $\vee (q \vee r)$.

| *p* | *q* | *r* | *p* · ~*q* | ∨ | ~*p* · ~*r* | ∨ | *q* ∨ *r* |
|---|---|---|---|---|---|---|---|
| T | T | T | F | F | F | T | T |
| T | T | F | F | F | F | T | T |
| T | F | T | T | T | F | T | T |
| F | T | T | F | F | F | T | T |
| F | F | T | F | F | F | T | T |
| F | T | F | F | T | T | T | T |
| T | F | F | T | T | F | T | F |
| F | F | F | F | T | T | T | F |

$[(p \supset q) \cdot (q \supset p)]$ reduces to a tautology. On the other hand, a complex proposition may be such that regardless of the propositional state of the world (i.e., for every propositional state), the truth value of the complex proposition is false. In such a case, the proposition expresses a *contradiction*. An example of a contradiction is the proposition $\sim(p \lor q) \cdot p$. Finally, a proposition may be such that it is true for at least one but not all propositional states. Thus, for example, $\sim[(p \cdot q) \lor (\sim p \cdot \sim q)]$ is true only if $p$ and $q$ individually take different truth values. The truth of such propositions is contingent on some subset of propositional states. We designate such propositions *empirical*. However, to label these contingent propositions 'empirical' is to take leave of strictly logical analysis and draw attention to the problem of initially assigning truth values to the atomic propositions.

In the case of tautology or contradiction there is no real concern over the initial propositional state. Tautologies and contradictions remain what they are regardless of what truth values we assign to the atomic propositions.[4] But in the case of empirical propositions, we must look to the truth conditions of the atomic propositions if we are to ascertain whether a complex proposition is true. With respect to our display board of lights, for example, we could formulate a complex proposition describing the world at a given time. This complex proposition might simply express the enumeration of all the lights that are on at a given time. Then the truth of the complex proposition would be a function of the truth of the atomic events strung together in a multiple conjunction. Thus we note that empirical propositions require only that (1) the complex proposition be an extension of (a reduction to) a set or sets of particular atomic events (i.e., of allowable propositional states), and (2) some reliable procedure is subsumed for assigning truth values to the atomic propositions.

The critique of logical atomism calls for detailed criticism of these two requirements, but for the time being if we assume that these two requirements are met, then the truth functional (extensional) thesis of language does promise a systematic mapping of the world. For any universe of $n$ atomic facts there are $2^n$ sets of elementary propositional states. Applying the operators of the logical calculus, we may then in principle generate all true propositions about all possible worlds. We have, in other words, the program and tools for perfect descriptions. Thus Wittgenstein could write:

> 4.51   Suppose *all* elementary propositions were given me: then we can simply ask: what propositions I can build out of them. And these are *all* propositions and *so* are they limited.

---

[4] Wittgenstein wrote "I know, e.g. nothing about the weather, when I know that it rains or does not rain." (*Tractatus:* 4.461). He could also have written that he would know nothing if he were told "It is raining and it is not raining."

4.52   The propositions are everything which follows from the totality of all elementary propositions (of course also from the fact that it is the *totality of them all*). (So, in some sense, one could say, that *all* propositions are generalizations of the elementary propositions.)  (*Tractatus*)

Moreover, it does not matter whether we build or reduce complex propositions, whether, in other words, we construct worlds, hypotheses, lawlike descriptions, or whether we reduce (as a method of testing) hypotheses and other possible logical constructions to their appropriate atomic constituents.[5] In summary, the logic of propositions, as sketched under truth functional analysis, outlines the program for the logically perfect language and for the perfect mapping of the atomized world. It affords us criteria for classifying propositions as to their meaning status. And it affords us the means of rigorous testability, of reducing complex propositions to atomic propositions whose truth values are assumed to be indubitable.

However, this program is rather too elegant in its simplicity. Questions arise. How are we to decide what is an atomic proposition? How do we decide the truth value of such a proposition? Are there any propositions which as scientists and empiricists we find useful but which prove unamenable to truth functional analysis? Is the system of logic itself adequate to the job of perfect descriptions?

For a discussion of these questions and others we turn directly to the logical atomism of Bertrand Russell and, to a lesser extent, that of Wittgenstein (cf. N4.2).

## LOGICAL ATOMISM

At the beginning of his essay "Logical Atomism," Russell writes:

THE PHILOSOPHY which I advocate is generally regarded as a species of realism, and accused of inconsistency because of the elements in it which seem contrary to that doctrine. For my part, I do not regard the issue between realists and their opponents as a fundamental one; I could alter my view on this issue without changing my mind as to any of the doctrines upon which I wish to lay stress. I hold that logic is what is fundamental in philosophy, and that schools should be characterized rather by their logic than by their metaphysic. My own logic is atomic, and it is this aspect upon which I should wish to lay stress. Therefore I prefer to

[5] It is tempting to apply the schema to an atomistic neurophysiology. Suppose that the on–off state of each neurone in the central nervous system is, in principle, knowable. Then all conceivable descriptions and all true hypotheses would be expressible in the development and elaboration of the propositional argument. According to the schema a neural hypothesis would be meaningful only if it were constructible from a set of atomic propositions, and it would be true only if it were reducible to a set or sets of propositional states.

describe my philosophy as 'logical atomism,' rather than as 'realism,' whether with or without some prefixed adjective (1956, p. 323).

In brief, realism is to be tempered by logic. Now it is of interest to observe that Russell came to conclusions such as those expressed in the above paragraph only in his philosophical maturity. His first love had been mathematics; he professed to search for sure knowledge, only to find the mathematics of the time both inconsistent and improvisational. The *Principia Mathematica,* written with Whitehead's help, was the result of their endeavors to make secure the foundations of mathematics. As a result of this great work, most of pure mathematics was derived within the rules of logic and thereby became just as secure as logic itself. In the process, Russell was able to improve upon traditional logic. Furthermore, Russell's contact with Wittgenstein lead to the realization that mathematical propositions and mathematical arguments are tautological. In short, they are conventional, they are true by the conventions of logic, and they are empty of content.

Now it had been apparent to Russell that pure mathematics was neither derivable from experience, as John Stuart Mill had proposed, nor given by virtue of *a priori* structuring, as Kant had argued in the transcendental aesthetic. However, it was by no means apparent what relation, if any, mathematical argument had to the real world. There was always the temptation to believe that mathematics was an instrument for tapping the real, Platonic substrata of the world. At one time Russell had succumbed to that temptation. However, realization that mathematical truths are tautological demolished the Platonic dreams; what was then left was a world of facts and a world of pure logics.

Facts and logic, is that all? In a sense, yes. But this is only to say that logic is external to the fact.[6] Atomic facts are independent of logic and they are independent of one another. As Wittgenstein wrote at the beginning of the *Tractatus,* "Any one (atomic fact) can be the case or not be the case, and everything else remain the same." (1.21) However, the relating of facts, the activities of grouping, classifying, and inferring by which we structure the world of fact, are the products of logic. This being the case, the structure of the world is not only a matter of empirics, it is a matter of applied logic. Our knowledge of the world is inseparable from logic and language. What the world is, other than the prerequisite census of atomic facts, is necessarily a matter of logical structuring.

## PICTURE THEORY OF LANGUAGE

We have previously given an informal account of picturing or mapping. The core idea of the doctrine is that of the similarity of structure between

[6] Not, as Bradley (1893) had asserted, internally inherent within the fact.

the fact and the propositional expression of the fact. Since within pure logic propositions have structures, and since the exhaustive set of logical operations is specifiable, then all possible descriptions of the world are contained in the set of potential logical structures. This doctrine has been the source of philosophical puzzlement. However, statements that draw attention to the similarity of factual possibility and linguistic conventions for representing or signifying such facts seem plausible enough. With his usual expository skill Russell writes:

> . . . I shall try to persuade you that in a logically correct symbolism there will always be a certain fundamental identity of structure between a fact and the symbol for it; and that the complexity of the symbol corresponds very closely with the complexity of the facts symbolized by it. . . . In a logically perfect language the words in a proposition would correspond one by one with the components of the corresponding fact, with the exception of such words as 'or,' 'not,' 'if,' 'then,' which have a different function. In a logically perfect language, there will be one word and no more for every simple object, and everything that is not simple will be expressed by a combination of words, by a combination derived, of course, from the words for the simple things that enter in, one word for each simple component. A language of that sort will be completely analytic, and will show at a glance the logical structure of the facts asserted or denied. The language which is set forth in *Principia Mathematica* is intended to be a language of that sort. It is a language which has only syntax and no vocabulary whatsoever. Barring the omission of a vocabulary I maintain that it is quite a nice language. It aims at being that sort of a language that, if you add a vocabulary, would be a logically perfect language (1956, pp. 197–198).

And in a series of papers seeking the classification of the concepts and premises of logical atomism, John Wisdom (1931, I, II; 1932, III; 1933, IV, V) analyzed picturing in the following way. Assume a proposition $S$ and a fact $E$; then

> " '$S$ sketches $E$, an elementary fact' means 'Every element in $S$ names one element in $E$, and every element in $E$ is named by one element in $S$, and the arrangement of the elements in $S$ shows the arrangement of the elements in $E$' " (1931, p. 196).

Emphasis should be given to *shows* for no further explication can be given to the bridge between the two sets of arrangements (cf. N4.3).

### Propositions

The foundations of logical atomism rest on the analysis of propositions. On the one hand, we have facts; on the other, the atomic propositions, $p, q, r, \ldots$, of our truth functional analysis. Facts and atomic propositions share a common structure. That is, the elements of the fact are the particular and the universal; the elements of the proposition are words or symbols which designate the elements of the fact. The particulars of the facts are the things to which we can point, give space–time coordinates, or assign logically proper names ('this,' 'that,' etc.). The universals of the fact are characteristics or relations. In propositional notation, a proposition expressing an atomic fact will have either the form $\phi a$, where '$\phi$' designates a characteristic and '$a$' designates the particular, or it will have the form $a\ R\ b$ in which '$a$' and '$b$' designate particulars of facts and '$R$' designates some relation.

It is tempting to think that a particular, as such, constitutes a fact. For example suppose '$a$' designates the thing to which I am pointing. Is this thing (to which I am pointing) not a fact? Not as such. It becomes a fact only with the assignment, or predication, of a characteristic or of a relation to another particular. For example 'this thing is sweet' and 'this thing is sweeter than that thing' express facts; 'the thing' does not.

So much is simple, or rather, it would appear to be simple. The common structure shared by facts and propositions gives rise to the doctrine of picturing. True propositions express facts, and facts are what make propositions true. What we have called 'the propositional state of the world' signifies for a set of propositions what the true state of the world is if in fact the truth value of each and every atomic proposition has been appropriately assigned. Molecular propositions are then constructible from a set of atomic propositions by the logical operations $\sim$, $\vee$, $\cdot$, and $\supset$. Thus for our example, 'Light $x_{11}$ on; light $x_{12}$ on; . . . ; light $x_{ij}$ off; . . . ; light $x_{10,10}$ on,' may express the atomic state of the world at a given time. 'If a light in row one is on, then another light in column one is on' may be a proposition derivable from the set of atomic propositions. Moreover, any complex proposition about our grid (world) is meaningful if it is capable of verification; that is, if it can be reduced to atomic elements whose truth values can be ascertained.

Unfortunately, perhaps, neither everyday language nor even the language of science possesses the simple precision of the ideal language outlined above. We seldom speak in atomic propositions, and the molecular propositions we use (even in neuroanatomy, for example) may be suspect. Nevertheless, granting the plausibility of a perfect language, we now ask the following questions. Just what propositions are atomic? What complex propositions are in fact derivable from a set of atomic propositions? And, what propositions are meaningless? Since the last question is perhaps the easiest to answer, let us proceed in reverse order.

## Meaningless Propositions

In answer to the third question, we should first observe that neither the propositions of logic, nor atomic propositions can be judged meaningless. Logical arguments are based on tautologies. Thus, for example, $[(p \supset q) \cdot (q \supset r)] \supset (p \supset r)$ is true for any set of truth conditions of the atomic elements. An atomic proposition cannot be meaningless, for a proposition $p$ is atomic only if there is a fact that makes the proposition true or false. But how about purported propositions that bear some semblance to a molecular proposition, but do not reduce by logical operations to atomic propositions? By our schema, such pseudo-propositions are obviously meaningless. There is no reductive access to a set of truth conditions that would make the proposition meaningful. Examples of some pseudo-propositions might be, 'The mind is free to activate the motor neurones,' or 'The self transcends its roles.' Assuming that 'mind' and 'self' designate composites and not particular items, other than by trivial definitions, it is unlikely that we can reduce either of them to a set of particulars. (On the other hand, the difficulty is increased if we treat 'mind' and 'self' as designating particulars. Particularity must be indubitable, like this thing, or that thing. But what kind of particular would 'this mind' refer to? Not an indubitable one to be sure.) Provisionally we can say, then, that metaphysical propositions, propositions expressing transcendental states, in fact all propositions that are neither factual statements nor purely logical ones, are meaningless.

## Complex Propositions

But what of molecular propositions? The difficulties are more subtle here. Russell was careful to emphasize there are no molecular facts, only molecular propositions (cf. N4.4). What makes a molecular proposition true is not a molecular fact, but a set of true atomic propositions that properly ramified by logical operations yield the molecular proposition. However, not all molecular propositions are of a $p$-plus-$q$ type. In fact, very few reduce to the ideal paradigm of the truth functional analysis. The data reports and other protocol statements of the physical and behavioral sciences are very complicated propositions indeed. And then, there are those odd sentences in which certain symbols appear to point to denotable things but which upon further reflection denote only in very ambiguous ways. For example, we may say "The hunger motive is operating here," or "The superego is the source of guilt." Why are these propositions puzzling? In order to answer this question, we must touch upon some distinctions made in Russell's Theory of Descriptions.

## Logical Constructions

First, consider terms like 'the hunger motive' or 'the average running time of subject K.' At first glance these terms may appear to differ as to precision. 'Hunger motive' may appear to be less precise than 'the average

running time.' However, that need not be the case. What is more significant is that neither phrase denotes a specified object; that is to say,
neither points to a specified particular that would be a legitimate constituent of a proposition amenable to direct truth analysis. Actually 'the average
running time' is a symbolic expression for a construction involving logical
operations upon a set of atomic facts. The set of individual times (particulars) as logically processed by means of the operations of summing and
dividing is a *logical construction* designated by the phrase 'the average
running time.' There is a subtle distinction to be made here between the
phrase and the logical construction which the phrase symbolizes. That
which symbolizes a logical construction is called an *incomplete symbol.*
An incomplete symbol is distinguished from other propositional symbols
by the fact that it denotes no particulars, it expresses no universal, its
meaning derives solely from its usage in the context of some set of facts.
Thus the incomplete symbol has "meaning in use only." 'Average,' 'standard deviation,' 'correlation' are all examples of incomplete symbols. When
such a symbol occurs in a proposition it is used only to designate some
logical construction deriving from logical operations performed on a set
of facts. The semantic distinction between 'incomplete symbol' and 'logical
construction' need not detain us. What is significant is the realization that
logical constructions do have a kind of existential status; but whatever
"that kind of status" is, it is clear that it is not that of the factual particularity that we find in atomic propositions.

Terms such as 'average running time' clearly designate logical constructions (cf. N4.5). But how about 'motivation' and 'superego'? Here
the reductions (of what these terms presume to denote) to sets of facts
and operations is more difficult. Such reductions are not impossible, of
course; but whether the terms do designate logical constructions is a matter
of intention by the user of the language. If 'motive' translates into the
simple events of a deprivation schedule (Skinner, 1953) then motive is a
logical construction. However, 'motive' is sometimes taken to designate
something other than deprivation schedules, other than sets of physical
and behavioral facts. The superego may be other than a logical construction of atomic events—or, at least, this is sometimes intimated. But then,
if complex constructs are not logical constructions, what are they? In the
language of science, constructs that are not logical constructions must be
*inferred entities.*

Now the admissibility of inferred entities creates a breach in the
reductionist rubric of logical atomism. The hard core of atomic empiricism
is cracked if we admit entities that are neither atomic facts, nor constructible out of such facts. What should we do? If we follow the rigid requirements of meaning as stipulated by logical atomism, the answer is clear.
In Russell's words, "The supreme maxim in scientific philosophising is this:

*Wherever possible, logical constructions are to be substituted for inferred entities"* (1917, p. 155). We should not admit inferred entities. Or rather as Russell intimates, we should seek to modify our constructs (by refinement and experimental search) until we do succeed in reducing them to logical constructions.

## Theory of Descriptions

The status of inferred entities will be examined upon a number of occasions in the course of this book. But now, there is another way of looking at such terms as 'the superego,' 'the so and so.' Such terms do not directly *denote* some thing but they do *describe* a thing. This distinction leads to one of Russell's greatest contributions to philosophy, his Theory of Descriptions (cf. N4.6). The significance of this theory extends beyond the matters of reference and construction which we have been discussing; therefore, we will confine ourselves to examining a description such as 'the superego.' By superego, we mean to imply there is some thing that we are talking about. But that implication is incorrect if by "thing" we mean to state it is an existential thing like the particular in an atomic fact. Thus the thing we describe has a very nebulous status, something like being a possibility, or perhaps, again, an inferred thing, but not an existential thing.

Now in his theory of descriptions, Russell was able to clarify the puzzles and incorrect inferences concerning descriptions. He was able to analyze a description in such a way as to ascertain whether or not it is a designation of some thing with existential status. His solution seems disarmingly simple. Descriptions such as 'the so and so,' 'the superego,' 'the author of Waverely,' etc., really do not name or denote any thing, but are complexes of predicates in which it is required that the predicates should be of some particular thing. That is, say, the superego is not a thing but a set of predicates of characteristics and relations attributed to some thing. We talk as if the superego is some entity, but what the description reduces to is some existential particular, say, $x$ and a set of predicates $\phi_1$, $\phi_2$, . . . , $\phi_i$, . . . , $\phi_n$ such that the superego really expresses the proposition $(\phi_1, \phi_2, . . . , \phi_i, . . . , \phi_n)x$. Thus, a description is empirically significant only if there is some $x$ which has all the properties assigned by $\phi_i$. One can see, therefore, that the theory of descriptions takes us far in the clarification of the meaning of terms. A definite description is meaningful only if there is some particular, or set of particulars, which possess properties specified in the description.

By this sensitive analytic device, Russell was able to dispense with the existential status of such indefinite descriptions as 'the golden mountain,' and 'the round square.' How should we look at 'the atom,' 'the superego,' 'the motive,' etc.? These terms symbolize constructs, they also symbolize possible definite descriptions. The surest way to endow them with meaning is to make sure that atom, superego, and motive are logical constructs.

## Atomic Facts

We turn now to the final question, "What are the atomic facts?" It is the fact that makes the proposition true. In the ideal language we find particulars, universals, and relations as the elements of the proposition. A proposition $\phi a$ is true if $a$ has the property $\phi$. A proposition $aRb$ is true if $a$ stands in relation $R$ to $b$. Knowing $\phi a$ or $a R b$ is a matter of knowing the constituents of the proposition by acquaintance. The source of our acquaintance is sense data. From these sense data we directly judge whether or not the proposition is true. This is the thesis of empiricism. That all complex constructs are logically derivable from atomic events in the sense domain is the thesis of phenomenalism. But how about the atomic events? Are they as indubitable as we would like to think? Do propositions such as $\phi a$ and $a R b$ offer any difficulty so far as the assignment of a truth value is concerned?

In the quest for certainty it is often the simplest task that proves most intractable. We have a fair idea of the structure of atomic facts. What kinds of sentences, then, should serve as protocols? 'This on red'? for example, or 'This pointer on red'? There is of course a difference between the two propositions. 'This pointer' is a definite description. 'This' alone (except for pointing to the object which is the pointer) is a logically proper noun. Yet each of these symbols is subject to ambiguity. Let us consider the issue further. The confidence we invest in atomism surely rests in the feelings of certitude that we have about the denotation of particulars. I may say, 'This pointer reading,' as I point to the pointer on the dial; or I may say, 'That cat now in the box,' as I point in the direction of the cat. Surely these are symbolic expressions of atomic particulars. But are they clearly so? No doubt the physicist and the psychologist, who are more inclined to trust their denotative skills than are philosophers, would be satisfied that by the above action we have straightforwardly designated particulars. But have we? 'This' is a word which does indeed point, but 'the pointer reading' is a definite description. That is to say, it is a descriptive phrase that is potentially applicable to many particulars but that itself becomes a complete symbol only if a particular is assigned to it. We all know what a pointer reading is but we only know what it really is when we point to a particular pointer reading. And there is ambiguity in pointing. However, this hardly touches the surface of philosophical skepticism. Descriptive phrases are incomplete symbols whose denotative closure depends on our pointing unambiguously to the particular to be imbedded within that which the incomplete symbol ambiguously denotes. But if our finger wavers in pointing, or if the description is sufficiently ambiguous that we cannot detect that which is instantial to it, then we are by no means certain about the symbol which we assume to designate the particular of the atomic propositions.[7]

To carry skepticism still further, we name particulars by the indicative 'this' or 'that' followed by a noun that is really a class name; for example, 'this table.' Is 'table,' then, unambiguous? The raw data of the table are sense data; the table, though you may argue that it is perceptually given, is really a thing that is constructed out of sense data.[8] Thus table, clock, counter are all logical constructions reducible to sense data. Now the process of reducing these logical constructions to their sense data is a very tedious one, and one that frequently results in the ambiguities of existential assumptions about particulars and incomplete reductions. Thus to be absolutely sure of our basic propositions, we may seek to avoid logical constructions altogether. Instead, in our quest for certainty, we may admit only reports such as 'Red now.' The certainty implicit in these reports rests in the fact that they are pure sense data reports. But now our conservatism culminates in a predicament much like that of solipsism. We are precluded even from asking public support of our data, and the whole of empirical science is lost to us.

The questing philosopher has often put certainty high among his goals. Invariably it is the case that just as he perfects his instruments of observation and decision, the object image becomes blurred—just as the theoretical physicist who, having perfected the finest of microscopes for his thought experiments, finds that the sought-after image disappears in a smear of uncertainty. The logical atomism of Russell and Wittgenstein gave us fine instruments for the factual verification of propositions, but as in the case of the microscope, that pinpoint of truth is never quite isolated. It is well to observe at this time that neither logical atomism nor logical empiricism, which followed, were able to enunciate a complete program for an apodictic science. They did not succeed in their empirics nor did they quite succeed in the logic. However, they did succeed in establishing logical foundations for empiricism. And though the promise of ideal language and perfect knowledge did not quite materialize, we do find the

[7] Wisdom argues that if ambiguity is to be eradicated at all, then descriptive phrases would have to be replaced by logically proper names, such as 'this,' 'that,' and to increase the supply, 'thet,' 'thot,' etc. For precise picturing all particulars must be named and not alluded to by description. Thus a reasonably hygienic translation of 'The son of the brother of the mother of the boy kissed the girl with the almond eyes' is 'This son that, and that brother thet, and thet mother thot, and thot boy, and this kissed Sylvia.' This latter proposition contains only logically proper names and relations.

[8] If one wishes to assert that "No, it is not sense data but a table percept which is given," it will be permissible providing no assertion is made concerning material existence of the table nor concerning any other characteristic not immediately present in the table percept. Tables that we talk about in the laboratory are logical constructions. But these constructions are dubitable; we are inclined to endow them with enduring material existence, whereas the only thing we are certain of is our table percepts—which are something other than the table itself.

groundwork laid for an empiricistic theory of meaning which would meet head-on the objections to an intuitionist defense of knowledge.

Finally, in way of appraisal, one should avoid looking upon logical atomism as a school of philosophy, as an "ism," or as a movement. Neither Russell nor Wittgenstein tried to found schools. Although both of them greatly influenced the Vienna Circle, they stayed aloof from its organization and programmatic commitments. For one reason and another, then, there are few logical atomists, few christened disciples teaching from manifestos and spreading slogans. And this is somewhat strange, since Wittgenstein wrote in commanding philosophical epigrams and since Russell has been described as "that unrivalled master of the philosophical maxim." Aside from its contributions to logical and linguistic analysis, the logical atomism of Russell and Wittgenstein remains salutary in the philosophy of science. It improved upon the logical and linguistic tools of science. It laid the foundations for a near-perfect language of science. It gave empiricism the means and criteria for meaningful discourse. And, in its phenomenalism and in its verification procedures, it laid the foundation for the unification of the physical, biological, and social sciences.

# NOTES

## NOTE 4.1

Regarding truth functional analysis:

(1) Practically every text in modern logic has a section on truth functional analysis. These vary from the somewhat practical treatments (Kemeny, Snell, and Thompson, 1957) to the more strictly logical (Quine, 1950). Gottlob Frege whose book, the *Foundations of Arithmetic* (1884), greatly influenced Russell was the first to develop the modern techniques of truth functional analysis. Lukasiewicz, Post, and Wittgenstein popularized the techniques. (See Quine, 1950.)

Truth functional analysis may be regarded as propaedeutic to the logics of quantification. However, so long as we are dealing with finite universes, i.e., universes of $n$ atomic facts, and so long as we do not treat the structure of the atomic fact as problematic, then truth functional analysis and the thesis of extensionality are sufficient for the program of logical atomism.

(2) Propositional operations have something in common with arithmetic operations. For example, propositions obey the associative laws. Thus $(p \cdot q) \cdot r \equiv p \cdot (q \cdot r)$; and $(p \lor q) \lor r \equiv p \lor (q \lor r)$. Likewise propositions obey the laws of commutativity. Thus $p \cdot q \equiv q \cdot p$. However, unlike the case of arithmetic variables, conjunction is *idempotent*. That is $p \cdot p$ is equiva-

lent to $p$ and not equal to "$p^2$." Moreover, propositions as such are not subject to relations of transitivity; only the relations that are expressed within propositions can be transitive in character.

(3) There are various alternatives to actual methods of analyzing propositions. In the text, we use a system of bracketing from lowest to highest order propositions. Some writers prefer a numbering scheme (Kemeny *et al.*, 1951). The differences are inconsequential. However, there are systems of truth value analysis which simplify more complex propositions and which render truth tables unnecessary. (See for example, Quine, 1950; Suppes, 1957.)

## NOTE 4.2

(1) The term 'logical atomism' is due to Russell. His discussions of logical atomism are found throughout his writings. However, the following should be noted:

(*a*) "The Philosophy of Logical Atomism," published originally in *The Monist*, 1918, and republished in Bertrand Russell, *Logic and Knowledge* (1956). In this same book one finds a reprint of the article "On Denoting" (1905) and another article "Logical Atomism" published in 1927.

(*b*) Good accounts of Russell's phenomenalism and theory of descriptions can be found in chapters VIII and X of his *Mysticism and Logic* (1917).

(*c*) Generally Russell's own accounts of his theory of descriptions are easier to comprehend than are those of his expositors. This is even true of his account in *Principia Mathematica, Vol. I*.

(*d*) Also see Chapter 2 of *Our Knowledge of the External World* (1926).

(2) Wittgenstein's contributions to logical atomism are contained in *Tractatus Logico-philosophicus*, a book that Russell was instrumental in getting published and for which he wrote the expository preface.

(3) As for general sources, the following are to be recommended:

(*a*) Susan Stebbing, *A Modern Introduction to Logic* (1948). For a critical discussion of the theory of descriptions.

(*b*) J. O. Urmson, *Philosophical Analysis* (1956). For an excellent general discussion of logical atomism.

(*c*) G. Pitcher, *The Philosophy of Wittgenstein* (1964).

(*d*) Brand Blanshard, *Reason and Analysis* (1962). For an incisive presentation and critique of logical atomism. Blanshard is an astute and readable critic of modern empiricist philosophies.

(*e*) John Wisdom, "Logical Constructions: I–V," a set of critical essays published in *Mind*, 1931–1933.

(*f*) Gustav Bergmann, "The Revolt Against Logical Atomism" in his *Meaning and Essence* (1960).

(4) Credits for logical atomism are to be accorded many people, but especially Russell and Wittgenstein. Wittgenstein, who as a young man studied

aeronautical engineering, went to Cambridge to study with Russell. It proved a fruitful interchange between student and teacher. Specifically, Russell convinced Wittgenstein of the independence of atomic particulars, whereas Wittgenstein convinced Russell of the tautological character of mathematical propositions.

## NOTE 4.3

The puzzlement over picturing stems primarily from the tendency to confuse propositions and facts. A proposition is said to express a fact. If we say a proposition '$p$' is the expression of the fact $p$, then we must be careful not to read into '$p$' the structure of what it asserts. To say 'the book is on the table' by no means gives utterance to anything resembling a book on the table. However, if we examine '$p$' factually, that is look at the fact of its logical structure, then indeed it does have something in common with the fact the book is on the table. It is just what is common to the two which is the picturing (Urmson, 1956).

Trenchantly considered, the doctrine of picturing is ontologically significant. That is, if logically perfect languages picture facts, then we are permitted access to a real world that is beyond the perceptual reach of phenomenalism. However, such an aseptic treatment of picturing presumes that all facts are pictureable, i.e., that the constituents of facts can be signified unambiguously. Russell himself insisted upon negative facts and general facts; but signification of these strange facts proved difficult, to say the least. One can, for example, grant a general proposition '$P$' and a general fact $P$ but it is difficult to arrange the constituents of each such that the constituent for constituent picturing would bridge the gap.

If one carries picturing to its ontological reach then the doctrine suffers from its own linguistic refinements. That is why picturing treated as a mapping analogous to cartographical mapping has a plausibility that a strict logical picture does not have. For finite worlds at least, a truth functional analysis presents an ideal map, if not a very useful one for the working empiricist. The thesis of extensionality does prescribe the conditions for the testability and meaning of complex propositions. But, of course, if we leave finite worlds, or even restrict ourselves to finite worlds which deprive us of ready access to atomic facts, then the truth function stands to mock us for not living in ideal worlds.

## NOTE 4.4

As regards facts, several comments should be made:

(1) Russell's disbelief in any such thing as a molecular fact is in part derived from the belief that the particulars of facts are independent: "each particular that there is in the world does not in any way logically depend upon any other particular" (1956, p. 202). On another occasion, he draws attention

to the Chinese philosopher who counted three things in his farmyard when he saw there a dun cow and a bay horse; the third thing to be counted, of course, being the dun cow *and* the bay horse. Needless to say one might be the richer for counting his purse in this way, but the facts of finances are quite atomic. Russell is almost matter of fact in his discussion of facts. "I do not see any reason to suppose that there is a complexity in facts corresponding to these molecular propositions, because as I was saying, the correspondence of a molecular proposition with facts is of a different sort from the correspondence of an atomic proposition with a fact" (1956, p. 211).

(2) With typical disregard for the purists, Russell introduced *general* facts and *negative* facts, neither of which fit neatly into the extensional pattern. It is not sufficient to say that "all the lights are on" reduces to the set of propositions which stipulate that each light is on. In addition, Russell claims, one must know that *this is all the lights that there are*. Generally, universal propositions use a quantification schema such as $(x)\phi x$, and $(x)\phi x \supset \psi x$, which read "for all $x$, $x$ has the property $\phi$" and "for all $x$, if $x$ has the property $\phi$ then $x$ has the property $\psi$." If the domain of the variable $x$ is unlimited, then, of course, the truth of such propositions cannot be reduced to a finite set of atomic facts. Can we then assign meaning to such propositions? F. P. Ramsey (1931), a brilliant younger contemporary of Russell and Wittgenstein, said no, not in a truth functional rubric at least. Rather he proposed that general propositions of this type are really pseudo-propositions, not propositions at all but conventions for making inferences—"inference tickets" as Gilbert Ryle happily called them. It can only be noted here that such stratagems for escaping one's logical traps are not in keeping with the mission of linguistic rigor. One cannot say that some propositions are meaningless, castigate metaphysicians are talking nonsense, and then good-naturedly say, "But general propositions are different, I need them." However, as was pointed out in Chapter I, positivistic philosophers, most of them with less good humor than Russell or Ramsey, have often defended the critical foundations of their own philosophy by means of propositions highly suspect by their own linguistic criteria.

Russell also improvised negative facts (1956, pp. 203–216). He almost had to in order to be consistent in his assertion that facts are what make propositions true. For example, we may have '$\sim p$' or its equivalent '$p$ is false.' What kind of fact falsifies a negative proposition? For systems of simple binary predication, e.g., light on, light off, there would seem to be a fact supporting the proposition 'the light is not on.' But how about the proposition 'the apple is not sweet'? Sourness may not be the exclusive alternative to sweetness. Thus 'being not sweet' expresses not a fact but a class containing all qualities of taste but sweetness. In information terms, there is more information in the predicate 'sweet' than in the predicate 'not sweet.' However, one fact contains just as much information as another fact. There is no uncertainty in atomic facts. In a sense, they contain all the information there is. From this point of view propositions such as $\sim p$ are really not atomic. Rather it is the case $\sim p \equiv (q \vee r \vee s \vee \ldots \vee z)$, where $q$ to $z$ designate the complete set of possible alternative facts. But then we must also know that this is the complete set of alternative facts; we are, therefore, confronted with a general proposition.

Thus, negative facts require general facts. Given a general fact, then any proposition expressing a negative fact reduces to a molecular proposition of denumerative disjunction. And given the disjunction, then there is a general proposition such as to reduce that molecular proposition to an atomic one expressing a negative fact.

## NOTE 4.5

We sometimes hear of statistical reporters being taken to task for reifying such phrases as 'the average man,' or 'the average income,' etc. This, of course, might be legitimate criticism providing that the reporter has been guilty of endowing his logical constructions with particularity. On the other hand, he could retort: "In using the language of averages I am not reifying, I am using incomplete symbols which have meaning only in a context of facts. In a specific context the meaning of my incomplete symbol is clear, it designates a logical construction which does reduce to a set of facts."

The ontological status of logical constructions is rather unclear. They are neither symbols nor facts, nor yet relations between particulars, such as $a R b$. They are contingent upon logical operations being performed on facts. Even Russell was at times unclear about the distinction between incomplete symbols and logical constructions. G. E. Moore (1959), Wisdom (1931–1933), and Stebbing (1948) did much to clarify the analysis of the two. A logical construction always reduces to a set of ostensive sentences, and the relation of the logical construction to the incomplete symbol may be expressed as follows:

> "Any $X$ is a logical construction" means "The symbol '$S$' occurs in expressions expressing propositions which would commonly be said to be *about X,* and in the case of every such expression '$S$' is so used that '$S$' is an incomplete symbol; and if the expression in which '$S$' is so used were transformed into a set of pictorial sentences jointly equivalent to the original expression, then '$S$' would not occur in any of these pictorial sentences, nor would any symbol in them represent $X$" (Stebbing; 1948, p. 157).

Thus in the phenomenalistic argument that 'table' does not designate a thing but a logical construction (see the text), Stebbing writes:

"The point to be emphasized is that every statement which would commonly be said to be a statement about *the table* can be transformed into a set of statements [about sense data] which can be jointly substituted for the original statement, but no grammatical element in the substituted set will be *used with the same meaning* as any grammatical element in the verbal expression of the original statement" (1948, p. 504).

## NOTE 4.6

The theory of descriptions has significance both for logic and for theory of knowledge. Traditional logic, which carried the influence of Aristotle right through to the twentieth century, analyzed propositions by means of the subject–predicate paradigm. If what was predicated by the proposition was in fact true then that proposition was true. The truth of the proposition was contingent upon the predicate. But what of the subject of the proposition? What is the status of the subject should the predicate be such as to render the proposition false? For example, I may say "The light is on" when it is really off. The proposition expressed is false, but nevertheless there seems to be some denotation for the subject 'the light.' Thus it has been implied that subjects of all propositions have some subsistent status; i.e., they are thought to exist in some sense. For example, consider the following propositions. 'This light is on.' 'The superego is the agent of anxiety.' 'The King of France is bald.' 'The round square does not exist.' The subject of the first of these propositions, even though it is a description, seems to have straightforward denotation. The subjects of the other three clearly do not. In fact, for the last proposition, there is no one thing which is itself both round and square. However, if we say the proposition 'The round square does not exist' is true, we are invited by traditional logic to ask just what is it that does not exist, and what is it that is not both round and square.

Although these puzzles of nonexistence are philosophically interesting, the problems they suggest are more general. Many people will claim that the proposition 'The superego is the agent of anxiety' is meaningful. Consequently, so would be the proposition, 'The superego exists.' There are others who would declare these propositions to be false. Is there any means of arbitrating the issue? By virtue of our empiricism we would say, yes. The facts will tell us. But the facts are always structured by their particulars and universals. What is the particular, or set of particulars, that constitute the subject, 'the superego'?

According to the theory of descriptions things or objects are known either by acquaintance or by description. If the thing or object is known by acquaintance, then in so far as it is the denotation of the subject of the proposition there is no difficulty; we observe whether the predicate applies. But if an object is known only by description such as "the so and so," then our knowledge of that object is contingent upon some one thing having the properties specified by the description. Thus Russell writes: "I shall say an object is 'known by description' when we know that it is *'the* so and so,' i.e., when we know that there is one object, and no more, having a certain property; and it will generally be implied that we do not have knowledge of the same object by acquaintance" (1917, p. 214).

The use of definite descriptions as subjects of propositions is therefore a complex matter. The analysis of the definite description shows that it breaks down into a proposition, or a set of propositions, namely, into those propositions that assert that one and only one thing possesses the defining properties of the description. Thus, the proposition 'The superego is the agent of anxiety' breaks down into 'There is one and only one thing that is the superego, and it is the agent of anxiety.' It is clear then that we must have precise specifications of the superego in order to know whether there is anything that possesses the properties specified. Existence propositions are somewhat different. Since the time of Kant, it has been argued that existence is not a predicate. Consequently, we may find that an adequate analysis of 'The superego exists' is simply to analyze the definite description. Thus the superego exists, as it were, if in fact it is the case there is one thing and one thing only which possesses the properties of the superego.

Existence propositions, in fact all propositions using definite descriptions, are best analyzed by the logical tools of quantification. For example, if we were to deny existence to round squares, we would have

$$\sim E! \, (\imath x)(\phi x) \cdot \equiv \, \sim \{\exists c \, \phi x \cdot \equiv x = c\},$$

which is to say,

" 'The object having the property $\phi$ does not exist' is equivalent to saying 'It is not the case that there is an object $c$ and $x$ has the property of $\phi$ if and only if $x$ is $c$.' " Cumbersome? Perhaps, but it is helpful to logicians.

The significance of the theory of descriptions can be summarized nicely for us by the following statement of Russell:

> Many universals, like many particulars, are only known to us by description. But here, as in the case of particulars, knowledge concerning what is known by description is ultimately reducible to knowledge concerning what is known by acquaintance. The fundamental epistemological principle in the analysis of propositions containing descriptions is this: *Every proposition which we can understand must be composed wholly of constituents with which we are acquainted* (1917, p. 219).

# CHAPTER 5

# Logical Empiricism I: Positivism

THERE ARE MANY PEOPLE, and fairly well read ones at that, to whom "logical positivism" *is* modern philosophy. To them, logical positivism is the spirit incarnate of tough mindedness, to be condoned or condemned, as the case may be. Here is a philosophy to chip away the heavy poesy of traditional tongues, to let the facts stand clear and thenceforward to ramify in the crisp tones of logic and mathematics. Here, too, is a philosophy that eschews the linguistic quest after the good and the beautiful. Banished are the dreams, the embroideries, the comforts of a world of transcendent beings and essences. We are condemned to take our pleasures and pursue our hopes in the prosodic domains of logic and science.

That logical positivism should stand as the cynosure of present-day philosophical critique is not hard to understand. From its inception in Vienna, it has been a brash movement, conscious of its own destiny and garlanded with manifestos and programs to enlighten the critical public. Its spokesmen have been articulate, direct, poignant. And when the decade of Hitler brought about the diaspora of the renowned Vienna Circle, the world was assured continuation of the work and thought of some of the ablest and most dedicated people ever to combine self-consciously into a philosophical fraternity (cf. N5.1). But what is more important is the fact that the positivists found sympathetic audiences. The scattering members of the original circle found students, confederates, and university chairs awaiting them in England, Scandinavia, and America. Their way had been prepared, for logical positivism was little more than the programmatic exploitation of ideas that were well entrenched in American pragmatism and English empiricism. The three movements have common roots.

Furthermore, the choice of order in which we should treat logical atomism and logical empiricism is somewhat arbitrary. The two movements have much in common. They draw from common sources; indeed, Russell

104

and Wittgenstein stand as important contributors to both. If a person were to say that the function of philosophy is to be critical, that logic is the fundamental language, that experience is to serve as the support of basic propositions, and that much, at least, of metaphysics is by virtue of language and experience nonsensical, then, to be sure, it would not be surprising were we to learn that that person regarded himself an atomist, or a positivist, or for that matter, a pragmatist. Be that as it may, there is the matter of continental origins. Atomism was the product of two notable individuals, Russell and Wittgenstein, who approached philosophy through logic. Positivism erupted as the work of men who were trained primarily in mathematics and physics and who wished to unite philosophy and science into a common critical discipline.

At the close of the twentieth century, the critique of science was in ferment. Basic conceptions of physics were being clarified and revised. Long accepted ideas of the ether and of space and time which served as the matrix of classical mechanics had become suspect. The applicability of mechanical description, with its deterministic premises, was being questioned. The underlying realism, the faith that science somehow puts one in touch with reality, was being rejected. Philosopher–scientists such as Mach and Einstein undertook the correction and reinterpretation of classical mechanics, thereby depriving it of its claims to enduring truth. Historians and philosophers of science such as Rey, Duhem, and Poincaré pointed out that the truths of science had time-bound conventional character. Thus scientific truth was found not to be absolute, enduring, and ontologically basic, but rather to be contingent upon the frames of reference, the constructions, the conceptual premises that give to the scientific argument its unique possibility. Science lost its ontological status. One might think, therefore, that the boast of scientific empiricism had been shattered or that the scientific quest had failed. This was not the case. What the positivist capitalized on was the fact that neither logic nor experience, as such, gives us license to dogmatize about the world. The idea of the indubitable character of basic scientific propositions, as generated, for example, by the Kantian synthetic *a priori,* had to be abandoned. Positivism sounded the retreat from the Kantian position of strength. It took its own position in Humean skepticism, in phenomenalism, in constructualism, in the host of all "isms" which coupled the empirical support of knowledge with the renunciation of metaphysics. The movement, of course, was not new. The positivists acknowledged their indebtedness to Hume, to Comte, to Mach and Kirchhoff, to Duhem, to Poincaré, to Russell and Wittgenstein, and to many others. Perhaps the only surprising aspect of this new positivism rests in the fact that its skepticism was motivated not so much by its despair over methaphysics, but rather by the failure of science to render enduring its dogmatic pronouncements.

If science was not the means to reliable knowledge, what then was?

The answer was a reaffirmation of scientific empiricism. Rather then looking for the enduring truth, rather then accepting the ontological commitment that the quest for truth implied, positivism set out to show in what respects the empirico-scientific route to knowledge was more reliable, more to be recommended, than any other.

We have previously indicated what the themes of modern empiricism are: (1) the importance of logic and language in structuring our knowledge of the world, (2) meaning, as factual verification, and (3) the rejection of metaphysics as an instrument of indubitable, reliable, or factually meaningful knowledge. The last point need hardly concern us in the philosophy of science, but the first two are of crucial significance. Let us begin then with a discussion of syntax.

## LOGIC AND SYNTAX

It is the character of all language to show a structure independent of its specific contents, i.e., of the meanings of its words, of its denotations, of its idiomatic colorations. But because of the colorations and the ambiguous reference of its components, it is difficult to show that natural language is a reliable instrument of knowledge. We are often trapped or seduced by its verbal magic. Many analysts believe that our philosophical perplexities derive solely from the fact that our natural languages are syntactically and semantically corrupt. Now a syntactically pure language would lead us out of some of our quandaries, but unfortunately we would be left with a sack of empty variables and operators which might satisfy our zest for hieroglyphics but little else.

We have already seen how a syntactically pure calculus operates. In the truth-functional calculus of the last chapter, we saw how propositional variables are introduced with the sole qualification that each basic proposition be judged true or false. Then by virtue of logical operations such as conjunction, disjunction, negation, and implication we could in principle develop all arguments conceivable under the set of the syntactical rules. The thesis of extensionality asserts that an argument within the syntactical system is a function of the truth conditions of the atomic propositions. Thus the propositions of the argument are either tautological (analytic), or contradictory, or synthetic, as the case may be. This syntax is sufficient for a finite set of atomic propositions (or events), but it will not do for the universe in which the quantification of atomic events is left open. We do sometimes speak of *some*, or *all*, not knowing precisely what is the denumeration of the events in our universe. The purpose of syntactical study is to show the character of logical argument independent of such contents as give natural language its significance.

Consider an assertion in a natural language. It reveals its propositional structure *Px,* where '*x*' designates a particular; and '*P*' designates a characteristic or a relation. This is the familiar subject–predicate form. When we examine propositions of the kind *Px* in their logical purity, we note, however, that *x* and *P* are, respectively, variables and class symbols specifying nothing independent of what values are assigned in the addendum on their semantic translations. As such, the rules for structuring well-formed statements are purely syntactical. An argument can progress without at any time our having to ascertain whether the symbol stands for any discernible thing in the world of fact. Moreover, we find that the letter '*P*' is a class symbol, by which we mean there is a set of things, variables, which have the property defined under *P*. Again, it is not necessary to assert that there is a palpable thing possessing a characteristic that may in fact be characteristic of palpable things. That is to say, classes do not presume to ontological status, they do not wear the aura of the Platonic reals, they are not in any way given. They are conventions, the plastic agents of our own whims for class inclusion. To assert *Px* is to assert that the thing that is *x* is in the class of the things that are *P*.

We note also that '*x*' itself can be the sign of a class of events. Should the '*x*' of the natural language signify a class we will need to quantify the variable according to whether we indicate all members of the class or just some. For example, we may take *Px* to be "the boy," symbolized by '*x*,' "is obstreperous," symbolized by '*P*.' If '*x*' does not refer to a specific boy but symbolizes the class of all boys, then we would have recourse to the convention '(*x*), *Px*'; i.e., for all *x*, *x* is *P*, or for all selections of a boy, the boy is obstreperous. On the other hand, if only some members of the class of things designated *x*, are *P*, we adopt the convention '∃*x*, *Px*.' There is at least one *x*, such that *x* is *P*. These are the most basic elements of logical quantification. We need not carry the logical schemata further. The important thing is to recognize that expressions such as '(*x*) *Px*,' are perfectly readable regardless of whether or not they symbolize a counterpart in the world of objects.

Why do we make so much over what appears to be so trivial? What appears trivial here has some profound philosophical consequences. The fact is that all languages are symbolic systems. What differentiates the language, say, of *Principia Mathematica* from our natural English is the rigor of the syntax. We are inclined to treat words as if they are materially connected with objects rather than as what they are, symbols in a syntactical system. It is just because we think in terms of content that we get into difficulty. For example, by virtue of the theory of descriptions (cf. N4.6) we find that propositions about noninstantial things lead to puzzles about their existence. This is because we are inclined to assume that whatever is named in a natural language must be something rather than nothing at all. The rhapsodies on nothingness, which we owe to Heidegger, reflect just such confusions. The proper analysis of the so-called "existence" proposition entails our analyzing it into a compound proposition, one part of which asserts the subject, the other part of which asserts the predicate. The ontological fog is dissipated when we make sure that our propositions are composed wholly of constituents with which we are acquainted.

The matter of verbal reification is more general than the paradigms of "golden mountains" and "round squares" intimate. According to Carnap (1937), it is the source of most of our ontological confusion (cf. N3.10). When we use language in its natural form we use words as if they refer to objects or as if their meaning has concrete significance. Thus any sentence of the structure $Px$ is thought to imply that there is some thing $x$ which has the property $P$. Perhaps it is a simple enough matter to ascertain whether a sentence $Px$ is true by factual reference. However, there are examples of words in the natural language that are purely syntactical; they have no reference beyond their own conceptual frameworks. Number words are an example. All statements about numbers are about logical conventions. Yet many of us speak as if we are talking about a real world of numbers, as if numbers were subsistent entities, even having those pervasive properties that sing the harmonies of the heavens. Some of us, like Pythagoras and Kepler (and in our own time, Eddington and Jeans) believe that the structure of the universe is mathematical; and because of this structure, the language of mathematics will spell out the synthesis of a unified science. Others are less elegant. Like J. S. Mill, they believe that mathematics falls within the synthetic repertory of our knowledge. Consequently disputes about mathematics (such as those over the postulates of Geometry) are to be referred to experience. When we realize that these disputes arise out of the puzzles of our own conventions rather than as empirical problems, they disappear or are delegated properly to the realm of logical critique. In the *Logical Syntax of Language,* Carnap gives us a veritable catalogue of pseudo-sentences based upon such syntactical confusions (cf. N5.2). We need not go into detail. Suffice it to recognize that some "philosophical" problems are hardly problems at all. Syntactical purity is one thing, meaning through semantical reference is another. The profundities of much dialectical metaphysics derives from a confusion of the two.

Briefly, now, we look at the principles of syntactical systems. Carnap writes, "By the *logical syntax* of language we mean the formal theory of the linguistic forms of language" (1937, p. 1). Although the adjectives 'logical' and 'syntactical' are often times used as synonyms, Carnap recommends that 'syntax' should refer to the analysis of linguistic forms, whereas 'logic' should refer to rules for manipulating propositions. This distinction is not always observed, but we should note that a syntactical system includes both syntactical and logical rules. In the former, we are concerned with rules for forming statements, for defining the primitives, for establishing the conditions of synonymity, and for defining the conditions which render a statement analytic, contradictory, or synthetic. Thus we codify the procedures for making well-formed statements in the system (cf. N5.3). In addition, we have logical rules for manipulating the propositions expressible in the system. Transformation rules and rules of deduction enable us to elaborate a set of premises into a complex proposition; or, on the other hand, they enable us to reduce a complex proposition to a set of basic elements. We have, therefore, to incorporate into logic the theory of construction, reduction, and proof. The great achievement of the Russell and Whitehead *Principia Mathematica* is that it presents just such a syntactical system, a system remarkable for its applicability not only to natural language but also to the foundations of the whole of arithmetic.

Our cursory treatment of syntax shows only that statements must abide by the conventions of form and transformation. We have not spoken of their having content, nor have we more than intimated how they are to acquire content. This, indeed, is the problem of meaning. And to that we now turn.

## MEANING AND VERIFICATION

The cornerstone of positivism is the verification theory of meaning. Its inscription reads "No nonsense!" And its significance is such that if it were removed the whole edifice of logical empiricism would begin to topple. Consequently it comes as a bit of a surprise to find that the masons of positivism were already pulling at the stone before the grout had set. Waismann, who was later to recant almost entirely, declared the motto of verification in the first volume of *Erkenntnis*:

> If there is no way of indicating when a statement is true, that statement has no meaning at all; for the meaning of a statement is the method of its verification. In fact, anyone who makes a statement must know in what circumstances he would call the statement true or false; if he is unable to do so, he does not even know what he has asserted (quoted in Black, 1934, p. 1).

"The meaning of a statement is the method of its verification." Here is a statement so casual in utterance that it strikes us as if we were being told something as factual as "the dollar is a unit of exchange." However, the statement is not factual; it is not at all clear what its meaning status is. Furthermore, our second thoughts show the verification principle to be destructive of much of what positivists would agree to be significant. As W. T. Stace writes:

> Most of them [objections to the verification theory of meaning] turn
> upon the consideration that the verificational theory is so narrow that it
> excludes as meaningless, not only those wordy disputes of philosophers
> and those poetical effusions of mystics which we are glad to see be-
> laboured, but also many sober propositions which the most hardheaded
> men of common-sense everywhere in the world have always believed to
> be plain statements of everyday fact (1935, p. 422).

But before we examine examples of excluded statements we note
that the phrase "the method of its verification" is itself seriously ambiguous.
What do we mean by the method of verification? Is there one method?
two? or several? Is the method of intuition as acceptable as that of empirical reference? Do we mean by method rules to assign meaning? If
so, is it not somewhat confusing to assert that the meaning of a term is
a set of rules? Even mottos should be more to the point than this. It is
strange that of all the statements concerning verification this is the one
singled out to carry the significance of an empiricistic theory of meaning.
We note, however, that the quotation of Waismann does adumbrate some
fuller explication of the meaning of verification. We must know what the
circumstances are for one's calling a statement either true or false. Presumably, these are to be empirical circumstances; that is what empiricism
is about. But are they? Let us have a look.

Terms and statements have meaning. Some terms are ostensive. They
denote objects and that denotation, itself, is their meaning. Other terms
are logical terms, e.g., connectives, operators, whose meaning is a matter
of syntactical convention and whose contextual significance occurs only
in conjunction with other, ostensive terms. Still other terms are definable
only by yet other terms, the nonlogical members of which are ostensive
(e.g., terms like 'committee,' 'duel,' 'gravitation'). Statements, of course,
are more complex. First, there are syntactical rules for constructing well-
formed statements in the subject–predicate format. Not only must we have
subject terms and predicate terms, but only certain types of predicates
are assignable to a given subject (e.g., 'The hills laugh through purple
chasms' may look like a well-formed statement, but it is not). Second,
each term in the statement itself must be meaningful. This seems straightforward enough, but is it? There is still confusion here. Look, for example,
at what Ayer writes with respect to the meaning of a proposition.

> We are asking what are the propositions to which the proposition in ques-
> tion is reducible. . . . These propositions are in turn reducible to others
> until we reach the elementary propositions which are not descriptive but
> ostensive (1934, p. 337).

This passage continues in such a way as to indicate that Ayer himself
would emphasize the activity of ostensification. However, the quotation
suggests one of the sources of difficulty which confronts the logical

positivists in their efforts to spell out the mechanics of verification. On the one hand, we may speak as if the meaning of a term or the meaning of a proposition is equivalent to another set of terms or set of propositions. If this is the case, meaning is a linguistic reduction, and verification seems to be a strange word to apply to the procedure of definition. Yet we note that Neurath and Carnap adopt this manner of speaking in support of the syntactical foundations of physicalism (cf. N5.2). On the other hand, if the ultimate reduction is betokened by our arriving at ostensive terms, then the problem is not a syntactical one but one of empirical reference. Rather than the ultimate meaning involving logical relations between words, it involves the relation of denotation between the word of the basic vocabulary and the object of experience. This is a different problem, and a more difficult one if we were to make secure the connection between word and object. These issues will crop up in later discussions; we will not pursue them here. Suffice it to say that the attempt to treat all meaning within the boundaries of syntax is not generally regarded as being successful. Rather, most empiricists are inclined to agree with Ajdukiewicz (1935) when he prescribes three kinds of meaning rules which involve both syntactical and empirical procedures: axiomatic, deductive, and empirical meaning rules (cf. N5.4).

To point to additional difficulties in the principle of verification, we need a somewhat more explicit statement of it. In the context of the passage quoted above, Ayer goes on to say:

> . . . to give the meaning of a proposition is to give the conditions under which it would be true and those under which it would be false. I understand a proposition if I know what observations I must make in order to establish its truth or falsity. This may be more succinctly expressed by saying that I understand a proposition when I know what facts would verify it. To indicate the situation which verifies a proposition is to indicate what the proposition means (1934, p. 337).

This article of Ayer was, incidentally, one of the first in English to enunciate the positivistic principle of verifiability. Its intent was to distinguish sense from nonsense, propositions from pseudo-propositions, and to banish all excursus in metaphysics (cf. N5.5). The arbiter for distinguishing between the factually meaningful and the meaningless was to be observation and experience. Can the line thus be clearly drawn? It is simple enough to banish the metaphysics of the transcendent, but how do the hypothetical statements which scientifically minded empiricists find useful fare? And, how are we to verify laws stipulated in terms of the universal quantifier *all?* How about hypothetical *if–then* statements, such as "if the universe began as a primordial atom, then its present rate of expansion at the boundaries of our telescopic vision is such and such"? And how about all statements pertaining to historical events, and about hypotheses of as yet unexperienced events (such as the presence of other planetary systems in our galaxy)? Clearly these are meaningful statements; but the states of affairs to which they allude are intimated only as being possible, not actual. One may claim no more for metaphysics.

Most of these difficulties were recognized from the start. But lest we give up in despair and disqualify verification as a criterion of meaning, we should look at what that criterion intends. From its inception in the writings of Locke and Hume, empiricism has attempted to distinguish between that which is indubitable and referential in character and that which is a matter of opinion, conjecture, or intuition. Statements coming out of these latter pretensions to knowledge are not, at first glance, meaningless. They are neither contradictory nor poorly structured. Still we do not trust them, for neither their assertion nor their denial can be assessed. We have no means for bringing experience, or any other publicly acceptable instrument of arbitration, to bear upon their evaluation under a system of truth functional analysis. Furthermore, as the skills of logical analysis became more fully developed, the efforts of logical empiricists were directed toward ascertaining the classes of assertions whose meanings were, by public agreement, unequivocal. For example, there is little or no doubt concerning the semantical status of analytic propositions. They are true and meaningful by the public convention of logic. There is also little doubt concerning public observation reports. These refer to events that are common to the experience of all appropriately stationed observers. There may even be tentative agreement that statements that presume to express transcendental states of affairs are meaningless. However, there remains a large mixture of propositions that are neither analytic nor unequivocally empirical yet that are considered meaningful by the empirical scientist. For example, we might postulate that parallel lines do not intersect, or that the total mass–energy complex of the universe is constant. One cannot test these statements empirically. And if they serve as postulates, their analyticity can be denied. Yet, one suspects they are in some sense meaningful.

Now, in this context the critics of the principle of verifiability were quick to point out that certain types of statements, though useful to science, may fall within this class of undecidable propositions. We have already mentioned them briefly. First, universal propositions and general laws can never be verified by a finite set of observations, no matter what the empirical implications of the law. Each singular observation may exemplify the law, but neither it nor any finite set of observations can cover the infinite range of possible empirical instances. Are laws then to be given some provisional status? If so, are we not then in danger of smuggling in some ontological presentiments? Second, some statements express hypothetical constructions that become essential to the chain of scientific inference. They too are beyond the reach of direct verification, if, indeed, they are even in principle capable of verification. For example, one may speak of electrons, of genes, of "hidden" variables, each of which, regardless of its eventual scientific status, serves as a focal unit of speculation. Yet there may be no direct evidence of their experiential existence. And in some cases (not all) their connection to fact is no more secure than the status of the antecedent in a material implication. Third, historical statements are incapable of direct verification. The evidence in support of historical statements is indirect. All documentation at best indicates a chain of possible events bridging the present and the past. Archaeology, paleontology, history, all assert hypotheses about occurrences which are impossible to verify. Predictions of the future fare no better. And fourth, the so-called counterfactual conditional assertion is also problematic. "If Rhodes were to sell all his diamonds, their market value would drop." "If it turned warm, there would be a flood." "If he fell on that traverse, he would surely die." These statements, and those like them, are somewhat like our hypothetical statements and somewhat like predictions. Actually they are complex propositions involving premises and rules of inference. Yet though their consequences affirm empirical states of affairs they cannot be verified. And it is unlikely they will be tested. (Chisholm, 1946; Goodman, 1947, 1955)

There are other problems as well, problems that are common to all empirical philosophy. We have met them before, in our discussion of phenomenalism, and again in our discussion of logical atomism. Yet in the present context they are best discussed in conjunction with the diverse developments within logical positivism itself. Note 5.1 reports how logical positivism crystallized about the Vienna Circle. The Circle borrowed and profited from its immediate contact with Wittgenstein. It also engaged in sympathetic exchange with the Berlin Society for Empirical Philosophy, and with some members of the community of British empiricists. However, within the Circle itself a divergence of opinion was developing over the proper role and interpretation of the principle of verifiability. On the one hand, Schlick, the founder and leader of the Circle, proposed a direct unsophisticated connection between statements and fact; on the other hand, Neurath and Carnap proposed a syntactical treatment of the problem of verification such that meaning was contingent only upon the connection of statements with other statements. This indicates an important divergence in approaches. The nature of the approach one adopts not only influences the kind of semantic treatment he undertakes, but also the kinds of problems that will be selected for analysis.

Continuing our discussion of meaning and verification, we divide the approaches within the positivistic movement into the empiricistic and syntactical schools. Under the first, we place Schlick and Ayer (as well as most English empiricists); under the second, we place Neurath, Carnap, and Hempel. It will pay us here to examine the thinking of each of these groups. In addition, we will want to consider Karl Popper's alternative to verification. As the culmination of British empiricism, analytic philosophy perhaps warrants a separate chapter. However, since it has been influenced by Russell, Wittgenstein, and Ayer, we will treat it as an addendum to the present discussions.

## Experientialist School

Following Feigl (1943), we classify under this heading those people who propose that the meaning of a statement is expressed as a relation between syntactical symbols and objects of experience. Thus, if the meaning of a sentence rests in its method of verification, the method itself is that use of symbols to denote objects and relations among objects in accordance with semantic rules. Whether a sentence is used appropriately and meaningfully is a matter that is contingent upon the object situation to which it purportedly refers. In brief, meaning is a matter of factual reference (cf. N5.6).

(1) *Moritz Schlick.*    Schlick follows Waismann in defining meaning as a method of verification. In an early article, he writes:

> . . . in order to find the meaning of a proposition, we must transform it by successive definitions until finally only such words occur in it as can no longer be defined, but whose meanings can only be directly pointed out. The criterion of truth or falsity of the proposition then lies in the fact that under definite conditions (given in the definition) certain data are present or not present (1932, p. 87).

And later he writes:

> Stating the meaning of a sentence amounts to stating the rules according to which the sentence is to be used, and this is the same as stating the way in which it can be verified (or falsified). The meaning of a proposition is the method of its verification (1936, p. 341).

Now Schlick is aware of the ambiguity of 'method,' 'verification,' and 'proposition' and sets about being more explicit. First, he notes that implicit within the definitions and meanings there is a note of expectancy. That is to say, the meaning of a statement lays out a plan of possible experience such that if the sentence is true then we know what factually or observationally to expect. Second, he lays emphasis upon the possibilities both of language and of states of affairs. The language must be sufficiently flexible and complex to convey the meaning of any possible state of affairs, and yet it should be bound by the restrictions which experience does in fact place on possibility.

This in turn leads him to some important distinctions. First, there is the distinction between logical and empirical possibility. Logical possibility is laid out by the syntactical rules of the language. Thus statements must conform to the appropriate sentential structure, although in fact they may or may not be meaningful. For example, the sentence 'The sky in Palo Alto is three times as blue as it is in England' is at least logically well structured, even though as it stands it lacks the possibility of empirical meaning. On the other hand, empirical possibility is that possibility laid out by the laws of nature, or if you wish, by the fact that nature is as it is. Thus logical and empirical possibility do not coincide, although the set of empirical possibilities are representable by a selection of statements from the domain of logical possibility.

Second, there is an important distinction to be made between verifiability and verification. It is important to note that the empiricistic theory of meaning is based upon *verifiability* rather than on *verification*. What is the difference? Schlick writes, ". . . when we say that 'a proposition has meaning only if it is verifiable' we are not saying '. . . it is verified,' " (1936, p. 344), and again, "Verifiability means the possibility of verification." Thus the principle of verifiability states only that verification should be in the realm of empirical possibility, not that it actually be carried out. Statements about the other side of the moon, about the distribution of galaxies behind the milky way (but not about the simultaneous position *and* velocity of the electron) have meaning, although in Schlick's time at least, no direct evidence had been taken. So long as there exists the empirical possibility of verification, then the sentence is in principle verifiable—even though the sentence may turn out to be false.

Finally, Schlick differentiates between sentences and propositions. Some such distinction follows from the earlier treatment of possibility. Within the realm of logical possibility is the set of all possible statements. Not all of these will be meaningful, as we have seen. But any meaningful statement must be expressible as a logical possibility of our system of syntax. The "grammatical rules" of verification require this. It is not clear in Schlick's exposition what precise connection propositions have to facts. Nevertheless, a proposition stands in a relation to the relevant facts such that the facts are sufficient and necessary to the meaning of the proposition. Sentences that are meaningful are transformed into propositions, which, by virtue of the sentence, are expressed in some definite language. This is suggestive, therefore, of the conventional distinction between the proposition as being the meaning of a set of equivalent but linguistically alternative sentences and a sentence as being an explicit statement possibly expressing a proposition. We may note that all propositions are meaningful, and they are meaningful by the method of their verification. Not all sentences are meaningful, however; just those which express propositions (cf. N5.7).

There is a linguistic as well as an empirical element in Schlick's treatment of meaning. Not only are facts necessary to the meaning of a proposition, but what facts are selected and attended to are determined in part at least by the logical conventions we adopt for verifying sentences. Syntax does in a sense determine the meaning of a proposition. 'A is next to B,' for example, is true if, and only if, A is next to B, but the fact that A is next to B is in part determined by the logical relation of juxtaposition which is one of the conventions of our language. In order further to explicate meaning along these lines, Schlick writes:

> Verifiability, which is the sufficient and necessary condition of meaning, is a possibility of the logical order; it is created by constructing the sentence in accordance with the rules by which its terms are defined. The only case in which verification is (logically) impossible is the case when you have *made* it impossible by not setting any rules for its verification. Grammatical rules are not found anywhere in nature, but are made by man and are, in principle, arbitrary; so you cannot give meaning to a sentence by *discovering* a method of verifying it, but only by *stipulating* how it *shall* be done. Thus logical possibility or impossibility of verification is always *self imposed*. If we utter a sentence without meaning it is always *our own fault* (1936, p. 351).

Meaning, therefore, has its conventional element. In this, Schlick is in agreement with the syntactical school of Carnap and others. But he is not so extreme as they; the agent of ultimate verification is always experience. Facts are selected according to the logical structure of the sentence; but unless there are facts to transform the sentence into the meaningful proposition, then regardless of the niceties of syntactical conventions, that sentence will be meaningless.

It should be noted that Schlick's article, "Meaning and Verification" (1936) was written in response to objections to the positivistic theory of meaning raised by C. I. Lewis (1934). Lewis, who by and large, has been sympathetic to empiricism, raises questions concerning the radical empiricism suggested in the early writings of the Vienna positivists. First of all, he notes that the intended object (the cognized object) always involves more than the immediate data, the cognitive act by which verification takes place involves conceptual structuring and a filling in of detail. Perceptually, at most, we receive only minimal cues. Spelled out in a logical framework, experiencing always involves the conceptual *a priori*. Specific to the discussions of verifiability, Lewis raises questions concerning (*a*) the meaning of statements about the surface of the other side of the moon, (*b*) the meaning of theoretical constructs, (*c*) the meaning of existential statements if all minds were to disappear, and (*d*) issues specific to assertions about immortality and other minds. We need not go into Schlick's point by point rebuttal of Lewis' argument but it should be noted that his conventionalist and "possibilitarian approach," if we may so stigmatize it, has little difficulty in coping with the issues of possible verification, of immortality, and of other minds. However, Schlick is somewhat less successful in dealing with the status of propositions about the external world if all observers were to disappear (cf. N5.8).

(2) *A. J. Ayer.* Undoubtedly the most important factor in the spread of logical positivism was the scattering of the continental positivists into the English speaking world during the 1930's. There was another important factor. Ayer, who had visited Vienna prior to this scattering, published his *Language, Truth and Logic* in 1936. This was an immediately successful book; its incisive and admittedly aggressive style turned positivism into a household gospel. However, the publication of this book was preceded by the article "Demonstration of the Impossibility of Metaphysics," a work that proved equally provocative among Ayer's native philosophical colleagues (cf. N5.9). We have already quoted him concerning verification and meaning (p. 110). But in that quotation he suggests that the meaning of a proposition is given in terms of other propositions. To emphasize the empirical character of the ultimate propositions, note that he says ". . . to give the meaning is to give the conditions under which it would be true and those under which would be false." He makes it clear that such conditions are facts and observation. Here he is in agreement with Schlick. Meaning ultimately involves a relation between proposition and fact; not a relation between one proposition and one or more other propositions. On another occasion Ayer writes:

> . . . when Professor Schlick says that the truth of a synthetic proposition consists in its agreements with reality, and not merely in its logical compatibility with other propositions, we may assume that he is attempting to show what is the criterion that people actually apply to their beliefs (1935, p. 29).

Ayer's own wrestling with the problem of meaning and verification exemplifies the retreat from dogmatism. In *Language, Truth and Logic,* he distinguishes between a "strong" and "weak" sense of verifiability:

> A proposition is said to be verifiable, in the strong sense of the term if, and only if, its truth could be conclusively established in experience. But it is verifiable in the weak sense, if it is possible for experience to render it probable (1946, p. 37).

This statement of weak verifiability is not very precise. For experience to render a proposition probable, it must do so in face of the fact that the proposition may assert some state of affairs for which the actual observations are insufficient evidence. This would be the case, for example, if the proposition asserted the absolute existence of some state of affairs, or if it asserted a proposition about the past, or if it asserted a universal. Therefore, in order for experience to render a proposition probable, some linkage involving auxiliary hypotheses or assumptions is necessary. Thus the weak versions of verifiability (as rephrased in the Introduction to the second edition of *Language, Truth and Logic*) should be written:

> . . . a statement is verifiable, and consequently meaningful, if some observation-statement can be deduced from it in conjunction with certain other premises, without being deducible from those premises alone (1946, p. 11).

In the first edition of his book Ayer did not take the trouble to specify what is the nature of those premises. But critics found it easy to provide applications of the schema which generated weak verifications of dubious statements. For example, Berlin (1939) pointed out that any major or minor premise in a syllogism would provide weak verification for one or the other premise on the grounds that the conclusion was true. "This logical problem is bright green, I dislike all shades of green, therefore, I dislike this problem" would provide weak verifiability for "This logical problem is bright green" on grounds of my disliking the problem. Agreeing with Berlin, Ayer was able to provide his own example of dubious verification (1946, p. 11). Let the proposition to be verified be "If the Absolute is lazy, then this is white." Supplement this with "The Absolute is lazy" as the auxiliary hypothesis. Then together they entail "This is white." Thus the auxiliary hypothesis in conjunction with the observation statement provides verification for the dubious hypothetical.

It was necessary, therefore, to impose a restriction as to the character of the auxiliary hypotheses. In the Introduction to the second edition of *Language, Truth and Logic* (a significant addendum to the original), Ayer is able to restate his thesis of verification:

> I propose to say that a statement is directly verifiable if it is either itself an observation-statement, or is such that in conjunction with one or more observation-statements it entails at least one observation-statement which is not deducible from these other premises alone; and I propose to say that a statement is indirectly verifiable if it satisfies the following conditions: first, that in conjunction with certain other premises, it entails one or more directly verifiable statements which are not deducible from these other premises alone; and secondly, that these other premises do not include any statement that is not either analytic, or directly verifiable, or capable of being independently established as indirectly verifiable (1946, p. 13).

But even this is unsatisfactory; it only carries the problem of factual verification back a step now to focus on the supportive premises. As Hempel was later to point out (1950), the supportive premise can involve the conjunction of a factual and a dubious metaphysical component. We must, then, seek the verification of the auxiliary hypothesis as also satisfying the empirical criterion of meaning.

It is not surprising then that in his later treatment of meaning Ayer should turn to phenomenalistic reductions. In spite of the artificiality of sense data from the perceptual point of view, the language of sense data became essential to the distinction between illusory and nonillusory experience. If one perceives an object he cannot be sure that he is not being deceived by illusion, hallucination, or for that matter, Descartes' demon who maliciously sets out to deceive us as to the existence of an objective world. On the other hand, one cannot question the experiencing of, or having, a sense-datum; the sense-datum is the indubitable given. Beginning with *The Foundations of Empirical Knowledge,* published in 1940, and culminating in the collection of essays written later in the decade, the *Philosophical Essays* (1954), Ayer maintained a restricted phenomenalist position. No set of sense data entails a material object: ". . . . it must be clear that what the statement that material things consist of sense data must be understood to designate is not a factual but a linguistic relationship" (1940, p. 232). What is this linguistic relationship? A purely linguistic one would be "All statements about material objects translate into sense data statements." But there are two objections to this treatment. One, it does not distinguish between statements that are linguistic conventions (logical constructions, such as chairs, etc.) and statements that are not determined by conventions. And two, and more significant for Ayer, denying a purely conventional translation, no set of sense data statements is sufficient to establish the truth of the material-object statement. To overcome such objections, he then proposes that the relation between object and sense data is a hypothetical one. "A protasis, which will itself include a number of subsidiary hypotheticals" is the antecedent and specifies the object. This is followed by an apodisis "which would describe such sense experiences as would be sufficient to verify the presence of a physical object," and that also would contain subsidiary hypotheses sufficient to rule out the possibility of illusion. In such an hypothetical, the confirmation of the consequent is only the sufficient condition for the truth of the antecedent. But, as Ayer suggests, "to formulate the sufficient condition in purely sensory terms is the most that the phenomenalist can reasonably hope for" (1954, p. 164). Along these lines, one can give "a *general* account of the way in which objects are 'constructed' out of sense-data."

But then by 1956, Ayer had re-examined the issue. In *The Problem of Knowledge* he writes:

> If the phenomenalist is right, the existence of a physical object of a certain sort must be a sufficient condition for the occurrence, in the appropriate circumstances, of certain sense-data; there must, in short, be a deductive step from descriptions of physical reality to descriptions of possible, if not actual, appearances. And conversely, the occurrence of the sense-data must be a sufficient condition for the existence of the physical object; there must be a deductive step from the descriptions of actual, or at any

rate possible, appearances to descriptions of physical reality. The decisive objection to phenomenalism is that neither of these requirements can be justified (1956, p. 124).

Thus the odyssey of verifiability in one man's life.

I have dwelled at length upon Ayer's treatment of the problems relating to verifiability in order to show how the retreat from apodictic verifiability results in our surrendering bits of our confidence at every step of analysis and clarification. No further comment need be made to realize that the position of verifiability had become a weak one. Nor need we be surprised that the flood of articles on verifiability and meaning through the 1930's had by 1950 dried to a trickle.[1]

# NOTES

## NOTE 5.1

Brief histories of logical positivism can be found in the opening chapters of each of the following books:

Ayer, A. J. (editor) *Logical Positivism* (1959),
Frank, P., *Modern Science and Its Philosophy* (1941),
Kraft, V., *The Vienna Circle* (1953).

The acknowledged predecessors of the positivism of the Vienna group were Hume, Mach, Rey, Duhem, and Poincaré. Mathematical logicians such as Frege, Hilbert, Russell also figured significantly into the early deliberations of the positivists. Schlick, the most active of the early founders of the Vienna Circle, reserved special credits for Wittgenstein although the latter never participated directly in the formal deliberations.

Schlick followed Mach, Boltzmann, and Brentano at Vienna in the chair in the Philosophy of the Inductive Sciences. He soon gathered about himself a group of like-minded empiricists: Carnap, Frege, Hempel, Kaufmann, Kraft, Neider, von Juhos, Waismann and Zilsel, all philosophers; Hahn, Menger, Gödel, Radakovic, mathematicians; and Neurath, an economist. From the beginning, the Circle found sympathetic confederates throughout the world. Philipp Frank, physicist and philosopher from nearby Prague, was a frequent participant. Close exchange was maintained with the Berlin Society for Empirical Philosophy under Hans Reichenbach. Members of the latter group included Kraus, Herzberg, Parseval, R. von Mises, Dubislav, and Grelling. The Austrian Karl Popper was a frequent correspondent, although he went his

---

[1] Indeed J. Evans exhumed the corpse in 1953, only to pronounce it dead again . . . presumably by analytic suffocation.

own way on the issues of verification and was never a member of the Vienna Circle as such.

The publication and promotional activities of the Circle were successful from the start. *Erkenntnis* served as the original outlet for the members' publications. Contacts were made throughout the philosophical world, in Scandinavia, England, America. Perhaps the most influential early work was Ayer's *Language, Truth and Logic*.

The age of Hitler brought about the scattering of the group since, despite the disclaimers concerning the possibility of normative sciences, its members politically were liberal and extremely critical of the rise of the dictatorship. Carnap, Feigl, Bergmann, Hempel, Reichenbach, von Mises, all ended up in America. Waismann and Popper went to England where Ayer, Stebbing, Braithwaite, and Wittgenstein had been influential in empiricistic exegesis sympathetic to that of Vienna.

Schlick himself was murdered by a demented student, a tragedy of the highest order. He was a dominant figure at the time of his death. Better read as a philosopher than most of his confreres, he exercised a stylistic charm and wit which were seldom again to obtrude into the logic-heavy treatises of his heirs.

Members of the Circle naturally thought of themselves as carrying on the positivistic and empirical tradition of Hume, Comte, and Mach. Schlick liked the term "consistent empiricist." The enduring (but not endearing) title "logical positivism" appeared in a 1931 article by Feigl and Blumberg. In time most positivists came to prefer the name "logical empiricism," a term that Herbert Feigl and C. W. Morris share credits for popularizing.

## NOTE 5.2

Carnap's *Logical Syntax of Language* (1937) warrants a place among the outstanding philosophical works of the present century. Coming after *Der Logische Aufbau der Welt* (1928), it represents a shift of attention from his earlier phenomenalism to logic. In the *Syntax* Carnap attempts to bring all philosophical problems under the purview of logical analysis. Problems arise because statements that purport to be about the world are really about words. Consequently, the proper analysis of such statements is syntactical.

Most of the important analytical distinctions are made in Part V of the *Syntax*. First, we must distinguish between object-questions and logical questions. The former deal with objects, their characteristics and relations. The latter "may be concerned either with meaning and content of sentences, terms, etc., or only with the form of these" (1937, p. 277). (Carnap was later to delegate meaning to the realm of semantics.) Second, we distinguish between the *material* mode of speech and the *formal* mode. By the material mode of speech is meant the treating of sentences and terms as if they were about objects. Thus Carnap assigns to the material mode of speech "any sentence which is to be interpreted as attributing to an object a particular property, this property being quasi-syntactical, so that the sentence can be translated into another sentence which attributes a correlated syntactical property to a designation of the object in question" (1937, p. 238). On the other hand, a syntactical sentence is solely about syntactical elements, about words and the conventions of usage and manipulation. The formal mode of expression is therefore in terms solely of syntactical sentences. Note, for example, the difference between, "Five is not a thing, but a number" and "Five is not a thing-word, but a number-word." The material mode of speech intimates a referral to a world of objects and other subsistent entities whereas the formal mode of speech reduces what is asserted to a statement about syntactical conventions.

Try out this distinction with any of the reductive fallacies. For example: "Material objects are nothing but ideas" would translate formally into "Material-object statements translate into idea-statements." Whether or not the statement in the formal mode of speech is true is contingent not upon any "real" nature of the world but rather upon whether the syntactical conventions will indeed permit the translation.

Carnap concedes that the material mode of speech is not in itself erroneous. However, it leads us "to a *disregard of the relativity to language* of philosophical sentences."

As an example of the obscurity that derives from confusing syntactical expressions as pseudo-object sentences, Carnap points to the disputes over realism. "The controversy between positivism and realism is an idle dispute about pseudo-theses which owes its origin entirely to the use of the material mode of speech" (1937, p. 301).

It should be noted that, elegant as Carnap's syntactical approach to philosophical disputes may be, it is not a popular one among contemporary analysts. Our disputes are not alone about words but also of the relation of words to things, or even the relation of things to things. We try to say what we have difficulty saying. This to the analyst is the source of his perplexity. Were disputes purely syntactical there would be no occasion for his own quandaries.

## NOTE 5.3

Establishing the conventions for forming the simplest of subject–predicate propositions is itself a subtle matter. We consider briefly Russell's *theory of types.*

"Be wary of the obvious!" Suppose you say to me: "You should not believe the obvious." I reply, "Yes, that is obvious." Thus my affirmation can be made to read, "It is obvious that I should not believe the obvious." But here we have a paradox. For I can believe what I say only if I disbelieve it. There are a large number of such paradoxes which can find expression in natural language. (See, for example, Suppes, 1957.) All appear to be well-formed arguments, all appear to follow the rules of syntax and logic.

It was Russell who proposed a solution to this set of paradoxes. As a prescription, his theory of types is ingeniously simple: do not use a propositional function as a value for its own argument. Thus, if we have the propositional function $P(x)$, and we propose an argument of a general form such that $x = P(x)$, then the resulting proposition $P[P(x)]$ may be a paradox. Thus by rule, no propositional function is to be the value of its own argument.

Applied to the above paradox, we have the set of all obvious propositions $\{x\}$; the property all these propositions have is that of disbelief. Thus, $P(x)$ is the expression predicating disbelief in an obvious proposition. Suppose now that $P(x)$, which asserts disbelief in an obvious proposition, is itself obvious; then if it is obvious, we disbelieve it. Thus $P[P(x)]$ means we disbelieve the propositional rule by which we assign disbelief.

The argument is somewhat telescoped here. More explicitly, we have:

$$x = \text{any proposition,}$$
$$O = \text{property of being obvious,}$$
$$D = \text{property of being disbelieved.}$$

Then our initial premise is expressed

$$(x)\ Ox \supset Dx$$

namely, for any proposition if the proposition is obvious it is to be disbelieved. But this itself is a proposition. Let us call it the proposition '$x_p$,' the proposition that expresses the premise of the argument. Our second premise is then that this special $x_p$ which belongs to the class of all $x$ is itself obvious. Then the argument is:

$(x)\ Ox \supset Dx$ (premise 1)
$x_p = [(x)\ Ox \supset Dx]$
but $x_p$ is a member of the set of all propositions, $\{x\}$
and $x_p$ is $O;\ Ox_p$ (premise 2)
therefore, $x_p$ is also $D;\ Dx_p$.

Thus if our valid conclusion is to be regarded as true then the initial premise by which we reached our conclusion is disbelieved.

Now, it is this type of argument that is disallowed by the theory of types; $x_p$ cannot be a value of the initial propositional function (premise 1). The paradox arises when, following our defining a class of propositions as all those having the property $D$, we then in turn take the proposition defining that class as itself being a member of the class. According to this theory of types, predicates such as $D$ have status in a hierarchy of types. One type is higher than another type by virtue of its inclusiveness. Thus to predicate something of all sentences that are disbelieved one must now go to a more inclusive class of predicates than that of disbelief.

## NOTE 5.4

Ajudkiewicz' (1935) three types of meaning rules are

(1) *axiomatic* meaning rules; i.e., definitions with the status of axioms in a deductive system;
(2) *deductive* meaning rules; i.e., rules of logical substitution and derivation;
(3) *empirical* meaning rules; i.e., those ostensive statements with empirical reference.

These meaning rules are not exclusive of one another. Terms and state-ments meaningful under one type of rule may involve terms and statements meaningful under other types of rules. Thus empirical statements will have both syntactical structure and semantic content, with the content being provided by empirical reference.

Ajdukiewicz then integrates his types of meanings into the thesis of *world perspectives*. Such perspectives are the product both of the conceptual apparatus and the materials of experience; thus, a true logical empiricism. It was largely through discourse with Polish logicians and philosophers (especially Tarski) that the followers of the syntactical school of positivism turned their attention to semantics.

In this context it should be noted that semantics, as the study of meaning, involves expressions whose meanings are either analytic or synthetic in char-acter. It is the latter type, however, that prove recalcitrant to our semantical analyses. Whenever we relate a term or a statement to an empirical state of affairs, we are in the position of having to single out, point to, or otherwise designate, that empirical state of affairs. We are then inclined to express our designata again in verbal terms. Thus we are no closer to the thing or state of affairs designated. We have previously noted these difficulties of "pointing to" in our discussion of logical atomism.

## NOTE 5.5

Ayer's "Demonstration of the Impossibility of Metaphysics" (1934) antedates his classic *Language, Truth and Logic*. If anything it is more brash than the latter work, which itself was effective for its impudence.

> My purpose is to prove that any attempt to describe the nature or even to assert the existence of something lying beyond the reach of empirical observation must consist in the enunciation of pseudo-propositions, a pseudo-proposition being a series of words that may seem to have the structure of a sentence, but is in fact meaningless . . . I call this a dem-onstration of the impossibility of metaphysics because I define a meta-physical enquiry as an enquiry into the nature of the reality underlying or transcending the phenomena which the special senses are content to study. Accordingly if I succeed in showing that even to ask whether there is a reality underlying the world of phenomena is to formulate a bogus question, so that any assertion about the existence or nature of such a reality is a piece of nonsense, I shall have demonstrated the impossibility of metaphysics in the sense in which I am using the term. If anyone considers this an arbitrary definition, let him refer to any work which he would call metaphysical, and consider how it differs from an enquiry in one of the special sciences. He will find, not that the authors are merely using different means to derive from the same empirical premises the same sort of knowledge, but that they are seeking totally different types of knowledge. The metaphysician is concerned with a reality transcending the phenomena about which the scientist makes his generalizations. The meta-physician rejects the methods of the scientist, not because he believes them to be unfruitful in the field in which the scientist operates, but because he believes that by his own metaphysical methods he will be able to obtain knowledge in his own metaphysical field. It will be shown in this paper

not that the metaphysician ought to use scientific method to attain his end, but that the end itself is vain. Whatever form of reasoning he employs, he succeeds in saying nothing (1934, p. 335).

Ayer is uncompromising in his indictment of metaphysics. It is only when he has a look at the character of statements expressing laws and universals that he begins to show that hesitancy which characterizes a change of pace from the therapeutic to the affirmative counsel. Scientific laws and universal proportions have "grounds" of support; they exhibit a potential for generating statements having observational consequences. But in a world that clamors for the conditions of truth and falsity the support is rather uneasy. As for the principle of verifiability, that, too, is a bit sticky. However, Ayer here follows the example of Wittgenstein's admirable self-confrontation. When finding that his own propositions were meaningless by the empiricist criteria of meaning, Wittgenstein dissolved his own support: "My propositions are elucidatory in this way: he who understands me finally recognizes them as senseless, when he has climbed out through them, on them, over them. (He must so to speak throw away the ladder, after he has climbed up on it)" (*Tractatus*). Ayer, too, embraces what I am tempted to call "hay-loft metaphysics." Never mind how we got here, to this, the vantage of correct discernment; but granted we are here, then the rules of discernment are to be rigously applied.

## NOTE 5.6

Although explicit statements of the principle of verifiability were due to Waismann and Schlick, anticipation of it as a significant analytic tool can be found in Wittgenstein's *Tractatus*. The doctrine of picturing and logical atomism clearly suggests a verification standard with respect to both atomic and molecular propositions (the latter by truth functional reduction). His treatment of propositions is also suggestive (4.45 to 4.463); for a proposition to be meaningful, it must be such as to bear a "truth-argument." That is, it must either be tautological, contradictory, or empirical. Since tautologies and contradictions are logically, and thus *a priori,* true and false respectively, it leaves to us the task of assigning truth values to empirical propositions.

Wittgenstein makes no direct statement of verification and verifiability but the following are suggestive, and are, no doubt, part of that fund of debt acknowledged by Schlick.

4.024   To understand a proposition means to know what is the case, if it is true.
(One can therefore understand it without knowing whether it is true or not.)
One understands it if one understands its constituent parts.

4.031   In the proposition a state of affairs is, as it were, put together for the sake of experiment.
One can say, instead of, This proposition has such and such sense, This proposition represents such and such a state of affairs.

> 4.0312   The possibility of propositions is based upon the principle of the representation of objects by signs.

> 4.06   Propositions can be true or false only by being pictures of reality.

But Wittgenstein also says that the logical form of the relation between the proposition and what it represents cannot itself be represented by a proposition.

> 4.12   Propositions can represent the whole of reality, but they cannot represent what they must have in common with reality in order to be able to represent it—the logical form.
> To be able to represent the logical form we should have to be able to put ourselves with the propositions outside of logic, that is outside the world. (*Tractatus*)

Thus all we can prescribe are the rules for assigning symbols to objects. If the object is this or that, the symbol is such or so. However, beyond the assignment of the symbol we cannot show how it, the symbol, relates to the object. The symbol itself is an object, a special kind of object, a sign. What its relation to the other signified object is can be shown, it cannot be said.

The problems involved in our trying to say that the meaning of *a* sign, which is not *the* object, involves a relation to *the* object has led people such as Carnap to explicate meaning solely in the syntactical domain of symbols. Schlick (1932, 1936), on the other hand, chose to ignore this problem of trying to interpret the logical form of the connection between the proposition and the experience which verifies the proposition. "Accordingly, in order to find the meaning of a proposition, we must transform it by successive definitions until finally only such words occur in it as can no longer be defined, but whose meanings can only be directly pointed out" (1932, p. 87).

## NOTE 5.7

Since this issue is rather central to the position Schlick takes as an empiricist, we give a relevant passage in detail. After distinguishing sentences that may or may not have meaning and propositions that always do, he writes:

> If we adopt this terminology we can now easily get rid of our paradox [as to the meaning of sentences and propositions] by saying that we cannot inquire after the meaning of a proposition, but can ask about the meaning of a sentence, and this amounts to asking, "What proposition does the sentence stand for?" And this question is answered either by a proposition in a language with which we are already perfectly familiar, or by indicating the logical rules which will make a proposition out of the sentence, i.e., will tell us exactly in what circumstances the sentence is to be *used*. These two methods do not actually differ in principle; both of them give the meaning to the sentence (transform it into a proposition) by locating it, as it were, within the system of a definite language; the first method making use of a language which is already in our possession, the second one building it up for us. The first method represents the simplest kind of ordinary 'translation'; the second one affords a deeper insight into the nature of meaning, and will have to be used in order to overcome philosophical difficulties connected with the understanding of sentences (1936, p. 340).

## NOTE 5.8

The other minds controversy, that important derivative of the solipsistic predicament, always arises to plague the empiricist. How can the verification of statements about one's own experience be public, how can I know that the content of another's experience of an event be the same as the content of my own experience of the event, where the only thing common to our experience is the description of the event? Schlick (1936) responds by adopting the position of Mach. The primitive experience is neutral; it becomes private, so to speak, only upon the reflective construction of an ego. My pain is private, to be sure; but aside from this personalistic construction, this is only to say that my pain has specifiable space and time coordinates just as has any other event. To ask that I experience another's pain, or even to suggest that the impossibility of experiencing another's pain is a philosophical puzzle, is not to appreciate the fact that spatio–temporal events are independent of one another. We do not ask of one clock that it experience the telling of time by another clock. Nor should we ask that one individual feel another individual's pain. At least, we should not at all be puzzled if the answer to the latter question is the inevitable negative one.

Schlick's answer to the question "Will the world go on existing after the observers have died?" is less convincing. First he would rephrase the question: "Does the existence of the stars, etc., depend upon the life or death of a human being?" Schlick then insists that only logical possibility of verification is required for stating the continuing existence of the world, "verification without a 'mind' is logically possible on account of the 'neutral,' impersonal character of experience" (1936, p. 369). But this is not satisfactory. Since Schlick's criteria of meaning depend upon his adopting conventions of definition and methods of verification, it is difficult to see how the conventions would have enduring status were there no individuals to embrace them. Conventions are arbitrary and contingent upon the collective of individuals. No doubt something would survive the ultimate human holocaust; but whatever it is, it would be some subsistent universe which, being now transcendent of particular conventionalistic descriptions, would lose its factual status. It is only if these conventions were routes to absolute truths that the case would be otherwise. Then, indeed, would the world be conformal with such possibilities as are reified through the privileged conventions.

# CHAPTER 6

# Logical Empiricism II: Physicalism and Analysis

THE TASK of relating statements to material objects, as such, proved difficult to say the least, so difficult that it is doubtful whether a very substantial defense of empiricism could be constructed on that basis. Does the syntactical approach to the problems of verification, meaning, and construction fare any better? Let us see.

Three people stand out as important contributors to the physicalistic movement: Neurath, Carnap, and Hempel. In many respects Carnap is the most important philosopher to come out of the Vienna Circle; certainly he has done the most to implement the logic of logical positivism. He has underwritten positivism with a rigorous syntactical foundation; meaning, reduction, theoretical structure, probable inference, have all received formal treatments. There are those, in fact, who would suggest that the syntax has subverted the empirics, that although Carnap may act like an empiricist, he talks like a formal logician who is more interested in symbolic systems than in the empirical structure of knowledge. What kind of philosophy is this?

## CARNAP'S PHENOMENALISM

With Carnap, we start a new odyssey: from pure phenomenalism, to syntactical physicalism, finally to a semantics that encourages yet does not altogether please the more empirical confrere. The first adventure, then, is into phenomenalism.

In his first important book, *Der Logische Aufbau der Welt* (1928), Carnap attempts to do what the logical atomists had failed to do—to undertake the rational construction of the basic elements of experience.

Rather than assuming something so psychologically unreal as abstract sense data, he first isolates units of consciousness in the "cross-section" of perceptual experience. He then applies a type of psychophysical method for structuring that experience into its basic elements. First, one must identify the "ground" elements of experience. These ground elements, known as *erlebs,* are phenomenally concrete, they are "full momentary cross sections of the total stream of experience" (in Goodman, 1951, p. 116). Since these elements are epistemologically primary, they are as yet unanalyzable into a subject–object structure. Second, a method is needed for analyzing the erleb into its basic constituents. Here formalized techniques of introspection are required. "The problem of abstraction is to define in terms of the primitive relation of concrete individuals, the conditions under which a set of such individuals have a common quality" (in Goodman, 1951, p. 125).

Let us briefly examine this method. First, assume that the objects of experience partake of qualities. Then we may regard the quale of a given object as belonging to some quality class. The quality class is ascertained by sorting, with the subject making the quality comparisons among a set of erlebs. The sorting is to follow two straightforward rules: (A) all erlebs in a sorted class must have some property in common; i.e., be quality "akin"; (B) selection of the class, or quality, should be such that the sorting will result in the greatest class satisfying rule A. The sorting itself, however, requires additional requirements. Two erlebs are to be judged *part-similar* if they are perceived to possess some basic constituent in common. Then classes of part-similar erlebs which overlap are said to define a quality class for the dimensions of the overlapping properties. Thus, if one set of part-similar erlebs have the following structures, $\{rgh, rsm, ref\}$, and another set, the structures $\{rkd, rkp, rkw\}$, then they overlap on the constituent $r,$ and $r$ is the basis for defining a quality class.

Since erlebs are sequential and nonoverlapping in time, one must assume that the effect of time on sequential judgments is nil. Ordering of quality classes is achieved through comparison by juxtaposition of quality classes so as to yield near-place, quality-identical pairs. Two colors, for example, are quality-identical if they expand the place dimension of one or the other quality without changing the character of that quality. And a sequence or ordering of quality classes can be achieved through the analysis of matches which do not match. For example, A and C may match with B but not match each other. Thus, in the context of non-transitive matches, one can order a set of quality classes. Sense classes are also introduced as being more inclusive than quality classes. In traditional psychophysics, the quality classes would roughly approximate to discriminable differences, and the sense classes would approximate to sensory modalities.

Carnap and later Goodman (1951) both could point to situations wherein the system would lead to nondefinitive results. The system was realistic, as opposed to nominalistic, in the sense that the quality-classes came near to wearing the aura of Platonic universals. But what was more distressing was the fact that the procedure entails treating the phenomenal quale as the basic ingredient of physical structure. By following this analytic procedure we are taking as basic ingredients the data of our private experience. How, among observers, can we bring order into quality classes when each observer's data are private unto himself? In fact, how is it possible to represent the observer's qualia? In answer to these questions Carnap adopts a methodological solipsism. The fact that different observers do agree suggests that we adopt conventions and perhaps methods of instruction such as to facilitate public agreement. Thus we are, in a sense, publicly trained for private observation. There is no bridging the gap of the inaccessibility of one another's experience; we must accept the fact that the erlebs are localized, unsharable (but not unverbalizable) phenomena. There is, however, a means of avoiding complete solipsistic entrapment. There is analogy among one another's worlds, but these analogies are incomplete. The world of one observer is not quite like that of another. Thus there are gaps and areas of disagreement between the solipsistic subsystems in the system of all observers. In order to achieve public agreement over those areas of experience deficient by incomplete analogy, we seek by means of a public language the "intersubjective coordination of solipsistic subsystems." And for the person caught in the solipsistic predicament, it means bringing all his own subsystems (i.e., what subject A reports, B reports, etc.,) into some synthetic agreement. Even though he cannot escape the privateness of his own data, he is to act as if it is a public world.

However, Kaila (cf. Kraft, 1953), Weinberg (1936), and others were critical of Carnap's phenomenalistic program. Methodological solipsism is a rather poor makeshift to the person who is by temperament a fact-oriented empiricist. Such a person wants a substantial world to be shared and not preempted by the given observer. The "consistent empiricist," and that is what Schlick thought the logical positivist ought to be called, must always face the issue of solipsism; he has no direct evidential support for other worlds, or for agents of his subsystem of perceptions. Conventions for ignoring or obviating the predicament do not, unfortunately, succeed in laying the issue to rest; for always, always, the only indubitable data upon which to construct the experiential world are the bits of experience itself—the sense data, the erlebs, the perceptual contents which flit through the sensorium of one's private consciousness.

It is not surprising, then, that Carnap gave up pursuing the program of *Logischer Aufbau* against the taunt of solipsism. With the logical skills at his disposal, he joined forces with Neurath to promulgate the doctrine of physicalism.

# THE LOGICAL SYNTAX OF LANGUAGE

Before turning to the doctrine of physicalism we need first to consider the character of Carnap's logical syntax; for syntax, and not empiricism, is both the skeleton and the flesh of physicalism.[1] By the logical syntax of a language, Carnap means "the formal theory of the linguistic forms of that language—the systematic statement of the formal rules which govern it together with the development of the consequences which follow from these rules" (1937, p. 1). After laying out the prospectus for analysis, he then proceeds to consider syntax in its purest form. First, syntax is to be distinguished from logic, in that the former considers the formation and structure of propositions and the latter considers the rules for manipulating these propositions. But the distinction is not rigidly adhered to; the utility of a linguistic system rests in the consequences to be drawn within the system. Any given language is a calculus providing, of course, that it conforms to syntactical rules. However, it should be possible to enunciate such syntactical requirements independently of a given calculus. Therefore, pure syntax concerns such rules.

Carnap then proceeds to consider the syntactical structure of two symbolic languages. One he calls a definite language, the other, indefinite. These languages have their propositional structure in common. That is to say, propositions admissible to the two languages must be interpretable within one of the following categories: analytic, contradictory, synthetic, or equipollent (cf. N6.2). All argument proceeds from admissible propositions. The type of argument one gets is contingent upon the type of calculus one adopts. There is, therefore, a conventional or "intuitionist" character of the specific language. Rather than ask: "What *is* this or that like?" we should rather ask *"How do we wish to arrange this or that in the language to be constructed?"* Or, from the theoretical standpoint, "What consequences will ensue if we construct a language in this or that way?" (1937, p. 46). Thus the class of existential sentences has its constructural element: ". . . an existential sentence may only be stated if either a concrete example can be produced, or, at least, a method given by the aid of which an example can be constructed in a finite, limited number of steps" (1937, p. 47). These are the requirements imposed by conventionalists such as Hilbert and Poincaré, but Carnap apparently is willing to accept them providing a provision is made for the admission of universal statements.

Syntactical conventions and rules are, of course, prescriptive; that is, some forms of expression and argument are excluded from the calculus

---

[1] The order is somewhat reversed here. Carnap first published *The Logical Syntax of Language* in 1934, after an exchange over physicalism had already taken place with Neurath in *Erkenntnis* articles.

while others are admitted. The primary function of the calculus, however, is to generate the consequences of the allowable argument. We must therefore emphasize the positive aspects of the conventionalism. Carnap proceeds then to italicize his *Principle of Tolerance in Syntax: "It is not our business to set up prohibitions, but to arrive at conventions."* It is obvious that these conventions are to be guided by some kind of pragmatic sanction. As an example, we seek a body of convention which would enable us to circumvent the crippling effects of any system that would require apodictic verification. This is one of Carnap's intentions.

In describing the syntactical structure of his language, Carnap first adopts a schema of arithmetization in which, following Gödel, numbers are to represent the required logical symbols. However, this is somewhat arbitrary for one could as well stay within the schema of *Principia Mathematica* except that the latter is not so amenable to formulating statements about its own language. Carnap then proceeds to build the syntactical system. First, one must establish conventions for forming both logical and nonlogical terms within the language. Second, rules for forming definitions and for creating the propositions of a calculus are required. "Whether a given sentence is an admissible definition in a particular calculus is dependent solely upon the form of the sentence and upon the formation rules of the calculus" (1937, p. 67). Definitions are thus conventional, they cannot be contradictory unless in fact they violate the formation rules. Finally, there are the transformation rules which by means of allowable substitution permit us within the calculus to move from one set of propositions to another set. Just as in mathematics we can transform one mathematical expression into another by the conventions of subsituation, so can we derive a conclusion, or a consequence, from a set of premises.

The simplest of languages is that which includes only definite concepts over a finite domain. Thus all propositions are of particulars or of conjunctions of particulars. And every argument has a finite set of steps. When we turn to unlimited domains, we introduce indefinite concepts and must augment the language accordingly. We introduce unlimited operators and quantifiers to handle the infinite domains. We must augment our schema of proof, and we must provide some kind of analysis of problematic sentences expressible within the system. Explication of these matters belongs primarily to the logical analysis of proof and lies beyond the purview of the present chapter. However, it can be noted that a distinction can be drawn between mathematical and logical proof, and between deduction in a definite number of steps and that which is indefinite. Because Gödel has shown formal systems such as that of *Principia Mathematica* to be incomplete, it is unavoidable that deduction should involve indefinite steps. However, this indefiniteness and incompleteness of deductive inferences is resolved by Carnap with ingenious simplicity. A proposition is determinate in the language if it is either analytic, or contradictory, or synthetic. But a proposition is judged to be synthetic if it is found neither to be analytic nor contradictory. Thus, all propositions which are indefinite within this language belong to the class of synthetic propositions. That is, their truth status is as yet indefinite; the question of truth is open and can be ascertained only as the truth of any synthetic proposition is ascertained, by experience. One might say that since there is no general algorithm of logical proof, then the validity of an indefinite proposition is in its way contingent upon the discovery of a proof.

In turning to science and to natural languages, we must have a recourse to a *general* syntax which is descriptive of all languages, natural as well as hypothetical. General syntax like pure syntax requires formation and transformation rules, but in addition we here face the task of translating from one language into another, i.e. of translating from the natural language into the calculus, and vice versa. It is here that Carnap's distinction between the material and the formal modes of speech becomes significant, for one is inclined to treat words in the material mode as ontologically different from words in the formal mode. But as Carnap argues, we shall free ourselves of pseudo-arguments and pseudo-sentences if we commit ourselves to treating all languages in the formal mode. (cf. N3.10; N5.2; N6.1). General syntactical systems do, however, include a class of conventions not included in pure logical syntax. Logical syntax includes the logical language in which proof is undertaken, the L-language; but in addition, there is a natural language of science, the P-language, which includes general rules of inference (laws). There may also be some translation rules in the form of operational definitions. Thus this P-language always involves some provisos in the way of general rules which are not included in a purely logical calculus. A consequence of the L-language is analytic and cannot be contradicted; but a P-consequence is contingent, not only upon logical rules of a calculus, but also upon the status of the general rule which is included in the P-language. Although P-consequences are analytic, they are so only if the general rule is true. That is, one may wish to deny the P-consequence on the grounds that the general rule is not true. If one wishes to hold the status of the law indefinite, he could then, if he so chose, endow the P-consequence with synthetic properties not at all applicable to purely analytic L-consequences.

In summary, although Carnap appears to be analyzing syntactical systems for their intrinsic logical interest, his discussion of general syntax culminates in its application to the logic of science. It is true that science has syntactical structure, but what is just as significant is the fact of its having protocol sentences that are assumed in some way to be descriptive of empirical facts. There is no effort in *The Logical Syntax of Language* to show what is the nature of the relation of protocol propositions to fact, other than to allude to the requirement that a syntactical system must have its formation rules. Ironically, the problem of factual reference is regarded as a pseudo-problem. If we adopt this strategy, then the issues of reduction, P-consequences, and verification are easily dealt with. If a set of protocol sentences agrees with a derived hypothesis that is a P-consequence of a scientific calculus (i.e., an L-consequence of a law), then the hypothesis is confirmed; at least, that agreement contributes an increment of confirmation in a probability calculus of confirmation. On the other hand, if the protocol sentences are not in agreement with the derived hypothesis, the hypothesis is disconfirmed. Note that this schema is contained within the boundaries of the syntax. All relations are those between propositions. Thus they are matters of logic. No reference is made to the ineluctable relation of proposition to fact, none is made to the verification of an hypothesis in terms of facts, nor to meaning as a method of verification. Thus, if the syntactical approach to problems in epistemology is tenable, then many of the issues and questions raised by Schlick, Ayer, and others are resolved. This syntactical approach provides us now the rubric for the doctrine of physicalism.

## PHYSICALISM

According to Carnap, "The thesis of physicalism maintains that the physical language is a universal language of science—that is to say, that every language of any sub-domain of science can be equipollently translated [i.e., by equivalences] into the physical language" (1937, p. 320).

The substance of this doctrine has been given in the preceding paragraphs. The following points need to be kept in mind. One, physicalism proposes to structure empiricism within the boundaries of syntax. Language, its sentences and transformation rules, provides the content as well as the structure of our knowledge. Meaning comes under the purview of syntax. Two, the basic elements of the syntactical system are the protocol sentences which, though customarily taken to signify physical observations, are in fact both determined and defined conventionally. For a theory to be meaningful in the physical language, it must through a reductive chain yield hypotheses expressible solely in terms of protocol sentences. Three, contrary to the innuendoes in the direction of physical materialism and realism, the meanings of the protocols have no ontological connection with facts or with material objects. Protocols are self sufficient. Their meanings are explicated entirely within the formation rules of the particular syntactical system.

Together, the conventional and logical requirements of such linguistically pure systems do not require a physicalism. We could just as well adopt a different set of protocols and call our system a phenomenalism, or, with additional modifications, a mentalism. This makes for a very puzzling doctrine; for if we seek its justification, we can find no grounds solely within syntax itself which will enable us to choose one set of protocols over another. Why physicalistic protocols, then?

It is interesting that early attempts to tie the syntactical system to experience by means of phenomenalistic protocols met with resistance among the physicalists. Neurath, creator and outspoken supporter of the doctrine, considered all efforts to relate protocols to objects as smacking of metaphysics. Thus he was critical of Carnap's early efforts in *Logischer Aufbau* to put phenomenalism on a rigorous analytical basis. And in this matter, he had the support of Hempel. Carnap, himself, did not see that the disagreement was in any sense fundamental; at any rate when he laid aside his phenomenalistic enterprises for purely syntactical ones, agreement among these three members of the Circle came much more easily. But to return to the question: Why physicalistic protocols, rather than any other set? The answer to this question unfolds in three phases.

*Phase one:* Efforts to apply a rigorous criterion of verification proved impossible. Phenomenalistic reports are private, they are subject to ambiguity, they cannot be considered reliable in any circumstance. Thus even Schlick's basic statements (*Konstatierungen*) such as "Here now red" are suspect, for how can we ascertain whether the person reporting is reporting honestly? Furthermore, phenomenalism suggests the seeking of absolute grounds for truth (i.e., phenomenalist reports are to be considered indubitable), but that effort is to be regarded as involving a pseudo-problem. One requires only a conventionalist standard of truth. Hempel states the case as follows: "Indeed the phrase that testing a statement is comparing it with facts will very easily evoke the imagination of one definite world with certain definite properties, and so one will be easily seduced to ask for the one system of statements which gives a complete and true description of this world, and which would have to be designated absolutely true" (1935, p. 55). Although sentences are not to be related to fact, they are to be selected so as to provide an empirical system of protocols. The apparent contradiction between the acceptance of an empirical system of protocols by convention and the rejection of the ontological pretensions of so-called factual propositions is easily resolved. We should seek a body of protocols that has proved publicly acceptable. We should look for coherence and consistency within the language.

*Phase two:* The thesis of extensionality was to go the way of the empiricistic criterion of meaning. Wittgenstein's treatment of the meaning of propositions is reductive; that is, the question as to whether a proposition is to be judged analytic, synthetic, or contradictory is decidable in the truth functional calculus. The extension of the protocols (atomic propositions) thus decides the truth of falsity of any appropriately formed proposition within this system. For a finite set of protocols, the system puts into effect a strong criterion of meaning. Yet, however, strong that criterion appeared to be, the physicalists were to drop the system of atomism for three reasons. One, the doctrine of atomic propositions and the picturing of facts carried with it undesirable overtones of metaphysics. Two, universal propositions could not be treated as extensions of any finite set of protocols. There was no place in the system for a universal quantifier. The physicalists needed universal propositions in order to treat scientific law within the physical language. They introduced them as conventions, not as summaries of a set of protocols but as convenient devices to supplement the transformation rules within the physical language. Such conventions were to be regarded as aids to inference, not themselves formally deducible or decidable within the system. And three, but not independent of one, atomic propositions were assumed to have factual reference. The physicalists wanted to avoid problems of factual reference.

*Phase three:* If factual reference is denied of protocol statements, how, then, are we to distinguish true protocols from false ones? Or as Hempel asks the question, how do the views of Carnap and Neurath enable us "to distinguish the true protocols statements of our science from the false ones of a fairy tale?" (1935, p. 57). The answer seems ingenuously simple:

> . . . there is indeed no formal, no logical difference between the two compared systems, but an *empirical* one. The system of protocol statements which we call true, and to which we refer in everyday life and science may only be characterized by the historical fact, that it is the system which is actually adopted by mankind, and especially by the scientists of our culture circle; and the "true" statements in general may be characterized as those which are sufficiently supported by that system of actually adopted protocol statements (1935, p. 57).

But there is more to the answer than meets the eye here. Pragmatism, conventionalism and logic converge to produce an agreement concerning a consistent body of protocols. What emerges is the proposal for a coherence theory of truth.

The atomism of Wittgenstein and the doctrine of phenomenalism both subsume a correspondence between facts and the propositions that assert those facts. In general, correspondence theories of truth assume this fundamental truth-relationship between fact and proposition. However, with the physicalists' rejection of factual reference as being metaphysical, some alternative theory of truth is required. A provisional answer is given in terms of true propositions' being "true" by concerted agreement among scientists. There is no reason, though, why mankind cannot be deceived by fairy tales just as it had been deceived in times past by succumbing to metaphysics. Here some special prerogatives are granted to the scientists. The protocols of scientific observation appear to be the most coherent among possible alternatives; they evoke the most stringent kind of agreement; and, once the arts of the observation language are learned, they appear to be indubitable. The coherence theory of the truth of a statement prescribes only that the following condition should obtain: ". . . a sufficient agreement between the system of acknowledged proto-col-statements and the logical consequences which may be deduced from the statement and other statements which are already adopted" (Hempel, 1935, p. 54).

But the protocols themselves figure in the deduction of other proto-cols. One faces the problem of justifying general statements (laws) from which the particular protocols are deduced under suitable conditions. Once again, there may be possible alternatives to choose among, and another choice to make between truth and possible fiction. An additional principle is required, a principle of *formal simplicity*.

> A general law cannot be formally deduced from a finite set of singular statements. Each finite set of statements admits an infinite series of hypotheses each of which implies all the singular statements referred to. So, in establishing the system of science, there is a conventional moment; we have to choose between a large quantity of hypotheses which are logically equally possible, and in general we choose one that is dis-tinguished by formal simplicity as Poincaré and Duhem often accentuated (Hempel, 1935, p. 52).

This amalgamation of agreement, formal simplicity, and empirical fact needs itself to be accentuated. At first glance we are confronted with the most abject kind of relativism—just as Schlick and von Juhos im-plied (cf. N6.1), but it is after all a relativism that reflects a state of scientific knowledge at a given time in history. Most of us have grown used to relativism in theory. Theories are contingent upon the character of one's analytic tools, frames of reference, and postulates. But does the relativism extend to the primary data, as physicalism seems to imply?

This is an interesting speculation, and one to which all manner of realists take exceptions. What is the defense of an "empiricism" which stipulates that the physical language, its syntax and laws, determines the character of its data language? If we could ascertain that the state of a theory determines the observational data, then indeed we would have pragmatic support for adopting the syntactical approach of physicalism. We should remember, however, that in our ordinary material mode of speaking facts are treated as though they are independent, discoverable entities. It is this mode of speaking that we must now deny; for if theory does in some sense determine the facts, then facts are as much a matter of creation as they are of discovery.

There are several sources of support for regarding facts as having the contingent, conventional character suggested here. These sources are em-pirical, i.e., psychological and sociological rather than syntactical in char-acter. First, from a psychological point of view, we know that what is observed is contingent upon certain dispositional factors. Psychologists have through the years invoked concepts such as "apperceptive mass," "psychological field," and "cognitive structure" to account for an observer's unique perceptual sensitivities. The state of the person's knowledge, his attitudes, the momentary states of his organism, etc., determine what he as an observer will isolate, attend to, and structure in the flux of experience. The psychologist often makes inferences concerning the dispositional aspects of the person on the grounds of that person's perceptions. But he could just as well predict the nature of the perception from a knowledge of the person. The cognitive potential of the person is determined by what is already in the cognitive apparatus. The state of one's knowledge, i.e. his learning and his cultural milieu, determines the facts of his own world. No reference need be made here to the fund of experiments that demonstrate perceptual distortion. Pathological perception is not the issue. What the constructs of cognitive sensitivity imply is that all facts of observation involve searching, selecting, and structuring on the part of the observer. To take a trivial example, one could hardly expect of the peripatetics of Greece that they should have perceived objects as accelerating, bound as they themselves were to their oxen and their sailing craft. One had to learn to perceive velocity as itself being in a state of flux. The state of physics and technology in antiquity did not provide the potential for a perceptual breakthrough. Such matters are perhaps too obvious to pursue further, but they should indicate that the state of the observer's knowledge is just as important to the discovery of facts as are technological inventions such as the telescope and microscope.

A second source of support derives from the sociology of knowledge. Whether we consider the immediate cultural locale or the broad sweep of ideology, there is little question but that the milieu creates a kind of mystique in which observations of some unique character become possible. Ideologies do have the effect of focalizing the scientist's interests, his theoretical formulations, and his observations. No doubt most of us cringe at the prospects of the censorship and controls that an ideology may impose upon scientific endeavors. But censorship, so to speak, need not be in the hand of the commissars of ideology in order to be effective. A free society has its own ideology. No matter how free the milieu, no matter how open to thesis and counterthesis, we are in large measure bound to our traditions, our training, and our technology. For example, as has been pointed out, the directions psychology has taken in recent years have been contingent to a large extent on technological innovations prompted by our preoccupations with war and defense. The nature of our models reflects that this has been the age of electronics. Witness, too, that the direction research takes is determined by the interests and investments of the supporting agencies. Thus the impetus is from within the society, the search and research are predetermined according to the interests, anxieties, the whole inventory in the charisma of its members. And what of "historical fact" wherein each epoch generates its own interpretive perspectives? All of these factors would indicate that facts have a social setting.

A third argument for the contingent character of fact derives from the philosophy of science itself. One can point to a number of people who stress the personalized aspect of fact, but here I shall concentrate on the argument as presented by N. R. Hanson (cf. N6.3). In his *Patterns of Discovery,* Hanson argues for a socio-psychological interpretation of scientific theory. He proceeds by distinguishing between "seeing" and "seeing as" as a basis for rejecting a naïve picture theory of language. Picturing presumes an object and an isomorphic relation between the picture and the thing pictured. However, we do not simply see objects as though they are veridical projections upon our retinas (or other sensory receivers), rather we see them as things in some cognitive context. We see them in relation to other objects, and in the context of the meaning of those objects. The atomists are correct in asserting that one atomic fact is independent of every other, if by fact they mean the elemental picture. Any picture can be fractionated into other pictures; but a picture that is merely a mosaic of other pictures is not a fact, a "seeing-something-as." No concatenation or juxtaposition of graphic pictures brings about its own synthesis; the synthesis occurs only in language, in the understanding that linguistic structuring brings about:

> When language and notation are ignored in studies of observation, physics is represented as resting on sensation and low-grade experiment. It is described as repetitious, monotonous concatenation of spectacular sensations, and of school-laboratory experiments. But physical science is not just a systematic exposure of the senses to the world, it is also a way of thinking about the world, a way of forming conceptions. The paradigm observer is not the man who sees and reports what all normal observers see and report, but the man who sees in familiar objects what no one else has seen before (Hanson, 1958, p. 30).

Hanson rejects any pictorial or sense data reduction of facts. If we insist, sense data are a reservoir of possibility. If from the same set of sense data we can draw different perceptual inferences, then for all observers there is an open range of protocols appropriate to their data. Were it not for this equivocality of fact, we would indeed become caught up in the fruitless metaphysical task of trying to distinguish the true fact from the vast fund of pseudo-facts.

A second part of Hanson's argument involves a critical evaluation of the hypothetico-deductive method (HD). According to the classical model of HD, testable hypotheses are derived from a theoretical model, and these hypotheses in turn lead to the experimental search for confirmation. Hypotheses, therefore, are regarded as a kind of prospectus on possible facts, the scientist himself a prospector making discoveries. This notion, Hanson contends, ignores the impact that one's present knowledge has in the matter of creating the theoretical model. The model itself reflects that the person is already seeing a phenomenon as such and such. The work of creative vision has already transpired in the building of the theory. If the new vision proves ingenious, such as that of a Copernicus, or a Kepler, or a Galileo, then subsequent possibilities of fact will be determined in large measure by that new vision.

The foregoing treatments of fact have a subjective overtone. Fact involves the state of the observer's knowledge, his inventions and his conventions. But facts also allow for the factors of experience and logic. The one is the raw material of fact, the other is the syntactical rubric that is as essential to the structure of the fact as the data themselves. What can we say, then, for the status of the syntactical theory of science? At first glance, the doctrine seems extreme, abstract, and, in its logical rigor, divorced from fact. It is weakest where many of us assume it should be strong, in the choice of protocols and their linkage to empirical data. We do not like to be told that our concerns for an empirical criterion of meaning and for factual reference are pseudo-problems that can be dissolved once we agree to speak in the formal mode.

To counter these disgruntlements, one can show that there is a contingent, arbitrary, even subjective, dimension to our facts. We may appear to select one factual statement over another because one happens to be true and the other not; but what is true remains a perceptual matter. We do submit to convention, both in the sense of Poincaré and in the sense of the public conclave of observers and users of language. Perception is contingent not just upon the raw data that intimate something external to the observers but also upon the observers' penchants for construction. One thing we should agree upon; the idea of the absolute truth of some absolute factual reference is suspect.

Still we would feel more comfortable if the protocol sentences were tied more irrevocably to the facts we observe. The purely syntactical approach to meaning has not proved popular. It has been a source of distress to many positivists, a source of amazement to some of the analysts, and a source of some discomfort to Carnap himself. There have been some compromise solutions in which the protocols are assumed to be factual statements either of sense data or of thing-object reports. Carnap, however, steers something of a middle course. His semantic fills out his treatment of problems of meaning.

## Physicalism and Psychology

Two practical themes permeate the accounts of physicalism: one is that of logical or methodological behaviorism; the other is that of the unification of science. Consider first methodological behaviorism. Carnap states the case succinctly in his little book *Philosophy and Logical Syntax*. Traditionally, psychology has been plagued with two languages, the one mental, the other physical. Let Sm stand for a sentence in the mental language, and Sp for a sentence in the physical language. Then for some event in the person's life there is an Sm-Sp pair that effectively describes the psycho-physical character of the event. This would be the case if Sm-sentences were allowable. But according to physicalism they are not; only Sp-sentences are included in the formal developments of science. How, then, are we to resolve the problem of the two languages? The answer is, by equipollent translations. Assume a psycho-physical parallelism at least provisionally. Then a person A at time $t$ will be describable in the mental language by the quality predicates Qm. For the same time $t$ he will be described in the physical language by the physical predicates Qp. A combination of these sentences and predicates will then represent a description of the psycho-physical event. Thus:

$$(Sm):Qm\ (A,t_1)$$
$$(Sp):Qp\ (A,t_1)$$

indicates the set of sentences and the assignable predicates in both languages for the description of the event. Now the thesis of physicalism asserts that every so-called mental event is to be regarded as having physical manifestations. For example, a person's anger is not only manifest in the fact that person feels anger, but also in the fact that his body is in such and such a state, he utters words such as 'I feel angry,' etc. If one language translates into the other language, then we may write

$$(x)\ (t)\ Qm\ (x,t) \equiv Qp\ (x,t).$$

That is, we may express the equipollent translation, that for any person and any time if a certain complex of mentalistic predicates then a certain complex of physicalistic predicates, and vice versa. In Carnap's analysis the equivalence is not strictly analytic but only P-valid; that is to say, it asserts only that the conventions of language as based upon synthetically derived psycho-physical laws prescribe that one language is substitutable for another.

There are objections to this formulation, but they disappear if we treat equipollent translatability simply as the substance of a set of procedural rules to be conventionally adhered to. For example, Carnap is asked if we can have Qm without Qp:

> My answer is that there cannot be such an untranslatable quality-sign or predicate in the psychological language. For if in this language there is a predicate 'Qm' with a meaning, then the sentence 'Qm $(A,t_1)$' must be empirically examinable; the psychologist must be able to recognize under suitable circumstances whether a person A is in the condition Qm or not. But this recognition depends upon the observable physical be-

havior of A; hence there is a corresponding quality Qp, to which this behavior is linked (1935, p. 91).

It should be obvious that this argument does not represent a logically sufficient support of his answer should the skeptic wish to maintain that somehow there is some psychosis without neurosis. What is given is a procedural rule whereby we agree to restrict the mental language such that the equipollent translation is part of its structure.

The movement towards the unity or unification of science can now be dealt with summarily. So long as psychology admits protocols from the mental language (raw feels, conscious contents, etc.) then it stands uniquely apart from the physical sciences whose protocols are all public observation statements. Suppose now that all statements about mental events are translatable into statements in the physical language, that, furthermore, no untranslated mental statements are admitted to the language of psychology. Psychology would then share with the physical sciences the property that all protocols are among the public-observation statements of the physical language. The actual unity of the physical and behavioral sciences has been variously interpreted, e.g. unity of data, unity of explanation, unity of language (Feigl, 1939), but the intention of Neurath and Carnap was clearly linguistic unity. Unity means sharing the language of public observation statements. The implication is clearcut, all science is to have its foundations imbedded in "hard" data expressible solely in the physical language.

People sometimes get the impression that the doctrine of physicalism was deliberately contrived to bring psychology into the brotherhood of the sciences. This is a mistake, and one for which Carnap and Neurath bear much of the responsibility. Physicalism cannot be divorced from its syntactical foundations. What it stipulates is that all protocols should be in a language acceptable to the community of linguists. It is a purely arbitrary choice that the protocol language be a physical one. But unless it is one about which there is no dispute, unless it has signification common to the experience of all people, then the choice of one language would have been no better than the choice of another, and the syntactical elaboration of science would have been little more than word magic.

Still, the emphasis Carnap and Neurath have given to a psychological physicalism is understandable. Unless protocols are to be restricted to statements in the physical language, then problems of reference would obtrude into the selection of the basic language. Why not admit psychic, raw-feel protocols? Their consistency with physicalistic protocols could be taken care of by means of definitions, and every psychological event statement could be reduced to a pair of psi- and phi-statements. Who should care if the parallelism was not substantiated in fact? Being concerned with propositions in the syntactical system, we are not concerned with fact. But this will not do. Regardless of their syntactical aloofness, Carnap and Neurath are concerned with facts. Psi-statements are not to be included in the class of admissible protocols because their factual reference is of a different type than that of the phi-statements. Though they may maintain their silence to insure their formal integrity, Carnap and Neurath do enter into that abhorrent material world to make their choice among propositions. What the physical statements refer to are publicly observable facts; what the mental content statements refer to are privately observed facts.

The tactic here is that of methodological behaviorism. Let us act as if mental contents have no meaning, as if they do not exist, or as if we can conveniently ignore them. Then the physicalist language exhausts the remaining possibilities for a publicly acceptable language. And the formal mode of speaking will protect us from the tiresome problems of factual reference. Physicalism and methodological behaviorism are to be interpreted as tactical agreements as to how we will restrict the universe of discourse. They do not as such present an analysis of science but only an agreement to treat just these and no other statements as meaningful.

## Semantics, Meaning, and Truth

The syntactical approach to meaning has been found wanting. Although it avoids some of the metaphysical problems of a naïve theory of verification in which statements in some way correspond to facts, it is open to the charge of arbitrariness. It makes the physical language preemptive. The choice is prescriptive, but in order to support this prescription over every other one, the votary of syntactical coherence must become pragmatist and enter the material world that, as a manner of speaking, he finds repugnant. The coherence theory of truth will not do; but there are other alternatives which do not require a complete abandonment of the syntactical analysis of science.

In his subsequent writings, Carnap vacillated between an empirical and a semantical implementation of the syntactical system. On the one hand, his treatment of meaning and verification comes close to that of Schlick and Ayer, (Carnap 1936, 1937); on the other hand, meaning is to be treated in the context of Tarski's semantical conception of truth (Carnap, 1946, 1947, 1949).

We consider first the Carnapian empiricism. Phenomenalism is to be rejected; whatever empirical qualifications are introduced, they are to be incorporated into the system of physicalism. The truth of a sentence is contingent upon the truth of its predicates. Thus to verify a sentence (and give it meaning, in a sense) is to verify its predicates. As physicalism suggests, it is only the primitive predicates (i.e., those of protocols) that are verifiable. Concepts and predicates that are remote from the primitive predicates must therefore qualify for verification through reduction chains.

These reduction chains utilize either material implication or the equivalence connectives, such that the truth status of the remote predicates is formally tied to the truth status of the primitive predicates. Both dispositional terms (e.g., 'soluble,' 'volatile,' 'flammable') and theoretical terms (e.g., 'electrons,' 'cerebral engrams') are related to observable terms by sets of reduction chains (cf. N11.2).

So much is straightforward logical empiricism. But now, how do we verify primitive predicates? Here Carnap distinguishes between testability and confirmability. This distinction is somewhat reminiscent of Schlick. A predicate '*P*' is *confirmable* if it is reducible to a class of observation predicates. A predicate '*P*' is *testable* if in fact a method of testing is available whereby the relevant observation predicates can actually be obtained. Not all predicates are testable, but all must be confirmable (i.e., testable in principle). But what are observations? How are they reported? How do they get into the physicalist language? Here Carnap proceeds gingerly. He takes pains to define an observable predicate as one which a knowledgeable person is willing to entertain under suitable conditions of observation. This brings the physicalist closer to his protocol milieu, but Carnap is still reluctant to say that the predicate '*P*' is true because what it asserts is true.

In another essay he comes as close as he dares to joining hands with the empiricists (1949). There are observation statements and predicates, and there are observations. Confirmation requires that these must be conjoined in some sense. The concept Carnap applies in this context is confrontation (again reminiscent of Schlick). The proper observation predicate is chosen at the confrontation of an observation relevant to that predicate. "Confrontation is understood to consist in finding out as to whether one object (the statement in this case) properly fits the other (the fact) . . ." (1949, p. 125). But he is careful to point out that this relation is not one of comparison. Only things having some property in common can be compared. The sentence as such and the observation germane to this sentence have no property in common. Carnap, moreover, warns against endowing objects with structure and properties which belong only to language.

In this same essay Carnap briefly entertains the semantical issues that occupy him in his later books (1946, 1947). Here the truth of statements again become linguistic problems, but at a more subtle level than that treated under physicalism. In developing the semantical issues, Carnap follows Tarski (1944).

Generally, we think of semantics as being the study of the relation of terms to what they designate. Knowledge of these semantic relations enables us to establish the proper usage of the what and where of our vocabularies. It is, in a sense, *the* problem of meaning. Tarski, for example, writes, "Semantics is a discipline which deals with certain relations between

expressions of a language and the objects (or 'states of affairs') 'referred to' by those expressions." (Feigl and Sellars, 1949; p. 56) This
looks like the familiar problem of factual reference. But it is not, or at
least it is factual reference at a more subtle level. The gist of the semantic conception of truth is as follows. Terms and sentences are name
symbols; they designate, but they are different from what they name.
Thus 'Snow is white' is a name, and the name is properly used if what
it names is the case. The paradigm, then, of the semantic conception
of truth is

*'Snow is white' is true if, and only if, snow is white.*

Now a sentence is true if, and only if, what it asserts is true; but the
sentence is not what it asserts, rather it is a name for that; i.e., a symbolic
expression used in conjunction with what it asserts. But in order to express
this relation, we need to designate what is asserted by the sentence. This
must itself be expressed by a sentence $p$. Let us now take $X$ as the name
for that sentence. Then we have $p$ and the name of $p$, which is $X$. The
semantic conception of truth then says: *X is true if, and only if, p.* In this
statement $X$ (a sentence) is the name of a sentence and $p$ is the sentence
named. Thus there are different levels of language operating here. If we
go to the basic level of factual reference, then we are bound to express
in sentential form that which a sentence refers to. This can only be a
sentence, i.e., a $p$. In expressing the relation of naming, a sentence cannot
name a fact but only another sentence; or, we can say the fact that is
named is the sentence $p$. What is the relation of a *sentence* to a *fact*?
We answer this by utilizing a sentence to designate the *sentence* and a
sentence to designate the *fact*. We then arrive at " 'Snow is white' is
true if, and only if, snow is white."

   This semantic conception of truth stipulates that meaning is explicated
*within* some primary language (the "object language") and by a metalanguage. But meaning and its truth conception remain within the boundaries of language. By means of a suitably rich metalanguage we can discuss the relation between the name of a thing and the thing named. This
leads us uncritically to think in terms of factual reference. But the fact
itself can only be expressed linguistically; thus semantic truth is always
a relation between a name and the sentence named.

   What advantage, if any, does this conception of truth have over a
syntactical one? Or rather, why should the semantic defense of physical
protocols be superior to the syntactical one? This is hard to articulate.
Some sentences are basic, we take them as fundamental. They are the
sentences that express facts, express our observations, if you will. If one
counters that facts are somehow different from sentences, that at some
place one must point to the relation between a name and a fact, then
there are two alternatives that may exemplify his intentions. One, he can

ostensively point to objects, to states of affairs, and to other names. But by doing this, he is giving a psychological demonstration of how indeed we do learn to use words. It is not the explanation of semantic reference. Two, he can verbalize the fact, regard this verbalization as a protocol, and then proceed in the type of analysis laid out by Tarski. The defense of this "semantic" protocol over the "syntactical" one rests on its confrontation of physical objects and states of affairs. At least here, the protocol is required to face the facts; whereas in the syntactical analysis of physicalism, protocols are what that name implies: resolutions and agreements prescribing a kind of linguistic etiquette.

Carnap's treatment of the semantic basis of truth follows Tarski, but it is somewhat differently expressed. Let $p$ be a sentence, let $S(p)$ be a designation of that sentence, then we have

$$p \equiv S(p) \text{ is true.}$$

For example, by making proper substitution, we can say that "The substance in this vessel is alcohol" and "The sentence 'The substance in this vessel is alcohol' is true" are logically equivalent. This formulation of the semantic conception of truth lends itself to the discussion of criticisms brought against it.

Is it reasonable to postulate that the equivalence of "$p$" and "$S(p)$ is true" is explanatory of truth? Kaufmann, one of the members of the original Vienna Circle, disagrees (1942, 1944). The formulation would give synthetic propositions an invariable truth status, whereas it is their character to be contingent upon experience. "Knowledge of invariable truth of synthetic propositions (whether perfect or imperfect) is unobtainable, not because of limitations of human knowledge but because the conception of such knowledge involves a contradiction in terms" (1945, p. 60). Cousin (1950), on the other hand, objects that "$p$" and "$S(p)$ is true" cannot be equivalent, for one is in the object language, the other is in the metalanguage, and although the latter can include the sentences of the former, the reverse inclusion is not possible. By its formulation, the metalanguage is necessarily richer than the object language. However, Cousin goes on to express a more general criticism of the semantic conception of truth. It is weak and, as Tarski himself realized, it is remote from what we usually mean by meaning, just because it does ignore the psychological factors of meaning. Talking about sentences must always be done with other sentences. This is a semantic trap. But sentences also serve a cognitive function, they are useful in our finding our way about in the world. They have pragmatic as well as semantic sanction. It is true that the two divisions of language, pragmatics and semantics, can be treated as having different subject matters. Still the separation of the two in discussions of meaning has resulted in the aseptic but artificial excursions into pure linguistics.

# FALSIFIABILITY: KARL POPPER

The thesis of verifiability runs into difficulties with respect to certain classes of statements which are essential to scientific knowledge (e.g., lawlike statements). We now ask if there is any alternative stratagem that will give veridical support to the various statements of science.

In response to his own questions, a child acquires information regardless of whether he receives a "yes" or a "no" answer. In epistemology, similar informational stratagems hold. Every question can be rephrased as a declarative statement, yielding a hypothesis, as it were, either to be affirmed or to be denied. Attending then to one particular statement, we find that it is "meaningful" if it is falsifiable. Now as we have seen, some statements are nonverifiable. Is their meaning status clarified at all under a strategy of falsification?

Suppose we are asked: Is the country in a state of economic depression? A "yes" or "no" answer is required under the criteria of meaningfulness. We rephrase the question in the form of a hypothesis: "The country is in a state of economic depression." What is the meaning status of this statement? First of all, the statement is meaningful if, and only if, there are some means of determining whether it is true or false. Assuming that it is not a tautology, we proceed then to ascertain what conditions will make the statement true. If these conditions are fulfilled then the statement is confirmed. Otherwise not. But we could just as well proceed by holding the statement true and deducing from it the set of predicates essential to its meaning. Then looking at each predicate in turn we pass or fail the statement contingent upon whether what the predicate states is true or false. Let us say the term "depression" contains in its definition the predicates "national income below such and such level," "rate of unemployment above such and such level," etc. Proceeding to test by falsification we hold true the hypothesis, depression, so long as each test of a possible predicate results in the verdict "true." Thus we hold the hypothesis provisionally true until it is falsified. Once it is falsified then we reject it. We are not at all concerned with the fact that some economist might wish to argue that the country really is in a state of depression even though one of the many tested predicates has been found to be false. We are engaged in a game, so to speak, with unambiguous procedural rules. A country is in "a state of depression" if, and only if, every one of the defining predicates is true.

In the present example, our definition (of the country being in "a state of depression") contains a finite set of predicates. Therefore, our hypothesis is in principle both verifiable and falsifiable. Ultimately, one strategy of testing is as good as another. But what is the case when the statement, or hypothesis, has an unlimited number of predicates? What if the hypothesis is a scientific law? Then under the conditions of test-ability, the hypothesis is falsifiable but not verifiable. Because of this fact, Karl Popper has proposed analyzing the logic and method of science under conventions that are deductivist rather than inductivist, and that stress falsification rather than verification. What follows derives primarily from his *The Logic of Scientific Discovery*.

## Deductivism versus Inductivism

In the history of science, laws and other general statements are frequently regarded as being summary statements of individual observations. But they are also treated as implying more than this, for they are sometimes used as rules of inference for future observations. Thus we find laws being utilized both as summary statements and as unrestricted generalizations. Epistemologically the two usages differ. The one is subject to analysis by verification; the other is not. This fact led Hume and the empiricists who followed him to skepticism concerning the inductive support of lawlike statements. Moreover, skepticism reaches further than this; it touches existential statements that purport to be ontologically secure. No finite number of observation statements can verify an absolute existence statement. Consider both existential and lawlike statements as being in the nature of general statements. We are to conclude then that inductivism, unsupported by intuition or by transcendental conjecture (Kant), is inadequate for the support of general statements.

Popper finds the difficulties of this kind of inductive inference to be "insurmountable." In place of induction he substitutes deduction. One begins with an hypothesis, which may be an unrestricted universal statement as in the case of a law. Such a hypothesis has a tentative or provisional status. It is held to be true until proved false. That is, its "truth" has a conventional rather than a dogmatic character. All the same, the hypothesis is held to be true for whatever epoch it endures as free from falsification.

Two difficulties must be immediately faced, however. First, how do we arrive at such hypotheses? By experience presumably. But, as Popper points out, this is a problem of psychology, not one of epistemology. The fact is we start with a hypothesis and deduce testable consequences from it. The etiology of the hypothesis may be of interest to the psychologist or to the historian, but it has nothing to do with its truth status. The second difficulty concerns choice among alternative hypotheses. In the given factual, historical context we may be confronted with alternative hypotheses. How do we go about evaluating their truth status? What criterion do we have for making this evaluation? In this case, it is perhaps best to think in terms of complexes of hypotheses which in their unity compose a theory. Rather than alternative hypotheses we consider alternative theories. By virtue of the logical embellishment of statements concerning the state of the system (i.e., those specifying the independent and the state variables within the theory), we are able to deduce testable hypotheses. This is the familiar hypothetico-deductive model. Proceeding now to answer our question, we consider alternative hypotheses generated from alternative theories. Deductivism prescribes that that alternative (in this case, some theory) will be regarded most highly which is most fruitful in generating testable consequences (in this case, hypotheses). In other words we are to select that theory having the greatest potential for falsification (cf. N6.4).

Mention of the hypothetico-deductive method should not, however, lead one to assume that a deductivist procedure (in the sense of Popper) is invariably being invoked. The contrary is often the case. The hypothetico-deductive method is utilized to generate positive tests of the theory; i.e., experimental hypotheses are generated by the theory for given experimental conditions. If the experimental hypothesis is confirmed, then such confirmation is considered as support for the theory. But this involves the strategy of verifiability. Accordingly then, this, the customary use of the hypothetico-deductive method, exemplifies inductivism and not deductivism, as mere words may incline us to think.

## Logic of Falsifiability

The thesis of deductivisim is that a statement is meaningful if it is falsifiable. This does not rule out the meaningfulness of verifiable statements. But the only clearly verifiable statements are those asserting particulars, and they have but limited applicability in the logic of science. Two matters now concern us. One, what classes of statements are falsifiable? And two, what is the method of falsification? The issues here are interdependent, so no effort will be made to keep separate the answers.

Popper's primary concern is with scientific laws and with hypotheses generated by theories. Both of these classes of statements are general in character. Under suitable conditions, each leads to the deduction of statements about classes of events. Rather we should say they lead to statements that we should consider basic in the sense that they specify events. We might say these basic statements, and all such statements as specify particular events, are experimental hypotheses. Psychologically they determine our expectations. If such expectations are not fulfilled, the experimental hypothesis is falsified.

We should not, however, get lost in this psychological description. It is irrelevant to the logical foundations of falsification. I have intimated that events falsify statements, but according to Popper, this is incorrect. He stands with Carnap and Neurath in maintaining that statements can only be falsified by other statements according to the conventions of logic. Facts, as such, do not falsify, they have no logical relation to statements. He agrees with them, too, that a basic protocol language is required, although he is suspicious that Carnap in particular has not avoided psychological contamination in his selection of protocols. To clarify his own position, Popper calls the simples of his system *basic statements*. Like protocols they are the fundamental statements that give to science its putative empirical character. They are tied to occurrences, events, the observables, but not, Popper claims, in a psychologistic sense.

Phenomenalism and the language of sense data are to be eschewed. Rather we are to specify observational reports in terms of "position and movement of macroscopic physical bodies." "Or we may lay it down, more precisely, that every basic statement must either be itself a statement about relative positions of physical bodies, or that it must be equivalent to some basic statement of this 'mechanistic' or 'materialistic' kind" (1959, p. 103). One cannot justify the use of the observational over any other language, for only logical arguments can be justificatory. But the observation language is intersubjective and, therefore, fulfills a requirement of testability. Popper, therefore, proposes that "observables" be regarded as undefined (cf. N6.5).

Basic statements, then, are about observables. They are needed to determine whether a theory is in fact falsifiable. Certain conditions are now required in order to assure falsifiability. One, no basic statement can be strictly deduced from a universal statement without initial conditions being imposed. (Just as a syllogism requires two premises in order to assure a conclusion.) And two, basic statements must be such as possibly to contradict a universal statement. Popper claims that these two conditions are met by all statements of singular existential form. Such basic statements are subject to falsification, but by convention and by agreement within the community of linguists, and not by virtue of any kind of logical compulsion. Under certain circumstances (what Schlick might call "confrontations" and what Popper would call "observations") certain basic statements are held to be true.

Falsification of hypotheses and theories, however, does involve logical manipulations. A theory, for example, is falsifiable "if the class of its potential falsifiers is nonempty." This criterion requires the following conditions be met: one, the theory, in conjunction with statements of initial conditions, must yield hypotheses expressible as classes of basic statements that are descriptive of events; and two, for any given test, the class of all possible basic statements must divide into two nonempty subclasses, one subclass being that of the hypothesis tested, the other being the class of "potential falsifiers of the theory." It should be obvious why stress is placed on "nonempty." A theory that generates an hypothesis including all possible basic statements would not be subject to test. A statement true under all specifiable conditions is true regardless of any test; it would be vacuously true as in the case of a hypothesis derived from the general rule: all swans are either black or not black.

Now that the conditions of falsifiability have been enunciated, how is falsification actually to be achieved? In Popper's terminology, one might be tempted to answer, "By the absence of the basic statement appropriate to that hypothesis," (or, in the material mode, "By the absence of fact"). But in the laboratory, the absence of a fact is a fact itself. For example, if the instruments of an experimental apparatus do not record any radiation effects they may fail to verify an hypothesis, but the description of the apparatus at a given time is a factual description. Or, for example, an animal may not respond in the predicted way but in some other way. Rather than speak of negative facts now (as, for example, Russell did), and rather than speaking of one basic statement negating another, Popper proposes that all basic statements germane to an empirical test be divided into two classes of hypotheses, the one class being derivable from the theory being tested, the other class containing such hypotheses as cannot be derived from the theory. Our decision, then, to hold or reject the theory is contingent upon experimental outcome. Since an experimental hypothesis is indicated by a basic statement or by a complex of basic statements, a falsifying hypothesis can always be specified in terms of the basic statement of the experimental hypothesis *except for* the exclusion, negation, or deletion of some element or complex of elements. (For example, suppose the experimental hypothesis, $H : pr$; a falsifying hypothesis might then be $H' : p \sim r$.) This strategem would assure us that the class of falsifying hypotheses would not be empty, providing, of course, the basic statements $p, r, \ldots$, themselves, are falsifiable.

In way of appraising the doctrine of falsification, the following points can be made. One, it is especially suited for the testing of general statements, the scientific laws and hypotheses derived from theories. In this respect it overcomes a major objection to the verification of theory of meaning. Falsification of a general statement is conclusive, whereas its verification is not. Two, it holds theories and hypotheses to be true until falsified. Even though this is a truth that is to be regarded only as conventional and tentative, it is the result of a strategem that avoids the skepticism endemic to inductively supported hypotheses. And three, in Popper's mind at least, the method of falsification best represents the actual practice of the experimental empiricist (cf. N6.6). The method of falsification is the method of finding the range of application for the veridically held theory.

The appraisal is not complete, however, without our including an objection and disturbing qualification. Just as a universal statement is not conclusively verifiable, so a statement with an existential quantifier ("some $x \ldots$," "at least one $x \ldots$") is not conclusively falsifiable. Popper counters this argument by saying that such existential statements have little place in science. We are invariably concerned with general statements or a class of general statements derivable from theories. But can we really do without the existential statement? Let us look for a moment at the procedure for falsifying a theory. We conclude that a theory is falsifiable. Why? Because we can divide the class of all possible basic statements into the subclasses of verifiers and possible falsifiers. However, the theory is falsifiable only if neither one of these complementary subclasses of basic statements is empty. But how do we ascertain whether the subclass, say, of potential falsifiers is nonempty? One can, of course, arbitrarily place putative basic statements into subclasses, but by Popper's acknowledgment basic statements are tied to observations. We only know whether a statement is a possible basic statement if there is an observation that will be the occasion for just such a basic statement. We may conclude, then, that a set is nonempty if, and only if, it is in fact nonempty. Furthermore, the hypothesis of the nonempty set must be expressed in terms of a statement containing the dubious existential quantifier. Thus, the following argument: a theory is falsifiable if, and only if, the class of potential falsifiers is nonempty; a class is nonempty if, and only if, it contains at least one member; but a statement containing an existential quantifier is not conclusively falsifiable; therefore, a theory is falsifiable only if it satisfies a condition (an hypothesis) which itself is not falsifiable.

## SUMMARY

This review of logical empiricism has been confined almost entirely to matters concerned with an empiricistic theory of meaning. The fact that the people considered here do not form a unified group, and do declaim against one another and against being called positivists at all, should not divert our attention from the fact they are united in defense of a critical philosophy. The function of philosophy is analysis and the clarification of knowledge. Philosophy should state explicitly the logical and empirical foundations of such knowledge. Without these, and only these, foundations, what would pass for knowledge would be suspect. The union of the people discussed here comes about by their common dedication to empiricism. They are agreed (1) that logic and language are indispensable to the structuring of experience and knowledge; (2) that all assertions about the world must reduce to their basic and supportive empirical counterparts, in whatever mode these are expressed; and (3) that traditional metaphysical speculations not concerned directly with epistemology are fruitless.

But any program of critique which attempts to place all knowledge on grounds as secure as those of logic will be subject to misgivings and revision. The complexity of the problems produces the diversity of the solutions. First of all, there is the problem of reference between language and fact. There is no logic among facts, only among statements and the conventional symbols. Yet it is to fact that the logical empiricist must relate his knowledge. Positivism has become linguistic and syntactical out of its deference to logic; but the victories it has achieved against an onto-logical search for meaning have been empty except that it always concedes a point by endowing the basic, the protocol language with some kind of empirical reference. The syntactical solutions of Carnap, Neurath, Pop-per, and their students are efficient ones; but whenever any of these philosophers disengages himself from empirics, he, often as not, sounds just as metaphysical as any dogmatic idealist.

And then, there is the problem of truth itself. How does the logical empiricist confirm or disconfirm conclusively? For many of the signifi-cant statements of science, he cannot establish their truth status conclu-sively. Or rather he cannot make these statements fit the prototypes for rational discourse. What of theories? What of dispositional models whereby we counsel against a course of action? What of theoretical con-structs? What of law itself? The paradigms of scientific inference them-selves are suspect. If this is not sufficient to encumber the quest after indubitable principles, there is always the problem of the primacy and privacy of sense data. The pursuit of empirical certainty leads one but to his own sensorium.

Finally, it is asked, why this theory of meaning? How is it to be falsified? Can it pass its own test? Statement of the empiricist criteria of meaning is itself neither tautologically nor empirically true. It, too, like so much we have had to say about basics, is a matter of convention, of pragmatically justifiable taste. The positivist's own defense belongs to the realm of value theory. Either the theory of meaning is meaningful by its own criteria, or it too is but a bit of metaphysics (Wisdom, 1953).

The positivist is most effective and most incisive when he is speaking of the philosophy of others, when, for example, he can call up the tran-scendental myth-makers to the pillory post. On the other hand, there is always some blush of embarrassment when he himself is called upon to be self-reflective. The irony is that he has in large part brought the situa-tion upon himself. Seeking certainty and elevating demonstrable proof to the role of exemplary knowledge, he has succumbed to the invitation to justify factual inference on the same apodictic pretense as logical inference. He knows better, of course, than to accept the invitation. Since Hume, it has been common knowledge that experiential inference can never be the subject of demonstrable proof. All forms of inductive infer-ence have just this property that distinguishes them from deductive in-ference: they always contain a conjectural element which, in the argument for rational inference, is itself not capable of proof. Still inductive inference is, and has been, widely utilized and relied upon by the most sophisticated of skeptics. When one reads tortuous efforts to discredit the principle of verification on grounds that the number of tests sufficient to pronounce a verdict is in effect infinite (e.g., see Waismann, 1952), one can suspect the critic manufactures the issue on the suppressed assumption that both inductive and deductive inference should be judged by the same standards of justification.

Reichenbach (1938, 1940, 1949), who has recognized these susceptibilities of his fellow empiricists and scolded against them, placed the case in defense of empiricism on purely pragmatic grounds. As concerns our knowledge of the world, what alternative is there to empiricism? True our confidence in inductive inference and test procedures is always qualified; but should the world happen to be as we in our philosophically naïve moments conjecture it to be, even should it be the chimera of the demons of deceit, then our efficient test procedures would be as defensible as any means of inference we could contrive. Should the world be an enduring uniform macrocosm, then our empirical explorations should reliably reflect that fact. On the other hand, should the world be ephemeral, changing the structure within each new epoch, then the empirical test procedures, such as we have roughed out here, would be as efficiently corrective as any we can conceive.

## LINGUISTIC ANALYSIS: AN ADDENDUM

In spite of the call to unity which emanated from the Vienna Circle, diversification rather than unification has been a distinctive feature of recent empiricistic thinking. Rather than a singular movement with well defined objectives and a codified discipline, what has emerged has been a set of movements each with its unique preoccupations, but all combining uneasily under the banner of what is now called philosophical analysis. Logical Atomism, Logical Empiricism, Logical Positivism, Linguistic Analysis: these are the names we have come to recognize. These movements are united by a distrust of metaphysics, an emphasis upon observation as a source of knowledge, and the commitment of philosophy to the critique of meaning and understanding. We have already seen how the interests and even the methods of logical atomism and logical positivism have converged, so that whatever their incompatibilities they can be resolved under a common interest in making secure the foundations of empirical knowledge. Yet among the groups mentioned above, the linguistic analysts do not entirely share in this convergence of interests. They stand apart. Why?

To begin with, it should be noted that linguistic analysis is primarily an English development. The coterie of analysts is spread throughout the world, but the center of the analytic movement has unquestionably been Oxford University. This is somewhat strange, for the two philosophers who have contributed the most in way of method and charismatic inspiration have been G. E. Moore and Ludwig Wittgenstein, both Cambridge men. Second, it should be emphasized that despite the presence of Russell, Wittgenstein, and Popper, and despite the dramatic success of Ayer's *Language, Truth and Logic,* English philosophy never fell under the sway of positivism to the extent, say, that American philosophy did. This, too, is a bit surprising; for despite their differences, the positivists felt a close affinity to Russell and Wittgenstein. What, then, is distinctive about linguistic analysis? And why should one be at all hesitant to include it among the empirical philosophies contributing to the understanding of science?

As the name indicates, linguistic analysis concerns the analysis of language. But so does logical analysis, the practice indulged in both by positivists and by atomists. What is singled out for linguistic analysis, however, is natural language rather than the ideal languages of logistics. One attempts to unravel the tangle of traditional philosophical puzzles by an analysis of ordinary language. The major thesis of an analysis is that philosophical problems arise from the abuse of ordinary language. Thus problems dissolve when we ascertain the correct uses of our natural language.

This argument is, of course, much more subtle than it first appears; its disarming character is due to G. E. Moore. Moore was a Cambridge contemporary of Russell and Wittgenstein, yet he maintained his own unique approach to philosophical analysis. He was neither atomist nor positivist, yet neither was he to join the emerging analytic group that he did much to create. Where he was singularly influential was in his method. In a series of essays, Moore attacked philosophical puzzles by giving what appeared to be offhand common sense answers and then showing point by point how a philosophical problem arises when we abuse the linguistic context in which the question is put. For example, in one of his most famous essays, "In Defense of Common Sense," Moore (1925) proceeds by giving common sense answers to philosophical questions all of which have received memorable negative answers. Does matter exist? Is time real? Is there another mind besides my own? Against the subtle and sometimes tortured exegetics of Bradley, McTaggart, and Berkeley, Moore steps forth to defend the obvious. Of course, time is real! I was in my room yesterday, I am here now, and providing no mishap I shall be here tomorrow. If these events are not in time, what is their context? Clear enough to the man of common sense, so what is the argument? Or on another occasion, Moore shows his two hands, first one, then the other; and then he exclaims for his witnesses: "At least two objects exist!" How then can Berkeley claim matter to be unreal? Moore's answer is that we know the meaning of our statements directly and simply. But it is difficult indeed to analyze just what that meaning is. It is only because a philosopher like Berkeley gets trapped by his own reductive analysis that he comes to absurd conclusions. It is true that what Berkeley has to say is interesting, and that what he says has some significance, but what emerges from an analysis of the argument is the realization that at some point the philosophical idealist has committed himself to using a term or a phrase in a way which is contrary to ordinary usage. For example, after following Berkeley through the *Dialogues*, one might say, "Oh, I see! Of course, *'Esse est percipi!'* " but then on further analysis, in the Moore fashion, he would add, "But, of course, one is not really denying the existence of matter." Until one develops the skills of diagnosing linguistic pathology and tries his own hand at this type of analysis, it is hard to appreciate its effectiveness. Moore's great influence is testimony to that effectiveness. Where paradoxes are found in philosophical discussions, analyze carefully the meaning of each term that iterates the paradoxical answer. At some place philosophical enlightenment will come. What appears to be a problem is not a problem at all. It is an ambiguity in ordinary usage. We are invited then to consider ordinary language as a very viable instrument of knowledge. Abuse it, exploit the oddities of grammar, such as in tense, and we may find ourselves trapped by the vagaries of that language into denying what our good senses tell us is really so. One should be cautioned, though, against thinking the analysis of a meaning is an elementary task. Witness, for example, the despair of all empiricists in trying to explain simply and lucidly how the meaning of a sentence is tied to some empirical state of affairs. This latter is the very problem that led Moore to proclaim the difficulty of analysis, and led Wittgenstein finally to abandon the doctrine of picturing.

If Moore gave to the analysts the light but reasoned touch of innocence, Wittgenstein was to contribute the ponderous element that made the analysts aware of their original linguistic sins. Moore gave simple answers to serious questions. Wittgenstein countered with serious answers to simple questions. These two Cambridge friends and colleagues complemented one another; Moore could persuade the skeptic to accept the obvious, but Wittgenstein would dissect the obvious in order to discover the meaning implicit in our heritage of common sense.

Before turning to Wittgenstein's analytic philosophy, it should be mentioned that he exercised an influence on two diverse trends in empirico-analytic philosophy. We have already seen that the *Tractatus*, Wittgenstein's own unique presentation of the arguments of logical atomism, was stimulus and source-book to Schlick and the Vienna Circle. To this day it is one of the most assayed, most referred to books, in all of the literature of positivism. On the other hand, the *Philosophical Investigations* is quite another book (cf. N6.7). It represents Wittgenstein's conversion to analytic philosophy, more directly concerned with language and philosophical puzzles than it is with the empiricist's inveterate interests in science and empirical knowledge. This is the work that has had great influence on the Oxford analysts. In it Wittgenstein reneges upon the earlier positivistic epistemology of the *Tractatus*. Rather, he now finds that philosophical quandaries are symptomatic of linguistic pathology. The practice of philosophy should be therapeutic analysis, to cure the philosopher, as it were, of his own preoccupations.

Like the *Tractatus*, the *Investigations* is a distinctive book. Its style is desultory, like a philosopher's commonplace book in which ideas appear too profound or difficult for sustained discourse. This book, too, is interspersed with quotable apothegms, but their brilliance is perhaps neither so enduring nor so original as in the *Tractatus*. The doctrine of analysis which Wittgenstein now develops is pretty much that of the pragmatists. Charles Peirce (1878), for example, maintained we are to seek the meaning of a proposition in the set of its possible consequences. Wittgenstein now argues "Do not look for the meaning of a statement, look for its uses." Do not look for essential meanings, correspondences, or isomorphic configurations, do not look for *the* meaning, or *the* use of a term or statement. Rather, examine the context. Let analysis lead the retreat into linguistic relativism. However, by relativism one does not suggest that meaning loses its enduring significance, or that a statement fails to possess some essential character within its own grammatical context. It is simply that analysis of meaning requires our gaining knowledge of the roles of the language as they are applied to given language-experience contexts.

In brief, Wittgenstein argues that hidden or enduring essences of meaning independent of context must be given up. As Ryle and other analysts were later to argue, philosophical perplexities are to be regarded as discordancies in linguistic use. Paradoxes derive from a lack of agreement as to the way in which terms are to be used. They result from our failure concertedly to adopt linguistic conventions appropriate to the experiential context. Thus words and phrases possess no absolute dictionary, nor can we prescribe for them a uniform ritual of verification. We must seek their meaning in behavioral settings. That is to say, the meaning of a term is situational, it prescribes rules for our response in a given situation. Each word is a sign post, as it were, directing us to behave in certain ways; to stop, to go this way rather than that, to treat the rock as a solid piece of matter, rather than as the diaphanous mist of an idealist's imagination.

There are several strands to this argument. Emphasis upon this lingual-behavioral context rules out the possibility of private language. Using language is like playing games. There are rules to follow, but no one set of rules for the games we play. Therefore, the meaning of a statement becomes the progeny of its many uses. When we speak of the idea represented by a term or phrase, we speak not of its unique meaning but of the family of its several meanings. Thus ontology succumbs to the population explosion. Yet a language consistently spoken is itself a form of life; *a* form, not *the* form. Philosophical theory thus suffers the presumption of privileged and transcendent judgment, when in fact it too is but one in the family of all life forms.

What is Wittgenstein's counsel, then? To analyze! Thus to leave things pretty much as they are in their proper setting of natural language. "What is your aim in philosophy? To show the fly the way out of the fly-bottle" (1953, p. 103). The linguistic analysts were to agree in every detail; but what is more they were to emphasize that it was the philosopher's cleverness, his metaphysics, even his critique, that lured him into the bottle in the first place.

It is this thesis that has impressed the linguistic philosophers to the point of elevating analysis to a mystique. There are no insoluble philosophical problems. The issues that have preoccupied philosophers through the centuries do not at all present legitimate problems. They arise only from the philosopher's abuse of ordinary language. This theme leads to two notable consequences. One, ordinary language is elevated to a privileged status among all languages (at a time, incidentally, when other philosophers were inventing formal languages). Although our philosophical ills are precipitates of that language, the analysis of the structure of that language is also the cure for such ills. And two, the practice of linguistic therapy becomes the sole preoccupation of the working philosopher. He is to analyze and clarify propositions until the language is purged of the tangles that our metaphysical inclinations effect.

, Just as linguistic analysis has been compared to psychoanalysis (Wisdom, 1953) so ought it to have its method. Yet, as Passmore (1957) notes, when one looks for a discourse on method, he only gets another example of analysis. More often than not it is the contentious critic rather than the analyst who lays out the analytic plan (cf. Gellner, 1959). Generally the writings of the analysts are confined to relatively brief essays. Simple expressions of philosophical issues are analyzed, rather than the problems, the questions, the answers which serve to catalogue the metaphysician's preoccupations. Sometimes the analyst starts with a sentence (e.g., "Every event has a cause?", "Nothing can be red and green all over?", "Is there a problem about sense data?"), or sometimes with just a word (e.g., "Can," "Ought"). And sometimes he merely begins to speak casually about profound matters (e.g., "My object is to try to elucidate the nature of mathematical propositions and to explain their relation to the everyday world of counting and measurement—of clocks, and yards of material, and income tax forms.") (cf. Flew, 1951, 1953.) From the simple statement of the problem the analyst proceeds to examine the extant uses of the word, phrase, statement. He exhausts, as it were, the possibilities of meaning and, in doing so, shows that substantive questions, such as "Are causes real?" are commands to impose certain uses on words and not others. But the analyst shows, in Wittgensteinian fashion, that there are many language games and many linguistic contexts. We are all, in our ways, correct in saying what we do say. As philosophers we are invariably wrong in insisting the meaning of our expression is what it is, no more, no less. The analyst has been criticized for ignoring history, yet he has no need for the history of metaphysics. What he, the working philosopher, is doing is something new. His major calling is linguistic critique; if the task is properly done it will obviate the traditional callings of philosophy.

And how does this analytic philosophy read? Well, like an interminable fugue on simple thematic materials. First, the issue is stated, a major theme, a major meaning; then a counter theme is stated and taken up and ramified, and perhaps another counter theme. And then the whole ensemble of themes is recapitulated to remind the reader that the composition is complex. There is no finale, no coda, for there is no resolution into a single triumphant theme. The analysis simply tells us that here is a set of uses; if we think this use over that, it is only because we are blinded to the alternative perspectives. The therapeutic analysis now offers its own resolution of the issue out of which our initial quandary may have arisen. We now appreciate how different answers may have been given to philosophical questions, why each may be correct, why each may be incorrect, much like the therapeutic analysis of psychological phenomenology.

Doubtless throughout history philosophers have engaged in some type of analysis. This is their critical function. Contemporary linguistic analysts have been singled out for their being an offshoot or even a culmination of empirical philosophy. Yet, they remain an addendum to discussions on the philosophy of science; for in the period of their self-identification, they turned their attention to a reassessment of philosophy rather than to the analysis of scientific meaning as such. No doubt this in part stemmed from the disenchantment over their efforts to find in the theory of meaning preferential support for scientific propositions. But the fact remains, both in interests and methods, that the analysts diverged from the main channels of empiricistic thinking (cf. N6.8).

# NOTES

## NOTE 6.1

Schlick agrees with Carnap that the material mode of speaking "though not faulty" may "engender pseudo-problems if it is *employed without sufficient caution*," but as to Schlick's being "accused of being a metaphysician and poet" over his rejection of physicalism, he is more amused than stunned. Thinking of his own writing on the matter "as nothing but a gentle warning of a true empiricist against certain tendencies towards what seemed to me a rather dogmatic or rationalistic formulation of positivistic principles," he could write:

> If anyone should tell me that I believe in the truth of science ultimately because it has been adopted "by the scientists of my culture circle," I should—smile at him. I do have trust in those good fellows, but that is only because I found them to be trustworthy wherever I was able to test their enunciations. I assure you most emphatically that I should *not* call the system of science true if I found its consequences incompatible with my own observations of nature, and the fact that it is adopted by the whole of mankind and taught in all the universities would make no impression on me, . . . the *only ultimate* reason why I accept any proposition as true is to be found in those simple experiences which may be regarded as the final steps of comparison between a statement and a fact . . . (1935, p. 69).

In an exchange with Hempel, von Juhos objects to the radical conventionalism assumed under the formal mode of speaking. The physicalists had implied that protocols could be modified under certain circumstances in order to coincide with derived hypotheses. But this freedom to modify and to select protocols seems to defeat the empirical foundations of science. The defense of selecting one over another set of protocols cannot be based on convention alone. As long as one is confined to the formal mode of speech, one set of hypotheses is as good as another, one set of protocols as defensible as another. There would be no means of distinguishing between an empirical science and a nonempirical one. Noting also that experience includes the data of awareness for which there are no physicalistic counterparts, von Juhos concludes:

> If we strictly adhere to the physicalistic theses, we come on the one hand to formulations which the Empiricist eliminates as being meaningless, and on the other hand, while trying to verify the special position of true science in relation to the merely imaginable one, we enter a circle, a pseudo-formulation, that can only be avoided by a return to the empiricist mode of speech, which means giving up the physicalist (formal) mode of speech (1935, p. 92).

## NOTE 6.2

The distinction among categories of statements is essentially that one which has been in vogue since the advent of modern analysis:

*Analytic* propositions are those propositions that are true by virtue of their logical character alone. They may be simple equivalences, definitions, or other forms of tautology. Speaking of the logical character of an analytic proposition, Carnap states a proposition is analytic "when it is a consequence of the null class of sentences (and thus a consequence of every sentence)" (1937, p. 39).

*Synthetic* propositions are those propositions that can be classified as factual, i.e., the truth of such propositions is contingent upon a factual (empirical) state of affairs which is their reference. According to Carnap a proposition is synthetic if it is a genuine statement that is neither analytic nor contradictory.

*Contradictory* propositions are propositions that yield every proposition as a consequence.

*Equipollent* propositions are propositions having the same content. Logically such propositions imply one another. Equipollence is thereby the basis of synonomy.


## NOTE 6.3

Hanson's argument is to be found in *Patterns of Discovery* (1958) and in Feigl and Maxwell (eds.) *Current Issues in the Philosophy of Science* (1961).

Authorative accounts of conventionalism are to be found in H. Poincaré, *Science and Hypothesis* (1905, 1952); and, P. Duhem, *The Aim and Structure of Physical Theory* (1914, 1954).

One will find overtones of Hanson's argument in W. H. Watson, *On Understanding Physics* (1938); and S. Toulmin, *The Philosophy of Science* (1953). Both of these books, like that of Hanson, reveal the influence of Wittgenstein's *Philosophical Investigations* (1953). However, it is in the work of Henry Margenau (especially, *The Nature of Physical Reality,* 1950) that one finds one of the most explicit statements of the impact of the conceptual bias.

Schematically, Margenau analyzes cognitive experience into two epistemological components, the empirical data and concepts. The two are epistemologically inseparable. His model is very simple. Primary data are separated from the conceptual elements by what he calls the P-plane; on the one side, are the world and its perceptual potential, but devoid of that which would give it ontological significance; on the other side, is the conceptual field, that organization of constructs that participate structurally and inferentially in a reification of the world. As formally represented, the constructs in the C-field are interconnected by logico-mathematical relations. Visualize now a coherent theory. Constructs are interrelated by virtue of equations, such as $F = ma$, where each term represents a conceptual unit. Contact with the P-plane is then made through instrumental correspondences. Such correspondences fulfill the logical function of transformation rules. They have been referred to as "the dictionary" (N. R. Campbell), as "epistemic correlations" (F. C. S. Northrop), but most familiarly as "operational rules or definitions" (P. Bridgman). The fact is (and this is important for the operationist to remember) the rules are generated out of the conceptual apparatus. For example, without the conceptions of force and mass in a physical system, one could not generate the conventions for reifying these concepts at the perceptual plane. This much is obvious. But just as in Hanson's account of the hypothetico-deductive method, there is a feedback loop between the P-plane and the C-field. Data help to generate theoretical constructs. In turn, the constructs embellish a theory so as to generate additional epistemic correspondences with the perceptual world. The overall effect of the P- and C- systems is first for the scientist to seek data (by operational means) which reinforce the theoretical structure of concepts. But the seeking after data also introduces disparate data, unresolved images for the conceptual structure. Thus new modifications of the concepts, and additional data advance the theory in its ontological development. One can see that such a model can easily be adopted as a psychological schema of perception, where the apperceptive mass, though not so neatly formalized, now serves the function of the conceptual field.

One can also cite P. K. Feyerabend in this context (cf. 1958, 1962). Even though he and Hanson are frequently at odds, Feyerabend proposes that the data language itself is subject to shaping by any revision of a theory. Hanson would argue that so long as we are committed to the conceptions of classical physics, these conceptions will impose certain logical restrictions upon scientific explanation. Feyerabend maintains that we are by no means bound to accept the formal limitations imposed by any conceptual system; we can always modify, or even reject the assumptions of the system. For their exchanges on this and related matters see Feigl and Maxwell (eds.) *Current Issues on the Philosophy of Science.*

## NOTE 6.4

It is perhaps unfortunate that the discussion moves from testing hypotheses to testing theories. Howbeit, two confusions should be avoided. One, a theory which is a logically unified complex of "hypotheses" is itself not testable directly; it is testable only indirectly by means of testable consequences. Two, the hypotheses of the theory may be hypothetical constructions, not directly testable, whereas the hypothesis that is the consequence of the theory and the imposed state conditions is the testable experimental hypothesis.

One could, of course, speak of testing alternative hypotheses, in which the hypotheses are different generalizations up for test, e.g., hypotheses as to statistical frequencies. The argument would then require statistical foundations which, for the present at least, have not been assumed. An example of such a Popperian procedure, however, is to be found in the techniques of quality control wherein sampling is to be continued until one or another of two hypotheses is to be rejected.

## NOTE 6.5

In the face of rejecting the possibility of logical justification of the observation language, syntactical purists are always pressed to make a case for the privilege of that one language which also happens to be the one preferred by the more naïve empiricists. One takes the language which comes natural, which comes out of the conventions of rational linguists. If he rules out the pragmatic arguments, then there is no defense for his selecting his particular set of primitive statements. The syntactical purist thus makes an arbitrary decision to use a particular language, out of respect for consistency, to be sure, but partially in deference to that common sense which is characteristic of the person's confrontation of the world. With respect to observability, Popper writes:

I have no intention of *defining* the term 'observable' or 'observable event,' though I am quite ready to elucidate it by means of either psychologistic or mechanistic examples. I think it should be introduced as an undefined term which becomes sufficiently precise in use: as a primitive concept whose use the epistemologist has to learn, much as he has to learn the use of the term 'symbol,' or as the physicist has to learn the use of the term 'mass point' (1959, p. 103).

## NOTE 6.6

But not only in Popper's mind. Popper has appreciably influenced certain writings of P. K. Feyerabend which utilize deductivism and the principle of falsification as the basis for a realistic interpretation of scientific knowledge (1958, 1962). Feyerabend agrees with Popper in holding a well tested theory as provisionally true. However, he goes on to attack the ideas of formal reduction within theories and the idea of an invariant observational language. The data language of science cannot be interpreted independently of the theory that gives it significance. Should one change the theory, say, by introducing innovations to make the explanatory range of the theory more comprehensive, the data language itself will then be modified by such innovations.

The proposal that the data language is contingent upon the theory in which it is imbedded would appear to be a rejection of realism. However, that is not the case. It is only when we treat the data as invariant and subject theory to pragmatic adjustments that we succeed in making science into the conventionalistic by-play of inventive people. Conventionalism, therefore, deprives science of realistic roots. On the other hand, when both theory and the observation language which the particular theory articulates are subject to epistemic revision, then one may consider the growth of scientific knowledge as a continual shaping of reality. No ultimate truth is visualized. But the growth process of test and revision of theory shows that the language of science serves an "argumentive function."

Feyerabend utilizes this thesis of the shaping function of the language of science as the basis for his attack upon philosophers of science supporting the Copenhagen interpretation of quantum mechanics. He joins Bohm, de Broglie, and Vigier in asking for a rejection of the classical invariant conception of physical data in the realm of microphysics.

## NOTE 6.7

The *Philosophical Investigations* was published posthumously in 1953, but the influence of its teaching antedates its publication by at least two decades. Wittgenstein stands as a unique figure in the English scene, and like all figures who become legends in their own time, a controversial one. After returning to philosophy in 1929, he proceeded by teaching, discussion, and example to develop a coterie of students and professionals dedicated to the kind of philosophical practice prescribed in the *Investigations*.

For interesting accounts of Wittgenstein's work and influence upon his students see essays by von Wright and Malcolm in Malcolm's *Ludwig Wittgenstein, A Memoir.*


## NOTE 6.8

As Bertrand Russell (1953) has frankly asserted, this is not the kind of philosophy to captivate the scientific empiricist. There have been some excellent analytic works which are of interest to philosophers of science (e.g., Ryle's *The Concept of Mind*). Still, if one gives the literature something more than a cursory examination, if he reads over the anthologies of exemplary work, if he reads the defenses of the analytic practice, he is disappointed in the contribution found there concerning empiricism and the philosophy of science. This need not be so. There have been first rate philosophers of science who have taken the lessons of Wittgenstein and Moore without succumbing to the temptations to play verbal games (e.g., Hanson, Toulmin, W. H. Watson). But it does indeed seem a question of which Wittgenstein you take. The *Tractatus* is a brilliantly contrived book; stylized and cryptic as it may be, it was addressed to the empiricist who was occupied with problems of meaning and epistemology. By contrast, I am tempted to say, the *Investigations* is sometimes trivial, often tedious, and only occasionally an insightful book. What is unique is not historically original. The substance of the argument can be found in James and Peirce. Does analysis of linguistic puzzles and philosophical perplexities offer more to the philosopher than logical analysis and the analysis of verificatory procedures? Not for the philosopher of science.

We could, of course, rest easier with the analysts' laudatory appraisals of the *Philosophical Investigations* if critics could agree. But they do not agree. Brilliant as the *Investigations'* handling of language games, the public character of language, and the nature of philosophical puzzles may be to some, to others these treatments range between the tiresome and the trivial. On the other hand, the *Tractatus* almost without question is a brilliant and stimulating work. Comparing it with the *Investigations,* one is inclined to accept Russell's appraisal (1959) of the two works: One might well suspect that the Vienna Circle took the better part of Wittgenstein and left to the Oxford therapists what, by contrast, is the dross.

But the issue does not by any means resolve to an appraisal of Wittgenstein's work. Natural language, to be sure, is significant to the empiricist. Regardless of his efforts to stiffen grammatical rules and to remove the vernacular, the empiricist must resort to ordinary language. And it is then that what he writes or tries to say is subject most to philosophical pitfalls. No one has been more persistent, nor more persuasive than Carnap in the matter. Yet, quite generally we find that the analysts disdain efforts to bring formal as well as ordinary language into the analytic picture. Certainly our logics, our calculi, are invented for good reasons; they enable us to avoid some of the snares concealed within the use of ordinary language.

Still, even this is not a reason to reject linguistic analysis. Nothing precludes the analyst from confronting the issues that are of interest to the scientist and the traditional empiricist. What is distressing is the paucity of critique and analysis concerning issues within the philosophy of science. It is not enough to be told that the old problems of philosophy are not problems after all. We should like to know more of the status and role of scientific theory as concerns empirical knowledge. What, for example, is the analysis of causality and determinism within physics and biology? What are the possibilities of meaning here? And what of logic and metalogic? How do we analyze the search for consistency and completeness? What of probability and inductive inference? Are there alternatives to operational treatments of probability? How can probability be applied to singular decisions? Finally, what are the limits and meaningful aspects of the mind–body problem as it applies to an empirical science of psychology? With notable exceptions, the analysts are silent.

Thus the information that there are no problems of philosophy, that all our perplexities succumb to therapeutic analysis within the natural language comes as a precious but dessicated condolence, when science and logic are presently so gravid with controversy. Indeed there is something perverse about our being told all problems of philosophy are solved, even if they are linguistic problems. One suspects that not all problems are linguistic. But even for those problems that are, the type of analysis that passes as therapeutic does not appear to make robust contributions to their solutions.

Certainly it can be argued that there is an important function for analysis to fulfill. Of this there is no question. Every philosopher should be analytic; and perhaps all first rate empiricists have been. The point is, however, that analysis should not become an end in itself, a Zeitgeist sucking up the very ablest of students into a gurge of linguistic scholasticism. And indeed, it should not be intimated that all of English empiricism is analytic in this pejorative sense. Philosophy at Cambridge, for example, has never been uniformly given to analysis, despite the presence of Moore, Wittgenstein, and Wisdom. None of these people have claimed to be analysts.

The argument here is that linguistic analysis has contributed little to the philosophy of science and not that it does not have a contribution to make to the philosophy of knowledge. Abraham Kaplan has poignantly expressed what, I feel, are rather general misgivings:

> Yet there is a certain clarity and vigor that its intellectualism gives to analytic philosophy, something clean and fresh, which allows us for once to breathe deep without being choked by the smog of so much European and Asian obscurantism. At the same time, I cannot help but feel that there is something seriously wrong with a philosophy, in the mid-twentieth century, that takes no notice of war, revolution, nationalism, nuclear energy, the exploration of space, or anything else distinctive of the life of our time save the magnificent sweep of the intellect in the achievements of pure science and mathematics (1961, p. 115).

Kaplan writes of all philosophical analysts. So far as the linguistic analysts are concerned even the pure science and mathematics are largely ignored.

Sympathetic accounts of philosophical (linguistic) analysis can be found in Malcolm (1952), Warnock (1958), A. J. Ayer (ed.) (1956), Ryle (1945). Critical accounts can be found in Blanshard (1952, 1962), Heath (1952, 1956), J. O. Wisdom (1959), Gellner (1959).

# PART II

# Psychology and the
## Philosophy of Science

# CHAPTER 7

# The Contents of Science

THE FOREGOING DISCUSSIONS of the foundations, limits, and possibilities of knowledge have brought us to the front of scientific empiricism. The way has not been easy, it has not always been free of misgivings. But from Locke to Kant to Wittgenstein we have been assured that the important problems of knowledge have been dissolved. It remains only for the scientist to get on with his work, to marshal fact and law and theory, and thence to cut the heart out of metaphysics. This is a sanguine picture, to say the least. After all, no layman need eavesdrop in order to learn of the scandals of science. The difficulties are advertised freely. Yet they are not difficulties that send us into epistemological retreat. Nor need they invite us to reconsider intuitionism as a significant alternative to empiricism.

## ON THE QUEST OF SCIENCE

What is it then that gives to science its endowment of epistemic privilege? One will not be much rewarded here by reviewing descriptions of what science is, or even descriptions of what it is that scientists do. Rather, he comes more directly to face the special status of science by considering what are the aims of science and what, at least, are the pretensions of its achievements. Whatever science is, its commitment to logic and observation have earned for it the fullest measure of public support. Its systematized knowledge, its methodological explorations of first principles, its reliance upon data seem somehow to bring to the person answers often more satisfying than any others he receives. As a rule, he does not question the "findings" of science. Facts, it would appear, are indubitable, even though they may not tell all the observer wants to know. But what is more important, science provides a kind of closure to curiosity; it gives answers that put an end to the person's search for meanings and explanations.

Observations and data, law, theory, and the rare synthesis of one theory within another theory: all these give comfort to the curious. These are the rewards of science. What is more, they provide answers to our incipient ontological enquiries. Whether the problem being considered is the machinery that makes the clock go round or the cosmologist's search for the origins of the universe, or whether it is even the psychologist's looking for the mechanism of perceptual constancy, the specific quest is always the same—a description of the world "as it really is." On first impression, we all seem to be realists. When the child sees the internal mechanism of the clock with its springs and gears, he is satisfied that there is no mystery to the rotating hands. If the cosmologist pursues the retreating galaxies for one more clue to an evolving universe, he is likely to think of himself as learning what the universe is, or was, really like. And if the psychologist sees perceptual invariance emerging from neural integration over equivalence classes of input, he is likely to put aside his heuristic devices and proclaim the truth as to the real nature of perception. Such satisfying states of knowledge have this in common: they bring the inquirer close to some kind of microstructure that lies concealed behind the larger phenomenon. That microstructure is what reality is.

By temperament, then, it would seem that scientists at first are realists. For them, the quest itself is real. True explanations lie behind the confusion, uncertainty, and unknowns concerning man's present state of knowledge. Although the most recent theories are subject to revision, or may yield to entirely new formulations, and even though each new experiment may provide only tentative conclusions, the postulate of terminal truth appears to be implicit—as if the quest should end eventually with apodictic success and allow the researcher to move on to other inquiries.

I say only at first brush with fact and theory do scientists appear to be realists. For soon doubt creeps into the picture. The road to scientific progress is bestrewn with the "debris of antiquated ideas." Concepts that once were held with confidence become the discarded relics of many presumptive worlds. The psychologist's entelechies, his instincts and faculties, join the calorics, the electric fluids, and aethers in our museums of scientific heirlooms. Nowadays we are more amused than impressed to learn that Newton could retire early from his memorable career in science because he felt the important truths were known, or to learn that Kant could proclaim that the absolute nature of time and space are forever embedded in the perceiving mind, or to learn that even today some scientists pronounce that the frontiers of microphysics are exhausted with only a few details remaining to be added. We are much too sensitive to the fragility of our theories and, alas, of our convictions to invest much faith in enduring scientific conceptions.

But there is another factor that is even more disconcerting to the naive realist. As the grain of microstructure is further refined, the hypotheses become further and further removed from the data that are their support. In physics there are technological and perhaps logical barriers to penetrating the hypothesized microstructures. All palpable properties of the material world evaporate. Cloud chamber tracks, scintillations, and Geiger counts are distant cousins to the postulated "entities" which compose the flesh of a theoretical calculus. Rather than a corpus we have a wraith incarnate in a deductive system, looking much more like an "idea" than any of the familiar grains of sand.

In psychology the logical barriers to microknowledge may not exist, but technology still does not permit our probing the fine structure of the nervous system. Like the physicist, the psychologist may turn to invention, indeed, even preferring it, say, to crude excursions into neuroanatomy. A system can be built with hypothetical entities having no more initial credence than the prospect that their theoretical role may lead to the deduction of confirmable hypotheses. It may even be that microphysiology is an encumbrance, since so little of it is known. Thus, a feeling of emancipation comes to a theorist who can say that theoretical constructs "need have no truth character at all" (Kendler, 1952). And among other strategies, he may proceed, as the cyberneticist does, to sketch out functional components of a system of behavior without specifying how any one of the components necessarily implements that function. Only the eventual output counts.

## CONVENTIONALISM VERSUS REALISM

We have breathed this air of conventionalism before. Science should not be so pretentious. It should be more modest in its aims, and leave to metaphysics all matters of ontology. The caution comes from positivism itself. Statements about the real world are hardly ever subject to test; either direct verification of an hypothesis is impossible, or the assumptions of verification are in doubt. Tests of theoretical constructs are always in terms of material implications, i.e., of *if–then* propositions. Therefore, the confirmation of the consequent is never sufficient to establish the truth of the theoretical antecedent. Only disconfirmation is straightforward. Furthermore, all tests of hypotheses are subject to qualifications. One always makes assumptions which, themselves, are not subject to test in the given experiment. If the assumptions are suspect, they may be subject to revision, with a subsequent discard or a reinterpretation of the original data. Thus test results are seldom conclusive.

In brief the conventionalistic character of assumptions and theoretical terms suggests to us that the scientist may be more concerned with predictive ingenuity than he is with "truth" or "the real," neither of which have proved enduring or accessible. In the words of Poincaré, certain conventions prove convenient for describing the processes underlying events. We should no more ask whether they are true than "ask if the metric system is true, and if the old weights and measures are false; if Cartesian co-ordinates are true and polar co-ordinates false" (1905, p. 50; and cf. N7.1).

The story is more familiar in physics than it is in psychology. This is because physics has a large number of formal theories that postulate theoretical entities only indirectly related to observation. Quite frequently the psychologist avoids speculating about internal processes intervening between observable states of the organism, between stimulus and response. Or, if he engages in any conceptual activities, he is likely to adopt constructs that are explicitly reducible to sets of observation terms such that the given construct is no more than a convenient means of designating a complex of data. Only rarely does he venture into the realm of microstructure wherein theoretical entities are postulated to explain behavior, not in terms of what is observed and given, but in terms of what might be in order that the data of behavior should be what they are. Now in physics the story is different. We come much more quickly to face problems of microstructure. Molar descriptions will not suffice, nor will the correlations of a crude empirical chemistry. We need to enter the smallest structure of matter in order to ascertain what it is that determines the binding and disintegrative properties of matter.

As is well known, the fine-grain constructs are "as-if" entities; they are not observed but are betrayed, as it were, by events quite gross on the observational scale. The structure of the hydrogen atom was initially inferred from scintillations on zinc sulphide screens, and from spectrograms. No nucleus, no electron of the atom was ever photographed, just tell-tale tracks in the ionized gas of a cloud chamber. Nor has the fine structure of a crystalline solid been photographed; all we have are gross patterns of reflected light. We say that the theoretical entities are "as-if" constructs, because the data suggest that it is *as if* there was such an atomic structure, or that it is *as if* atoms are arranged in Bragg planes (cf. N7.2). One cannot say that a theoretical construct is definitely true, for alternative constructions of theoretical entities may serve just as well to suggest the events. And it may be that no experiment can decide the issue among alternatives.

When he enters the labyrinths of mathematics, the physicist doubtless gives little thought to any hard-core reality. As Dirac has said, the physicist must get over thinking in terms of pictures and concrete models, and rather accept his constructs as possessing significance only in the context of an abstract, unconcretized mathematical model (cf. N7.3). He seems hardly concerned with questions such as: what is the world really like? or, where is the electron at this very moment? or, is a smallest particle hard like a grain of sand? Philosophers in turn have wondered whether theoretical constructs picture facts at all and whether the physicist has not entered into a world of disciplined fictionizing.

We need, therefore, to have another look at realism, or at least at the ontological status of theoretical terms. Are we playing games? Are we inventing convenient prediction machines? Or, do our constructs take the measure of a more substantial world? Second thoughts are likely to be sobering. An increasing number of empiricists maintain that existence propositions (these propositions have always been problematic) are not uniquely different from propositions about hypothetical entities (cf. N7.4). We attribute existence to an object if there is a set of observations which is taken as testimony to the real, not illusory, presence of the object. In other words, existence prescribes evidential bases for asserting the object. But then, are not theoretical terms used in just this kind of context? To assert the theoretical entity is to prescribe a set of observations which are evidential to the entity. In fact, it is very likely that the theory incorporating the theoretical entity has, through deductive inference, led precisely to the search for some evidential support in behalf of that entity. Photographs are not the objects they report, but they are evidential bases for objects occupying some slice of time and space. If we observe that the hands of a clock move and hear the ticking of the clock's escapement, we are satisfied as to the existential status of its mechanical guts. The existential extension of our world at any given time exceeds our immediate data. Perceptually, we process only minimal cues, the rest of the construction is done by inference. One cannot conceive what it would be like to perceive each and every detail of the composite event—not only, for example, to witness another person's smile, but to perceive the state of each and every cell that composes that person's being. Even the smile is evidence for an hypothesis—an hypothesis, say, about some interpersonal attitude. That attitude is no less real because it cannot be pointed to directly, as we can "point to" the worm in the case of the jumping bean.

We are led then to reconsider the status of our theoretical terms. The descent into microstructure has meant that we have had to give up formulating existential propositions in terms of simple empiric equivalences. The data suggest what we would assert, but only indirectly; yet, the data-inference rubric itself spells out what it is we mean to assert by our maintaining existential status for our theoretical constructs. Could we separate the data from the hypothesis, the case might be more clear-cut for separating the two into exclusive epistemic classes. But this cannot be done. The state of one's knowledge, his hypothesis, if you will, indicates how the complex of data input is to be processed—what, for example, is to be the figure and what, the ground. It takes training, i.e., hypothesis, to read an electro-encephalogram, just as the star in the cloud chamber photograph can only be existentially read by a person conversant in the field of cosmic ray research. The student who is new to his science is blind to the facts put before him. He has to learn to see what is in the microscope, he has to learn to detect the significant patterns in an oscilloscope—just as a music student must learn to detect harmonic structure in a musical composition. One does not just open his eyes and see, he brings with him perceptual hypotheses. Otherwise, he remains blind to facts.

One other comment should be made before we leave this preview on theoretical entities. Existence and existential status carry overtones of permanence. The evidential basis of our data should not signify one thing at one phase of hypothesis and another thing at another. The rhythmic pattern of the electro-encephalogram, for example, cannot be the evidential basis for *both* spontaneous electro-cortical response *and* mechanical vibrations of the brain substance. The red-shift in the galactic spectrum cannot indicate *both* a static *and* an expanding universe. The state of our knowledge determines how we interpret the data, what hypothesis we bring to them, and consequently, what the real world is like at any given time. Why speak of the real world or existential status at all? Why not accept the predicament and acknowledge all constructions to be ephemeral? And what of alternative theoretical entities bound to the same data complexes? These are sticky ontological problems. However, much of their apparent difficulty resides in our naive commitment to simple empirical equivalences (again, like our looking for the worm in the jumping bean). Nevertheless, hypotheses do affect what we perceive and hypotheses do determine how we construct entities out of data. A good hypothesis is one that serves to crystallize data into the meaningful configuration we call the entity. One does not claim permanence for his entities but only that in any given historical context those "entities" serve unambiguously and consistently as approximations to the real. To be sure our ideas, even the most basic ones like those of force and motion, are subject to modification with the changing state of our knowledge. Yet they change not so much because we were mistaken but because at any given time the data and hypothesis are such that just this particular construction should be given to the world and not another. One does not catalogue his textbooks of biology and physics as fiction because he knows in time their hypotheses will be outmoded. There is an element of time-boundedness in existence, and in truth, just as Margenau and Whitehead, for example, have pointed out.


## LAWS OF NATURE

When scientists speak the word "nature" they often do so with just a touch of reverence, as if "she" is that cosmic entity hiding a treasury of secrets for us to share piece by experimental piece. And it is not always clear whether or not they are speaking metaphorically. What are laws? On initial inspection the question resolves to whether nature, the cosmic entity, conforms to some *a priori* set of regularities which do in fact detail the cosmic processes, or to whether laws are man-created generalizations which facilitate both his description of his world and his predictions concerning specifiable events in certain familiar surrounds. Are laws true descriptions? Or are they conventions? No doubt our metaphorical predilections commit us to think of laws in terms of cosmic decrees. Events must obey laws; indeed, they have no alternative. However, one need not think of decrees and cosmic agents to support this view. Mechanists and determinists may arrive at such a position merely by assuming that lawfulness is a characteristic of the given universe.

Now it takes but little reflection for us to reject this metaphysical point of view. The scientist inclines more toward methodology than metaphysics. He may proceed as if he believes there are cosmic regularities, but his belief is hardly more than a procedural agreement. The history of his subject reveals that laws are subject to revision, disconfirmation, and withdrawal. They are more like hypotheses than decrees. He uses them to predict, not necessarily to command. An event that violates a law of nature is still an event. It is the law that must yield.

In this context, two comments from the philosophy of science are worthy of attention. One, the certainty that man finds compelling belongs only to logic. Events themselves, though their relations may be expressed in a language of rigorous syntax, are not compelled to follow any prescribed pattern. As we have seen, a purely empirical contingency is the basis of Humean skepticism. And two, laws are adopted as instruments of understanding and prediction. In this context they have been called "inference tickets" (Ryle, 1949; Kneale, 1949); but happy as the phrase may be, this is not quite the appropriate metaphor. Rather, laws are the credentials which enable the scientist to justify asserting his expectations. Laws, therefore, assume a personal reference. They are the expressions of our states of knowledge, they are not ontological contracts held to be binding upon nature.

The issues here are not so poignantly drawn in psychology as they are in physics. Psychologists need little persuasion as to the provisional character of their laws. Laws of learning, of reinforcement, contiguity, and recency, for example, are hardly more than empirical surveys of certain classes of learning experiments. The fact that a law like that of reinforcement has only limited extension over the range of all possible learning situations is implicit in the prevalence of two-factor learning theories. And the Weber-Fechner law, $S = k \log R$, offers a classic example of the well-tempered law.

As is well known, the Weber–Fechner law, which prescribes that perceived intensity over scales such as loudness or brightness varies directly with the logarithm of the intensity of the physical stimulus, holds only for the intermediate range of intensity. The law breaks down at the extremes.

That is to say, the law is a useful generalization over a certain range of stimuli but not over others. It is for the psychophysicist to determine the range of application by experiment, and not to pronounce, as Fechner did, that some underlying principle of nature had been defined (cf. N7.5).

Laws are useful, then, as devices of inference, but they are to be tempered, as it were, by the search for their extensions. Thus, like theoretical constructions, they have a conventional character; they are inventions that serve as hypotheses concerning events. But as before, one need not conclude that laws are thereby unreal. To say a law is true is merely to say that there is a class of events for which the lawlike statement serves as a convenient summarization.

## THEORIES

If, ontologically speaking, theoretical entities and laws have only a contextual status, then theories, too, can be interpretably real only in the context of convention and procedural agreements. Is a theory a picture of the world? Is it some description of actual events? Or is it a model and deductive system by means of which we infer lawful relations among observables? A theory could, of course, be both a picture of an actual world *and* a deductive system. Yet, if we are not careful we will impart to our naive phenomenology the properties of the deductive system. This temptation to reify fails us in matters concerning laws and hypothetical entities. All the more reason, then, that it should fail for theory.

Though ultimately concerned with data, theories begin with conventions, laws, and rules of inference. Only somewhat belatedly does a dictionary tie the theory to the world of experiment. The foremost considerations are that the theory be consistent and comprehensive. It must protect against generating contradictory hypotheses; it must have a secure foundation in tested scientific traditions. But of the truth of a theory, one may only speak with reservation. Theories are useful and they are "contextually true," but only to the extent they generate well-confirmed hypotheses. Their extension is empirically determined and provisional. They make no claim to an absolute truth status that would enable us to prejudge the world and retire from the ontological quest.

Yet, at some critical point each well-supported theory may be disconfirmed. The false hypothesis condemns it; and the temptation may be great to declare the theory false and ourselves, in that moment of humble reckoning, mistaken. To succumb abjectly, however, would itself be a mistake. The history of science would show us that no theory can be true in any lasting sense, for no theory endures without modification. Should we then presume that science can make no claims for any special epistemic resource?

The mistake here is to confuse enduring logical truths with contingent factual ones. One expects that logical truths will endure throughout all time; he cannot conceive what it would mean to say that the laws of arithmetic or those of syllogistic inference might be disconfirmed, for data have no part in logic. This is not true, however, in the domain of fact and theory. It is the nature of fact that it should be subject to revision. To the scientific empiricist, fact is inseparable from theory. It is an hypothesis, a conjecture germinated in theory, which guides the scientist in his search for evidence. What kind of world one finds is determined by what kind of structure that world is assumed to have. Rather than facts standing alone to be discovered at the blink of an eyelid, they emerge only in conceptual focus. They are the product of the theory and its dictionary, for it is the latter which conjointly direct the evidential search. The events, the data, the facts that reward the sophisticated exploration may have an identity of their own which evokes their special credence; but nonetheless, that identity is inseparable from the conceptual framework. To alter a theory, even to reject it, is ultimately to alter, even to reject, the fact. A rejected theory is thrust aside not so much because "the" facts belie it as because alternative theories with new conceptions extend the factual interpretation of the available data. Thus the world is no longer flat, nor does the sun revolve about the earth, nor do objects in motion seek their natural position. Yet each of these at some time was the fact of observant men. There are innumerable examples wherein a new conceptual-factual context introduces a different excursion into reality.

No obvious advantage accrues to us in trying to force this treatment of the truth status of theories into traditional philosophical molds. It is better to do as Campbell (1921) and Toulmin (1953) recommend: reserve the language of truth for matters of logic where its use is nearly unequivocal. Theories, rather, should be regarded as "holding" over the range of facts which their hypotheses generate. They are the instruments for deriving experimental hypotheses, the truths of which are attested to by the data. The only danger inherent in this language is the suggestion that the instrumentality should be regarded any the less real because it does not translate directly into the truth functional language which our simple empiricistic conventions dictate. Yet, when we learn to accept the contingent character of all empirical propositions and the inseparability of fact and conceptual framework, we will appreciate the suggestion that strict truth-reductive translations are not appropriate to the language of science.

## SCIENTIFIC EXPLANATION

No doubt the retreat of the scientific empiricist from naive realism is a source of amusement to his critics. It is also a source of embarrassment when he hears his confrère adopt the language of fictionalism to describe tasks of theory construction and scientific explanation. This freedom of invention is the heritage of pragmatism, and like pragmatism it too has been interpreted as sheer license happily purchased by the coin of clever people. However, a close reading of Charles Peirce or even of William James (and of contemporary instrumentalists such as Nagel) would reveal that the emphasis upon fiction misrepresents the case for scientific invention. One needs only reflect upon the character of scientific explanation.

In general, events are explained by one of two strategies: by instantiation, or by higher order deductions. In the one case, a particular event is expressed as some particular value of a variable in a general proposition (law); in the other, the law, of which the event is a particular instance, may itself be a hypothesis deducible from within a theory. In neither case does one have the fictionist's freedom to construct just any explanation that aesthetic whim may dictate. Theories, for example, contain laws, theoretical constructs, a logical calculus, and a dictionary. To a large extent the calculus and the theoretical terms are inventions. There may also be a conventional element in the statements of laws and the dictionary. However, in no case are the inventions peremptory. They reflect the factual conceptual traditions of the given science. They also reflect the selective principles of comprehensiveness and simplicity which, at a more subtle level of ontology, are the guides to theoretic evaluation and theoretic convergence.

It is one of the interesting speculations of conventionalists that every theory is salvagable. This is a corollary of fictionalism. But no one, not even Pierre Duhem (cf. N7.6), has thereby argued that every theory is worth saving. The complex hierarchy of many scientific theories makes some particular set of constructions preferable to another. It is well known that Ptolemy, Tycho Brahe, and Copernicus could each provide a model of the solar system, each with a different set of constructs, and each with confirmational success. Yet, the construction eventually selected was the one that fitted most readily into a more comprehensive system. Kepler and Newton assured us what kind of inventions would be eligible for scientific license. And the issue of the freedom of invention was thereby closed.

When we turn to the idea of a hierarchy of explanation, we especially realize there is a guidance implicit within scientific invention. One seeks not only an explanation of a particular set of events but also a theoretical construction that itself is derivable from within some still more basic science. Chemical explanations, for example, were conceived in terms wholly unique to the phenomenology of chemistry itself. But the advantages and the guidance of atomic constructions are now all too apparent. Geneticists could have continued to think in terms of the gross characteristics of genotypes, but the molecular models of biochemistry offered explanations of the duplicative powers of the genes. And psychology can continue to build hypothetico-deductive models in learning theory, knowing (perhaps unconsciously) that issues of alternative theories will be resolved by developments in neurophysiology.

Perhaps nowhere in science are the issues of reductionism and of the hierarchy of explanation more debated than they are in psychology. The gap between psychology and any lower order discipline is wider than that between any other set of hierarchical cousins. One can feel comfortable in reducing thermodynamics to statistical mechanics, or genetics to biochemistry, or even meteorology to thermodynamics. It is "natural" to seek their respective reductive explanations. But it is a long way indeed from behavior and the constructs of learning and personality theory to the microstructure of physiology. No one pretends to fit motivational or reinforcement theory into the family of hypotheses deducible within an extant neurophysiology.

Nevertheless, one suspects that disclaimers against reductionism and against the hierarchical scope of explanation are passing predilections. The psychologist must implement explanations of behavior by chains of inference mediating between observables. If he is theoretical at all, he must make constructual conjectures; their locale can only be the organism itself. One does not claim, therefore, that psychologists should be physiologists. But lest the psychologist think he need only contrive heuristic gimmicks, he should be reminded that it will be the lower order science that will eventually dictate the veridical selection from among alternative constructions. As between stimulus and response there is the mediating process. One can model that process in any way he chooses, but there is a sense in which there is an "actual" microstructure. It is that set of descriptions which will be deducible within a mature next-order discipline. It is in the hierarchical context of explanation that one can indeed make claim for ontological convergence.

# NOTES

## NOTE 7.1

As a philosopher of science, Poincaré (1905, 1913, 1914) has gained renown for his exposition of the conventionalistic implications of positivism. Since direct verification of theories is not possible, the status of theories must be couched in terms of their success and convenience in accounting for the data. The "hypothesis" of science is an invention. It predicates how we are to look at things; that is, how we are to represent events and how we are to construct the world that underlies appearances.

Because of the contingent status of science, conventionalists have at times been accused of being rather flippantly arbitrary about serious matters. But a reading of Poincaré's popular philosophical works reveals that he was considerably more cautious and conservative than the reader is likely to assume on first acquaintance with the off-hand relativism that seems to characterize his treatment of time and space. "It is not nature which imposes them [the frames of time and space] upon us, it is we who impose them upon nature because we find them convenient" (1913, p. 13). This seems to set the tenor of his work. And it is supplemented by the fact that he stresses intuition and not logic or observation as the source of mathematical and scientific invention. Yet Poincaré was critical of any treatment of conventionalism which would lead to a radical nominalism. He contends against his contemporary LeRoy who argues that conventionally "the scientist creates the fact." Certainly there are limitations to observation, and certainly we are unable either to perceive or to comprehend total pictures, but this is no reason to conclude that what we do comprehend and conventionally construct is either an unreal or a distorted picture of the world.

Language is conventional, it is also the source of invention; for

> . . . without this language most of the intimate analogies of things would have remained forever unknown to us; and we should forever have been ignorant of the internal harmony of the world, which is, we shall see, the only true objective reality (1913, p. 13).

Then speaking directly to LeRoy, Poincaré writes:

> Some people have exaggerated the role of convention in science; they have gone so far as to say that law, that scientific fact itself, was created by the scientist. This is going much too far in the direction of nominalism. No, scientific laws are not artificial creations; we have no reason to regard them as accidental, though it be impossible to prove they are not. Does the harmony the human intelligence thinks it discovers in nature exist outside of this intelligence? No, beyond doubt a reality completely independent of the mind which conceives it, sees it or feels it would for us be forever inaccessible. But what we call objective reality is in the last analysis what is common to many thinking beings and could be common to all; this common part, we shall see, can only be the harmony expressed by mathematical laws (1913, p. 14).

Moreover Poincaré distinguishes between the conventions of mathematical representations and the postulates of science itself. One does not ask of a geometry whether it is true.

> *The geometrical axioms are therefore neither synthetic a priori intuitions nor experimental facts.* They are conventions. Our choice among all possible conventions is *guided* by experimental facts; but it remains *free,* and is limited only by the necessity of avoiding every contradiction . . . What, then, are we to think of the question: Is Euclidean geometry true? It has no meaning. We might as well ask if the metric system is true and if the old weights and measures are false; if Cartesian co-ordinates are true and polar co-ordinates false. One geometry cannot be more true than another; it can only be more convenient (1905, p. 50).

On the other hand, physical postulates, such as the law of inertia, are descriptions of ideal states of affairs. They may serve as useful conventions for making calculations, but they are in a sense subject to empirical check. In other words, it is conceivable that a state of affairs might obtain which would entail our rejecting the postulate. This is a useful distinction, but the example of geometric representation of space is perhaps ill chosen. Astronomical data at present are thought relevant to determining whether our space is Euclidean or Riemannian. Poincaré does wish to assert, however, that the truth of Euclidean propositions, as such, in no way is contingent upon the properties of our own space.

## NOTE 7.2

In the philosophy of science, discussions of theoretical entities often take atomic physics as their reference. It is here that the bombardment of particles culminates in the cloud chamber photographs whose gross detail supports our impression of a world composed of fragile billiard balls. But from the tracks made by the minute condensations of water vapor to the inferred structure of the atom is a tortuous inferential path.

Another example of theoretical inference, simpler in detail yet of equal subtlety, is that involving crystalline structure. The pattern of inference is ingenious and is perhaps worthy of more attention than expositors in the philosophy of science have given it.

Until the early part of this century, crystallography was, for the most part, a descriptive science. Considerable knowledge had been gained from classifying different types of crystals, observing their properties, and even formulating lattice networks in which to describe the structure of the crystal. Little attention had been given to the internal structure of crystals other than to assume that homogenous sets of molecules, or atoms, which seek a minimal state of potential energy tend to arrange themselves in regular assemblies so as to minimize their volume of occupancy. This was a matter of speculation. Was there any means of inferring the dimensions of the intracrystalline structure itself?

In 1912 Max von Laue proposed an experiment in which a crystal was to be treated as a diffraction grating on the basis of its molecular structure. Although the purpose of the experiment was to detect the wave properties of x rays rather than crystalline structure as such, the subsequent contribution to crystal analysis was a notable one. The actual argument is a simple one to grasp. If it is assumed that the molecules of zincblende, say, are arranged regularly along sets of planes, then the sets of molecules in the strata of planes should serve to diffract light as a diffraction grating does. First, consider diffraction effects. When any physical wave front (air, water, light) meets a barrier with a relatively small aperture, the wave front squeezes through, as it were, only to fan out as a diffraction front as it emerges. An essential condition is that the aperture be small relative to the wave length (the space between successive wave crests). Now, if we have series of such apertures or slits, such as is the case in a diffraction grating, light passing through those slits is diffracted according to the spacing of the slits (usually 15,000 to 30,000 slits per inch of grating surface) and the wave length of the incident light. Light of different wave lengths is differentially diffracted. Consequently, the grating diffracts sunlight just as a prism does. If we mount the grating in a reflecting spectroscope, as in Figure 7.1, we note that a source of light from S hits the grating G at an angle of incidence equal to *i,* and an adjustable focal target F determines an angle of diffraction $\theta$. By adjusting F we find the image of S diminishes and decreases in brightness as a function of this angle $\theta$. The reason for this is that the wave front from S strikes A on G before it does B. In

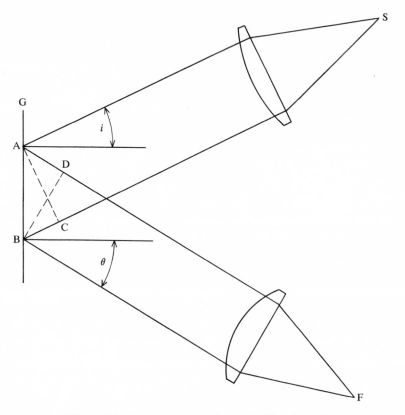

**Figure 7.1**   Spectroscopic analysis of diffraction effects

fact the distance BC measures the extent of *retardation.* The wave front emerges from A before it does from B, and its diffracted retardation is equal to AD. One gets the brightest image at F if the sum (or difference) of the retardation effects is such that the successive wave fronts from G reinforce one another (i.e., superimpose trough upon trough and crest upon crest). This relationship can be expressed by the equation

$$AD - BC = b\,(\sin i - \sin \theta),$$

where optimal images are obtained at values of $\theta$ such that AD − BC is equal to some whole number times the wave length. The details of this sketch are not difficult; what is important for the subsequent argument is the fact that if one knows the wave length of the incident light and the angles $i$ and $\theta$ he can determine $b$, *the distance between slits on the grating.*

Turning now to an analysis of crystalline structure, let us visualize the particles of a crystal arranged equidistantly along a plane A, as in Figure 7.2. Each particle serves as a reflector such that it radiates light in all directions. However, it is only along the wave front P'C that the crests reinforce one another. As in a mirror, the angle of reflection $r$ equals the angle of incidence $i$.

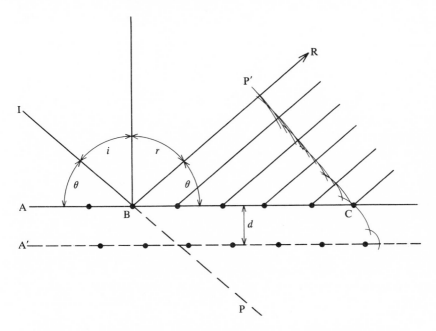

**Figure 7.2** Scattering of waves for the analysis of crystalline structure.

Suppose now we consider another array of particles on plane A'. Although the new set of radiating crests from the plane A' is not shown, they will not reinforce those from the plane A unless the following relationship holds:

$$n\lambda = 2d \sin \theta,$$

that is to say, unless some multiple of the wave length is equal to twice the product of the sine of the glancing angle $\theta$ and the distance $d$ between lattice planes. This amounts to saying that $n\lambda$ is a quantity representing the magnitude of retardation of incident light as between adjacent lattice planes. The image in the direction of R is optimal only when $n$ is some whole number.

Let us now consider the problem of inferring the structure of the crystal. We would like to determine the distance $d$ between lattice planes when $\lambda$ is known and when $\theta$ is chosen such that the image from the several planes reflected is optimal in the direction R. This is easily determined by

$$d = \frac{n\lambda}{2 \sin \theta}.$$

If the incident light is adjusted such than an optimal image is obtained at its primary reflection R, then $n = 1$ and the calculation of $d$ is straightforward.

This is a simplified picture of what actually occurs. First, it only shows the wave front advancing in the plane of the page. Second, troughs of reinforcement occur on more than a single front. Hence, in the second, third, and higher orders of reflection, one finds the effects of the usual diffraction patterns. And third, in order to obtain the actual data one must pass an x ray through a crystal which is rotated upon its own axis. As different planes and glancing angles $\theta$ come into play, unique patterns of cancellation and reinforcement are generated on a cylindrical photographic emulsion. This is known as the technique of a rotation photograph. The resulting photograph presents a gridlike matrix of darkened spots, i.e., of reinforcement nodes. From it, one can infer the distances between possible lattice planes and thereby construct the interatomic spacing within the crystal itself.

What is interesting here is the fact that structure is inferred from photographic data none of which actually pictures the crystalline structure itself. Only indirectly do we arrive at the nature of the crystal. And then only by initiating assumptions that are not at the moment testable. For example, we assume that x rays are wavelike. We also assume certain regularities in the transmission and reflection of the waves, to say nothing of the assumptions concerning the apparatus and the character of the x rays themselves. Only then do we proceed to deduce the data on the basis of our crystalline model.

Doubtless the crystallographer has other good reasons for assuming the latticelike arrangement of particles in a crystal. That is another story. What is significant is that he infers details of a structure that cannot itself be observed directly, and that cannot be constructed without his making assumptions of a particular atomic world and of an explicit crystalline model. Should one note the laminated character of mica, he may well appreciate the postulated arrangement of molecules. But flakes of the mica crystal are not evidence for the particular model being tested. Much less real, it would seem, is that large-scale recording of a somewhat regular distribution of dark spots on a white background which the rotation photograph displays.


## NOTE 7.3

In the preface to his *Quantum Mechanics,* P. A. M. Dirac writes:

> The classical tradition has been to consider the world to be an association of observable objects (particles, fluids, fields, etc.) moving about according to definite laws of force, so that one could form a mental picture in space and time of the whole scheme. This led to a physics whose aim was to make assumptions about the mechanism and forces connecting these observable objects, to account for their behavior in the simplest possible way. It has become increasingly evident in recent years, however, that nature works on a different plan. Her fundamental laws do not govern the world as it appears in one mental picture in any very direct way, but instead they control a substratum of which we cannot form a mental picture without introducing irrelevancies. The formulation of these laws requires the use of the mathematics of transformations. The important

things in the world appear as the invariants (or more generally the nearly invariants, or quantities with simple transformation properties) of these transformations. . . . The new theories, if one looks apart from their mathematical setting, are built up from physical concepts . . . which cannot even be explained adequately in words at all (1947, p. vii).

In this and other passages, Dirac is not arguing for a mere conventionalistic representation of the physical world. There is ontological significance to the fact that as we enter the world of microparticles, of photons and quantum effects, it is no longer possible to draw pictures or to visualize objects. Rather one must look for the invariant properties of mathematical expressions. What the language tells us is that underlying reality is remotely and subtly related to the world of objects with which we are familiar.

He also writes, "In order to give absolute meaning to size, such as is required for any theory of the ultimate structure of matter, we have to assume *that there is a limit to the fineness of our powers of observation and the smallness of the accompanying disturbance—a limit which is inherent in the nature of things and can never be surpassed by improved technique or increased skill on the part of the observer*" (1947, p. 3). Thus there is a point at which any conception of a material world that would postulate palpable properties of objects behind the barrier of observation is not just contradictory within the theory, it is both logically inconceivable and unreal.


## NOTE 7.4

The literature on the "existence" of hypothetical entities is extensive. We shall return to it later in the discussions concerning hypothetical constructs and intervening variables. However, in an important sense, the issue is more demanding in physics than in psychology. The physicist's examination of microstructures necessarily results in his reaching limits and barriers of observation. He cannot "illuminate" objects whose dimensions are of the order of the wave length of light. Such objects diffract the light, creating a penumbra of locale known to us as the uncertainty effects. Moreover, any effort to enhance our resolution of the object by using sources of illumination with shorter wave lengths increases the impact that such sources have on the submicroscopic structures being studied. Thus, there comes into play the complementary set of uncertainties under which simultaneous accuracies cannot be obtained for both position and momentum of a particle. (This, of course, is to say nothing of the technological limitations upon our even carrying out the "thought experiments" proposed by people like Bohr, Heisenberg, and Einstein.) Questions of existence, therefore, are more pressing to the physicist than to other scientists. He cannot produce palpable evidences in the way that other people can. Since the submicroscopic entities are necessarily inferred, the question arises whether such entities can be considered real at all. The temptation is great to consider them convenient fictions, with a different status than that we attribute to objects that are the direct reductions of sense data.

The ontological predicament with respect to submicroscopic entities has been discussed by Nagel (1961), Bergmann (1961), Hanson (1958, 1963),

Feyerabend (1958, 1962, 1963). Ontological predicaments must, however, succumb to linguistic analysis. What is an existence statement? What is "evidence for"? Are we asking for anything more than a classification of the logical status of hypothetical physical entities? For a nontechnical presentation of the issues from the point of view of linguistic analysis, see B. Mayo (1954). For a defense of realism built upon linguistic analysis see G. Maxwell (1962a,b) and J. J. C. Smart (1956, 1963).

Physicists themselves (e.g., Bohr, Heisenberg, Born) have been outstanding proponents of pragmatic instrumentalism. In an important book, *The Structure of Science* (1961) Ernest Nagel sees the issue as essentially a terminological one.

## NOTE 7.5

In recent years an alternative psychophysical law has been refined and emphasized by S. S. Stevens (1951). Rather than the Fechnerian logarithmic function, $S = k \log R$, he obtains a power function by varying the operational context of judgment. Thus, instead of requiring subjects to discriminate as between physical stimuli, Stevens requests that they make direct estimations of sensations as such. For example, a subject is given a reference stimulus and instructed to assign some arbitrary number of units to it, and then he is given a variable stimulus and is asked to adjust it until it is $\frac{1}{2}$, $\frac{1}{3}$, $\frac{1}{4}$, . . . units of the standard. Note that the units are not assigned physical weights; the scale is presumed to be strictly psychological. If the experimenter then plots the logarithm of judgment against the logarithm of stimulus intensity, he finds that the median judgments tend to plot on a straight line with slope $n$. The slope then determines the exponent for the appropriate psychophysical law:

$$S = k R^n$$

where $S$ and $R$ represent the values of sensation and stimulus intensity, respectively.

On examination the difference between the power and the logarithmic laws poses some interesting philosophical questions. Is one law correct, and the other incorrect? Is one just a better approximation to a true psychophysical relation than the other? Or, are there really two laws? And even perhaps more important, do the direct estimation procedures really get at subjective judgments in contrast to the response-oriented discriminations of the classical procedures?

These are interesting questions, and only peremptory responses can be given here. Doubtless the role of experimental instructions plays a part in these differences of laws. With respect to magnitude estimation, Stevens shows that direct estimation and classical discriminable difference techniques give different results. But with respect to the fractionation technique mentioned above and the classical technique for giving the plot of j.n.d.'s, it can be shown in some cases that the power and logarithmic measures are essentially equivalent. The difference is conventional. It depends upon whether one prefers to take $\Delta S$, the increment of sensational difference as a constant over the range of all physical intensities, or whether one wants to take the ratio $\Delta S/S$ as the constant. According to one's preference, he will obtain a logarithmic or a power law. In the one case, the constancy of $\Delta S$ means the equivalence of discriminable sensational differences over the range of physical stimuli. In the second case, the constancy relates to comparisons of sensation alone, not to stimulus intensities. Treisman (1962) has argued that the direct estimation (or "private data") hypothesis is not at all uniquely different from the traditional discrimination procedures. No operational test exists for choosing among the procedures. There is no reason to believe that direct estimation techniques come any nearer to quantifying the private data of consciousness than Fechnerian techniques.

Criticism of direct estimation from another quarter is discussed by Attneave (1962). Following up a suggestion by Garner (1954), he proposes that direct estimates utilize some numerical scale which, though undefined by the experimenter, is itself a psychophysical function. The magnitudes of numbers themselves are discriminable on a logarithmic scale, although in pure number theory the magnitude of the move from one number to its successor is the same throughout the set of all integers. When one takes into account judgment of the number continuum as itself a psychophysical function, then "the discrepancy between 'equal-interval' and 'direct magnitude' scales might disappear" (Attneave, 1962, p. 624).

The purpose of this digression is to show that putatively different laws may differ only with respect to their conventions. To this extent it is clear that ontological issues are not at stake. As Stevens and others argue, direct estimation techniques may possess certain advantages for scaling; but such pragmatic considerations should not be taken as a basis for arguing that we are dealing with essentially different realities in the two psychophysical procedures.

## NOTE 7.6

Pierre Duhem (1906), in a classical discussion, argues against the conclusiveness of experimental tests of hypotheses. He is especially critical of the notion of the "crucial experiment." No test can resolve theoretical controversies, first, because specific hypotheses cannot be isolated from the presumptive fabric of the total theory and, second, because any given hypothesis of the theory can be modified so as to alter the theory's testable consequences. Thus he writes:

> In sum, the physicist can never subject an isolated hypothesis to experimental test, but only a whole group of hypotheses; when the experiment is in disagreement with his predictions, what he learns is that at least one of the hypotheses constituting this group is unacceptable and ought to be modified; but the experiment does not designate which one should be changed (1914, p. 187).

He then proceeds to argue against the Newtonian inductive method of deducing integrative principles of theory from observations and established laws. Theoretical synthesis rests on the creative fruits of hunch and intuition, and not on logic. With respect to Ampère's preference for Newtonian inductivism, Duhem writes:

Very far from its being the case that Ampère's electrodynamic theory was *entirely deduced from experiment,* experiment played a very feeble role in its formation: it was merely the occasion which awakened the intuition of this physicist of genius and his intuition did the rest (1914, p. 199).

But if theories are freely modifiable, and intuition and ingenuity alone determine what conceptions the scientist is to introduce into his theoretical framework, how is one to judge which of the hypotheses ought to be abandoned? Duhem says "good sense" ought to be the judge. Unfortunately, discussions of good sense are likely to be no more incisive than those of intuition. As to the eventual choice among alternatives, all that Duhem can offer is faith that in the end good sense will prevail. "The day arrives when good sense comes out so clearly in favor of one of the two sides that the other side gives up the struggle even though pure logic would not forbid its continuation" (p. 218). One suspects that Duhem's own good sense led him to prefer formal simplicity.

In the writer's opinion, good sense for the conventionalists must eventually rest in preferences for hypotheses supporting theoretic convergence.

# CHAPTER 8

# The Language
# of Psychology

IT IS COMMON PRACTICE to title works in the philosophy of science as the language of this or that science. The analyst claims that all philosophical analysis is about language and therefore all analytic works should be so acknowledged. Unfortunately, this shifts attention from what it is we are trying to say to the language itself. By our attempting to show that philosophical puzzlement stems from linguistic muddles, we sometimes forget that there is a world of experience about which, we presume, there is something to say. Aside from syntactical conventions, we are concerned with problems of meaning. We feel on fairly safe ground when our expressions have explicit extension, when they point to recognizable "facts" and relations. We feel less sure when our expressions have intentions but no explicit set of defining events (cf. N8.1). Nevertheless, we encounter both types of expression in science, and presumably both have claim to anchorage in the indisputable data of experience.

In the language of psychology both types of expressions find their place. We initially speak of the data language, the observation language, the factual language. This is the language of the observables, of the dependent and independent variables as stated in formal expressions of empirical relationships. But we may also speak of the language of mediating processes and of mediating variables. Here factual reference becomes somewhat more remote. And for the empiricist, the lack of an immediate empirical reference for the mediating variable presents an occasion for some philosophical reflection. Even more remote are the languages of inference, constructs, and theory. They involve matters requiring special attention. Discussion of these languages will be deferred until later chapters. Here only the language appropriate to the variables of description and connection is considered.

# FACTUAL LANGUAGE

What is a fact? This is one of the most disarming of questions. At first glance it calls for a straightforward answer. "Facts are facts! Waste no time over the obvious, when there are really significant problems for the empiricist to contend with." It is as if we were to say that facts, like sense data, are the givens. The facts are given and the facts decide. But immediately it may occur to us that there is a difference between sense data, sense impressions, or whatever we would call the raw data of awareness, and the facts that are constructed of these raw data. Furthermore, we are a bit cautious about embracing the naive inductive method of our Baconian inference. According to Bacon we proceed from the enumeration and collation of similar facts to generalizations, laws, and other universal-like statements. Yet, we are immediately reminded that observation requires skill. An observer who could claim no other credentials than those of naïveté would see very little that would be of interest to the scientist (cf. N8.2).

Consider the factual language of behaviorism itself. From Watson on, behaviorists have concurred that the basic data of psychology are to be behavior itself. That the basic facts of psychology are to be publicly observed responses was taken so much for granted that few writers were to give more than passing attention to the concept of response itself. Strangely, however, psychologists who could reach significant methodological agreements differed as to the language of fact. Behaviorists generally have agreed that the response language is a molar rather than molecular language; it speaks of complex coordinations and movements of the organism rather than of reflexes and muscle twitches. Yet the terminology adopted by the theoretical behaviorists shows such diversity that we know it is impossible to separate the language of fact from that of a theory.

Recall the cat in the Thorndike puzzle box. It claws, bites, struggles, strikes, and finally escapes. Simple facts it would seem. Yet to Thorndike it was a random trial-and-error sequence of responses supported by an initial, instinctive, response-repertory; whereas to Tolman, such a sequence of events could be seen as a demonstration of persistence and "docility" culminating in the subject's responsive orientation toward its goal-objects (Tolman, 1932). Something in this behavioral situation is identical for the two observers and something is very different. It is as if the data are the same, but the facts differ. Yet even here we must speak as if the data are the unexpressed givens. When these data find expression in the language of fact, cognitive processes have transpired to transform them ontologically from their status of potentiality to one of actuality. One does indeed get a different picture of the data of behavior if he reads Tolman than, say, if he reads Thorndike, Guthrie, Hull, or Skinner. One gets a different picture of the primate's behavior if he reads Köhler, rather, say, than Yerkes or Harlow. And it is not necessarily the case that one is a better observer than another. The observers may differ only as to their theoretical dispositions. The argument over facts may very well turn upon which observer operates from the more defensible set of preconceptions.

The story now becomes the familiar and often trivial one of perceptual and cognitive relativism. It is the story of frames of reference (Sherif), of the new look in perception (Bruner, Goodman), of the cognitive structure (Lewin, Krech, Crutchfield), of psychological phenomenology (Koffka, MacLeod, Snygg, Combs). Explicitly told, it is as old as the Herbartian doctrine of apperception where "apperceiving attention is a combination of imagination, which works from within, and the sensation coming with external impression" (Herbart, 1898; p. 209).

The doctrine is so self-evident nowadays as to be a truism. We perceive according to our inclinations, our beliefs, predispositions, sets—according to our apperceptive mass. One does not arrive on the scene as a naive observer recording facts on a blank tablet wherein such facts are to repose in their own pristine integrity. Rather the data of pre-perception are neutral until configurated under the clutch of the apperceptive mass. Observation is not merely a matter of bringing data into the focus of awareness but rather one of assimilating them into the prevailing conceptual system of the person. Still, what is so obvious to the student of ordinary perception may appear less significant to the student of science. Facts of science are presumed to warrant a privileged status. They are often expected to transcend conceptual frames of reference. Koch, for example, directs his respondents to describe their empirical independent and dependent variables in a "theoretically neutral . . . immediate data language" (1959, p. 679); and a group of expositors of modern learning theory responded to the question, "Is the data language explicit and theoretically neutral?" as a touchstone of scientific sophistication (Estes et al., 1954, p. xviii).

Thus, it is thought that the facts of scientific observation can be quite different from the facts of everyday perception. The rigors of operational procedure, the checks, the precautions against bias, give to them a degree of reliability not found in the "facts" of the untutored observer. It is as if the scientist is tutored to overcome his biases and to safeguard against his preconceptions. Presumably, then, facts are to stand apart from the conceptual frameworks in which the observer operates. Operational procedures may prescribe certain conceptual limits for scientific facts, but then once the operational rules are accepted by conventionalistic agreements, the facts as thus derived should be neutral with respect to theoretical points of view converging on given experimental issues.

Now, one should suspect any such pretentions to factual neutrality as are suggested in the preceding paragraph. Historians and philosophers of science (e.g., Hanson, 1958; Feyerabend, 1962), students of language and knowledge (e.g., Whorf, 1956; Wittgenstein, 1953), as well as students of perception agree that factual statements are conceptually contaminated (cf. N8.3). How a scientist sees the world is no more a matter of veridical observation, *in any absolute sense,* than is the way any culture-bound person sees the world that is unique to his frame of reference. The welter of pre-perceived events may be factually and theoretically neutral, but just how our events-as-experienced are precipitated from this neutral stuff is a complicated constructual matter involving sensitivity, selectivity, and the entire epistemic apparatus of structuring which is prior to the experience itself.

## PARADIGM OF LOGICAL ATOMISM

As an initial approach to the clarification of factual statements consider a perceptual rubric based upon the schema of logical atomism. Potential punctate inputs can be treated as statements of atomic facts, either true or false. Perceptual configurations can be treated as molecular propositions that are extensions of the atomic facts, but that achieve a figure-ground pattern in the following way: each atomic fact, i.e., each potential input, is judged true or false according to whether it has some given property. Inputs having the property contribute to the figure, all other inputs, regardless of their properties contribute to the background. Thus any perceptual configuration is a molecular proposition obtained over the census of all inputs taking true or false values.

Doubtless this is a simplified schema of actual perception, but it is relatively easy to think of applications that exemplify this dichotomizing, census-taking model of perceptual construction. Imagine the following apparatus and experiment. At the nodes of a 20 by 20 grid are light sources such that each source emits either a subdued white, blue, or yellow light. Thus any random stimulus pattern would look much like an Ishihara-type card, and a particular stimulus pattern in relatively coarse grain would be achieved by setting up a nonrandom figure in a particular hue against a random background. Suppose further we undertake the following experiment. Three sets of stimulus panels are constructed such that barely detectable single-digit numbers are imposed on a random background. Set one gives a figure in blue, Set two gives a figure in yellow, and Set three gives two different but partially overlapping figures, one in blue, the other in yellow. Assume two groups of subjects, such that members of Group one are trained on the blue-figure panels and are rewarded every time they make a correct response to a brief stimulus exposure, while members of Group two are similarly trained on the yellow-figure cards. The experimental test comes when members of both groups receive the

Set-three cards in which the superimposed figures are presented. Doubtless we should find (on comparison against a relevant control group) that the blue-reward group would tend to perceive the blue figure, whereas the yellow-reward group would tend to see the yellow. This much we can infer from related experiments in the literature (e.g., Schafer and Murphy, 1943). And if we wished to draw a preliminary conclusion, we could say that the conceptual framework of one group was bluish figure and the conceptual framework of the other was yellowish figure, that the conceptual framework emerged as a function of reinforcement, and that the factual apprehensions of both groups were "correct" in their respective conceptual frameworks.

However, there is another conclusion to be drawn. Consider the stimulus world of a given subject, say from Group one. Each 20 by 20 card can be regarded as a true–false extension where a light is coded "true" if it is blue and "false" if not blue. Thus in all there would be $2^{400}$ possible stimulus configurations. These are the potential inputs. Suppose now the subject sees and names a six. The naming of the six belongs to his factual language. But the six can be relatively small or relatively large; it can be displaced to one or the other margin of the panel; it can be tipped, distorted, broken; etc. The naming of the six simply indicates that the particular configuration belongs to a class of many molecular propositions, each member of which possesses the property of being like a six. The language of fact does not report the *particular* stimulus configuration, i.e., the particular extension of atomic events, but only that the configuration belongs to a particular class of molecular propositions.

It is important to distinguish between a particular molecular proposition with its extension of atomic events, and a factual expression that indicates only that the molecular proposition warrants a specified class membership. The one is semantically anchored to a unique world occurrence, whereas the other only classifies the occurrence according to a set of many possible occurrences all possessing the defining property. One names *the* occurrence as an event in its ontologically given state; the other names a class having no such ontological status. Failure to appreciate this distinction leads to many philosophical perplexities.

When speaking in a factual language, we must, therefore, be careful to distinguish whether we are alluding to molecular events and their atomic extension, or whether we are attributing class membership to these events. Although there are troublesome initial conditions for judging an atomic event to be true or false, once these judgments are made then there remains no conceptual freedom for ascertaining whether molecular propositions are true or false. It was in this sense that logical atomists could take their atomism as ontological bedrock. However, what class a given proposition belongs to is quite another matter. Class membership depends on definitions wherein the conceptual framework is all-important. As Wittgenstein has said, what is or is not to be judged a cow is for the public to decide. It is not at all a matter of ontology.

In the foregoing sense, then, a fact is a general proposition determined by the conceptual predispositions of the factual classifier. We must distinguish the raw data of pre-perception from their factual reification through conceptual conventions. The raw data are neutral, so to speak, but they are unexpressed. Facts cannot be neutral for they reflect our classificatory penchants.

When we consider the concept of response the issues come into vivid relief. The raw data underlying our factual representations of response are the states of the effector elements and they are amenable to truth functional analysis. Responses are integrated over time, as it were, to compose the continuity of the parcel of molar behavior. For example, "turning left," or "running toward the goal," or "entering the cul de sac" are all molar behaviors involving complex sets of molecular responses. But the factual statement of molar behavior is a general proposition. It specifies only that certain observable events must obtain in order for us to classify a particular set of response events as a member of the class of such and such behavior. "Turning left" means only that the animal was seen to enter and disappear past the door to the left alley. It does not specify just what complex of response states should implement the behavior. In fact, many of the response factors may be considered irrelevant, such as position and movement of the head, the side of the alley passed, or even aspects of hesitancy and rate of movement. There are many ways of an animal's turning left but the myriad of possible response states is irrelevant to defining the class of act itself.

Why, we should then ask, just this set of defining properties for the factual class and not another? Why, for example, is not the rate of locomotion significant? In some cases it is judged not to be. And what of vicarious trial and error? And the momentary exploratory episodes? And what of whisker and tail performances? We do not even bother to report so many events because they are conceived as being nonsignificant and irrelevant to the description of the phenomena in question. This much can be taken for granted, but the question remains: What determines the relevant items of response from the irrelevant? What determines the defining properties of behavior? Doubtless the answer is to be found in the conceptual framework which the behaviorist brings to his study of learning.

In maze learning one may conceive of running a maze as a concatenation of discrete behavioral events marked off at various choice points. Therefore, running the maze is a complex affair of many behaviors with sequential connections (e.g., Hull, J. A. Deutsch, 1960). Many facts compose the sequence. One may also conceive of the running of a maze as an almost unitary act in which the minutiae of sequential behaviors are irrelevant as compared with the goal-orientation and goal-pursuing activities of the animal subject. What then, is the unit of behavioral description? It depends upon what one is predisposed to consider as relevant. A contiguity theorist may entertain many behaviors with small time spans, and purposive overtones are likely to be missing in the factual descriptions. A purposive behaviorist may entertain only meaningful units of behavior with a longer time span including a terminal response (e.g., Muenzinger, 1942). For the two people who observe the animal, the raw data are in a sense the same. But the facts differ! Different sets of factual propositions are considered appropriate for describing observation.

## ROLE OF THE *A PRIORI*

The thesis expressed here is that, one, a distinction is to be made between the raw data and the facts of experience, and two, factual reification of these data entails a conceptual framework. This is the empiricist counterpart of the Kantian doctrine of apperception. Kant distinguished between *noumenon,* the unknowable thing in itself, and *phenomenon,* that which is known by virtue of the transcendental unity of apperception and the categories of understanding. His great lesson is that the flux of raw data would remain an unperceived flux were it not for prior structuring according to certain categories of understanding which reify events on a space–time frame. It is the nature of a perceived event that it has structure, that it be seen as isolable in the welter of sensory flux. The principle of association would be inoperable were it not that events are impressible in familiar categories of experience, were it not that prior dispositions order events in the associative complexes that we do in fact understand.

Subsequent empiricists have taken exception to Kantian dogmatism about the innate character of *a priori* associative propensities. The classical space–time rubric of Newton has been modified. The conceptual framework is not so indubitable, nor so compelling of all possible experience, as Kant had thought. Nevertheless, the question: "How are synthetic *a priori* judgments possible?" is one of profound significance. Without the *a priori* element no synthetic judgment, that is, no factual propositions, would be possible. To be sure, we have had to modify our conceptions of the *a priori* (Lewis, 1923, 1929). A conceptual framework need not be conceived as something that is built into the mind, unchanging, enduring, and forming the foundations of a common understanding. Rather, it represents the epistemic hypothesis for our classifying complex events into their factual categories. The fact itself is not seen, but unless we can see complex events as instantiations of fact we would not see them as things at all (cf. N8.4).

The *a priori* element of structuring signifies only that a conceptual framework is prior to the experiencing of the fact. The conceptual framework itself may emerge in the interplay of experience and hypothesis. Thorndike, for example, witnessed the cat's scratching, clawing, biting in its puzzle box confinement. It occured to him that the behavior was random. A response occurred in which the catch to the door was released. The cat escaped and the successful response was stamped-in. For the psychologist, a conceptual framework emerged, one of trial and error and reinforcement. And it was this conceptual framework that predisposed the psychologist to define behavior in the way he did, as a set of acts upon the environment. But another conceptual framework includes the goal object, the end state that terminates the behavioral episode that is of conceptual interest to the cognitive psychologist. Clawing, biting, etc., are now seen as means–end hypotheses. They are not seen as mere random sequences of acts but as acts toward some end.

To the naive empiricist it would seem that the facts of latent learning experiments, for example, are the same for any person regardless of his theoretical leanings. Indeed, one hardly contests the reporting of the results of such experiments. However, the facts that one incorporates into his theoretical discussion may be quite different for different analysts; for on the one hand, making a correct response is seen as a reinforced act, and on the other, it is a sign of expectancy (cf. N8.4). The act of classifying response-sets into categories of behavior is a conceptual affair. Initially superficial agreement as to factual propositions may be reached among people of diverse theoretical dispositions, but then a closer scrutiny reveals that the defining properties that the theoreticians choose to emphasize may be quite different. The raw behaviors that they seek to classify in terms of factual propositions may be seen as instances of different classes. And the difference in kind may be at the source of subsequent discrepancies in theoretical accounting.

## RESUMÉ OF THE CONCEPTUAL ACCOUNT OF FACTS

Several implications follow from this account of facts. Let us pause to consider each in brief:

(1) Are facts theoretically neutral? One may as well ask, can one express himself verbally without recourse to language. The language of fact cannot be purified of the conceptual framework from which the defining characteristics of class memberships are taken. The raw data of pre-perception may be neutral but then we cannot speak of them. There is no way to report such data in factual propositions (cf. N8.5).

(2) Are facts true or false? The inclination is to treat all facts as true; otherwise they would not be facts. However, the language of truth

does not wholly apply. Putative instantiations of facts may be true or false, and for any given event complex, we can assert whether or not it is a member of the class named by the factual proposition. Still the same event complex may be classified according to different factual propositions, in which case it is seen differently. But the difference is in the set of defining properties. Different emphasis may be incorporated and different sets of irrelevances, such that when the same event complex yields different factual statements, it can be attributed to differences in the conceptual framework in which the factual propositions are stated.

(3) Are crucial tests possible? This familiar question has several ramifications, but in the present context, we would have to insure that the *sine qua non* of a crucial test is that the experimental facts should be theoretically neutral. The defining characteristics for the factual propositions should be independent of conceptual frameworks. But, as maintained here, this is not the case. Facts that are seen to agree in name display at the experimental confrontation an open texture of interpretation. They may possibly be seen as supportive of discrepant hypotheses. Thus the facts of latent learning experiments have never been conclusive. This open texture has always provided an escape clause, as it were, for the avoidance of crucial decisions.

To these implications, the following points may be added:

(4) Determination of facts according to the conceptual framework is neither strictly an empirical nor strictly a logical matter. Rather, it concerns the psychology of scientific invention. It cannot be an empirical matter without our introducing an element of circularity. We would have to assume that the nature of fact is itself to be decided as a matter of fact. Nor is the nature of fact a matter of logic, for logic like factual propositions begins with definitions and rules. To say that the determination of factual propositions is a matter of the psychology of invention is merely to say that factual propositions derive from the conceptual potential for *a priori* structuring.

(5) Emergence of a new conceptual framework results in the modification of factual propositions. This follows from the fact that new ways of conceiving result in new ways of perceiving. This is inevitable, for fact and conceptual framework are inseparable.

(6) Since the growth of a science involves a hierarchy of conceptual frameworks, principles of choice must operate for ascertaining which classifications and which factual propositions provide the preferred catalogues of perception. The inductive issues of decision are treated more fully in Part III of this work. But conceptual frameworks implicit within theory construction are subject to such noninductive criteria of selection as simplicity, comprehensiveness, reducibility, and correspondence.

## OBSERVATION VARIABLES

Let us now look more closely at the implications that the foregoing thesis has for the factual language of psychology. For example, the language of S-R habit elements and the language of cognitive or purposive behaviorism reflect not so much a difference in the raw data of response as a difference in behavioral classification. This being the case, it is not clear that issues which are devisive, e.g., latent learning, are such that they can be settled by experimental design. We come more to the point, however, when we examine the language of observation itself, of the independent and dependent variables. Behaviorists, as a group, have been notoriously lax or inconsistent in their definitions of stimulus and response. Considering their early polarization in the stream of physicalism and logical empiricism, this comes as a bit of a puzzle. One would think that with public verification being elevated to the role of epistemological doctrine, behaviorists should have agreed upon what it was they were to observe. But this was not the case. Nor is it now. We have only to consider some definitional efforts.

### Stimulus Variables

Stimuli, environmental conditions generally, and the facts of organismic control exhaust the classes of independent variables. Other things being equal, it is the stimulus variable that is salient. But what is a stimulus? The lack of conceptual agreement is well publicized (e.g., Gibson, 1960). Koch states the situation for both stimulus and response:

> It has become a truism to observe that early behaviorists were systematically ambiguous in their definitions and applications of the concepts "stimulus" and "response." The term "stimulus" was indiscriminately applied to states of affairs ranging from the physical energy change operating on a single receptor to the behavior evoking effect of a complex social situation, while "response" could designate anything from the contraction of a single muscle cell, to the name of a class of end results brought about by a widely varying range of movement sequences (1954, p. 9).

It is not clear that the situation has improved. The following usages are in vogue. Stimuli may be proximal, they may also be distal. As external energy changes they may be the actual elicitors of receptor activities or they may be potential elicitors residing in an object world. They may be specific energies activating the single receptor unit. They may be situations playing upon the entire sensory manifold. They may be only external energies, they may include activity within the organism. Is this sampling, then, a sign of conceptual confusion (Gibson, 1960)? Or is it more a sign of conceptual diversity necessitating different factual classifications? Consider the following:

*Distal versus proximal stimuli.*          This is the well-known distinction of Koffka, 1935; Brunswik, 1944. For the most part Hull, Tolman, Skinner, each in his individual treatments, considers the effective stimulus to be distal. For example, Tolman defines stimuli as "environmental entities which evoke expectations, i.e., sign-gestalt-perceptions, memorizations or inferences; . . ." (1932, p. 451). And for Skinner, " 'stimulus' refers to any part of the environment that is related to some specified operant or respondent according to the laws of the system" (Verplanck, 1954, p. 293). In contrast Hebb prefers what appears to be a definition of proximal stimuli: stimuli "are events which excite the neurone from outside the CNS . . ." (1958, p. 93). And Hayek in the same vein defines stimulus as "an event external to the nervous system which causes (through or without the mediation of special receptor organs) processes in some nerve fibres which by these fibres are conducted from the point at which the stimulus acts to some other point in the nervous system" (1952, p. 8). If there is any doubt as to the locus of the proximal stimulus, Hayek adds that it is "the last known physical event in the chain which leads to the production of the impulse" (1952, p. 8).

Now it should be apparent that the differences in these definitions are indicative of conceptual preference rather than conceptual confusion. Tolman, for example, conceives of stimulus as a goal-object with positive and negative valence as reflected in the expectations of the organism. The conceptual framework is adaptive and cognitive. It requires treating stimuli as meaningful goal objects. Skinner, on the other hand, conceptually suppresses the cognitive element in the event complex and treats stimuli as cue-occasions for response. Cognitive implications of the stimuli are accommodated by his insistence that only events tied to a response (i.e., effective stimuli) can be classed as stimuli. In any event, with these two conceptual frameworks at our disposal, we know in each case what constitutes the empirical evidence of a stimulus. With Hebb and Hayek quite different conceptual frameworks are involved. Both Skinner and Tolman are radical behaviorists in that they eschew any internalization (physiological analysis) of behavioral process. Hebb, on the other hand, thinks in terms of neural processes, the cell assembly and the phase sequence, as mediating behavior. He is committed, therefore, to a stimulus concept that fits into his conceptual system (1949). In similar fashion, Hayek is concerned with the internal processes for classifying various sensory orders. He is a constructualist somewhat in the sense presented in this chapter. Classification is a function of stimulus equivalence, generalization, and transfer. It is a function of apperception and not of some object structure as independent of sensory organization. Therefore, his conceptual system requires a neutralist treatment of the stimulus event. And the best way to assure the neutrality of the stimulus is to define it as a proximal event.

*Potential versus actual stimuli.* One can, of course, be eclectic about defining stimulus just as the Hullians seem to be. Stimuli can be either external or internal, potential or actual. Spence (1956), for example, finds that the term "stimulus" performs several different functions. It can designate "independent stimulus variables that the psychologist was said to manipulate" (1956, p. 39). Some stimuli are *intraorganic;* some stimuli are *situational,* e.g., levers, alleyways, card symbols, auditory cues, shocks, etc. Only if some response is connected with the stimulus can it be said to be *effective.* Skinner (1938; cf. Verplanck, 1954) and Tolman (1932, 1959) make stimulus contingent upon its evoking, or being the occasion for, some response. Thus all stimuli are effective stimuli. But Guthrie and Estes insist upon the situational enumeration of stimuli wherein both potential and effective elicitors and cues are included. For Guthrie, stimuli are "the physical changes which are *potential* occasions for the initiation of sense organ activity and consequent afferent activity leading to response" (1959, p. 178). And Estes writes ". . . it should be emphasized at the outset that by *stimulus* and all the variants of the term I refer to environmental conditions describable in physical terms without reference to the behavior of the organism" (1959, p. 455).

Again we may ask, is there conceptual confusion concerning whether stimuli must be actual or merely potential? Or is the choice one of conceptual necessity? For both Skinner and Tolman, but especially for Tolman, a stimulus must be an occasion for response, otherwise what purports to be a stimulus does not at all figure into the behavioral situation. But with Guthrie and Estes the situation is different. Response occurrence is a probability function with respect to stimulus sampling (Estes 1950, 1959; Voeks, 1950). One could not entertain this kind of sampling concept unless within the domain of stimulus elements he included some stimuli which would be noneffective.

## Response Variables

Just as one should distinguish between a member of a class and the class itself, so should he distinguish between a molecular response that is an explicit set of effector events and a molar response that is formulated as a factual proposition naming a set of many such molecular responses (all equivalent only in that they share some defining property, such as pressing the lever). Just what the defining property is for the factual proposition is a conceptual matter[1]: In its preoccupations with learning,

---

[1] No consistent distinction is made or maintained between response and behavior. It is tempting to take response as some specific set of effector events and behavior as the classificatory factual proposition—as is done for expository purposes in Chapter 12. However, this is contrary to current usage of the term 'response.' Thus its meaning is left somewhat ambiguous and is clarified only where confusion would be likely.

behaviorism incorporated the reflex arc and the conditioning model into its conceptual framework. Understandably, then, response was limited to the designation of muscular contractions and glandular secretions where specific sequential tracing from stimulus to response was, at least, conceptually possible. When concern with adaptive function rendered the reflex concept inadequate, larger units of response description became necessary but with a concomitant loss in specificity. It was not that the facts supported the molar over the molecular point of view. It was simply that different facts emerge as intrinsic to our moving from reflexology to functionalism. Where behaviorists now take the pains to define response, it is clear that their differences of opinion are dictated by their conceptual preferences and not by discoveries or confusions about real response entities in the world apart.

As it is with stimulus so it is with response. Not only does the conceptual framework determine the definitions of the observation terms, it determines the type of experiment undertaken. The apparatus of operant conditioning was invented and perfected by the Skinnerians, and not by Tolman, for example. And there is more to this historical fact than the possibility that Skinner may have been the more mechanically inventive of the two. But if the psychologist believes that organisms in some sense apprehend the world and are insightful, the response opportunities need be somewhat richer than those provided by simple lever devices. A complex apparatus for measuring pupillary reflex can be a fine piece of equipment but it would not provide data of interest to a psychologist who defines his subject in terms of means-end activities.

A very few examples will suffice to illustrate. Focusing upon the molecular elements of response, Hebb defines behavior as "the publicly observable activity of muscles or glands of external secretion as manifested in movements of parts of the body or in the appearance of tears, sweat, saliva and so forth" (1958, p. 2). No need for the scope of response that would give play to expectation, means-ends, or even consummatory acts. The conceptual system is one of brain function and it dictates a response concept the facts of which can be implemented by specific sets of efferent outputs.

Skinner (1935) and Estes (1950, 1959), on the other hand, refer to response as a class of many sets of events. Their treatments of response are thereby akin to the treatment of a factual proposition as outlined in this chapter. A given response, such as withdrawing from the grid in the presence of light, pecking the target, etc., is a class of many possible event-complexes and names no specific occurrence except generically. Note what Estes writes, ". . . the term response refers not to a physiologically or anatomically defined unit, but to the class of activities, e.g., all behaviors which result in depression of a bar, all behaviors which result in cutting a photocell beam or entering an endbox . . ." (1959, p. 392).

Although Tolman makes no explicit mention of the logical status of his response terms, it is clear that he too is interested in classes of acts and not specific concatenations of response. Thus he writes: "I also felt response could not be defined as a specific muscle contraction but must in some way be defined as a directed, goal-oriented manipulation or 'performance'" (1959, p. 59). And, "responses are for me to be conceived of as 'performances' rather than as specific muscle responses or gland secretions" (1959, p. 147). 'Conceived of,' to be sure, is the proper expression. Tolman's purposive orientation requires that the response variable has sufficient scope to include goals and ends. One has no need for specific response, for means-utilization is both flexible and manifold. Specificity of response would indeed become an encumbrance to the theoretical system, as it would in fact be for any system that makes reinforcement contingent on acts as complex as pressing a bar or taking one path over some other path.

## Venn Maps of Stimulus and Response

To summarize, recourse can be made to simple Venn diagrams. We can think of the Venn domain as the universe of all possible raw data stimulus points, or, on the other hand, of all possible raw data response points. Then any class of stimuli as represented by a factual proposition can be represented as a class within the domain; *mutatis mutandi,* for response. Now consider the case wherein two conceptual frameworks are brought to focus upon the same domain of raw data response points. According to the present thesis, the relevant language of response may be different for the two conceptual systems and the two response classes, for their more or less coincident behavioral episodes will not be the same. Suppose a cognitive behaviorist and a reinforcement behaviorist are concerned with behavior at the choice point of a simple T maze. Then the response classifications might be represented by Figure 8.1. Let $R_r$ designate relevant response for the reinforcement behaviorist, such as turning right or turning left. Let $R_c$ designate relevant response for the cognitive behaviorist. Note that $R_r$ is wholly contained in $R_c$. That is to say, every response ("turning left" or "turning right") in the classification schema of $R_r$ is a response in the classification schema of $R_c$. Assuming $R_c$ is the response class for the cognitive theorist, then some points are considered responses in his conceptual system which are not considered so in the system of the reinforcement theorist. For example, these might be the vicarious trial and error motions which are significant to the cognitive theorists but are not so to the reinforcement theorist.[2] Continuing in the same

[2] This is not to suggest that reinforcement theorists need necessarily ignore VTE, but initially the extension of response classes to incorporate VTE was undertaken by purposive behaviorists (Muenzinger, 1938; Tolman, 1939).

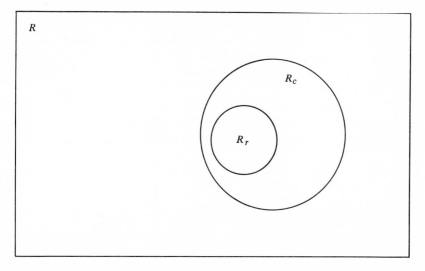

**Figure 8.1**  Response classes for two different conceptual systems.

vein, a possible schema of stimulus classification is found in Figure 8.2. Here the classes of stimuli $S_e$ and $S_h$ are defined from different conceptual systems. The stimulus classes that are of interest are

$\{S_e\}$, the stimulus class for E,

$\{S_h\}$, the stimulus class for H,

$\{S_e \sim S_h\}$, the raw data points included in E's stimulus world but not included in H's,

$\{\sim S_e S_h\}$, the raw data points not included in E's stimulus world, but included in H's,

$\{S_e S_h\}$,    the raw data points which are included in the stimulus world of both E and H.

As an application of this schema let E stand for Estes and H stand for Hebb. Then $\{S_e S_h\}$ is the class of stimuli where both Hebb and Estes concur; for example, stimulus objects to which the subject attends and responds. Next $\{S_e \sim S_h\}$ is the class of unactualized, potential stimuli, i.e., objects in the stimulus world which for one or another reason do not elicit significant receptor activity. And $\{\sim S_e S_h\}$ may be the class composed of internal afferent events and, for that matter, might also contain the spontaneous unelicited firing of the sensory neurones.

One can, of course, construct other schemata to represent other conceptual differences of opinion. But unless the class compositions of the factual propositions coincide exactly, there will be inconsistencies and conflicts as concerns comparisons of the factual language. As noted, the classical conditionist may see many events as response which do not at all find their way into the response vocabulary of a purposive behaviorist.

Such a predicament is quite understandable and need not be troublesome providing opposing theoreticians recognize that one factual language may be different from another, and that the hypothesis of one theory is not testable by the factual language generated within the conceptual framework of another theory. Linguistic difficulties seem to arise when the ontological status of the language of fact is misinterpreted.

It has already been emphasized that factual propositions, as class designations, have referents of a different type than that of simple existential assertions. Although a named class can have a finite number of members, and thereby its name names the concrete aggregate, we do not often

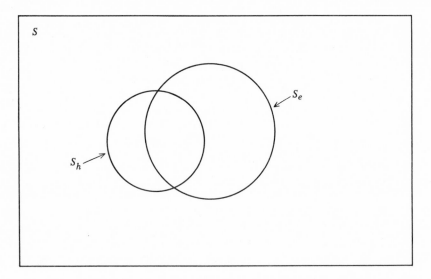

**Figure 8.2**   Stimulus classes for two different conceptual systems.

correctly apply the name to designate the aggregate. Rather we use the name as if it names a thing and not the selected aggregate. Suppose we say, "Subject S turned right." This is the fact. From this, we can infer that the actual response occurrence, as an explicit event sequence, was such that, by virtue of the applied defining properties, it could be assigned to the given class. By using the term "turning right" we point to no specific act or event. We only assert that whatever the specific and unique act, it had the defining property "turning right." Thus to assign a property over a set of variables is to construct a class.

Consider once again Figure 8.2. Every point within the domain represents a molecular proposition whose truth is an extension of its atomic elements. Each point, therefore, is ontologically basic—its represents a possible occurrence or state of the stimulus world, such that if the possible occurrence does take place it takes place as a recognizable event in the universe. What has been here called the event is a point in the domain or universe. It is the existent, it is neutral, and it is not a fact! The status of fact arises only when apperception allows us to assign a given property to the specific event. What properties we assign to the event are not alone determined by the event, for the property emerges only as it functions in a conceptual framework.

The Venn diagram should not be taken too seriously as a model for the distinctions that have been made. For one thing, the mere need to speak of raw data means that we deprive them of their neutral status. And merely to call such events points in the phenomenal flux is surely to give them an identity which it is hard to describe except in factual terms. These difficulties cannot be avoided. Nevertheless, granting certain conventions for isolating events in the domain of possible experience, then constructions and classifications will be relative to conceptual schemata. We can, for example, agree as to the molecular elements of raw response. But whether a response sequence is one of reflex brevity, or one of means-end expanse, or one which is always terminated by a reinforcement episode, is not a definitional matter that can be decided by one's looking to the domain of possible experience with an open and unbiased mind.

## MEDIATING VARIABLES

There would be more homogeneity to the themes of this chapter were we to confine our attention to observables and the language of fact. Mediating variables fall into a different category. Since they serve to mediate between the independent stimulus variables and the dependent response variables they do not appear to reside within the precincts of the observation language. There is, however, a sense in which we use mediating variables as part of the observation language. We refer to internal states as if they are writ large on the surface of observable events. For example, we deprive an animal of food so as to reduce it to eighty percent of its ad lib weight. The animal is active, it looks hungry; "Looking hungry" is part of the observation language. However, the state of hunger itself may not be among the set of observable events. We may insist that hunger is some internal state of the organism; tissue deficit, biochemical disbalance, or some other unspecified state. In that case, the data of observation can only serve as the grounds for inference for the hypothetical internal state.

How much of the mediating variable is inference? How much is construct? This is the significant question. When Woodworth (1929) made room for mediating organismic variables in the stimulus–response schema, he did so in recognition that organisms were not simple processors, such as one might expect of tropismic or reflex organisms. Behavioral laws are not so simple. The statement of the external stimulus conditions yields insufficient information for the making of response predictions. The past history of the organism, drive, permanent and momentary disbalances in organic function, attitudinal structure, these and many more conceptual processes intervene as the executives for the response mechanisms. Some of these mediators were tied to the side of manipulatable independent variables. Thus their locus falls more within the stimulus complex, as for example, need and deprivation. Some of the mediators were tied more to the unmanipulatable dependent variables. Such factors as momentary oscillations and unknown rhythms of the organic systems were located in the response complex. Initially though, all mediators were inferred from response. Why, for example, under these stimulus conditions does just *this* response occur and not some other? It is the behavior that signifies the mediator.

As Hull and Tolman undertook their systematic developments of behaviorism, the issues of the status of mediators became more refined. The emphasis was to be upon public observation, otherwise the hard won advantages of empiricism would be lost. Hypotheses and conjectures can be useful if they lead to discoveries and to the opening of new factual vistas. But if hypotheses merely serve some weak explanatory function with little possibility either of fitting into the body of established science or of achieving existential status, then like all progeny of metaphysics they are distractive, and they are dispensable. Under the circumstances, it is safest to stay within the boundaries of the observation language. In such a case mediators are not to be internalized. They are to be logical constructions constituting a more explicit statement of the behavioral setting.

## Mediators as Constructs

Consider need, for example. As a construct, we ignore any aspect of its hypothetical residence in the internal milieu. What the need statement signifies is that certain environmental conditions, such as history of food intake (hunger) or history of sustained disapproval (sense of failure), are antecedent to given response options. Statement of need supplements to a substantial extent the fund of independent variables. We can, of course, concentrate on response rather than stimulus setting. What we then construct is a kind of dispositional term whose meaning is explicated in terms of test-conditionals. The subject displays certain kinds of behavioral dispositions (demands, expectations, fears, etc.) if under a given set of stimulus conditions a specified response or set of responses occurs. In either case, however, we are concerned with logical constructs. Regardless of whether the mediating variable is a construction from the complex of independent variables or from the complex of dependent variables, no existential status is attributed to the mediator aside from the aggregate of constitutive events reported in the observation language.

## Mediators as Inferred Entities

Now a physiologist, for example, may not be satisfied with such empiricistic conservatism.[3] The complex S-R connections lead him to place the mediating variables within the organism itself. States, mechanisms, entities are inferred which when incorporated into the model of the behavioral system permit the deduction of response hypotheses. A motivational state is not explicitly definable in terms of the independent variables. Need is more than a maintenance schedule, demand is more than response under a given set of stimuli and behavioral options. Somewhere within the organism, it is hypothesized, there are structures for which the evidence is now only indirect and incomplete.

The question as to what mediating variables are, or should be, has evoked considerable discussion in the psychological literature. MacCorquodale and Meehl (1948) were the first to clarify the distinction for psychologists. Intervening variables as treated by Tolman, by Skinner, and to large extent, by Hull are logical constructions; hypothetical constructs as conceived, say, by Hebb (1949) and Duffy (1962) are hypotheses concerning entities for which the evidence is both indirect and incomplete. Contrary to what some writers (Bergmann, 1951; Kendler, 1952) have intimated, the question appears to the present writer to be a significant one. But its significance rests in the assessment of the role that mediating variables are to play in our choosing among alternative theories. The question and the issues shall come up again in subsequent discussions.

## MENTAL LANGUAGE

Before closing the door upon the language of psychology, we should consider the question of mental states, raw-feels and other data of consciousness. After all, there was a time when the mental language, and the shared physical language, was *the* language of psychology. Now the contemporary behaviorist is inclined to accept the verdict of Watson, " 'States of consciousness' like the so-called phenomena of spiritualism are not objectively verifiable, and for that reason can never be the data for science" (1929, p. 1). The muddles over consciousness have been a bar to scientific progress.

Such has been the judgment of learning and response oriented psy-

---

[3] It would seem that "conservatism" is the correct word here. Why people adopting this conservative attitude have been called "radical empiricists" (e.g., Skinner) rather than "conservative empiricists" is, for etymology, one of the curiosities of semantic irrelevancy.

chologists. There is no need for consciousness and mind as private, mentalistic referents. Still consciousness and the introspectable contents of "mind" keep cropping up. Our language is so traditionally steeped in mind stuffs and in qualities and dimensions of consciousness that it is difficult for the behaviorist to carry off his operational reductions of such terms as meaning, thinking, cognition, perception without having the old ways of thinking obtrude. As a result textbook writers allude deferentially to the historical efforts of the introspectionists, take Watson's brash but poignant judgment as the text for a discussion on methodology, and then proceed to use the language of their ancestors, larded as it is at the sinews with the overtones of consciousness and introspectable feelings.

Yet it is not alone out of carelessness that the vocabulary of mentalism will not be suppressed. Clinicians and personologists are no longer unique in their need for speaking of levels of awareness. With the successful probing of the subcortical centers of the central nervous system, neurophysiologists have given new heart to the dead issues of psychophysical parallelism. "Activation" and "awareness" need not be part of the psychological language, as the behaviorists were careful to point out; yet when a group of neurophysiologists convened to discuss this important work in subcortical structure and function, the title of the proceedings became *Brain Mechanisms and Consciousness* (Delafresnaye, 1954).

So, what of the mental language? Is there something to say for the mental domain? If so, does the mental language say it? These are the significant questions.

Doubtless there is something to refer to. 'Raw-feels,' 'sense-data,' 'sense-contents,' whatever term we use to refer to the stuff of consciousness, that stuff seems indubitable. It is not clear that the behaviorist or the physicalist has ever denied consciousness as such. Watson, we may think, comes close when he writes, "The behaviorist finds no evidence for 'mental existence' or 'mental processes' of any kind." But this presents a puzzle. For what is evidence but the stuff of consciousness? What would constitute evidence of mental content and mental process? It is like asking, what is the evidence of evidence. We may ask, what is the evidence that some putative structure is real, but it is quite a different matter to ask what is the evidence of that evidence we use.

There seems to be no justifiable argument for denying consciousness —for ignoring consciousness and its raw data perhaps, but not for its outright denial. That being the case, is there a reliable mental language? Can we develop a mental language as precise and publicly teachable as the physical language, without our begging some kind of privilege? The one is a public language, the other is private. The objects of reference, the particulars of the physical language, are publicly observed objects. One has recourse to the court of public approval as to whether a term in the language is used properly. This is not the case, however, for the private language. The particular content of consciousness, the "thing" that is referred to, is private. There is no public access to the data referent. Such are the linguistic implications of the egocentric predicament, of solipsism, of subjectivism, of that whole panoply of variations on the privacy of the primal data.

One difficulty of a mental language, then, is its lack of reference to data in a public domain. Only if the data are public can the semantic requirements for ostensive definitions be fulfilled. Another difficulty, and equally disturbing, is one alluded to by Wittgenstein (1953). I cannot be sure, even in the private domain, that I have learned to use the mental language correctly. The ostensive use of terms derives from our associating words with objects. Correct usage then is contingent upon my seeing whether the object possesses the defining properties I associate with the word. For example, the object in my pocket is a member of the class "eraser." I can say the object is an eraser, because it can be compared with other existent objects possessing the defining property. But can I claim the same for the private data language where the objects to be classified and named are the raw data of consciousness? Suppose I am experiencing a red sense-datum. What ostensive check is there upon my having used "red" in my private data language correctly? Proceeding as above, I would have to refer my red sense-datum to a class of many such data, i.e., to call up other members of the class. But it is the character of such data that they are transient, occupying, as it were, the momentary span of consciousness. Recall will not help me here; for even had I vivid imagery, I could not recall any past experience, be sure it was the one I had intentions of recalling, and still retain the present sense-datum there in the focal vortex of the sensorium. Thus, not only does a mental language lack public criteria of correct usage, we are not even sure that it is amenable to treatment under any conceivable set of private criteria.

Here end for the time being our misgivings over the mental language (cf. Chapter 12). Still we continue to use mentalist terms; and like Feigl (1950, 1958) and the neurophysiologists (Delasfresnaye, 1954), we continue to recognize the provisional dichotomy of the mental and the physical. However, whether there is a true mental language, or whether what purports to be a mental language contributes anything to the description of psychological events which is not translatable into the dispositional language of physicalism, is a matter for analysis. In the present book, the context for this analysis is established in the subsequent discussions on reductionism. The thesis to be maintained is that terms in the presumptive mental language are contaminated by behavioral reference. In the writer's opinion, no psychologically feasible method (i.e., an experiential method precluding intuition and recourse to postulation) exists for learning a strictly mental language. Nor is it clear of what use it would be, if we did in fact have one.

# NOTES

### NOTE 8.1

"Intension" and "extension" are here used in their customary philosophical senses. The *intension* of a term or phrase is the set of defining properties such that if any event exhibits those properties it then belongs to the class of objects named by the term or phrase. The *extension* of the term or phrase is the de-numeration or identification of all such objects as one intended by the term or phrase. Intension refers to the matter of defining the class, whereas extension refers to the discriminative acts of populating the class.

Analogs are *connotation* and *denotation; sense* and *meaning.* For short discussions of shades of meaning see Stebbing (1948), Black (1949), and Pap (1949).

### NOTE 8.2

Further clarification is required concerning raw data. In general these are the neutral inputs as concerns the raw material of perception and observation. But where should we locate them? In the world, as Russell does with his "sensibilia"? or as J. S. Mill does with his "permanent possibilities of sensation"? Or in the receptor system where we can give them a coding as input? Because of its amenability to treatment in the paradigms of logical atomism, the latter alterna-tive is preferred. This, however, introduces a difficulty. Set, conditions of the receptor, and other phasic states affect the sensitivity of the receptor. Thus raw data are subject to dispositional factors of the organism just as are perceptual events, and, therefore, they cannot be theoretically neutral.

This is an unfortunate predicament and one that is difficult to avoid. To place raw data in the physical world as independent of any receptor activity is an indefensible metaphysical gambit. Yet to place raw data in the receptor activity is to destroy their neutrality. It would seem that the "counsel of despair" is to regard them as relatively neutral. That is, raw data are coded as sensory input under "optimal" conditions of observation . . . from which we infer that for every punctate input there is a source of physical energy sufficient to elicit firing of the receptor.

We do, of course, infer a world external to ourselves. It is on this basis that we assume a certain neutral stuff, or a thing in itself, or a real, which we use as the backdrop for our perceptual pluralism. Since this world-as-stimulus-potential is presumptively one of physical stimulus energies, we may think of the world as potentially elicitive of complex sets of punctate receptor response, in which the set for a given observer takes its unique space–time coordinates. Thus each such set of punctate receptor elicitations represents a space–time perspective. But then one might ask: how can these sets be neutral? For, each observer carries with him a unique space–time perspective. True, but the neutrality rests in the fact that the perspective affords a vantage and an aspect of the object and not a vantage or an aspect of the perceiving organism. The raw data space–time perspective is not contingent upon the attitudes, momentary sets, and other dispositional conditions of the organism.

The substance of such a doctrine can be found in the phenomenalism of Mach (1897) and Russell (1917). It is interesting to speculate what implications there are here for any substantive world. Since objects are systems of stimulus energies they cannot particularly be anywhere, until detector systems located at specific space–time positions process the information contained in the energy inputs. It is not simply a case of *esse est percipi*, but of how any system of ambient energies could crystallize into a world of objects without the presence of detectors with unique space–time perspectives.

## NOTE 8.3

1.   Note these two quotations of Goethe:
"Were the eye not attuned to the Sun
The Sun could never be seen by it."
(quoted by Hanson, 1958, p. 4)

and,

"All that is factual is already theory."
(quoted by Klüver in his introduction to Hayek, 1952)

Thus we run the gamut of factual relativity, from naive phenomenalism to what Feyerabend (1962) calls the *pragmatic theory of observation*. The theme has become a truism, yet people continue to speak as if facts stand apart ontologically, as if they have an eternal validity, or as if the ingredients of those facts (e.g., sense data) possess that enduring status.

In the text it has been argued that the raw material of experience out of which factual classifications are made as repositories of perceptual knowledge is itself not subject to factual description. Feyerabend has made a somewhat similar distinction as the basis of his lucid exposition of a pragmatic theory of observation—in the writer's mind, as explicit and perceptive an account of factual relativism as can be found in recent literature. He writes:

. . . the fact that a statement belongs to the observational domain has no bearing on its meaning . . . Whatever restrictions of interpretation we accept are determined by the language we use, or by the theories or general points of view whose development has led to the formulation of this language (1962, p. 39).

If one insists upon ontological bedrock for observation, all we can say is that observation is caused, and that specifically it is caused by the behaviors or acts of observation:

An observation sentence is distinguished from other sentences of a theory, not, as was the case of earlier positivism, by its *content*, but by the *cause* of its production, or by the fact that its production conforms to certain *behavioral patterns.* This being the case the fact that a certain sentence belongs to the observation language does not allow us to infer anything about its content, more especially, it does not allow us to make any inference concerning the *kind* of entities described in it (1962, p. 36).

Our instrumental and operational tactics in science should make for ready appreciation of the pragmatic aspect of observation.

Taken by themselves, the indications of instruments do not mean anything unless we possess a *theory* which teaches us what situations we are to expect in the world, and which guarantees there exists a reliable correlation between indications of the instrument and such a particular situation. If a certain theory is replaced by a different theory with a different ontology, then we may have to revise the interpretation of *all* our measurements, however self-evident such a particular interpretation may have become in the course of time. . . (1962, p. 37).

And speaking of the meaning of observation, Feyerabend writes:

Nobody would dream of demanding that the meanings of observation statements *as obtained with the help of measuring instruments* remain invariant with respect to the change and progress of knowledge. Yet, precisely this is done when the measuring instrument is a human being, and the indication is the behavior of this human being or the sensations he has, at a particular time (1962, p. 37).

(Behaviorists should take note, for results are, with but rare exceptions, reported as if the facts of response have existential status independent of the observational behavior of the experimenter. That this observational behavior is dictated by the experimenter's conceptual framework has been a major theme throughout this chapter).

Feyerabend draws two significant conclusions from his analysis of observation. One, he rejects the idea of *reductionism,* in which the facts and theoretical constructions of one science can be reduced to those of another. Two, he is critical of the idea of *meaning invariance,* i.e., the idea that facts once agreed to are invariant so far as concerns all subsequently developing theoretical perspectives. In rejecting meaning invariance, Feyerabend finds he must also reject the idea of reducing one science to another.

2.    Hanson (1958) approaches the problem of perception and factual construction somewhat more informally. He notes that scientist and nonscientists alike may receive the same data, but as individuals they see different things. "There is more to seeing than meets the eyeball." Physical states of two different observers, for example, may be very nearly alike, but what is seen can be quite different. The findings of perceptual studies of ambiguous figures, shifting perspectives, and impoverished cues all indicate that different things are seen for what proximally are identical stimuli.

Furthermore, one cannot separate interpretation of visual data from the apprehending of a thing seen; "theories and interpretations are there in the seeing from the outset." Hanson is critically sympathetic to the Wittgensteinian notion that language is instrumental in structuring fact. "Knowledge of the world is not a montage of sticks, stones, colour patches, and noises but a system of propositions" (1958, p. 26). Expressing some reservations on Wittgenstein's doctrine of picturing (*Tractatus*), he interprets the formal structure of science as placing limitations on factual perspectives. Thus in supporting the Copenhagen interpretation of quantum physics, he feels that so long as the formal structure of microphysics is as it is, there is no alternative but to accept uncertainty (Heisenberg), complementarity (Bohr), and unvisualizability (Dirac), as unavoidable aspects of our factual presentation.

The debates between the contemporary determinists and the votaries of the Copenhagen interpretation cannot be gone into here, but mention should be made that, as one of the former, Feyerabend (1957, 1961, 1962) believes that overemphasis upon the intrenched and inflexible character of language results in pessimism. Bohr was an obdurate spokesman for his Copenhagen point of view on grounds that the observational problems of quantum mechanics were not to be overcome. (Bohr writes ". . . it is decisive to recognize that, *however far the phenomena transcend the scope of the classical physical explanation, the account of all evidence must be expressed in classical terms*" (1949, p. 209).) Thus the uncertainty principle places an inescapable limitation upon observation and upon further penetrative speculations concerning hidden variables. Feyerabend's critical discussion of quantum measurement problems can be found in Körner (1957) and in Feigl and Maxwell (1961). Hanson also speaks to the issues in the latter volume. Also see Feyerabend (1958) and Hanson (1958, 1962).

3.  In a series of articles Katsoff (1947, 1949, 1953) makes some of the same points on behalf of an interpretative theory of observation. Responding to the question: "If facts are known what is it that is known?" Katsoff answers that the fact is a proposition whereby supportive perception is the interpretation of sense data in the context of an existential hypothesis. The hypothesis constitutes the interpretative framework. "Every scientific observation involves a set of categories *a priori*" (1947, p. 688).

Katsoff's argument yields the following conclusions:

(a) Sense data, as such, are not facts (a rejection of naive empiricism and radical positivism).

(b) Facts result only as the interpretation of sense data (therefore, rationalism is insufficient).

(c) Every scientific observation presupposes a set of categories (the requirement of the *a priori*).

(d) A differentiation is to be made between the sense data events (the *ding an sich*) and the facts. Factual propositions are expressive of interpretative perception, never of the sense data.

Katsoff cautions against an inflexible factual language, on the one hand, and uncritical relativism, on the other. For example, he takes to task Snygg and Combs for their statement: "A fact, we find, is not *something,* an independent thing that we can memorize and depend upon and know that it will always be true. It is true only in its own frame of reference, which means that it is false in others" (Snygg and Combs, 1949, p. 4).

It is the last clause that is clearly exceptionable. A fact in a foreign frame of reference, so to speak, is not false, it is simply meaningless. To endow factual propositions with general testability from alternative frameworks is to lose sight of the fact that such propositions are meaningful and capable of validation only in their own framework.

## NOTE 8.4

Kant made it clear to subsequent generations of scientists and philosophers that the conception of a naively impressible perceiver is inadequate. His analysis of the basic spatio–temporal framework and categories of perceptual construction was to the point. Even though his perceptual idealism was rejected on the grounds of its presuming enduring epistemic propensities of the mind (non-Euclidean geometries and theories of relativity put an end to these aspects of Kantian *a priori*), the *a priori* foundations of knowledge were clearly recognized by pragmatists, positivists, empiricists, and mere epistemologists. Defenses of the *a priori* presuppositions of knowledge subsequent to Kant can be put into the following categories:

(1) *Intuitional a priorism.* Essentially the argument of Kant. As noted, it had to be rejected because of radical innovations in mathematics and physics.

(2) *Psychological a priorism.* Here restricted to the generic principles and schemata of associationism. If ideas are to be associated by similarity, contiguity, and contrast, then principles of the relevant classifications and associations must be incorporated into the processing mechanism prior to any experience. Otherwise initial experience could not be processed, no associative configurations and classes could emerge.

(3) *Epistemological a priorism.* All *a priorism* referred to in this note has epistemological significance. Here we are concerned as to how the *a priori* functions in the matter of existential enquiry.

Feyerabend and to some extent Hanson, as reported in Note 8.2, would be designated as defending epistemological *a priorism,* as could be Katsoff. However, the most explicit statements (in terms of *a priorism* itself) have been made by Lewis (1923, 1929), Pap (1946, 1949), and Schlick (1930).

Lewis' pragmatic conception of the *a priori* has been very influential in contemporary philosophy of science. Rejecting the absolute intuition and categories of Kant, Lewis still finds an imperative for *a priori* presuppositions so far as the empirical sciences are concerned. Empirical knowledge without the *a priori* schemata of our "definitive concepts" would be impossible. "We cannot even interrogate experience without a network of categories and definitive concepts." Thus he writes:

> A name itself must represent *some* uniformity in experience or it names nothing. What does not repeat itself or recur in intelligible fashion is not a thing. When the definitive uniformity is a clue to other uniformities, we have a successful definition. Other definitions cannot be said to be false, they are merely useless. In scientific classification the search is, thus, for *things worth naming.* But the naming, classifying, defining activity is essentially prior to investigation. We cannot interrogate experience in gen-

eral. Until our meaning is definite and our classification correspondingly exact, experience cannot conceivably answer our questions (1923; 1949, p. 289).

Laws are *a priori*. They define our concepts and the categories by which we classify our facts. Thus:

> In the case of an empirical law, a mere generalization from experience, if the particular experience does not fit it, so much the worse for the 'law.' But in the case of the categorical principle, if experience does not fit it, then so much the worse for the experience (1929, p. 224).

As Pap (1946) points out in his discussion of Lewis, the categorical, or *a priori*, propositions are true in intension. They include the set of defining properties essential to the classification of the facts. But the actual search of events and classification is a matter of the extension of an *a priori* proposition. One knows the extension of the proposition only *a posteriori*. But note that what is a fact to be classified can only be a fact in a classificatory schema.

Pap himself has undertaken a defense of the *a priori* in science. He draws upon Dewey, Lenzen, and Cassirer as well as upon Lewis and finds himself in substantial agreement as to the prerequisite of *a priori* classificatory schemata. However, he gives somewhat greater attention to the empirical origins of these *a priori* categories. Defining concepts arise by our noting similarities among events, by our relying, it would appear, on some kind of intuitive credence. But once formulated, empirical laws function analytically in the following way. Suppose an event is perceived as conformal to the defining concept. Then it is appropriately classified, as it were. The event is known. But suppose it is nonconformal in some respect. How will it be seen? If no available defining concept and class is available, it will be seen against the backdrop of some available class as being, in some sense, incomplete, aberrant, or refractory. For example, suppose the defining concept is the law of reinforcement. The class of learned responses then may include this law *a priori* as among its defining principles. But now suppose some behavior has many symptoms of a learned response yet is not wholly amenable to classification as reinforced response (e.g., as in some latent learning experiments). In such cases, the definitive concept must either serve to exclude the deviant event or it must undergo some modification itself in order to admit the deviant event. But so long as the category remains unchanged, it can only function to exclude the deviant event.

This argument crops up again in discussions of conventionalism and instrumentalism as pertains to law. What it clearly points out is that a question as to whether a given phenomenon is or is not a member of a given class (e.g., whether a behavior is a learned behavior or not) is not a question that can be easily settled by experiment. It is often a question of analysis.

(4) *Linguistic a priorism*. Not to be rigorously distinguished from epistemological empiricism so long as the state of knowledge is formulated in purely linguistic terms. Wittgenstein (1953) utilizes this type of *a priorism* when he emphasizes the conceptually limiting (or should we say "expansive") influence that language has on seeing and on picturing. And Stebbing (1933), in agreement with Lewis, prefers to formulate the conceptual framework in terms of linguistic instruments. She writes:

What use can we make of *a priori* propositions? Fortunately, I can reply very briefly. We do not use *a priori* propositions in order to obtain true generalizations concerning matters of fact. Such a procedure would be impossible. I accept Wittgenstein's statement: "In life it is never a mathematical proposition we need, but we use mathematical propositions only in order to infer from propositions which do not belong to mathematics to other propositions which equally do not belong to mathematics." The same may be said with regard to logical principles. As for conventions and definitions—we *use* them in order to enable us to arrange what we know in an orderly system (1933, p. 197).

Stebbing does not admit an empirical principle for the *a priori;* she is not interested, as Pap is, in the etiology or the psychological origins of the *a priori*. However, the difficulty for Pap is that the problem of psychological origins of the *a priori* involves him in an infinite empirical regress. That is why intuitive credibility on limited experience is taken by him as supportive of the empirical foundations of the *a priori*.

(5) *Physiological a priorism*. In some respects, one of the most obvious treatments of the *a priori* requirements for experience. Just as Brain (1951) speaks of physiological idealism, so might we speak of physiological *a priorism*. Without some innate properties and structures of the nervous system, no experience, no perceptual construction (not even that ultimately derived from learning) would be possible. This was a thesis defended by early nativists (e.g., Hering, Müller) with respect to spatial constructions. Physiologically, these nativists were Kantians. And following them, empiricists such as Lotze, Helmholtz, and Wundt never fully succeeded in freeing themselves of *a priori* principles. Even though the doctrine of local signs (Lotze) rejected the notion that spatial characteristics were given implicitly within the perceptual data, it had to allow innate propensities of the mind for processing the data to cognizable spatial impressions and ideas. Doubtless in such terms, the doctrine of the *a priori* becomes all but trivial. Yet it serves to emphasize that the *tabula rasa* models of early empiricism are naive.

The Gestalt psychologists have been at the forefront of physiological *a priorism*. Their field models of brain process, the doctrine of isomorphism, and ultimately the principles of perceptual organization all suggest the notion of the *a priori* foundations of experience. There is, however, an important precautionary note. Kantian *a priorism* is disavowed by the Gestaltists; the principles of prior organization belong to physical theory and not to the inherent propensities of the knowing mind. Koffka, for example, writes:

> In our case the formulation that structure is innate but processes are not, adds very definitely to the understanding of the nature-nurture dichotomy. For it makes it explicit that each process depends upon a *set* of conditions, of which the innate structure is one, the factual stimuli are another, and the laws of organization a third . . . But as we have emphasized, the laws of organization fall entirely outside the scope of our dichotomy. The laws of electrical potential, of surface tension, of maximum and minimum energy, hold for *any* system and are quite independent of the particular system considered, much as the nature of those systems will determine the actual processes which follow from the universal laws. To call these laws innate is therefore nonsensical; for innate can only mean: dependent upon the particular nature of the system as it is on account of its biological origin (1935, p. 549).

Perhaps so, but even should the Gestalt theory prove satisfactory, the reason that just this set of physical laws prove applicable and not another is to be found in the structural development of the brain as coded in the genetic material. The whole point of signaling out the autochthonous factors of perception was to propose that certain unique laws of perceptual organizations (proximity, similarity, closure, Prägnanz) are explainable in terms of genetically determined structures. Allusion to the laws of physics notwithstanding, the Gestalt psychologists have seldom been successful in disavowing their Kantian heritage.

Speculations along this line are also found in Hayek's interesting but neglected book, *The Sensory Order* (1952). His major thesis, a kind of contingent phenomenalism, is that sensory perception is an act of classification in which the input is processed "isomorphally," as it were, by any number of classes of sensory processes which impart to the phenomenal event the properties it has. The specific class linkages can either be learned or species acquired—the ontogenetic and phylogenetic aspects of "linkage" acquisition.

However, no sensory input is perceived except that it can be isomorphally accepted by the classes of sensory order. No object or phenomenal constructions are possible except in terms of the prior apparatus of classification. Moreover, these are not classes with the ontological status of Platonic reals; the properties and qualities of sensory order are not of the objects themselves but are abstractive attributions of the nervous system. Thus, his central thesis is:

> . . . we do not first have sensations which are then preserved by memory, but it is as a result of physiological memory that the physiological impulses are converted into sensations. The connections between physiological elements are thus the primary phenomenon which creates the mental phenomena (1952, p. 53).

An impulse-complex within the nervous system will be processed and thereby perceptually reified only if the impulse elicits the activity of the classifying complex. Since many such impulses may activate the class complex, any given input loses its uniqueness in the process of perceptual reification. In other words, perceptual reification means that the phenomenon emerges as an abstractive reality.

The neurological speculations of Hayek's thesis, its implications for both philosophy and psychology, are too extensive to go into here. But apropos of *a priorism,* the following comments can be made:

(1) Perception is impossible without prior categories or classificatory assemblies for the processing of input.

(2) All perception is abstractive in the sense that it attributes properties which are class defining and thus are meaningless as unique descriptions.

(3) The classificatory structures or assemblies are either species determined or are learned, but in either case, they are prior to any experience.

Hayek offers us an analysis of perception that is the antithesis of that of certain existentialists (e.g., Marcel). According to them all classification is corruptive of the particular experience. Only particulars are real. As soon as an event is classified and surrenders its individuality to categories of shared properties, it is no longer an event. Hayek's model of sensory processing, on the other hand, adamantly asserts that without the "abstractive" classes there would be no phenomena at all.


## NOTE 8.5

There are contexts in physics where facts cannot at all be separate from their conceptual framework. A counterpart to the argument for the neutrality of facts is that a given fact should be one thing and not another. For example, an electron should be a particle, or it should be a wave. It should have sufficient integrity not to pretend to both. But according to the principle of complementarity, it is indeed both. Contingent upon the experimental set up, it is seen as a particle or it is seen as a wave. And all together, it must be seen as both. If a beam of electrons is directed through a slit, the usual diffraction pattern is observed which is characteristic of wavelike phenomena. Now, if the intensity of the beam is reduced so that only an occasional electron is emitted at the source, punctate scintillations occur at the screen according to a probability law that is isomorphic to the intensities of a diffraction pattern. However, the punctate scintillation must be seen as a particle striking the screen and not as a wave phenomenon.

But, you may counter, the electron is not seen at all. It is a kind of construction. True, but the light patterns on the screen *are* seen. And they can be seen both as signifying a wave interception and as signifying a particle interception. Moreover, they must be seen as both, each manner of seeing according to its respective conceptual frame. This is essential to completing the picture quantum physics has of its microphenomena.

# CHAPTER 9

# Theories and Models

NAÏVETÉ has been used in much of the foregoing discussion as a backdrop against which various themes of the empiricistic argument have been developed. We have addressed ourselves to the following questions: As observers do we apprehend facts as they occur in their pristine naive factualness? or are they apperceived from within some conceptual framework? Is the mind, the brain, a naive recorder of events with all the properties of an impressionable blank tablet? or does it possess certain inborn, or even developmentally acquired, propensities to organize experience in certain characteristic ways? The answer to such questions nowadays seems obvious. Perception involves conceptual frameworks. One cannot divorce the questing after fact and the search for empirical hypothesis from matters of theory. The significance of theory here is two-fold: one, theory prescribes the conceptual framework for our isolating and classifying facts; and two, it is the source of hypothesis by which we direct our fact-getting, fact-creating activities. Thus in certain important respects theory takes precedence over matters of acquiring data.

This has not always been so. Empiricists such as Francis Bacon and John Stuart Mill were eager to exploit the methods of experiment and induction almost to the exclusion of theory and system building. Nature with all its presumed regularities, its laws, its uniformities was there to be interpreted, at least for those who would use the correct empirical methods. Bacon's *Novum Organum* (like Mill's *System of Logic*) was in large part a book on method in the sciences—one of the first, in fact. Nature was "to be interpreted rather than anticipated," by which Bacon meant the observer was to free himself of preconceptions and anthropomorphisms that would prejudge all of experience. His faith in tools and inductive method was such that he believed all observers, regardless of native ability, could, with sufficiently simple and explicit methods, be equally effective in their inductive efforts. Good method was to prevail

over giftedness and inventiveness. Man's innate propensities, his predilections, his language, his traditions, conspire to deceive him. But, with
good inductive regimen, he could come to apprehend the formal aspects of
nature, those regularities which Bacon assumed for natural phenomena
(cf. N9.1).

But even as Bacon himself intimated, he was "more one to sound
the bugle than to marshal the troops." His own speculations about heat
were unfruitful and he is distinguished more for his ignorance and rejection of his scientific contemporaries than for any appreciation of the
theoretical turn that science must take.

Doubtless there is something refreshing in the absolute reliance that
the naive empiricist places upon experience. We find it in Bacon in his
attacks upon the pretensions of rationalism. We find it again in J. S. Mill
who, in a work ostensibly on logic (*A System of Logic*), was to reaffirm the tenets of naive empiricism against the intrusions of rationalism
and deductivism. Mill's famous methods of experimental inquiry (like
the Baconian method of positive and negative instances) were based on
a quaintly restricted conception of science: nature is uniform, it is lawful, and above all it is causally interrelated so that the propositions,
the language, we use to describe nature is a causal language. This being
the emphasis, there is no occasion to speak of theories. There are hierarchies of laws, to be sure. Thus, at the pinnacle of "the ultimate laws
of causation" would stand those of Newton. Below these are the derived
laws, such as those of Kepler, which, in accordance with the unique
factual coexistencies (sun and planets) of the system, are derivable from
the more inclusive laws. This has the touch of reducibility which we find
to be characteristic of formal theories. But ultimate laws are not theories.
They are not invented, they are not arrived at as an inductive gambit
of some kind; rather, according to Mill, they are to be *discovered* as other
laws are discovered—by the application of methods of experimental inquiry. Mill presents a pure empiricism built upon the presuppositions
of uniformity and lawfulness; but the presuppositions are invested in the
object world, and not in the mind of its perceiving subject. For the
radical empiricist such presuppositions are both important and hazardous.
They involve him in the circularity of inductive support. He must evaluate his presuppositions by the very methods the presuppositions were made
to support.

Be that as it may, Mill's empiricism was inviolate; he held consistently that all hypothesis is fundamentally empirical, that material causation, without any metaphysical implications of efficient causation, is alone
supported by experience, and that "experience cannot offer the smallest
grounds for the necessity of a proposition." The source of all law is empirical generalization.

Mill's empiricism has been found wanting for several reasons; for the circularity of his inductive methods, for his inductivist accounts of logic and the foundations of geometry, and (especially for us) for his treatment of hypothesis in scientific method. It is not that Mill ignored the role of hypothesis; in fact he found it indispensable. Rather, he intimated that all hypothesis was to be of an empirical nature, both as to content and as to origin. One needs hypotheses if he is to apply any of the respected methods of inquiry; he needs hypotheses if he is to derive by ratiocination verifiable consequences of the laws such hypotheses express. However, these hypotheses have a different origin from those which we may incorporate into formal theories. They, themselves, are suggested by experience rather than by the deductive requirements of some formal system. As such, their truth is to be directly affirmed or denied. It is the initial hypothesis itself which is verified and not the propositions derived therefrom. It is this treatment of hypothesis which contemporary empiricists have qualified or denied (cf. N9.2).

# HYPOTHETICO-DEDUCTIVE METHOD

In a sense Mill and the inductive empiricists pay lip service to the so-called hypothetico-deductive method of inference. But what they propose is not the same as the method of contemporary theoretical inference. The source of hypothesis was for them a kind of intuitive induction in which experience itself prompts the hypothesis to be tested. The empirical consequences of the hypothesis are more or less direct. One cannot really affirm the consequences of the hypothesis and deny the hypothesis itself. According to the hypothetico-deductive method of contemporary logical empiricism, the situation is quite different. The hypothesis may be constituted of a set of postulates. Then by virtue of rules of inference and correspondence rules one derives hypotheses or propositions the truth of which is an empirical matter. Linguistically, the postulates are statements in the theoretical language. Transformation rules supplement the logical manipulations, such that propositions amenable to interpretation in the observation language are thereby derivable. The postulates themselves may, or, as is quite usual, may not have direct interpretations (translations) in the observation language. "What then," we may ask, "is the truth status of such postulates, of the presumptive hypotheses of the system?" Can we say that they are true or false as Mill would claim for his own hypotheses?

Obviously not. The truth status of an hypothesis that serves as the antecedent in the logical schema of material implication remains indeterminate irrespective of the outcome of an experiment testing the consequent of the hypothesis. The truth of the consequent of the implication is necessary for the truth of the antecedent, but it is not sufficient. Thus every test of a hypothesis is provisional and tentative, in that a hypothesis is tentatively true providing it is not disconfirmed. Yet we are reluctant to claim truth status for the hypothesis other than to attribute to it a *plausibility* residing in its being sufficient to generate derived hypotheses that are not disconfirmed. If we are able to make a clear distinction between presumptive hypotheses which belong to a theory and derived hypotheses which belong to the data language of experiment, then it should be clear that the epistemological status of the two types of hypotheses is quite different. Hence our questions concerning the truth status of theories, of theoretical entities, of crucial experiments, of the ontological necessity of models, and so on.

These questions will come to occupy our attention, but first, a comment on the hypothetico-deductive method in the context of empirical testing. Almost from its inception, experimental methodology, based as it is upon sampling and statistical inference, has acknowledged greater confidence in procedures for rejecting hypotheses than in those for accepting them. John Arbuthnot (1710) gave us what apparently was our first essay in hypothetico-deductive testing (cf. N9.3), but it is Karl Popper, in our own lifetime, who has most keenly analyzed the hypothetico-deductive method as a strategy of disconfirmation (1959). (See Chapter 6.) Let us assume a theory $T$ constituted by a body of presumptive hypotheses $P_1$, $P_2$,..., $P_n$. By virtue of transformation rules, certain derived hypotheses are obtainable which then by means of correspondence rules are either partially or wholly translatable into observation statements. The derived hypothesis is the experimental hypothesis and is that which is subject to evaluation by our verification or falsification procedures.

We have seen earlier that certain types of propositions (hypotheses) are relatively easy to confirm—for example, existential propositions. Thus, if our hypothesis states what a given subject will do, such as choosing an alternative $X$ over an alternative $Y$, then a simple observation will attest to the truth or falsity of the hypothesis. But if the hypothesis is a general statement, say an empirical law, then confirmatory evidence from finite sampling is insufficient to establish the truth of the hypothesis. Thus a more conclusive result is obtained with disconfirmatory results, for the falsification of a general hypothesis is not subject to sampling doubts. Appropriately then, we find that the predominant strategy of experimental test is that of the null hypothesis; namely there is no difference between the universe sampled and the value of the corresponding parameter as deduced from some theory (often set up as the foil). If we then can reject the null hypothesis, our results and decision are relatively conclusive; but if we cannot reject the experimental (null) hypothesis, then by virtue of the decision policy of traditional significance tests we must accept the hypothesis. In that case our decision to accept is exposed to double jeopardy. One, it may be subject to sampling errors in which the "confirmatory" results prompt our accepting an hypothesis which may be false. This is a statistical problem, and though an important one, it does not concern us here. But two, a confirmatory experiment resulting in acceptance of the hypothesis, even should it be warranted statistically, only gets us as far as the truth status of the derived hypothesis. So far as the presumptive hypotheses of the theory are concerned, support reaches no further than the pragmatically tacit agreement that hypotheses which generate true results are useful, and, in some sense, justifiable.

Hence the strategy of so-called "deductivism" as against "inductivism." Presumptive hypotheses are justified so long as they lead to confirmed results. If alternative theories, with different sets of presumptive hypotheses, arise to generate the same set of confirmed experimental hypotheses, then the data, as such, are irrelevant to the assessment of the different presumptive hypotheses. The matter of choosing among theories, each leading to the same experimental results, rests on factors such as simplicity of structure, parsimony, comprehensiveness, and reductiveness which, themselves, are not part of the purely empirical activity of science. Looking at deductivism from the vantage of confirmation, then, it would appear that experiment serves to determine whether the given theoretician, with his creative penchant for presumptive hypothesis, should continue along his given direction rather than along another. Experiment tells him when something is amiss, when modifications in the set of postulates are called for, when he should restrict the range of the theory's application. This would be the case in event of negative results. Experiment also tells him when he can continue in the solace that his theory is a "sufficient" generator of interesting hypotheses.

Now this might appear to be a cavalier treatment of the seriousness with which the theoretical scientist takes his work. As a rule, he is not content with the suggestion that a good theory may be little more than a sufficient myth. But to get at this, he must look to the character of his provisional hypothesis rather than alone to the results of an experiment.

If deductivism, or the hypothetico-deductive method, is inconclusive as concerns positive assertions about evidential support of its presumptive hypotheses, it proves inconclusive also in the region of decision wherein presumably lies its strength. Namely, this is the region of disconfirmation. According to Popper, falsification and the criterion of falsifiability are to be defended on the grounds that they are more conclusive than verification and the criterion of verifiability. Doubtless the argument holds for general propositions and at least equally for existential propositions of the form, "the subject will perform the action $X$ and not the action $Y$ on trial $K$"; that is, an experimental disconfirmation is conclusive if we are concerned with the experimental hypothesis as such. But in the hypothetico-deductive test of the theory and its presumptive hypotheses, the situation is different. We know that experimental confirmation of the derived hypothesis is necessary for the truth of the theory. However, a theory is not a simple proposition. It is a body of presumptive hypotheses $(P_1, P_2,..., P_n)$ such that the falsity of the theory only means that one or more of its conjoint presumptive hypotheses is false. But which hypothesis (or hypotheses) is false, which needs to be modified, augmented, or withdrawn, is not a question that can be answered by the given experiment. As Pierre Duhem (1906) has argued, a theory contains both explicit and implicit assumptions; a disconfirmatory experiment means only that there is error somewhere in the presumptive structure of the theory. In time the theory may undergo modification, such as Hull's theory (1943, 1952) underwent with respect to its treatment of the results of latent learning and exploratory behavior. But the modification is not one made explicitly determinate by the outcome of the initial disconfirmatory experiment. The revision of hypotheses is teased out as the theory itself was teased out, by invention, by trial and error, by anything but the dictates of a logic of discovery (cf. N9.4).

The foregoing is not to argue that the inconclusiveness of experiment in the deductivist schema disqualifies in any substantial way hypothetico-deductive methodology as an instrument of inference and scientific construction. Quite the contrary, formalized theories being what they are, there is no alternative to this methodology. But one should be cautious about overemphasizing the empirics of the experimentalism, both in the constructual and the confirmatory aspects of a theoretical science. It has been sufficient here to point out that the truth status of the postulates and other presumptive hypotheses of a theory is not unequivocally determined by experimental facts. The postulates themselves need not have any direct interpretability in the observation language. Nor need they be a matter of conjecture arrived at by means of an intuitive induction embedded, as it purports to be, in experience.

It is this latter point that distinguishes contemporary hypothetico-deductive method from the deductivism of Mill. There is neither a logic nor an empiric of scientific discovery. Postulates are inventions. Conceived as they may be, as analogy, as inductive hunch, as abstractions to sets of ideal objects, or as uninterpreted variables in abstract calculi, there is no rule, no algorithm, for scientific invention. The Bacon–Mill reliance on intuitive induction wherein the hypothesis has been extrapolated from the complex of experience will not do as an article of systematic investigation.

Much has been made of the absence of any logic of discovery. Both Bacon and Mill would let good methods of inquiry do much of the work of discovery. But both had relatively naive conceptions of science. Neither conceived of a presumptive hypothesis being made independently of facts except as that postulated entity was assumed to be part of a causal complex. The situation in the nearly formalized theories of science is quite different. Initially the presumptive hypothesis may be so abstract or so idealized in its empirical reference that no conceivable defense of the hypothesis can be found on the basis of direct experience. In physics, the kinetic theory of gases assumes dimensionless and perfectly elastic particles of which there is no empirical counterpart. The laws of motion of Newton are purely presumptive, since no demonstration of the laws is possible except in that they lead to verified empirical consequences. In learning theories such as those of Guthrie and Estes, one-trial stimulus–response bonding is assumed although the simple S–R units are for the most part idealizations. But what is more distressing to the pure empiricist is the fact that the structure of the theory may contain postulates that have no ready interpretation at all in the observational language. We are then left with abstract calculi bridging the inferential gulf between antecedent empirical states and derived experimental hypotheses. There may be some argument, as I think there is, for rendering presumptive hypotheses less abstract and more reductive, as it were. But the hypothesis, the invention, determines the search for data as much as data suggest the presumptive hypotheses (cf. N9.5).

In summary, then, deductivism and the hypothetico-deductive method lead us to three somewhat obvious but important conclusions. One, experimental tests are always inconclusive and tentative—they do not confirm the truth of the presumptive hypotheses of a theory, but only attest that such hypotheses could be true. Two, the given experiment, if disconfirmatory, does not indicate precisely what presumptive hypothesis is in error. And three, the source of inventiveness of hypothesis rests in the theoretician. As yet, no device is known for manufacturing scientific discovery, nor does it look as if there ever will be (cf. N9.6).

## STRUCTURE OF THEORIES

'Theory' like 'hypothesis' is a term that belongs to the common language, its meanings running from description to explanation, from the abstract to concrete hypotheticals. With the work of N. R. Campbell (1920), however, the term 'theory' in the language of science has come to designate "connected sets of propositions" which serve as the formal basis for the prediction and explanation of phenomena (cf. N9.7). Generally, we are thought to have explained something whenever we can show that it is an instance of a familiar principle. Thus a law may serve as the major premise of a syllogism, or as the material implication in the *modus ponens*. The event in question now being inferred as an instance of the law is then said to be explained by the law. Instantiation of a law, to be sure, presents one level of explanation, but it should be clarified that a lawful explanation is not the same as a theoretic explanation, nor is a law the same as a theory.

Theories, of course, make use of laws, but they are distinguishable from laws, as such, in certain obvious ways. First, a theory embodies propositions, principles, and syntactical structure such that its corpus is sufficient for deriving experimental hypotheses in the form of empirical laws. Thus an experiment suggested by the theory seeks the instantiation of a law. Second, a theory involves presumptive hypotheses (i.e., theoretical constructs), which are not completely interpretable in terms of the observation language. They are the instruments for mediating theoretical inference, and are not subject to verification in the same way existential statements are. Third, a theory pulls together some set of laws. It performs the function of synthesis such that more than one law is inferable from its set of assumptions.

Now these properties of theories are very loosely specified. Theories can vary in their formal refinements, say from the nebulous meteorological speculations on the origin of air mass systems to an axiomatized mechanics, from theories of personality to an axiomatized theory of learning based upon stochastic processes. Yet regardless of their specificity and regardless of their pretensions, all theories aspire to fulfill their purpose as systems of inference—as unequivocal, consistent, and, of course, useful systems for deriving confirmable hypotheses.

One must note initially that formalization of the theory is desirable. This hardly needs saying in the physical sciences. But in the descriptive sciences, i.e., those of macrophenomena such as personology, ethology, etc., the point requires emphasis. Explicit statements of the postulates and correspondence rules of the theory are necessary for ascertaining whether a hypothesis does indeed follow from the presumptive bases of the theory. A postulate or a set of presumptive hypotheses which are ambiguous or which contain contradictions and inconsistencies can result in the derivation of contradictory experimental hypotheses (cf. N9.8).

Consider, for example, classical psychoanalytic theory. The basic concepts of the theory are a mixture of behavioral categories, presumptive hypotheses and interpretive facts. This is as it should be. The difficulty arises in our not spelling out either the classes of response or the logical implications of the postulates with precision sufficient to generate unequivocal hypotheses. Rationalization, compensation, ambivalence, reaction formation: these, to play the pun, are mechanisms that defend against any unequivocal test of the theory. In a sense these mechanisms are behavioral hypotheses. But they are imprecisely specified; they may ramify in such a way that both behavior $A$ and some other behavior belonging to the class not-$A$ are derivable from the same set of postulates. For example, both parental rejection of the child and parental over-protection can be derived from a set of postulates including factors of the id and superego. Thus the theory, as it stands in its loose formulation, may be incapable of disconfirmation (cf. Kaplan, 1961). One or another postulate may perhaps result in an unequivocal inference but together they may combine to generate any hypothesis you please. One visualizes a damping factor operating or an irony-variable, so to speak, such that from some total set of postulates, if behavior A, then one subset of postulates, if behavior B, then another subset of postulates. Together they achieve the irony factor: namely, that if some other behavior than the one predicted occurs, that deviant behavior is perfectly understandable in terms of an appropriately selected subset of postulates. Even Hull's theory, with its laudable aspirations to hypothetico-deductive formalism, has been criticized for being too loosely structured to permit precise and unambiguous deductions of testable theorems (cf. N9.9).

It hardly need be said that in the fields of psychology, theory is both multifarious and inchoate. Doubtless there is some inverse relation between the multiplicity of theories and their state of formal systemization. If one reads books on the theories of learning, the theories of personality, the theories of perception, etc., he finds compilations of relatively crude sets of propositions which are a mixture of speculation and gross generalization but which offer very little in the way of precise theorems deducible from an explicit set of assumptions. On the other end of the scale of hypothetico-deductive refinement is Euclidean geometry, whose axioms and postulates and derived theorems have proved useful in mapping terrestrial space. One, however, does not plead excepting the social or life sciences from the paradigms of scientific method. All theory, as here visualized, is to serve the purpose of generating precise hypotheses within the framework of the hypothetico-deductive method. The formal analysis of such theory is called for regardless of the state of a science. Without its formal structure, what may pass for a theory in a given science is little more than a masquerade.

## FORMAL STRUCTURE OF THEORY

One of the earliest of formalized theories in the history of science was that of classical mechanics. From a set of definitions and the laws of motion and gravitation, Newton was able to deduce the laws of planetary motion, the orbit of the moon, the patterns of the tides, and nearly every other phenomena of mechanical significance. By operating in this same framework of classical mechanics and by adding certain postulates about gas particles, perfectly elastic collisions, and random motion of the particles, Boltzmann and Maxwell were able to derive the classical laws of gases, thus extending the system to the range of phenomena covered in thermodynamics. By operating from within the same framework and by adopting the postulate of the constant speed of light and the Lorentz transformation, Einstein was able to derive the adjusted values of variables in a relativistic mechanics. This is an impressive array of intellectual achievements. The formal structure, in principle, is the same for all of the theories involved; and it is the same for all theories in psychology and psychoneurology which serve the function of generating experimental hypotheses.

In his classic work in the philosophy of science, N. R. Campbell (1920) writes: "A theory is a connected set of propositions which are divided into two groups. One group consists of statements about some collection of ideas which are characteristic of the theory; the other group consists of statements of the relation between these ideas and some other ideas of a different nature. The first group will be termed collectively the 'hypothesis' of the theory; the second group the 'dictionary'" (1920, p. 122). To these two groups Campbell added the set of propositions which would constitute the model of the theory. And then later a painstaking analysis by Braithwaite (1953) led to his making an important distinction between the calculus of a theory and its model. Thus, following Campbell and Braithwaite, the aspects of a formalized theory are

(1) *The presumptive hypotheses of the theory:* These constitute the postulates and axioms of the system; sometimes explicitly stated as such, sometimes stated as hypothetical constructs with provisional and instrumental status. A significant feature of the postulates is that their evidential support is usually indirect. There may be barriers of inaccessibility precluding direct evidential support of the hypothetical term; there may be no conceivable evidence in direct support of the term; or "interpretation" of the term may be the progressive gaining of evidential support through subsequent experimentation. In this rest the problems and critique of the theoretical terms. But as a theory is initially contrived, the concern of the theoretician is not so much with the truth of the presumptive hypotheses as it is with the empirical truth of the derived theorems. Only after he has empirical support of the theorems of his theory does he become concerned with the "status" of those hypotheses.

(2) *The syntax and calculus of the system:* Every theory requires a language in which it can be expressed. This is to be taken for granted. A significant feature about this language is the set of transformation rules by which values of one class of variables can be transformed into the values of another class of variables. Thus the calculus of a theory is represented by a set of equations or logical formula specifying operations to be performed on certain variables in the formal (theoretical) language of the theory. Thus for example we might find a theory utilizing a probability calculus or an infinitesimal calculus for continuous variables. As the

calculus stands, it is empty of content. That is, questions of interpretation do not belong to the calculus itself. The only requirement is that it be consistent and otherwise logically rigorous.

(3) *The dictionary of the theory:* Theorems derivable within the calculus of the theory will contain nonlogical, as well as, logical terms. Such nonlogical terms are empirically definable by means of the dictionary of the theory. That is, the terms are translatable into, or are true by virtue of, statements in the observation language. Thus the dictionary is that which ties experimental hypotheses in the theoretical language to their observational implications. Moreover, the dictionary provides the rules by which we assess the truth status of the derived theorems within the empirical context of verification. Terms such as "correspondence rules" (Carnap) and "epistemic correlations" (Northrop and Margenau) have also been used to designate the function of this dictionary.

(4) *A model of a theory:* The first article 'a' in this heading is called for (and not 'the') for two reasons. One, there is conceivably more than one model of a theory or a calculus; and two, it is a question for debate as to whether a model is indispensable to the formation and interpretation of a calculus. A model of a theory is some set of propositions, nonequivalent to the propositions of a calculus, which can be said to interpret that calculus. As a rule, models are of the nature of some material or theoretical analogue; but they need not be. The language of models also includes those "models" that are purely abstract. Families of equations may, for example, constitute a "mathematical model" which in its respective applications functions as an analogue as between two sciences, and which is given different interpretations by virtue of different dictionaries. As we shall see, the question whether models are necessary may be gratuitous. Models, analogues, and scientific metaphors play an all but indispensable role in theoretical invention.

Postulates, calculus, dictionary, and model: these constitute the ingredients of a theoretical system. Axiomatization of the theory does not add anything to the theory as such, it merely provides the metascientific language for a logically rigorous derivation of theorems within the applied calculus. Given some calculus then the calculus and its application can be axiomatized in such a way that all statements within the theory will be logically consistent.

Let us now consider an application of the foregoing schema. Attempts to develop postulate sets within psychology (e.g., Hull, 1943, 1953; Voeks, 1950; MacCorquodale and Meehl, 1953) are too complex and at the same time too crude for our initial purposes. Therefore, let us turn to an extremely simple world of behavior calling for simple theory.

Consider the world and behavior of dice, in which members of the species may or may not be alike. They live in a world, so to speak, having the following ecology. Any one or several of the dice are placed in a cup, shaken, and rolled. The "behavior" of the given die is simply its outcome as designated by the number of spots on the face-up side. We are not concerned with how the dice are picked up, shaken, and thrown; these factors are ignored just as in human behavior we may ignore such background detail as the fact that there is oxygen to be breathed and there is light to make stimulus cues effectively visible. The behavioral data are simply the outcomes as obtained singly or combinatorially for a given trial or for a sequence of trials. There are a number of questions that are of empirical interest. Do the two dice differ? Does one class of outcomes occur more frequently than another? Given certain data, can we make any inferences concerning the character of the dice thrown? In other words, we seek and perhaps expect to find certain regularities. And we can reasonably expect to develop laws and a theory concerning such behavior.

Let us now propose a theory based upon the traditional probability calculus. First, we proceed in purely formal terms, without regard, for the time being, for a complete set of definitions or a dictionary. There are various ways of doing this but let us adopt in abbreviated form a set of postulates and axioms after the fashion of Kolmogorov (1933). First, we define a sample space, such that any possible behavior (outcome) is mapped within the space. Furthermore, subsets of these outcomes can be taken so as to establish an event space over the same domain. Then, by virtue of relatively simple operations within the language of set theory, we can formulate the following set of axioms.

We will call the probability of the event $E$, $P(E)$; and the probability of $E$ conditionally upon a sampling procedure, $P(E|H)$. Now, without further specification as to the nature of $P(E)$

A1.   $P(E) \geq 0$

A2.   $P(S) \leq 1$, where $S$ is the domain of all possible events.

From this it follows that

$$0 \leq P(E) \leq 1,$$

since the definition of an event $E$ can include any, all, or none of the outcomes in the sample space.

A3.   $P(E_1 + E_2 + \cdots + E_i + \cdots + E_n) = \sum_1^n P(E_i)$ if the set $\{E_i\}$

is composed of mutually exclusive classes (i.e., for any two members of the set $E_i$ and $E_j$, $P(E_i E_j) = 0$).

From these axioms can be derived some basic theorems for the probability calculus.

T1.   $P(E) + P(\sim E) = 1$

T2.   $P(E \sim E) = 0$, where $\{E \cap \sim E\}$, from which this probability derives, is the null set.

T3.   $P(E_1 \cup E_2) = P(E_1) + P(E_2) - P(E_1 E_2)$

What is popularly known as the multiplication theorem in elementary probability theory is not precisely a theorem but arises by way of defining independence with respect to conjoint sets. Thus we may add

A4.   $P(E_1 E_2) = P(E_1)\, P(E_2 \mid E_1) = P(E_2)\, P(E_1 \mid E_2)$

As a precautionary note, $P(E)$ is the probability of $E$ without specification as to the domain to be sampled. If sampling conditions are to be imposed upon the sampling domain, this is indicated by the conditional $P(E \mid C)$ where $C$ is some event, hypothesis, or other factor relevant to a sampling procedure. From this axiom, we can define *independence* as follows.

D1.   $E_1$ and $E_2$ are independent if $P(E_1 \mid E_2) = P(E_1)$.

In addition, $E_1$ and $E_2$ are mutually exclusive if their conjoint set is null. Thus,

D2.   $E_1$ and $E_2$ are *mutually exclusive* if $P(E_1 E_2) = 0$.

Two other theorems can be deduced from the axioms to complete our probability theory. Letting $p = P(E)$ and $q = P(\sim E)$, we have $(p + q) = 1$ which can be expanded according to the binomial expansion. Thus

T4.   $(p + q)^n$

$$= p^n + n p^{n-1} q + \cdots + \frac{n!}{r!\,(n-r)!} p^r q^{n-r} + \cdots + q^n = 1.$$

Furthermore, if we assume two probability domains, one of events and the other of sampling domains themselves, we can apply A4 to derive the simplest form of Bayes' theorem. Suppose $E$ is the event, and $H$ is the domain sampled in which $H$ itself belongs to a specifiable probability space. Then substituting in A4 we obtain

$$P(H \mid E) = \frac{P(EH)}{P(E)}$$

$$= \frac{P(H)\, P(E \mid H)}{P(H)\, P(E \mid H) + P(\sim H)\, P(E \mid \sim H)}.$$

The formal theory is complete. But as a theory of behavior of the dice, it must have a dictionary. In fact, as exemplary of our formal schema of a theory, this theory of dice behavior should have a set of postulates, a calculus, a dictionary, and possibly a model. Let us see.

First, the axioms and definitions serve as the postulates of the theory. Some terms are undefined, such as 'occurrence.' Some terms are only formally defined (i.e., by implicit definitions), such as '$P(E)$' itself. At this point, we need not concern ourselves as to whether or not a given die has some property specified by $P(E)$. Second, the corpus of the theory serves as a calculus. Rules of arithmetic are, of course, subsumed, and actual calculations may be expedited by some elementary conventions of combinatorial analysis. Third, and this is the significantly pragmatic feature, a dictionary is derived by translating terms in the theorems into terms in the behavioral language. Then, by the conventions of this dictionary, we can ascertain whether a theorem which is true by virtue of the calculus alone is also true by virtue of true statements in the observation language. And fourth, any random device simulating the behavior of the dice might serve as a model (e.g., a lottery). However, the whole of our probability calculus has served as a model for many behaviors and could as well be designated the formal model of our theory.

We are ready now to apply the theory to the behavior of our dice. What hypotheses might we test? What would be analogous to testing a theoretical construct within the theory? As a presumptive hypothesis concerning the dice let us assume that implicit within the "structure" of each die there is a hypothetical factor which we will call its "random propensity." No structural details are given for this propensity, but it must be so stated in the theoretical language that observable consequences can be derived from it.[1] Some such consequence we designate an empirical hypothesis with respect to $P(E)$. How we derive this hypothesis is actually immaterial. But let us assume some rational of homogeneous structure of a perfect cube such as to give the hypothesis: $P(E_j) = \frac{1}{6}$, where $E_j$ is one of six equally inclusive classes which partition the total event space.

How can we test this hypothesis? It should be obvious that we cannot do so with the observation of a single outcome. Either the event will belong to the class $E_j$ or it will not; and, as some probability theorists have never tired of telling us, singular occurrences are not amenable to quantification or to interpretation in the language of probability. We can, of course, take a sequence of many singular occurrences. This, in fact, is what we do. By the aid of a dictionary it is possible to establish a correspondence between the language of set theory with its sample points and the language of occurrences and events in the behavioral language. An expression of the form $P(E)$ is translatable by the dictionary into a relative frequency of those occurrences having the property of the defining event with respect to the total number of all occurrences. Then according to our procedures for testing hypotheses we confirm or disconfirm our hypothesis on the basis of some prescribed decision policy. What that deci-

---

[1] See K. Popper (1957) for a propensity interpretation of probability.

sion policy is, is for the present immaterial. What we conclude upon our decision is whether or not our theoretical construct is plausible.

There are, of course, other hypotheses we might test. For example, we might test the hypothesis that one die has a greater propensity for one face than for another. We might test the hypothesis that two dice behave independently and randomly, as indeed they are assumed to do for their consort in the game of craps (simple combinatorial analysis is required in the calculus). One could test hypotheses for even–odd preferences (using the binomial theorem). Or, perhaps more interestingly, one might assume that an individual die has moods in which the mood phases themselves are describable as a random variable. Assuming two moods, $H$ and $\sim H$, and the probability distribution of each, and assuming that any given sampling of behavior is obtained under the same mood, then Bayes' theorem could be utilized for testing hypotheses about which mood is assumed to prevail at the time of sampling. Details of such tests need not be spelled out, although it would be a simple matter to do so. It is apparent from our theory that experimental hypotheses can be deduced against which actual behavioral tests can be made. What is interesting is the fact that we endow our behavioral objects with properties and dispositions not directly observable. Experimental hypothesis as elucidated within the formal framework of the theory gives us what vision we have of the theoretical constructs. Such vision is, of course, greatly restricted. If we would see the construct in some existential detail, presuming there is such detail, then we would have to probe the structure of the theory itself so as to implement a dictionary for the theoretical term under surveillance.

Aside from the system of axioms, the one theoretical construct upon which our theory rests is that of $P(E)$. Various terms and phrases have been used to describe it, e.g., 'propensities', 'dispositions', 'randomness', or just plain 'probability'. These uses have dispositional implications, such that if $P(E) = k$ then certain behaviors are expected. Indeed, we could define $P(E)$ in such a way that we would say $P(E) = k$ if, and only if, the relative frequency of $E$ to all events out of $n$ trials is exactly $k$. We would then have an explicit reduction of $P(E)$. That, however, is not quite how we used the theoretical construct in our theory. For one thing $P(E)$ could be equal to some real number, $k$, where $0 \leq k \leq 1$, and the actual relative frequency of $E$ in $n$ trials be some number other than $k$. That is to say, we expect sampling error. The relative frequency of $E$ in actual experiment could very well be $k + \epsilon$, where $\epsilon$ is reasonably small, we would still accept that experimental result as support of our behavioral hypothesis generated by $P(E)$. For another thing, there is an objection here to defining $P(E)$ as an explicit reduction to a finite set of trials in the history of the die. That is not what we mean when we set up the hypothesis $P(E)$, for the hypothesis is prior to any trials. It is an expectation, as it were, not a result. Finally, one can be quite unclear about the meaning of $P(E)$, as such, except that for every purportedly meaningful theorem of the theory there is a translation into the behavioral language. Thus $P(E)$ could be nothing more than a pragmatic gimmick.

Although our example here is somewhat trivial, it demonstrates quite clearly the quandaries that might arise about the meaning of our theoretical terms. All that we require of our postulates is that they have testable consequences. Should they have such consequences and should the experimental hypotheses stating these consequences be confirmed, then we more or less cautiously conclude that the postulates, the theoretical constructs, are plausible.

Still, we are inclined to look for more than a cautious predication of plausibility. What is it that is plausible? Does $P(E)$ have some kind of existential status? Is it a fiction? Is it pure invention? Is it a convention? Is it an inferential crutch? From such questions one can glean four different theses as concerns the nature of theoretical constructs.

(1)  The theoretical construct is a real entity. By this is meant that it is directly translatable into the observation language. Its name may designate a real object, however hidden that object may be from initial observation.

(2)  The theoretical construct is a logical construction. By this is meant that it is translatable into the observational language in which the translation indicates a set of logical operations performed on a finite set of particulars. There is no thing, as such, to which the theoretical term refers—only a set of things entering into certain completely specified logical operations.

(3)  The theoretical construct is a convention. As such, it has no existential status. It can be a fictional entity, a contrivance, an abstraction without exemplification. It could even turn out to be descriptive of something that is real. As a convention, however, it is a device, a component of a deductive system without existential pretensions.

(4)  The theoretical construct may be an incompletely specified postulate of real entities. As such it is translatable into an incomplete set of observational consequences. These specified observational consequences are the minimal set of conditions necessary to the truth of the construct. However, the construct has an open texture. In the surplus or as yet unspecified properties inherent in the construct, we find room to include the possibility of additional consequences. Thus the construct has a potential for ramification which it would not have if it were a convention or an explicitly definable logical construct.

For psychology the place to debate the nature of theoretical constructs is in the context of reductionism (Chapters 11 and 12). However, a few points should be noted. Alternative (1) above can be easily dismissed. If the theoretical construct is a hypothesis about some potential (as yet unconfirmed) real, then it serves merely as a place holder for eventual exemplification. One might say that under alternative (4), the surplus meaning view, we aspire to eventual reification of the construct. We act as if alternative (1) indicates the ontological status toward which theoretical terms move. But we cannot hold such terms as designating real states, for the evidences (even the indirect evidences) are as yet incomplete. There have been cases in the history of science where theoretical constructs that were initially hunches led eventually to their own reification under observational refinement (e.g., the case of genetic determiners, or of some types of viruses). To the extent we hope to achieve the progressive transformation of theoretical constructs from their status under (4) to their status under (1), we are interested in transforming all science into descriptive science (a position held by Mach).

The best place to examine the conventional character of theoretical constructs is in the section on models which follows. This leaves alternative (3). It will be argued in Chapter 12 that explicit definition of theoretical constructs removes such constructs from the domain of legitimate theory. An "explicit definition" is given for the purported theoretical construct if we can substitute for that term an explicit set of observational terms combined by means of a completely specified set of logical operations. Thus should one choose, he could define $P(E)$ explicitly as the logical operation of relative frequency (i.e., $P_f(E) = (\Sigma X/N)$ where $X = 0,1$ according to observation) over a finite number, $N$, of trials. But then, from the point of view of theory, the theoretical construct would be a tautology derived from its own extension over the set of observations. In effect: if $H$ then $P_f(E)$; but since $H = P_f(E)$, then if $P_f(E)$ then $P_f(E)$. That is to say, such theoretical terms (logical constructs) may be useful in the observation language (e.g., in the refinement of law, as argued in Chapter 12); but they can only serve in a trivial way as instruments of inference. This is the argument of intervening variables as against hypothetical constructs (cf. N9.10) and the issues can be summarized briefly as follows: If the theoretical term is to be given an explicit definition in the observation language and is to enter into the interpreted calculus of the theory, then the only hypotheses deducible from it in the language of the dictionary will be the logical consequences of its own set of observation statements. On the basis of a theory whose only postulates are intervening variables one will not get interesting hypotheses. Only by combining the intervening variable with other theoretical constructs that are not so extensionally limited, or by opening the texture of the intervening variable's own extension, as, for example, by analogy, will the theory generate experimental hypotheses that are not trivially evident within the presuppositions of the theory (cf. N9.11).

## MODELS

As philosophers of science have reached considerable agreement concerning the formal nature of theory and the ideal of hypothetico-deductive methodology, they have turned their attention increasingly to the problems of models and theories. The essential question is: Does a theory that incorporates an abstract calculus as the skeleton of its formal structure require an interpretation of that calculus in a language different from the calculus itself? Is a model indispensable to the utilization of a calculus within the theory? It would appear that the answer to both of these questions is "No, models are not indispensable." However, the debate that has occurred has stemmed, one, from a lack of agreement concerning the nature of a model, and two, from a mixing of logical problems in scientific inference with psychological problems of scientific inventiveness.

That the answer to our question appears to be "No" follows, by example from an analysis of the simple theory of dice behavior given in the preceding section. The calculus of probability as formally stated is purely abstract. The probability variable $P(E)$ is undefined except within the abstract system of real numbers. The theorems of the formal system are uninterpreted as they stand in the initial calculus. Utilization of the calculus in the theory of the dice occurs by means of our constructing a dictionary by which the theorem can be translated into our expectations concerning the frequencies of observable events. Or, with respect to state variables, certain operational conventions may be adopted for assigning values to $P$ within the range allowed by the relevant axioms of the calculus. But the calculus can be used without our conceiving any model for the variables of the calculus. Although, conceivably, one might make an *a priori* assignment to $P$ on the basis of the classical procedures of enumerating equally likely classes of outcomes, this is merely a convention (i.e., an arbitrary procedure, not at all entailed by the logic of the calculus) for assigning one value rather than another to the parameter $P$. Moreover, the calculus is indifferent, as it were, to our dictionaries. No model is required for the point-by-point elaboration of its theorems. The usefulness of the calculus is decidable on grounds of its serving as the basis of inferring verifiable hypotheses. Decidable, yes, but perhaps not alone decidable on such grounds. And that is where the utility of models enters the picture.

First, however, we must backtrack and pick up the argument with the discussion concerning the meaning of 'model' as it is used in the philosophy of science. Likely we are all prepared to accept the distinction between the model and thing modeled. That much is apparent. However, some models are much like the thing modeled, whereas other models are quite unlike the thing modeled in that they either are fictional or are logically abstract. Beginning with replicas at one extreme, we ascend the scale of abstraction from scale representations to conventions and on to abstract calculi themselves. When does a model cease to be a model? At the one extreme, that of the replica, the model converges on the object of theory itself; it may become a "true" description of that object. At the other extreme, the abstract treatment of a model may turn it into a calculus itself, so that the point of differentiation between a calculus and a model seems to be lost. This latter point is the source of some confusion in the argument for the indispensability of models.

## Types of Models

For the present discussion a distinction is made between *formal* models and *structural* models.[2] Questions of the realism of models are in the background but it is apparent that so far as formal models are concerned, the language of realism, if used at all, will have esoteric overtones not to be found in the realism of palpable structures. The logician tends to define a *formal* model as that by which any set of valid sentences of a theory are satisfied or represented by another set of entities which are the realization of the theory (Tarski, 1941; Suppes, 1957). As it stands this definition is somewhat remote from the actual models that scientists deal with. Two features, however, serve to bring out its specific applicabilities. One, there is a set of valid sentences of the theory in a language that is partly theoretical and partly observational (at the dictionary ties). Two, there is also a set of entities, such as those of set theory, in which the formal relations of the theory can be realized. It is the model that interprets the calculus, and the fact that one realization or model of the valid theorems of a theory can be achieved does not preclude the possibility of alternative realizations. The logician has one thing in mind when he seeks a model of a theory. For him a theory is a system. He wants to know if he can build a model for the theory such that every theorem of the model is isomorphic to a theorem in the theory. He seeks complete representation of one system, the theory, by another system, the model.

As remote as some discussions of logical models may be from the subject of concrete models, their relevance should not escape the theoretical scientist. For if he takes his own models seriously and holds out for them on the grounds of say their simplicity or their microreductive potential, he must be sure that his model, as rigorously expressed, does in fact satisfy the requirements of isomorphic representation.

[2] This is a simplification for expository purposes only. There is a fairly large literature in which problems of classifying models are touched upon. See for example, Hesse (1953, 1961, 1963); Gregory (1953); Hutten (1954); Apostel (1960); Suppes (1960); Lachman (1960); Beament (1960); Black (1962); Kaplan (1964); Rosenbleuth and Wiener (1945); Braithwaite (1962).

There is, however, a more obtrusive feature of formal models. This is the fact that the set of entities of the model need have no specific interpretability in the observation language. That is to say, theoretical terms in the theory when represented in the model may have no meaning other than that which they possess by virtue of their being parts of the abstract system. One notes, for example, that a model of the probability calculus may be purely abstract, as indeed it is in its axiomatization. And in some mathematical learning models, no effort is made to interpret in empirical or even familiar construct language the algebraic form of the models (Bush and Mosteller, 1955; Luce, 1959). The structure of the model is logical structure made explicit by a careful statement of the theory. Aside from its representation of valid experimental hypotheses, it stands aloof, as it were, from such mundane intermediating processes as might concern the neurophysiologist.

Presumably any rigorous theory can be axiomatized. It can be given a formal model which may or may not be anchored to statements in the observation language at various stages of some process function. Mediating process is, of course, not precluded from the formal model. However, the insistence that formal models are only concerned with representing valid theorems of a theory seems to license the theoretician to adopt any logical conventions he may find to be useful. Consequently, he may ignore mediating process where, so far as a traditional learning theory is concerned, the reduction of mediating variables is purely speculative. At least so far as the neuropsychologist is concerned, this may have certain heuristic disadvantages. The question of inventiveness becomes foremost; and it is by no means clear that a theoretician who is concerned primarily with rigorous formalization can continue to create and embellish upon scientifically interesting theories (Restle, 1959).

By *structural* models, I mean those models whose entities in some sense are more palpable than those we find in formal models. Two initial comments are in order. First, the fact that a model may possess palpable structure does not preclude its being axiomatized and formalized within a representative abstract model. Second, the meaning of structure is by no means preempted by its reference to palpable objects. Geometry and Boolean algebra possess structure, so to speak. It is the business of the logician to show just what structure various calculi have. Still this does not obviate the fact that some models are interpretable in other than abstract terms. A structural model, therefore, is taken to be one such that not only is it a realization of a theory, but the realization is such that some of its nonlogical terms are interpretable in an existential medium *different from that of the thing modeled.* By "existential medium" I mean some uniquely classified domain of predicates in the observation language. Thus for any abstract calculus of a structural model, if the model is well represented by that calculus, there are some variables whose values are determined by operational conventions. In the language of palpability, a structural model is something we can build, visualize, construct, put on paper, etc. Even though unconstructed in fact, the ultimate realization of such models entails a familiar space–time context. The problem of analogy, of course, remains open. One might have a mechanical analogue, say, of muscle action; it would be a structural model of the muscle but with limited analogy (cf. N9.12).

Most models in psychological theory, I think it is safe to say, are of a structural type. A formal model requires systematic axiomatization and successful efforts along this line are quite rare (Bush and Mosteller, 1955; Estes and Suppes, 1959; Luce, 1959; Fitch and Barry, 1950). In this context what one notes is not so much whether the theoretician has achieved a fully representative formalization in his abstract model but whether or not he wishes to remain aloof from giving an interpretation of the nonlogical variables of the system. It is interesting too that formal models have been achieved primarily (though not exclusively) in the area of statistical learning theory. Stochastic models and the probability calculus are particularly amenable to formalization. However, they need not be purely formal. There have been many efforts to build structural models that effect the random processes and behaviors describable in probabilistic language. For example, in the area of neurophysiological theory, we find structural models for random functions presented by Marshall and Talbot, 1942; Osgood and Heyer, 1951; Eccles, 1953; Pitts and McCulloch, 1947; Hebb, 1949; Milner, 1957; Rosenblatt, 1958.

*Cybernetic models.*     The subject of cybernetics, even as it is applied to psychology, is far too extensive to give it more than passing attention. Still, its emphasis upon functional units, feedback, and schematic functionalistic diagrams renders it especially relevant to the model-making enterprises of the behavioral scientist. The details of cybernetics belong to the communications engineer. We shall not be concerned with these. However, the method and analysis of the new discipline are quite relevant to problems of both modeling and scientific inference.

Norbert Wiener, who along with his colleagues is credited with inducing the birth and with christening the new science, defines cybernetics simply as "the entire field of control and communication theory, whether in the machine or in the animal" (1948, p. 19). This is a broad definition but the approach of the new science was at the time quite unique. Relying heavily on the principle of feedback, cyberneticists were able to lay down complex schemes of function which were descriptive both of physical and biological systems of communications and control. So far as the physical systems were concerned, the components implementing a system could be clearly identified and classified. In biology, however, only partial information was available; but by virtue of impressive analogy, cybernetics served as means both of description and hypothesis concerning certain biological processes.

The schematics of cybernetics are simply an elaboration on the old black-box principle. If no simple laws are ascertainable as between input and output or as between stimulus and response, and if interposed between the observables there are mediating complications, then it is convenient to introduce the black-box analogue. Thus Woodworth, in his remarkably successful textbook (1922), interjected the organism, O, between stimulus and response as a catchall processing center for all those factors that make S–R psychology a more complicated discipline than pure reflexology (cf. N9.13). As such, however, the black-box is a mere substitute for the enclosed brackets of ignorance. Certain functional relations may be implemented by the black-box but details as to mechanics, process, and structure are missing. Thus, the brain has suffered both the eminence and the indignity of being a black-box. Early ablation studies undertook the partition of the big black-box into smaller black-boxes, leaving mechanics and process untouched but adding a little to our knowledge of function and structure.

It should be noted, however, that black-box schemata are not quite the same as those of cybernetics. Black-boxes are, in logical terms, place holders; they are the guarded lacunae to be filled in by future generations. Cybernetics schemata, on the other hand, are structural and functional hypotheses which model the internal details of the boxes. In fact, the black-box itself must be partitioned according to the cybernetics hypothesis. The case here is trenchantly presented in a paper by Mario Bunge (1963). According to him, "a general black-box theory" enables one to describe mathematical functions as between input and output for crudely classified systems; but it does not give interesting results so far as scientific (i.e., theoretical) inference is concerned. Black-box theory is a kind of crude phenomenology; it states gross functional relations without elucidating any system for deducing hypotheses about those relations.

As compared with black-boxes, then, the distinguishing feature about the cybernetics model is that it partitions a behavioral system into meaningful functional units, the meaning of each unit being some explicit hypothesis as to how that function is achieved. Thus, for example, a system may require a memory unit. With the specification of the unit, one can prescribe certain mechanisms or hardware sufficient to effect the kind of storage the system seems to have. Furthermore, the application of cybernetics exemplifies a pragmatic rather than ontological approach to modeling. Although cyberneticists such as McCulloch and Pitts may be interested in constructing models of the nervous system with an optimal amount of positive analogy, the preliminary work entails constructing alternative systems that will achieve the types of function under study. A memory system, for example, can be implemented by IBM cards, magnetic tapes, magnetic drums, mercury cells, program panels, etc.; but when modeling the memory of the nervous system certain of these schemata can obviously be eliminated. Our anatomical knowledge of the nervous system might favor reverberatory circuitry, or permanent impress either on the circuitry or cellular structure itself (Gaito and Zavala, 1964) (cf. N9.14).

Generally then the difference between black-box modeling and cybernetics is one of functional detail. But that difference is a significant one. Where black-box analysis simply indicates the presence of a mediating process or unspecified structure, cybernetics makes a functional analysis of mediating components such as to propose various structures sufficient to effect such functions. As Gregory has pointed out (1961), black-box schemata, at their very highest degree of refinement, are blue prints from which a mere technician might produce a structure of given black-box components; but such schemata have no explanatory power. They contain no hypotheses as to how the components work. A cybernetics model, on the other hand, being concerned with the structures and functional details of the components and even with the design of components, serves as an explanatory basis of control systems. Gregory continues in a Cambridge tradition largely instigated by Kenneth Craik (cf. N9.15); namely, the structural and functional properties of systems are inseparable, and though there may be major differences between metallic and colloidal components, the analogy in function between inorganic and organic systems is sufficient for us to utilize cybernetics as the basis for at least lower level explanation. Gregory finds that both functional analogues and the language of physical control systems (e.g., criteria of efficiency) are useful in generating hypotheses concerning organic behavioral systems.

Perhaps the most poignant feature of his argument is to be found in a critique of ablation studies. There are several points to this critique which are worth noting. First, ablation studies are designed essentially for making black-box identifications. Impairment of behavior after ablation leads to isolating some component of neural tissue as being apparently indispensable to normal functioning of the organism. However, the level of explanation is quite primitive—like indicating the removal of some tube in a television set as the cause of certain aberrations of the picture. Second, disturbance of a system occasioned by ablation may have indirect effects not traceable by tissue removal alone. For example, if the system is not a simple telephonic network, mass removal of a cell complex may affect functioning of some cells which under normal circumstances are more or less independent of the ablated cells. In general, understanding of the functioning of complex redundancy systems, such as the central nervous system appears to be, is not likely to be achieved by means of ablation intrusions. And third, and perhaps most important, neurophysi-

ology needs theoretical models to define and specify what it is we are
to look for in the way of structural detail. Without hypotheses the search
is restricted to crude classification of anatomical detail. Cybernetics hypotheses as to memory function, attentional scansion, recognition, and
perceptual invariance suggest the possibility of neural networks and systemic interactions that very likely would remain obscure without that
theoretical guidance. Here Gregory touches upon a now familiar adage:
theory guides discovery, and not vice versa (cf. N9.16).

*Truth status of models.*     We have seen earlier that the terms
'true' and 'false' can be applied to theorems of a theory but not to the
theory itself. Is the situation any different for models? According to empiricistic conventions (and the thesis of extensionality) truth values can
be assigned to propositions which reduce to statements of observable
states of affairs. A model would then be a true model if all of its assertions were true. But models are models of things. If we take the "thing"
to be a theory, then the model of it could only be true if every nonlogical assertion in the model were true by virtue of its being a correct
empirical assertion. In that case the theory and its isomorphic model
would become a true description of the phenomena which are the subject
matter of the science. Should we choose to call the thing modeled "the
phenomena of the given science," then the model itself may be a theory
of the data. And if every nonlogical assertion of the model is true, then
just as above, the model again becomes a true description of the thing
modeled—so the argument would appear to go (cf. N9.17).

Now there are three features of the discussions of models which
militate against so restricted a treatment as is given in the preceding paragraph. One, in the open discussion of models, we have to include relatively abstract systems of postulates, axioms, and transformation rules,
as well as the potentially concrete artifacts we usually think of as being
appropriately named by 'model'. Two, in light of alternative models for
the same theory, such models may possess a conventional character in
which the truth status of nonlogical terms is indeterminate. And three, it
may not be our intention that a model be a replica of the thing modeled.
We may intend only that it be an entity with sufficient positive analogy
that we can understand and predict the phenomena to which that model
is applied. This touches upon the metaphorical aspects of models. Let us
briefly consider each of these points.

A set of statements which describes the terms, operations, and range
of application of some calculus may serve as the model of a theory. This
would include for the most part what a logician construes as the model of
a system. The essential feature of such a model is that it be isomorphic
with the thing modeled. That is to say, that for every statement in the
theory there is a statement in the model such that every theorem in the

theory is derivable within the model.[3] As an example, we might again take some model utilizing the probability calculus in its logical structure. Since the nonlogical terms of the calculus remain uninterpreted within the model itself, it would be quite irrelevant then to ask whether such terms were subject to truth analysis. In the astronomy of antiquity one might indeed have used the geometric models of the epicycle and eccentrics for generating theorems of planetary position without visualizing as matters of fact any of the myriad of motions which the geometric entities suggest. The only motion that is describable or representable so far as factual access is concerned may be that of the apparent planetary positions; thus, only hypotheses about such positions are subject to verification. In stochastic learning theories, $\theta$, the parameter sometimes designated as the rate of learning, may be just such an abstract entity. As such it designates no object, but its place in the formal model results ultimately in statements which by means of a dictionary can be tied to experiment. Is $\theta$ true? To be sure, since $\theta$ is a parameter, one estimate of $\theta$ might be better than another in that it generates truer hypotheses about behavior. Still it makes little sense to state that the confirmed hypothesis makes $\theta$ true, not even if the statement in the model which is isomorphic to the true hypothesis necessitates $\theta$ being some specific value. Or to put it another way, the only recourse we have to making $\theta$ true is to show that the true hypothesis can be generated by the model incorporating $\theta$, and *only by that model*. Such a condition would be realized only if all models were true descriptions of things in the sense of N9.17.

The second point follows on the first. If models are conventions and mere instruments of prediction, then no part of the model, no nonlogical term, carries with it existential pretensions—or if you choose, it carries with it *only* existential *pretensions*. There is no intention of making the models a true and exhaustive description of phenomena (cf. N9.18).

The third point asserts that it may not be our intention that a model be a replica of the thing modeled. In that case it would be irrelevant to ask of the model if it is true. Rather at most we should say of a model that it is more or less true. That is, it is true to the extent of its positive analogy, it is false to the extent of its negative analogy. But by being more or less true, it is neither. The language of truth or falsity is applicable only as a manner of speaking. What makes a model a metaphor (Black, 1962) is that it possesses some negative analogy. It is like the thing modeled, but not exactly. Some aspects of the model are thought inapplicable; they are either suppressed or idealized. Thus a gas can be thought of as a volume of perfectly elastic particles behaving much like,

---

[3] Pains are not taken here to bring in the fine distinctions between set theoretic, algebraic, and other abstract models; or between isomorphic and homomorphic relations. The reader is referred to Apostel (1960) for a general discussion and to Suppes (1957), Chapter 12, for a more technical discussion of these matters.

but not quite like, billiard balls. The negative analogy that tells the lie rests in the fact that particles of some finite mass have internal structure that contaminates the ideal of perfect momentum exchange. The psychology of tension systems and psychic energy is, of course, loaded with negative analogy. The model of the psychoanalytic energy system with its pipes, reservoirs, and overflow spouts (Hendrick, 1934) is hardly to be taken seriously at all. Yet energy systems, principles of least effort (e.g., Zipf, 1949) and other paraphernalia of mechanics seem to be such useful expository devices that we succumb to the enchantment of the metaphor and begin to reify what initially serves as a crutch for establishing certain crude descriptive categories.

The point is well stated by Hinde (1960) in an article titled "The Energy Model of Motivation." He reviews motivation models of Tinbergen, McDougall, Lorenz, Freud, and J. S. Brown, only to find that motivational energies do not systematically exploit the analogy to physical energy systems. 'Energizing' appears to be an appropriate term for describing behavior onset and activation; analogy comes to us so easily. Still even for those who seek physiological foundations of motivation (e.g., Tinbergen and McDougall), the energy manifestations of behavioral onset are only roughly analogous to energy transformations in physics. First of all, there is a confusion between behavioral and physical energy systems. One can speak of behavioral energies in a metaphorical sense, but he cannot make point for point identifications wherein the repositories of behavioral energy are also repositories of physical energy and where both satisfy conservation principles. A precise dictionary for translating the behavioral energy language into the physical energy language does not as yet exist. Secondly, one cannot use physical energy analogy (other than as expository metaphor) and *not* embrace a reductionist view of theoretical constructs. Physical energy is a very real thing, as close to ontological basics as we are likely to get. There is an element of insincerity in our holding to closed or open physical energy systems while playfully inserting "as if" constructs to mediate behavior. Hinde holds that MacCorquodale and Meehl are correct in their calling for neurophysiological reduction of hypothetical constructs. Thirdly, the analogues of energy storage and dissipation can be quite misleading when applied to behavioral science. The concept of energy level is inapplicable to behavioral analysis; where some behaviors conserve energy, others seek actively to dissipate it. A system that needs stimulation and energy dissipation more than it needs equilibrium or conservation (e.g., Heron, 1957) is hard to match against simple physical systems. The moral is, of course, that analogy, i.e., negative analogy, can be quite misleading if the person takes a model as a replica of the phenomenal system.

Let me now reiterate the foregoing argument. A model is to be judged by its positive analogy. To the extent there is negative analogy then some hypotheses as derived from the model are not true for the thing modeled. Models, therefore, are potentially misleading and corruptive. But lest one takes this as the salient lesson of modeling, he should hasten to note that models are also effective heuristic instruments. In terms of the conceptual framework, models enter into our apprehension and interpretation of facts. We bring positive analogy to focus upon the phenomenal flux. Both our classification and our understanding of phenomena are contingent upon analogy, upon what Pepper (1948) calls the "root metaphors" and what Black (1962) calls "conceptual archetypes."

*Are models indispensable?* "Yes!" say Campbell (1920), Hesse (1963), and Suppes (1962). "No!" say Duhem (1914) and Braithwaite (1953). "Helpful!" say Black (1962) and Nagel (1961). Even when these people agree, they come to their answers for different reasons. Let us briefly inspect their arguments. Consider the no's first. Duhem (1914) argues that all theories are essentially conventional so far as concerns their theoretical terms (cf. N9.19). Any effort to interpret these terms either existentially or as material analogues smacks of unwarranted metaphysics. Models will be misleading in that they suggest hypotheses not testable within the body of experimental theorems of the theory. Rigor in scientific thinking is achieved by attending to the derivation of testable hypotheses and not by postulating palpable entities presumed to be like those found in our concrete experience. He does not, however, disdain analogy. "The history of physics shows us that the search for analogies between two distinct categories of phenomena has perhaps been the surest and most fruitful method of all the procedures put in play in the construction of physical theories" (1914, p. 95). But analogies should not be confused with models.

> Analogies consist in bringing together two abstract systems; either one of them already known serves to help us guess the form of the other not yet known, or both being formulated, they clarify each other. There is nothing here that can astonish the most rigorous logician, but there is nothing either which recalls the procedures dear to ample but shallow minds, nothing which substitutes the use of imagination for the use of reason, nothing which rejects the logically conducted understanding of abstract notions and general judgments in order to replace it with a vision of concrete collections (1914, p. 97).

Braithwaite (1953, 1962), with his characteristic rigor in argument, gives a somewhat similar answer.[4] Both the theory and the model of the theory are interpretations of the same calculus. For the theory, the

[4] If one savors an irony here of the ample, empirically minded Englishman beating the rationalist Frenchman at his own game, he should not be too hasty. Symbolic algebras (such as the Huntington calculus which Braithwaite uses) belong to the spirit of the ample mind with its penchant for extensive classification.

derived formula, the laws, and empirical hypotheses are epistemologically prior to the theoretical terms, whereas for the model the theoretical terms are epistemologically prior. One cannot, therefore, claim that models are indispensable either to an interpretation of a calculus or to the development of a theory. Under some circumstances the positive analogy of a model can be heuristically fruitful but the factor of negative analogy can be as detrimental as the positive analogy can be productive. "The price of the employment of models is eternal vigilance" (1953, p. 93). It is, however, important to emphasize that a theory and its calculus can be uninterpreted so far as concerns the theoretical terms. The essential character of such terms is that they be open-textured and amenable to such modification as will enhance the explanatory and predictive possibilities of the theory.

One would think that an affirmative answer to the question posed in this section would indicate a point of view which is discrepant in some fundamental way from that of Duhem and Braithwaite. This, however, does not seem to be the case. If anything, what is at stake is the role that analogy and the reliance on palpable analogues plays in the psychology of invention. Suppes (1962), for example, renders models indispensable to theory by virtue of his making any systematic corpus of mathematical propositions or calculus a possible model of a theory. Any clear statement of the deductive system in the metascientific language of logic should satisfy the set-theoretic requirements of a model. Fundamental distinctions between mathematical models and formalized theories are not required. Therefore, a model, whether mathematical or physical, is essential to the theory. Moreover, a good physical theory will be well formalized and thus amenable to the axiomatization of so-called mathematical models.

In a series of publications, Hesse (1953, 1961, 1963) has argued for the indispensability of models on the grounds that without them extension of a theory would be impossible. The essential feature for the growth of any theory and for its extension is the positive analogy implicit within its model. Still what looks like a call for the kinds of models Duhem disdains turns into a qualified retreat. For by models, Hesse means to include such formal models as we claim for any systematic body of uninterpreted equations. The positive analogy rests in the fact that an interpretation of a theoretical construct in one science suggests an analogous interpretation of the nonlogical terms of the calculus when that calculus is applied to another science. But here the model can actually be the formal body of mathematical equations that are interpretable both in the fundamental science and in the analogue. Thus, for example, both the theory of heat and the theory of electrostatics utilize the same mathematical equations with, of course, their respectively different dictionaries. One theory with its interpreted calculus serves as the model for the other, the positive analogy being implemented through interpretation of those terms in the calculus which are common to the theory and its model. When Hesse argues for the logical necessity of models, she is not merely exploiting the role models play in the psychology of convention. She asserts that deductive structure is the *sine qua non* of a theory. Selection of an appropriate calculus is a matter of analogy. One calculus, with its formal components and interpretation in one theory, is selected over another calculus because of an analogy which makes it congenial to interpretation in the other science. In general, Hesse argues from the vantage of heuristics. New hypotheses, insights, and theoretical inventions come to us by virtue of the logic of analogy as implicit within the creative process.

Campbell's yes to the indispensability of models remains one of the most defensible answers to the question. Writing of analogy rather than models, as such, he argues not that analogues are heuristic devices or are mere instruments of invention but that they are essential to explicating the meaning of the theory itself. Anyone can invent a theory, i.e., a formal calculus by which he can deduce an established law. However, a theory without an analogy is meaningless (cf. N9.20). It may be true that a theory without analogy would lack heuristic potential but this is not the point. (We could as well argue that as often as not a person may be misled by what materializes in the model as negative analogy.) What is more significant is the fact that a theory would have no epistemological anchorage, no reference, no semantical overtones of any kind, if in fact it were uninterpretable by grace of an analogy. The analogy of a theory is epistemologically prior to the hypotheses and constructs of the theory itself. Thus not only are laws explained within the deductive framework of the theory but the analogy, by means of this priority, serves to explain why events should conform to the laws of the theory (e.g., see Sellars, 1961).

It would appear from these and other accounts of models (e.g., Black, 1962; Hutten, 1951, 1954; Nagel, 1961) that there are no fundamental differences of opinion concerning the need for a logical calculus of some kind in the development and application of a theory. Moreover, it also seems obvious that the purely formal part of a theory need not be interpreted; it need not be modeled in the physicalistic senses of modeling. For example, certain mathematical models in psychology and economics (Braithwaite, 1962) and some formal models in microphysics (Dirac, 1947) cannot be interpreted as a logical blueprint for any empirical process. Still what makes models real to people and what removes them from the domain of abstract contrivances ("for calculational purposes only") are their heuristic and semantic functions. Whether models are explicitly interpretable and convergent upon real descriptions or whether they remain abstract calculi is relatively unimportant so long as they perform the function of explicating the meaning of a theory. This they do by virtue of their analogy.

*Semantic functions of models.*    We should now examine more closely the semantic functions of a model and its analogy. If both formal and phenomenological analogy are allowed then the semantic functions that a model performs will be different according to whether a model is structural and phenomenological or whether it is primarily formal. Consider first the case of structural models. There is little difficulty in stating what one means by their fulfilling a semantic function. The theory and its model indicate to us that certain laws of physics, behavior, etc., are derivable by a set of postulates, theoretical constructs, or explicit mechanisms epistemologically more basic than the understanding of simple lawful descriptions. It is not just that our analogy suggests that this set of phenomena is like another set of phenomena by virtue of some similarity but that the analogy imparts an understanding of one set of phenomena on the basis of an understanding of another set of phenomena. Assume some abstract model M for a science and its theory $T_1$. Assume another science and theory $T_2$ also utilizing most of M. The application of M to $T_1$ is epistemologically prior to its application by analogy to $T_2$. What is the source now of that analogy? One cannot say that it is due to the fact that $T_2$ and $T_1$ have the same inherent logical structure, for as empiricists have persistently pointed out (e.g., Hume, *Treatise;* Duhem, 1914; Toulmin, 1953) logical relations are not properties intrinsic to physical objects. The source of the analogy is very likely perceptual. One sees positive analogy as between the phenomena of one science, for which $T_1$ holds, and the phenomena of the other science, for which $T_2$ holds. Because of the analogy, M (the language of formal inference and the postulates it includes) which is useful in deriving theorems within $T_1$ is also thought to be useful in deriving valid theorems in $T_2$. When one observes waves in a liquid medium, and then observes elementary beat phenomena in an acoustics laboratory, he does not see the fundamental wave equations as properties of the two sets of phenomena. Rather the phenomenological analogy is the source of his using the model as a common language for representing two different domains of experience. In bombarding gold leaf with a stream of particles and observing the effects, Rutherford could literally see the structure of the gold leaf as a set of minimally occupied orbital systems each analogous to a solar system. The model of celestial mechanics could therefore serve as the theoretical language for diverse physical systems.

Another example is to be found in the application of the model of information theory. Mechanical communication systems are so rich with analogy that when Shannon (1949) and others perfected a formal model for the analysis of communication channels, practically every other science of input-output systems, whether physical or biological, rushed to borrow the language and the schema of bits, negative entropy, noise, redundancy, etc. (cf. N9.21).

The first point, then, is that the analogy of models may derive primarily from the analogy of perception. Since two or more sets of phenomena may be perceived as having positive analogy they are also understood as having common structure wherein a given model, or a set of analogous models, serves as the language for expressing the nature of the structure.

Now one may also discover analogy by means of noticing the similarity in the formal models as postulates for sets of diverse phenomena. Say for a theory $T_1$ a model $M_1$ is developed. This may be the formalization of its postulates and equations. For $T_2$ a formal model $M_2$ may be developed. And now, and perhaps not until now, it is noticed that $M_2$ resembles $M_1$. Thus an analogy as between $T_1$ and $T_2$ and as between the phenomenological domains of each theory is discovered but the discovery is posterior to the recognition of analogy in the models. It is not easy to find examples in which the analogy between models materializes upon recognition of similarities between the formal systems of laws, as such. Newton's law of gravitation, Coulomb's law of magnetic attraction, and the law of the intensity of electromagnetic radiation revealed their homology before the latter two at least were incorporated by Maxwell into a unified field of theory (cf. N9.22).

Now it does not appear that the distinction between analogy by phenomenological similarity and analogy by formal similarity contributes anything, as such, to the imperatives for models. It does, however, serve to bring out what Hutten (1951, 1954) has called the semantic function of models. In the case of phenomenological analogy, the language of the model is common to the sciences that are bridged by the analogy. The meaning of the model is then transported from the science from which it was derived to the science for which the model is constructed. In the case of formal analogy, the language of formal models is found to be appropriate for the derivation of diverse sets of laws. The meaning of the formal model is amplified through its successful applications to phenomenological domains which would, except for that analogy, remain unrelated or more or less encapsulated within their respectively autonomous theories.

Much of the argument over the indispensability of models, as we have seen, stems from the failure to make the clear-cut distinction between formal and structural models. Without formal models, we might argue there could be no theories. This seems to be straightforward. But often the argument for models as the indispensable heuristic ingredient of theories is based on the assumption that such models are to be regarded as structural models, with at least some components of the model being either actually or prospectively interpretable in the observation language. This is a much less impressive argument, since formal systems as such are also open to invention and modification and can be suggestive of new hypotheses at the frontiers of experiment. Nevertheless a strong case can be made for the need for structural models, if not for their absolute indispensability in the sciences whose theories have been characteristically microreductive (and what sciences haven't been?). The proper place to examine the details of the argument is in the chapters on reductionism; the substance of the argument, however, can be briefly outlined.

A theory should not only serve the function of deriving its laws within the system of its postulates and calculus but also, where possible, it should evolve toward explicating the nature of its postulates. Or to put it another way, if empirical laws are to be derivable as the logical consequences of postulates, then it is legitimate to ask why one set of postulates is preferred over some other. There are several criteria that we may wish to impose here in defending our choice, e.g., simplicity, familiarity, comprehensiveness, heuristic richness, etc., but the foremost of criteria would be empirical confirmability wherever there might be some prospect that "sufficient" postulates could be formulated in the empirical language. In a word it is proposed that we keep in mind Russell's maxim: "Wherever possible substitute logical constructions for hypothetical entities." This does not mean that hypothetical constructs are never to be introduced. Indeed, it is these constructs that remove theory from the domain of pure description. But wherever a hypothetical construct serves as a logical mediator, and *where conceivably there is also a physical mediator,* then Russell's maxim would require us to seek the interpretation of the hypothetical construct in observational terms. Thus, as is to be argued in the chapters on reductionism, a stimulus-mediator-response psychology is conducive to the explication of the theoretical language. The criterion of microreduction is essential to behavioral theory. And although formalization of the model of a theory is essential to logical rigor, our aim, it is proposed, should be eventually to interpret the nonlogical entities of the theory in observational terms.

## LAWS

An addendum should be appended concerning the nature of law. As treated herein, laws when derived from within a theory are theorems of the formal theory. They are general propositions from which we infer, predict, or explain a given pattern of events. Not all laws, of course, fall within the corpus of theorems of a theory. In fact, considering the large number of propositions asserting lawful regularities, very few laws are explainable or deducible from within a theory. Moreover, the term 'law' even in science is ambiguous. The Newtonian laws of motion are postulates of a formal system; they are ideal descriptive generalizations only remotely applicable to any set of objects of physical systems. From them we can, of course, infer physical laws descriptive of observable events; but they themselves are idealizations whose truth is not something attested to by a given object or a set of objects in motion. We should, therefore, distinguish between lawlike statements that are postulates of theory and are, therefore, part of its theoretical hypothesis and lawlike statements that are theorems of the theory and are, therefore, part of the experimental hypothesis. Only the latter class of statements concerns us here. For the most part, laws are generalizations of relations and conformal patterns from which we may infer individual events, providing the individual events fulfill the conditions of the law's applications.

This last proviso seems, however, to be a qualification that deprives laws of any apodictic character. We should like to think that laws are enduring generalizations. At least if events are not to be looked upon as conformal cosmic imperatives, they should be considered valid statements of empirical regularities. Thus it would seem that it is the nature of a law to be true. However, nowadays these residues of Platonic realism have all but vanished. Laws have become the instruments of classification and inference. They have become "inference tickets" by which we categorize physical process and inferentially exploit our experience. But as to the truth or falsity of laws? Well, that language does not apply.

This is a thesis that has been popular with positivistic philosophers. One finds explicit statements of this instrumentalistic treatment of law in Campbell (1920a, b), Schlick (1938), Ramsey (1931), Ryle (1949), and Toulmin (1953). A law is not true or false in the way an existential proposition can be true or false. A law is a useful statement of properties and relations common to some given set of events. Just what the set of events is, just what is the range of events over which the law applies, is for us to decide. Thus according to Toulmin (1953), we are to ask not whether a law is true or false or probable but rather what is the range of its application. Statements about the range of a law's application can be true or false, but not the statement of the law itself.

There is, of course, much that is significant and insightful in this positivistic thesis. It is descriptive of our actual utilization and refinement of laws. The Boyle–Charles law of gases holds over the middle range of temperature and pressure but not otherwise. The Weber–Fechner law does not hold for extremes in stimulus intensity. And for all laws, their application is restricted to certain *ceteris paribus* conditions. Indeed, the applicability of a law is assured by our readiness to adopt provisos that will exclude all cases that falsify the law. Still this seems like a trivial way to keep laws inviolate. It is in some way reminiscent of

Victor Borge's uncle who invented a cure before he found the disease. One makes a law and then proceeds to discover the facts for which it serves, or rather he preserves its integrity by restricting its use.

Another point should be brought up before comment is made. That is the fact that a law, as an unrestricted universal statement, cannot be subject to verification in a world of finite sampling. All members of a finite set can be known to have some property. But this verification by enumeration is not possible for the infinite set to which lawlike statements apply. Ramsey and Schlick responded to this predicament by withdrawing lawlike statements from the catalogue of propositions. Such statements are pseudo-propositions which we utilize inferentially. That is all.

One can, I think, utilize laws in a slightly different way that would bring both of the foregoing arguments into focus. Laws, in a sense, are borrowed generalizations that carry with them an assumption of applicability. If pressed to demonstrate, we establish the truth of the law on the basis of a finite sampling of events. Thus the law will be true for just these events. Then by analogy, intuition, or any other crutch to inference, we utilize the restricted generalization for classifying some additional set of events, possibly some set of future events. We now apply the law to the extended set of events. If the law holds, then it is a true generalization of this now extended range of instances. If the law does not hold, it has been disconfirmed. That is to say, it is a false generalization for the extended range of hypothesized instances. In this sense of application, laws are hypotheses that are subject to confirmation or disconfirmation for the extended but still finite set of events.

Finally, a reminder that laws are not theories. We can give what are apparently satisfactory explanations of events by showing that they are instantiations of a law. Still, the law is not a theory. A theory logically binds laws together under the heritage of a common set of postulates and definitions. Thus the theorems of the theory compose the family of the derivable laws. And it is deducibility of a law within the theory that constitutes the formal requirement of scientific explanation.

# NOTES

## NOTE 9.1

In many respects, Bacon's inductivism was a prophylactic empiricism. It stressed protection from the diseases of the idols of false knowledge and it stressed prevention of misconceptions based upon anthropomorphism, metaphysical (rather than physical) causation, and premature generalization. As to the latter of these pitfalls, Bacon's admonition anticipates the counsel of some of today's anti-theoreticians:

> . . . if ever men are roused by my admonitions to betake themselves seriously to experiment and bid farewell to sophisticated doctrines, then indeed through the premature hurry of the understanding to leap or fly to universals and principles of things, great danger may be apprehended from philosophers of this kind, against which evil we ought even now to prepare. (*Novum Organum,* I, 64)

His enumeration of the idols that mislead is well known:

(1) *Idols of the tribe:* inborn penchants, aspects of human nature that predispose one to illusion and false perception.

(2) *Idols of the cave:* autistic confusion due to man's isolating himself from the checks of public discourse.

(3) *Idols of the forum:* misconceptions deriving from the exigencies of public discourse and the vocabulary and language thereby imposed.

(4) *Idols of the theatre:* conceptual restriction and corruption as dictated by prevailing schools, philosophies, sciences, and superstitions.

Nowadays we might list these as the sources of our conceptual frameworks. In light of the stress that has been placed upon our conceptual predispositions, one wonders what would remain of knowledge if all the Baconian idols were destroyed. According to Bacon, what would remain would be an experimentally purified perception revealing physical causality. But according to the point of view expressed in the preceding chapter, even physical causality and pure mechanics requires some apprenticeship at the altars of the idols of the forum and theatre.

## NOTE 9.2

It is quite easy to misconstrue what Mill has to say in this context. Speaking against Whewell's intuitionist philosophy of science, Mill writes in the *System of Logic:*

> It is true that for these simply descriptive operations, as well as for the erroneous inductive one, a conception of the mind was required. The conception of an ellipse must have presented itself to Kepler's mind before he could identify the planetary orbits with it. According to Dr. Whewell the conception was something added to the facts. He expresses himself as if Kepler had put something into the facts by his mode of conceiving them. But Kepler did no such thing. The ellipse was in the facts before Kepler recognized it, just as the island was an island before it has been sailed round. Kepler did not *put* what he had conceived into the facts, but *saw* it in them. A conception implies and corresponds to something conceived; and though the conception itself is not in the facts but in our mind, yet if it is to convey any knowledge relating to them, it must be a conception *of* something which really is in the facts, some property which they actually possess, and which they would manifest to our senses if our senses were able to take cognizance of it . . .

I do not conceive that the part which conceptions have in the operation of studying facts has ever been overlooked or undervalued. No one
ever disputed that in order to reason about anything we must have a conception of it, or that, when we include a multitude of things under a general expression, there is implied in the expression a conception of something common to those things. But it by no means follows that the
conception is necessarily pre-existent, or constructed by the mind of its
own materials. (Book III, Chapter II)

Then turning to "the proper use of scientific hypotheses," Mill writes:

An hypothesis is any supposition we make (either without actual evidence,
or on evidence avowedly insufficient) in order to endeavor to deduce
from it conclusions in accordance with facts which are known to be real,
under the idea that, if the conclusions to which the hypothesis leads are
known truths, the hypothesis itself either must be, or at least is likely to
be, true. . . . We want to be assured that the law we have hypothetically
assumed is a true one, and its leading deductively to true results will afford
this assurance, provided the case be such that a false law cannot lead to a
true result, provided no law except the very one which we have assumed
can lead deductively to the same conclusions which that leads to. . . . It
appears, then, to be a condition of the most genuinely scientific hypothesis
that it be not destined always to remain an hypothesis but be of such a
nature as to be either proved or disproved by comparison with observed
facts. (Book III, Chapter XIV)

These excerpts, suggestive as they are of hypothetico-deductive methodology, differ in two important counts from contemporary treatments of hypothesis testing. One, Mill makes it clear that the hypotheses themselves are factual
in character; they exemplify the rubric of causal analysis. But according to contemporary empiricism, a useful scientific hypothesis may have no immediate
observational consequences. Only through correspondence rules applied to key
propositions at the end of a deductive chain do facts come to bear upon
credence of the hypothesis. And two, Mill speaks of the truth and the verification of hypotheses as if the truth of a consequent in a material implication
affirms the antecedent. If hypotheses are to be treated as tools of inference to
factual propositions, then Mill has committed an error in logic. However, when
pressed to pin the error on Mill, we find that he retreats from adopting hypothetical modes of speaking as the basis of deductive inference. Rather such
modes are descriptive of phenomena and causal connections themselves, and
it would appear, subject to verification.

## NOTE 9.3

John Arbuthnot, physician to Queen Anne, occasional contributor to the Royal
Society, composer, and crony of Swift and Pope, argued in behalf of divine
providence on the grounds of testing alternative hypotheses concerning random
or chance events. In his short paper, "An Argument for Divine Providence,
Taken from the Constant Regularity Observed in the Births of Both Sexes"
(1710), he argues rather circuitously that the inequality of sexes cannot be attributed to chance. He used a simple heads–tails type model and shows that it
would be highly improbable that one would obtain exactly as many male births

as female in any given year. Incidental to his actual test, he then argues that a disbalance in the sexes must be part of the plan of "provident Nature" since:

> . . . we must observe that the external accidents to which Males are subject (who must seek their Food with danger) do make great havoc of them and his loss exceeds far that of the other sex, occasioned by Disease incident to it, as Experience convinces us. To repair that Loss provident Nature, by the Disposal of the wise Creator brings forth more Males than Females; and that in almost a constant proportion.

Then in order to dismiss the hypothesis of chance, Arbuthnot assumed the probability of a male birth to be one-half. Checking London birth records from 1629 to 1710, he then finds for each of the 82 years that the number of male births exceeds the number of female births. Applying the appropriate probability, $(\frac{1}{2})^{82}$, he finds the chance of such event ("by a Table of Logarithms") to be $1/(4.836 \times 10^{23})$.

On the basis of what is later to become the principle of Cournot and D'Alembert, namely that if an event is sufficiently improbable, we can say with apodictic confidence that it will not, or cannot, happen, he then concludes male births predominate over female births:

> From hence it follows, that Polygamy is contrary to the Law of Nature and Justice and to the Propagation of the Human Race; for where Males and Females are in equal number, if one Man takes Twenty Wives, Nineteen Men must live in Celibacy, which is repugnant to the Design of Nature; nor is it probable that Twenty Women will be so well impregnated by one Man as by Twenty" (1710, p. 189).

This probabilistic argument in the hypothetico-deductive mode became attractive to several early writers concerning certain astronomical distributions. Reverend Michell applied it early (circa 1767) to the hypothesis of a random distribution of double stars. And Laplace and DeMorgan each independently calculated the probability ($\approx 0.00000012$) that the inclinations of the planetary orbits should be confined to the small limits that obtain on the assumption that such inclinations could be treated as random assignments. On the grounds of the smallness of this probability, both writers rejected randomness "in favor of some disposing cause" (cf. Boole, 1854, p. 364). This mode of testing in favor of disposing causes is still with us. It is adopted by Newman and Scott (1956) in their tests of chance mechanisms operating in the scatter of the galaxies. It is also characteristic of the argument adopted by LeCömte du Nouy (1947) in his own quaint calculations in behalf of divine providence.

## NOTE 9.4

In one of the early expositions of the method of deductivism for the psychological audience, Hull states: *"Whereas argument reaches belief in its theorems because of antecedent belief in its postulates, scientific theory reaches belief in its postulates to a considerable extent through direct or observational evidence of the soundness of its theorems"* (1943, p. 9). The bridge to belief unfortunately is spelled out only in rather elusive terms of probability. Belief obviously cannot be a case of conclusive verification, for as Mill had pointed out in his treatment of deductivism, a hypothesis would be verified as true if, and only if, it and no other hypothesis could derive the experimental result. Hull intimates that truth status of the theory is a probability function of its true (by verification) theorems—each new verification increasing the probability "that the next theorem derived from these postulates in conjunction with a different set of antecedent conditions will also agree with relevant empirical determinations." There are serious difficulties in using probability here in the way Hull does (e.g., see Chapter 14); at least, his language would have to be qualified. Be that as it may, we support our belief in the postulates of our theory by means of empirical test. Acknowledging that disagreement between theorem and experimental result signifies that one or more postulates are in error, he goes on to say:

> When the breakdown of a generalization occurs in this way, an event of frequent occurrence in new fields, the postulates involved are revised if possible so as to conform [*sic*] to the known facts. Following this, deductions as to the outcomes of situations involving still other combinations of principles are made; these in their turn are checked against observations; and so on as long as disagreements continue to occur. Thus the determination of scientific principles is in considerable part a matter of symbolic trial-and-error (1943, p. 12).

Hull's use here of the language of conformity as between postulate and fact, along with his adopting a probabilistic support of belief, would seem to indicate that postulates ultimately would have factual reference and, one would surmise, should in principle be subject to direct test.

## NOTE 9.5

The problem of what logical systems can or cannot do is a highly technical branch of logic. The consensus seems to be that machines cannot be designed such that they can in principle solve all questions meaningful within their syntax. Whether machines as we now know them can simulate all human activities of reason and discovery is a question of some debate. However, it is clear that machines cannot exceed the limits put upon the logic of discovery by Gödel's theorem of the essential incompleteness of the logical system.

Nevertheless, when we retreat from the ethereal region of computers and science fiction, there is little question concerning the inventive proclivities of creative people. Incubation, insight, intuition, and, alas, accident are the clues to invention, not logic. Hadamard (1945) and Beveridge (1950) offer interesting accounts of the "irrational" aspects of inventiveness in the fields of mathematics and science. Einstein (1933) and Poincaré (1914) give interesting accounts of the intuitive aspects of creativity in their own work. And Russell adds his bit to the theme of the subconscious in his brief essay, "How I Write" (1956).

## NOTE 9.6

The issue is debated by Hanson and Feyerabend (Feigl and Maxwell, 1961) though both parties would appear to agree that a logic of invention is impos-

sible. Hanson takes as his historical example the works of Kepler. Kepler recorded his own inventive travails with painstaking detail. Though he engaged
in systematic trial-and-error exploration of hypotheses concerning the planetary
orbits, it was clear that neither logic nor intuition prescribed principles that
would assure him of eventual success. Strangely, Kepler toyed with the hypothesis of orbital ellipses relatively early in his travails, only to discover its successful application at a later time.

In his *The Concept of the Positron,* Hanson (1963) gives an account of
the interplay of invention, theory, and discovery in the story of antimatter. This
work is further elaboration upon the themes presented in the earlier *Patterns
of Discovery* (1958).

It is customary in discussions of logical design and simulation to ask if we
cannot design a machine that will invent hypotheses. No trouble at all. Machines
can be creative as random generators of hypotheses. They can also learn inductively (e.g., George, 1959, 1960; Scriven, 1960; Ashby, 1963). However,
no one has been able to design logical circuitry to assure us that whatever
theorem is proposed in a language the machine understands, the machine can
proceed to find a proof as to whether the theorem is true or not by virtue of a
reliable algorithm (Church, 1936). Although this issue is tangential to inventiveness it does seem to indicate that even a machine would require some unpro-
grammed intuition in order to resolve all questions that can be meaningfully
asked of it.


## NOTE 9.7

The account of theory given in the text borrows heavily from Campbell's classic
*Physics, the Elements* (1920), also issued by Dover as *The Foundations of
Science* (1957). This book has been very influential in the philosophy of sci-
ence, especially in the discussions of hypothetico-deductive methodology. The
Campbellian point of view is adopted and refined by two recent works of out-
standing merit, R. B. Braithwaite's *Scientific Explanation* and E. Nagel's *The
Structure of Science.* Campbell also gives a more elementary account of his
philosophy of science in *What Is Science?* (1920).


## NOTE 9.8

It is not the writer's intention to be critical of personality theory, or to avoid
its discussion, other than critically. The study of complex interpersonal behavior
is just as amenable to scientific study as say the interaction of bodies in their
gravitational fields. The argument is that theories are testable and useful only
to the extent they permit straightforward inference and can be assessed by our
confirmational procedures. The ontological status of theories, tenuous as it is,
can only emerge under a rigorous formalization of the theoretical postulates
and the principles of inference. In this respect it would appear that personology
is still in its preformal, pretheoretical stages of development.

One notes, of course, that simplified theories of interpersonal behavior are being constructed. Two-person interactions, simple dyadic relations, may not be very interesting or insightful so far as complex social behavior is concerned. But in this case, as in so many in psychology, simplification almost to the point of triviality is the price one must pay for syntactic and semantic precision.

## NOTE 9.9

In his last revision of his theory, Hull presents postulates from which theorems are derived without proof. Indeed the proofs would have to be informal; for in spite of some basic equations of $_sH_R$ and $_sE_R$, Hull's language is often phenomenological and basic terms are left undefined. It is apparent then that even in treating the postulates as a deductive system, the theorems can be no more precise than the language in which the postulates are stated. (See for example Montgomery, 1951; Koch, 1954.)

Examining some aspects of Hull's theory from the point of view of the precision and warrantability of its predictions, Cotton concludes, "Without clarification and simplification of the theory, it is believed that most predictions rigorously deduced from the theory would contradict or at least differ in form from Hull's empirical equations" (1955, p. 313). He explicitly shows that Hovland's equation of the relation between amplitude of response and number of reinforced trials (used by Hull in support of his theory) cannot be derived within the system of postulates *as stated* by Hull. Noting Hull's use of other workers' data in support of his own theory, Cotton writes:

> In fact no one has publicly questioned the presumption that the empirical data cited in *Principles of Behavior* is embraced by the theory. Yet this presumption is false. There was, to be sure, a romance between theory and fact, but the wedding did not take place. Hull never quite compared the implications of his theory with the data he discussed (1955, p. 303).

Cotton makes some interesting comments about the "degree of specificity" of the data as stipulated in theoretical predictions. Such data fall into three classes of hypotheses: (1) those expressing only inequalities such as greater than; (2) those expressing the general form, such as linear trends; and (3) those specifying numerical values of parameters. Much of experimental work involving classical learning theories specifies hypotheses merely in terms of inequalities: e.g., as between experimental and control groups. It is obvious, however, that alternative theories may easily yield predictions to the same direction of the inequality. More precise tests and more decisive results can be achieved, if, for example, the alternative theories are sufficiently refined so as to predict particular patterns and trends of the values of the dependent variables.

## NOTE 9.10

In the chapters of this section, frequent reference is made to the now classical distinction between intervening variables and hypothetical constructs. The original paper of MacCorquodale and Meehl (1948) has stimulated much discussion both in psychology and the philosophy of science. It makes what presumes to be a significant distinction between theoreical terms which are postulating constructions, i.e., explicit operational terms and theoretical terms postulating as yet unobserved entities and processes. MacCorquodale and Meehl write:

> We suggest that the phrase 'intervening variable' be restricted to the original use implied by Tolman's definition. Such a variable will then be simply a quantity obtained by a specific manipulation of the values of empirical variables; it will involve no hypothesis as to the existence of nonobserved entities or the occurrence of unobserved processes; it will contain, in its complete statement for all purposes of theory and prediction, no words which are not definable either explicitly or by reduction sentences in terms of empirical variables; and the validity of the empirical laws involving only observables will constitute both the necessary and the sufficient conditions for the validity of the laws involving these intervening variables. . . .
>
> As a second linguistic convention, we propose that the term 'hypothetical construct' be used to designate theoretical concepts which do *not* meet the requirements for intervening variables in the strict sense. That is to say, these constructs involve terms which are not wholly reducible to empirical terms; they refer to processes or entities which are not directly observed (although they need not be in principle unobservable); the mathematical expression of them cannot be formed simply by a suitable grouping of terms in an empirical equation; and the truth of the empirical laws involved is a necessary but not a sufficient condition for the truth of these conceptions (1948, pp. 103-104).

Subsequent literature on the subject has been extensive. A partial list of references follow, with grouping according to positions taken as regards the ontological status of theoretical terms:

(A) Emphasis upon theoretical constructs (H.C.'s) with realistic overtones, wherein the postulated entity carries with it the possibility of eventual reification: Cronbach and Meehl (1955); Feigl (1950, 1951); Hebb (1955); Hochberg (1961); Krech (1949, 1950a,b); Meehl and MacCorquodale (1948); Maxwell (1962); Sellars (1956).

(B) Operational reduction, with emphasis upon the intervening variable, although surplus meaning may be claimed for the strictly operational concept: Bergman (1951, 1953); Craig (1956), an article on the logical reducibility of *all* theoretical terms to statements in the observation language; Kendler (1952); Madden (1961); Marx (1951); Spence (1956); Tolman (1936).

(C) Conventionalistic interpretation of theoretical terms, no existential hypothesis implied by such terms: Deutsch (1960); George (1953), emphasis upon model; Kendler (1952); Kessen and Kimble (1952).

(D) Contextualist interpretation of hypothetical terms; close to the conventionalist position, but emphasis upon stating the meaning and ontological status of a construct in the context, and context alone, of the theory of which it is a part: Braithwaite (1953); Carnap (1956); Ginsberg (1954); Hempel (1951, 1958); Jessor (1958); Lindzey (1953); Mayo (1954); Meissner (1958); Smart (1956, 1963); Toulmin (1953).

(E) For critical exposition of aspects of the distinction: Beck (1950); Maze (1954); O'Neil (1953); Rozeboom (1956); Seward (1955).

**NOTE 9.11**

If by an intervening variable $I_r$ we were to mean a logical construction out of response variables (as in case of expectancy, cf. Hempel, 1958), then any theory in which $I_r$ would be the sole theoretical term could not, by virtue of its status in the calculus, generate more interesting experimental hypotheses than would arise from within the radical atheoretical stimulus–response psychology itself. That is, there is nothing inherent within the intervening variable $I_r$ that would lead to hypotheses which could not be derived from a set of laws eliminating $I_r$, as it were, by its utilizing only primitive terms in the observation language. Regardless of the aura of empirical respectability with which intervening variables have been endowed by people such as Tolman, Hull, and Spence, it is doubtful that anyone holds to a strict reductive definition of an intervening variable. There is always some presumptive factor beyond the empirical ingredients of pure logical construction. For example, if one were to define habit strength as a function of number of reinforcements, as Hull does, he very likely presumes that it is *any* set of reinforcements satisfying some rather general conditions, e.g., reinforced trials in a T-maze. When he speaks of the value of habit strength, he does not reduce the unique value to just this and no other set of $N$ reinforcement trials. In other words, he takes the $N$ trials to be evidence of a definite level of habit strength, but the level of habit strength is something indicated by a set of trials; it is not *the* set of some particular trials. And that is to say, the intension of the proposition about the level of habit strength is not limited to the specific set of ingredients of a logical construction.

Suppose we define $P(E)$ as a logical construction, i.e., as the relative frequency of $E$ for a particular set of $N$ trials. If $N$ were large, we might in fact prefer the estimate $P(E)$ of $p$ to some other estimate, such as that based upon the analysis of equally likely classes. But note the word "estimate". We assume that $P(E)$ is used in such a way that all propositions derived therefrom are not necessarily statements about just these $N$ trials. In fact, if we use the theory predictively, we are talking of some other set of trials of future sampling and so forth. We assume that $P(E)$, the relative frequency, will hold for future cases and in some way manifest itself in our expectations concerning many future trials. Thus, whenever $P(E)$ occurs in some theorem, we are not at all thinking of the particular set of $N$ trials from which $P(E)$ was constructed. For example, we could apply $P(E) = p$, $P(\sim E) = q$, in the binomial theorem and obtain the probability distribution for all possible outcomes in $N$ Bernoullian trials. Should we consider the probability distributions for the event occurrences of experiments involving ten rolls of the die, we would get the expansion

$$p^{10} + 10p^9q + 45p^8q^2 + \cdots + 10pq^9 + q^{10} = 1.0.$$

The terms $p^{10}$ (i.e., $[P(E)]^{10}$), etc., become meaningfully tied to event classes and expected frequency by means of a dictionary. Here $P(E)$ betokens a dispositional property not exhaustively defined by the original sampling from which its value was first determined. The point is that an explicit definition, without the presumption of its dispositional properties, would be forever bounded by its defining set of events. There is invariably a presumptive factor involved in the use of intervening variables. For that reason much of the controversy over intervening variables and hypothetical constructs is misdirected. The more important distinction seems to be that the surplus or presumptive meaning of hypothetical constructs is embedded in models and their positive analogy, whereas the surplus meaning for intervening variables is left unreified or downright suppressed.

## NOTE 9.12

The distinction between structural models and formal models one might think has an analogue in a distinction between the tough-minded and the tougher-minded. Structural models frequently suggest either actual structures of the thing modeled or mechanical analogues. Both the replica and the analogue suggest an actual hardware approach. The use of structural models is tough-minded in the sense that their builders leave no lacuna for irreducible agents of mediation such as intuition, entelechy, self-regard, etc. But a purely formal approach may be tougher-minded still. The reluctance to interpret any variables but those in the theorems that are anchored securely to the observation language reflects an attitude in keeping with the most radical of empiricisms. The data language and formal deductive models: these are admissible. There is no place for structural speculations.

## NOTE 9.13

It is of interest to follow Woodworth's adventures in search of O-structure through the many revisions of his famous *Psychology*. In the first edition of the book (1922), his stimulus response schema was S-T- $R_1R_2$ . . . in which T designates determining tendency. To this mediational state he sometimes added P, a preparatory set. By the second revision in 1935, T, and P were absorbed under O, with O indicating a general adjustment set including situational and goal sets. 'Structure' was beginning to appear in the vocabulary. Philogenetic and ontogenetic differences in brain structure were perfunctorily noted. Specifically, the O factor covered structure, condition of the organism, and activity in progress. By the third revision (1940), a contrast between permanent structure and temporary states was emphasized. The dynamism of motivation was beginning to appear and by the fifth revision (1949, in which Marquis appeared as co-author), greater detail was spelled out for the classes of organismic variables. Structure now meant bodily and anatomical structure as manifest in habits and skill. Suggestions were made as to the relevance of modification in brain structure, although it was noted that such internal states were inferred rather than observed. The language of the temporary states (the "conditions" of earlier editions) now made mention of emotional and motivational states, hunger, drowsiness, etc. Activity in progress refers to those states that are later to succumb to feedback analysis. Thus, the ontogeny of black-boxes. Little by little, light intrudes from the laboratory to illuminate the black-box, if not with the actual biomechanics, at least with functional hypotheses. The tradition of Woodworth continues. Note, for example, texts where explicit use is made of the cybernetic schema.

**NOTE 9.14**

Problems of special interest to the cyberneticist are learning, categorical perception, generalization, and constancy effects. So far as learning and basic adjustment are concerned, actual "hardware realizations" of cybernetic models have been achieved (Ashby, 1952; Shannon, 1951; W. Grey Walter, 1953; Uttley, 1955). But not all models, utilizing different networks and components as they do, can be equally good models of the nervous system. Analogies are more or less good. However, some models such as Uttley's conditional probability machines (1955, 1956), are interpretable in terms of logical nets which might very well be isomorphic with actual neural nets. Good discussions of the application of cybernetics to psychology can be found in George (1960, 1961).

It is of interest to note that the speculative neural network models of McCulloch and Pitts (1943, 1947) stemmed largely from McCulloch's early efforts to design machines capable of recognizing certain general aspects of a physical stimulus world (Wiener, 1948). The order of attempted discovery here is from one model, the cybernetic one, to another, the neural network. Explorations proceeded from functional to structural analogies.

**NOTE 9.15**

Kenneth Craik, a student of Bartlett's at the University of Cambridge, combined competencies in philosophy and experimental psychology with unique mechanical inventiveness. His experimental work was largely in the field of what we would now call human factors; but in large part, his reputation rests upon his little book *The Nature of Explanation* (1943).

After rejecting *a priorism* and skepticism, Craik argues that the most fruitful language of analysis and understanding is an out-and-out causal language. Thought processes themselves follow external processes. External processes can be translated into the symbols of thought, the thought then amplified through deductive inference and translated back into empirical hypotheses. The practical implications of the argument rest in Craik's thinking that some isomorphism exists between the structures of mental and physical process. Therefore, he firmly believed that it would always be possible to design a mechanical system that would imitate and predict mental processes. Whether Craik's critique of uncertainty and causality will hold up (he was critical of quantum physicists who rejected the principle of causality) is doubtful; but his contribution to the study of simulative procedures has been considerable. He was a dedicated cyberneticist before that science was christened.

Craik died in a bicycle accident while he was still a young man.

**NOTE 9.16**

One might wish to argue that refined black-box analysis does indeed offer point-by-point analysis of concatenated processes. Thus ablation studies systematically carried out would provide at least lower level explanations (Pribram, 1954). To be sure; but as Gregory (1961) and Deutsch (1960) have argued, inferences from anatomical studies of this type are only good in simple mechanical systems with point-by-point linkages. The neurological speculations of Hebb (1949), Sholl (1956), Milner (1957), Rosenblatt (1958) rule out specific connections in favor of randomized construction of cell assemblies and redundancy. Obviously ablation studies on systems that are neither homologous nor genetically specific cannot be very informative. One wonders how much of Lashley's failure to establish a generally acceptable theory of cerebral organization is due to his reliance upon ablation studies.

An interesting synthesis of ablation strategies and cybernetic modeling occurs in the work of Karl Pribram. In one work (1954), he enthusiastically calls for intensive ablation studies of the small structures of the forebrain. But in his excellent *Annual Reviews* article of 1960, he assimilates a selected review of recent neurophysiology into an elaborate and detailed cybernetic model. The heuristic value of the cybernetic model is also stressed in Miller, Galanter, and Pribram, *Plans and the Structure of Behavior* (1960).

## NOTE 9.17

When does a model cease to be a model and become the thing itself? An interesting question. One might answer: "When all the negative analogy is dissipated." Let us see. Consider a relatively simple type of model. Suppose an engineer were to construct a large suspension bridge. He might first want to construct a large model of it in order to test its behavior under wind conditions, load, stress, etc. Perhaps there is some doubt as to the feasibility of such a structure. But stress factors of metal cannot be modeled on any reduced scale regardless of how faithful the scale reduction. Thus, if one were to eliminate all negative analogy, he must eliminate all those features and properties of the model which are different from the thing modeled. In effect, the engineer must replicate the bridge if he is to be sure that all model-inferences about the actual bridge are to be correct.

Suppose the engineer includes estimates of his model in the actual construction of the bridge. He can be certain, *ceteris paribus,* as to the success of its structure if he can first build a model to the scale of the bridge itself. The question is, of course, whether the model is a model of a bridge, or is *the bridge itself.* If one wishes now to argue that to the "perfectly conservative engineer" the cost of a bridge is always twice the cost of the bridge, then he is free to name the "paradox" and puzzle it out for himself.

## NOTE 9.18

It is difficult, though presumably not impossible, for a mathematical-model man to escape the affinities of conventionalism. And empiricistic, nonconventionalist credos are sometimes easier to declare at the beginning of a work in theory than at the end.

For example, in their *Markov Learning Models for Multipersonal Interactions,* Suppes and Atkinson declare against conventionalism in their opening statements. Adopting the Estes–Suppes (1959) formalism of statistical learning theory, they contend "that in statistical learning theory we have a theory with the same kind of feel about it that theories in physics have." Theoretical postulates are well formed and predictions are non *ad hoc* and precise. "However beautiful the structure of a theory may be, if it does not yield stable, nonartificial experimental interpretations leading to new empirical predictions, it does not have empirical significance," (page 4). They reject the point of view "that by sufficiently distorting the 'natural' experimental interpretation of concepts, they may save any theory from failure." However, by the end of their work, these writers are somewhat less confident. In the face of some refractory experimental results, they stress the need for manageable models:

> In advocating this approach we are taking a methodological position with which some scientists do not agree. Our position is in contrast to one which asserts that a model should be discarded once it is clear that certain of its predictions are in error, but this position postulates a clearer connection between learning models and the actual behavior of organisms than we are willing to grant exists. Naturally, it is always better to choose from the available models the one that best fits the data, but in the present state of psychological knowledge, no single model is clearly superior to all others in every facet of analysis (1960, p. 279).

**NOTE 9.19**

Duhem made much of the distinction between the narrow but strong mind of the French and the ample but weak mind of the English (although it turns out that his example, *par excellence,* of the ample but weak mind is Napoleon). He was writing in a time when it was still popular to write of national character. After noting differences between the heroes of French and English literature, he attempts to show that Englishmen's "shallow" (not in the pejorative sense!) proclivities for empirics lead in physics to a weakness for mechanical models. Duhem's essay on the subject (Part I, Chapter IV) is too long to give in any detail, but the following gives the spirit of his thesis:

> In the treatises on physics published in England, there is always one element which greatly astonishes the French student; that element, which nearly invariably accompanies the exposition of a theory, is the model. Nothing helps us better understand how very different from ours is the manner in which the English mind proceeds in the construction of science than this use of the model . . . (1962, p. 69).

Speaking specifically to a science of electrostatics, Duhem writes:

> The whole theory of electrostatics constitutes a group of abstract ideas and general propositions, formulated in the clear and precise language of geometry and algebra, and connected with one another by the rules of strict logic. This whole fully satisfies the reason of a French physicist and his taste for clarity, simplicity, and order.
>     The same does not hold for an Englishman. These abstract notions of material points, force, line of force, and equipotential surface do not

satisfy his need to imagine concrete, material, visible, and tangible things . . . (1962, p. 70).

And in reference to the work of Oliver Lodge:

> Here is a book intended to expound the modern theories of electricity and to expound a new theory. In it there are nothing but strings which move around pulleys, which roll around drums, which go through pearl beads, which carry weights; and tubes which pump water while others swell and contract; toothed wheels which are geared to one another and engage hooks. We thought we were entering the tranquil and neatly ordered abode of reason, but we find ourselves in a factory . . . (1962, p. 70).

## NOTE 9.20

To make his point, Campbell allots himself "about a quarter of an hour" to elaborate a formally adequate but meaningless theory for deducing a theorem which in its dictionary translation states that "the ratio of the resistance of a piece of pure metal to its absolute temperature is constant" (1920, p. 122). To emphasize that formal sufficiency alone is not all that we require of a theory, we can take Campbell's vacuous formal theory (as a kind of formal analogue) and apply it to the deduction of Fechner's law. Consider the following:

$u, v, w$ are independent variables;

$a, b,$ are constant for all values of $u, v, w$;

$c, d$ are intervening variables such that $c = d$ and $cd/b = \log R$, where $R$ is stimulus intensity; $(c^2 + d^2)\, a = S$, where $S$ is the subjective estimate of the physical stimulus.

Then

$$\frac{(c^2 + d^2)a}{cd/b} = \frac{S}{\log R}.$$

Since, with $c = d$, the left side of the equation reduces to the constant $k = 2ab$, we obtain Fechner's law

$$S = k \log R$$

Quite simple! We have a formally satisfactory theory of psychophysics. It even possesses purely formal analogy with Campbell's theory of electrical resistance. All the same, as a theory, it is quite meaningless. It has no analogy by which we can comprehend it in the context of established theory which is understood.

## NOTE 9.21

As Attneave (1959) is careful to point out, information theory is not a psychological theory but rather a technique for handling data. Nevertheless, what distinguishes it from such techniques as chi square and the analysis of variance is the analogy that $T(x,y)$, transmitted information, $Hy(x)$, equivocation, and $Hx(y)$, ambiguity, have for all systems which fail to utilize or to process all information available to them; i.e., its analogy for all input–output systems.

It is perhaps a point for debate whether researchers and theoreticians come to informational analysis because of phenomenological analogy or because information theory has been elevated to the position of an ontological probe. One senses that the general popularity of information theory stems partially from people being first enamored of the tool and then going out in search of an application.

### NOTE 9.22

The discussion here is strikingly reminiscent of that between nominalism and realism. For nominalism, analogy inheres in objects; classes are conventions by which objects are grouped according to perceived similarities. For Platonic realism, the analogy inheres in the formal archetype of which phenomena are their partial empirical exemplifications; thus, for example, the emphasis upon calculi, formal models, and mathematical training for the philosopher-scientist.

Whether this dichotomy of labels applies to contemporary writers on theory and models is debatable. Few formalists nowadays endow their formal models with any more than a conventional status. At least the defense of mathematical models does not reveal the faith of a Galileo, who expected that his researches would reveal the underlying formal structure (the mathematical laws) of which all phenomena were manifestations.

# CHAPTER 10

# *Explanation*

ALTHOUGH much has been written on the subject of explanation, the literature is frequently less incisive and less definitive than that on theory and reductionism. The reasons for this are not hard to come by. Curiosity and the seeking of explanations are characteristic of us all, scientist and nonscientist alike. Logical attempts at explication aside, explanation is largely a personal matter. Curiosity and the need for explanation are the products of our intellectual development. Early in our lives we ask why? what? how? And, in turn, we accept "explanations." These explanations have this in common, they satisfy us. In some sense of cognitive completion, they satisfy. Yet it remains a source of puzzlement and amusement as to why the explanations we accept do, in fact, satisfy: why some people will accept a casual allusion to a general principle or to a causal agent while others pursue their inquiries into first principles, unmoved movers, ultimate unexplained explainers. In a sense nothing is explained; a thing or an event simply is, it needs no explanation. Yet what we accept as explanation gives us cognitive closure. Explanations terminate our curiosity and we are left free to attend to other events and move on to other inquiries.

Still this token of cognitive satisfaction is not easily codified. Satisfactory explanations are not always "true" descriptions of affairs. Hypotheses explain, so do fictions and lies, as well as what we might presume to be true descriptions. However, the language of truth is in doubt here. Since in science so much of explanation is of an hypothetical nature, it would be better to avoid making truth judgments at all concerning explanation and rather reserve such judgments solely for the domain of observation statements. Accepting this as the case, it is then important to distinguish between the cognitive requirements of explanation, on the one hand, and the formal or logical requirements of explanation, on the other. Failure to appreciate this distinction has led to much fruitless discussion over the meaning of explanation.

Consider, for example, the question of causation—a central issue for some although as Russell (1917) and others have pointed out (e.g., Campbell, 1920, 1921; W. H. Watson, 1938; Toulmin 1953) causality and causal laws are hardly mentioned in modern treatises of science. Still causality enjoys some precedence in matters of explanation. Causal antecedents are accepted as natural explanations of the events that follow. Consequently empiricists from the time of Bacon through Mill (1884) to the contemporary J. O. Wisdom (1952) have stressed methodology for the induction of causes; as if some algorithm of inference will assure us of isolating the antecedent event-complexes which in a very real sense serve to explain the effects that occupy our attention. There is something explanatory about concomitant variations, functional relationships, interdependence. The satisfaction we derive from such relationships is hard to overcome. And Humean skepticism has to be reaffirmed in each generation in order for us to see clearly that events just do happen, without necessary connection and without the occurrence of one event, alone and unaided by our principles of general inference, explaining the occurrence of another (Braithwaite, 1953).

By a cognitive requirement of explanation, then, I mean that an explanation is cognitively satisfying if its statement is accepted as an adequate answer as to "why" the occurrence of the event in question. The "why?" is a perfectly legitimate question. Still what is cognitively satisfying may be quite a personal matter. To hear that a virus is the "cause" of a disease may be quite a satisfactory explanation to the man who suffers the infection but it is hardly an adequate answer to the why that is posed by the biochemist. A falling barometer may explain the change in cloud cover to a backporch weatherman but to the meteorologist it is little more than a symptom in a large complex of relevant events. What the biochemist, the meteorologist, and the scientist in general want is not explanation based upon our pointing to empirical events with which we are familiar, but rather explanation based upon some larger deductive schema that generates inferences concerning many events not heretofore related. In such cases, our sets of explanatory statements must fulfill certain formal requirements.

By the formal requirements of explanation, I mean that an explanation is formally satisfying if the statement of the event to be explained is shown to be a logical consequence of principles, laws, and theories in generalized scientific systems. Thus a formal explanation may be one in which a theorem is derived within a scientific system such that the event to be explained is an instance of what the theorem stipulates. In the case of these hypothetico-deductive explanations, we are likely to come to greater procedural agreements as to what constitutes an explanation, yet we may not be cognitively satisfied with the character of the explanation. All formal treatments of explanation rest upon a deductive inference leading from either a theory or a law to a statement about a particular event. The details of the inference can be rigorously spelled out. However, the *explicans* (the set of statements which constitute the argument for the *explicandum*—the event to be explained) may be neither interesting, satisfying, nor otherwise psychologically adequate. Children, for example, seldom appreciate our adeptness at hypothetico-deductive explanations.

Now it is not just children who may disdain formal explanations. In psychology and other personalistic sciences, questions have been raised over whether any unique event such as the behavior of a given individual can be explained by recourse to hypothetico-deductive procedures or to the individual's being an instantiation of a law or set of laws. According to a more intuitional point of view, the explanation of behavior can only be achieved by its detailed, highly specific description accompanied by the observer's empathetic understanding. Thus only by projecting oneself into the event sequence will an explanation supported by an essential sufficiency of understanding be achieved. Laws, hypotheses, theoretical constructions, and all other classificatory schemata of the deductive procedures only serve to obfuscate description of the thing to be explained. This is a theme iterated by mystics, by existentialists, and by some personologists. It is argued on grounds that the classificatory schema does violence to the unique character of individual events. Only unique events have ontological substance, not classes, laws, or other abstractive repositories. This is a viewpoint that requires attention and in time we shall want to examine it further.

As a preview, we may list the types of answers and disquisitions that have been acceptable as explanations. First, the child's world, for this carries over into our subsequent demands for explanation. A child learns efficient causation largely through his early experiences in manipulating objects—by his causing them to move and to behave. He readily learns simple principles of mechanics, of the elements of momenta transfer. Thus he can understand why some objects move, why some fall, and how some objects cause other objects to move. Easily deceived by legerdemain, he is also easily satisfied as to how it all happens. It is as simple as the dynamics of the jumping bean. The child may be puzzled by the movement of iron filings on the table top, but if he is shown the magnet that is being manipulated under the table, he may appear quite satisfied that he understands the dynamics of the phenomenon—even though he has not the slightest conception of the principles of molecular structure. Another distinctive feature of the child's world is that he is likely early in his experience to accept as explanatory the omnipotencies that only later he refines into the arguments of first cause. Birth phenomena; the elementary economics of where does money come from; questions like that of Red Chief (O. Henry), why are oranges round?—all these are dispatched by facile references to God, banks, the government, daddy, and other agents of omnipotence. The etiology of such explanatory types is perhaps not difficult for the psychologist to discover but what is more interesting perhaps is the ease with which one moves from explanations by the omnipotent to explanations by the familiar.

Another phase of the child's cognitive development comes with his awareness of black-box agencies. This, we might say, is typically the jumping bean phase of explanation. Something is happening inside the box which accounts for its behavior. Thus, if the mechanical toy is opened so that wheels and springs are found, a primitive level of explanation is achieved. Considerable sophistication is, of course, required for thinking in terms of mechanical linkages. Still, if we can see the linkages and other media of concatenated events, we may find the gross behavior of the mechanism explained, even though explanation by phenomenological concatenation (i.e., of the familiar chaining of events) may be relatively primitive and leave entirely unexplained why such concatenations should occur. It has been argued that ablation studies in psychoneurology have frequently done no more than to exploit our primitive black-box criteria of explanation.

When the child has learned to structure sequences of events in terms of concatenation, concomitant variation, and other complexes of contiguity, he has gone a long way in becoming perceptually prepared for dealing with the problem of explanation. So long as he confines himself to his perceptual frameworks, his explanations, even his sophisticated explanations, will lead him to the problems of causal analysis. Thus to explain an event-sequence is critically to examine the "causal structure."

By then, of course, the child has become a relatively sophisticated philosopher. It is interesting perhaps to lay out the itinerary of his intellectual odyssey. First, he looks for linkages of events, which become familiar to him. Thus he takes for granted certain basic sequences of events. They become "unexplained explainers," as it were. And, if some event to be explained is found to be an exemplification of these basic patterns, that event is explained in at least a cognitively satisfying way. As a second adventure he may begin to wonder why such basic patterns actually obtain. He carries the refinement of inspection to a different level and begins to examine the microstructure of the events that appear to conform to the basic patterns. Thus as a relatively naive psychologist, he may direct his inspection from crude stimulus–response patterns of the object and behavioral world into the microstructure of the nervous system. As a naive physicist noting the phenomenological law of increasing entropy, he may wish to look into the structure of gases in order to find out why the second law of thermodynamics holds. The two examples here are somewhat different, for in one the microstructure is readily accessible, whereas in the other it is not; the microstructure is more hypothetical. Still the explanatory significance of the two microstructures is, in one sense, the same. If we were to see the given microstructure or to verify its hypothetical character (by microscopes, etc.), what would emerge is a finer grained picture of concatenated events; but in no sense would the psychological or the logical character of our causal analysis be altered. From crude contiguities, we go to finer grained contiguities. Still we get no closer to an agency of causal process transpiring in the finest grained of event sequences. This predicament leads the adventurer of our intellectual odyssey to his third and Humean port of call. There is nothing compelling about contiguity. The satisfaction of explanation arises from habit-established perceptual expectancies. Thus, the finest grained phenomenal conformities are described more than they are "explained." There is the uneasy feeling that the world need not oblige us by conforming to our descriptions and that if an observation violates our principles or our laws, the solecism will rest with us and not with the event.

For the radical empiricist, the end of the odyssey is Humean skepticism. Indeed, explanation and causal analysis can penetrate no further than the inevitable barriers of contiguity. We are often told that correlation does not mean causation, but as good Humeans, we can discount the argument by introducing certain space and time provisos with respect to stipulating the antecedents and consequents in a causal sequence. Correlation may not be causation; but causation *is* correlation unless, of course, we leave the domain of pure empirics—in which case it would be as well that we drop the language of causality altogether.

No effort has been made here to distinguish between causal relations and explanations. That is because I have concentrated on cognitively satisfying explanations and have proposed that what is satisfying is the perceptually familiar organization of experience. That causal analyses are explanatory is apparent not only from the work of empiricists but also of phenomenologists (from Kant to Michotte, 1963). However, if we wish to place explanation on firmer grounds than the nebulous standards of cognitive satisfaction, we will have to leave the psychological aspects of explanation and turn more directly to the practice of explaining events within science itself.

## LEVELS OF EXPLANATION

### Lower-Level Explanations

In *The Logic of Scientific Discovery*, Karl Popper writes: "To give a *causal explanation* of an event means to deduce a statement which describes it, using as premises of the deduction one or more *universal*

*laws*, together with certain singular statements, the *initial conditions*,"
(1961, p. 59).

Since the qualifier 'causal' is unnecessarily restrictive it can be removed and without substantial loss of meaning. What we have then is
a formal description of lower-level explanation; that is to say, of explanation by instantiation.

Let us be explicit. Suppose we wish to explain the behavior of a
pigeon in a Skinner box. He has learned to peck the target in order to
get food, or better, because the response is accompanied by a reinforcing
state of affairs. Or perhaps better still, his pecking the target is an instantiation of the law of reinforcement. The paradigm for this case might
be as follows: Let $x$ be any response, let $Sx$ be "the response $x$ accompanied by reinforcing stimuli," and let $Rx$ be "the response $x$ acquires
an increment of habit strength." Then the paradigm

$$(x)\ Sx \supset Rx$$
$$\underline{Sx_i}$$
$$\therefore Rx_i$$

is simply the familiar *modus ponens*. We assume that if a response is
repeatedly emitted it has habit strength. The habit strength, as expressed
in $Rx_i$, is then inferable from the general *law of effect*, $(x)\ Sx \supset Rx$, and
the statement of the initial conditions, $Sx_i$.

At first glance such explanations may seem trivial. One notes an
element of circularity here. If one defines response in such a way that
all response is accompanied by reinforcing stimuli and that the general
law of effect holds for every event we classify as a response, then indeed
it seems somewhat circular to explain an event by what amounts to an
arbitrary classificatory procedure (cf. N10.1). This may appear as trivial
as saying, for example, that we explain the fact that a particular swan,
Hisser, is white from the conjunction of "All swans are white" and
"Hisser is a swan." One might as well explain some particular as having
some characteristic (such as "John is accident prone") by saying that
all particulars like *that* particular have the given characteristic ("All
people just like John are accident prone").

Two comments are in order as concerns this conventionalistic or
circular aspect of explanation by instantiation. First of all, the general
law (or laws) takes precedence over the examination of a given particular.
As scientists, for example, we are familiar with these general laws and
classificatory schemata. If in fact a particular is found to exemplify a
law, then we do indeed understand that particular in light of our comprehension of a law that is part of our domain of familiar discourse.
The law of gravitation does explain events, although even the gravitational physicist is pressed to tell us why objects do appear to "attract"
one another as a function of their masses and distances. The language of

gravitation is a familiar one. It has the status of an explainer (an explicans) of falling objects, even though it presents a mere description of what we classify as free-falling objects. Why this language should prove a cognitively satisfactory explainer is not a question to be answered by a logic; it is a psychological question (cf. N10.2). Secondly, the element of cognitive enlightenment, of comprehension, of understanding, which is essential as the psychological qualifier of explanation, derives from the empirical inspection which results in our finding that a given event belongs to the class of events covered by the explaining law. In the general law, $(x)$ $Sx \supset Rx$, whatever it is, the element of cognitive enlightenment comes in our recognizing that some event can be assigned to a class of events designated by '$Sx$'. We first recognize that the event is a particular of the class of all particulars, $x$, to which we can assign $S$. This may not be immediately obvious to us, any more than it was immediately obvious to early scientists that magnetic and electrical events were describable by the same set of equations, or that judgments of value and judgments of sensory magnitude were describable by the same psychophysical laws. Lower-level explanations of the type we have been discussing would be circular only if we manufactured a law for each particular and its properties to be explained (cf. N10.1). But as we have seen, the laws take precedence. Explanations are achieved only when we find how to classify our explananda. At the level of instantiation then, explanation is a matter of putting our events to be explained, our explananda, into familiar slots, where the slots are general laws enunciated in the progress of science.

Superficially, these procedures of lower-level explanation look embarrassingly like the typologies which have been the scandal of psychology. A person displays such and such behavior because he possesses such and such a faculty, disposition, or personality type. The difficulty here is that one begins with behavior and from the classes of behavior "types" attempts to ascertain correlated characteristics in physiognomy, modes of expression, verbal report, etc. There may or may not be substantial correlations between, say, temperament and body type, but such correlations, even though they express "laws," cannot serve as satisfactory explanations in the sense discussed here. To find that all mesomorphs are aggressive is hardly an adequate explanation of why Hank is aggressive, even though Hank may be a mesomorph. The law does not take precedence over the class of particulars it now explains. That is to say, the law is not now found to hold for (and explain) a class of events not included in its initial formulation. Psychologically, what is satisfactory about lower level explanations is that a law (or laws) is extended to cover classes of events not visualized as being covered in its initial formulation. This aspect of lower-level explanation suggests: one, the explicandum is explained by a law not restricted to the class of events that are similar in all (cognitively germane) characteristics to itself; and two, the extension of the law itself is enhanced by virtue of the successful explanation.

### Higher-Level Explanations

The hierarchy of levels in explanation rests upon the regress in explanatory pursuit. Thus, if the explicandum $E$ is explained by the explicans $L_1$ and in turn we explain the predicates in the general laws of $L_1$ by another set of propositions $L_2$, then $L_2$ constitutes a higher-order explicans. Not only do we derive the sentences that truly describe $E$, but we derive in turn those laws and principles that are the instruments of inferring the description of $E$. Thus, for example, one can derive specific behaviors of the planets from Kepler's three laws of the planetary orbits; but also one can in turn derive Kepler's laws within the rubric of classical Newtonian mechanics. The explicans in the lower-level explanation is itself explained. Or again, we can explain certain changes in response pattern as an instance of the law of effect. But the law of effect might be explained in turn by a theory that postulates activation of cell congeries by the presence of reinforcing stimuli, thereby facilitating the emergence of cell assemblies that mediate the habitual response (e.g., Hebb, 1949; Milner, 1957; Rosenblatt, 1958).

In general then, theoretical explanations are higher-order explanations. The experimental hypotheses which are derived theorems within the theory are expressions of laws. These laws in turn might be the general principles serving in the lower-level explanations of particular events. Thus the idea of a hierarchy of explanations is simple to comprehend. However, the idea of higher-order explanations becomes particularly interesting when we consider explaining laws of one science in terms of the theoretical formulations of another. This is the familiar problem of reduction. It will occupy our attention to some considerable extent in subsequent chapters. But upon initial inspection, it is significant that reductive expanations themselves imply a hierarchy of explanations. A reducing science which constitutes the argument of an explicans is, in some sense, thought to be more inclusive or more basic than the reduced science. A successful reduction thereby provides us with a cognitively satisfying explication of events and laws in the domain of the reduced science.

## LOGICAL REQUIREMENT OF EXPLANATION

In the discussion of levels of explanation, we have been concerned with deducibility of the explicandum. It is time to give the rubric of deducibility a more explicit formulation.

The classic treatment of the logic of explanation is to be found in an article by Hempel and Oppenheim (1948). Their schema follows that suggested by Popper (1959) and is given in the following summary statements (1948, p. 138).

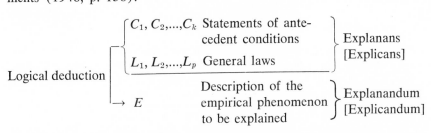

In light of the foregoing discussion, the elaboration of the summary statement should be obvious. 'Instantiation', 'deducibility', 'derivability', all are terms designating the procedure by which we arrive at a description of the event to be explained. Hempel and Oppenheim also prescribe the following logical conditions for the adequacy of the explanation:

R(1), The explanandum must be a logical consequence of the explanans. . . .

R(2), The explanans must contain general laws and these must actually be required for the derivation of the explanandum. . . .

R(3), The explanans must have empirical content; i.e., it must be capable, at least in principle, of test by experiment or observation. . . .

R(4), The sentences constituting the explanans must be true. . . . (1948, p. 137)

Strangely perhaps, this last requirement is the most curious of the four. As the requirements stand they imply that the schema applies only to what we have treated as lower-level explanations. What of higher-level explanations? The given schema would then have to be altered to include the possibility of hypothetical constructs among a set of postulates. (The completed theory need not include such constructs, but then, in the sense of a complete microreduction, no theory is itself complete.) Thus the explanans would include statements of antecedent conditions, general laws, *and* a set of postulates including whatever hypothetical constructs are sufficient for deducing all the theorems (experimental laws) of the science. This being the case, then there is some puzzlement as to the applicability of condition R(4).

Initially, the hypothetical constructs are theoretical entities of somewhat dubious existential status. They serve as devices in an if-then chain of reasoning. However, the only observational anchoring by which we may judge the truth of such hypothetical statements rests in the consequents of the chain of deduction. We thereby have necessary observational conditions for the truth of the hypothetical statements in the explanans, but we do not have the sufficient conditions. It is difficult then to see how we can hold consistently to condition R(4), unless, of course, we undertake a program to reduce all hypothetical terms to empirical entities. There is good reason for aspiring to such a program, as we shall see in the discussion of reductionism; but it is by no means clear that such a program is possible—as witness logical barriers to observability in microphysics.

## CRITIQUE OF THE DEDUCTIVIST THESIS

The deductivist thesis of explanation has been held by a number of distinguished scientists and philosophers (cf. N10.3). It ignores the subjective aspects of cognitive satisfaction and concentrates on the less equivocal requirements of deducibility. It forms an integral aspect of hypothetico-deductive method in the sciences. Still in spite of the pervasive character of this methodology in all ot the philosophy of science, serious objections have been raised against the gospel of deducibility. Some of these objections are as old as the systematic attacks on modern science, some are more recent. We shall attempt to sift them out by attending to the following questions: (1) Does deducibility in fact serve as the touchstone of explanation in scientific practice? (2) Are prediction and explanation symmetric, as the Hempel–Oppenheim thesis of deducibility maintains? (3) Are there events which in principle are unamenable to, or are otherwise refractory to, deducibility?

### Deducibility and the Analysis of Explanation

Several contemporary philosophers of science (Scriven, 1958, 1962, 1963; Goudge, 1958; Yolton, 1958, 1959; Hesse, 1963; Sellars, 1962; Feyerabend, 1962) have been critical of the deductivist analysis of explanation on grounds that the actual practice of scientific explanation is not so amenable to neat logical treatment as the deductivists claim. Of these, Scriven has been the most persistent in his criticism, and for the sake of brevity, we shall follow the line of his attack. First of all, if we look at the usages of 'explanation' we find that the term is used to designate quite diverse activities even in the restricted range of its applications in science. Not all explanations are deductive in nature; some are descriptive, many are causal, and many carry with them a kind of certificate of "primeval" assurance from within on the conceptual framework in which they occur. The language of science itself creates the conditions of understanding, it breeds its own intelligibility. Secondly, the schema of deducibility oversimplifies the process of arriving at explanations. It subsumes a finished body of laws, principles, postulates, such that explanations always occur in a finished corpus of theory. But this, according to Scriven (also see Yolton, 1958, 1959), is seldom the case. Only in "complete" theories, such as that of Newtonian mechanics where there are no unspecified nuisance variables, can we aspire to this placid ideal. Rather in most of our efforts, explaining requires the interplay of experimental hypothesis, factual language, and theoretical construction. These are contextually interrelated. Not only are theoretical systems incomplete but they are contextually dynamical in that events, i.e., the explicanda, themselves, may inspire some modification of the theory. Thirdly, deductivism concentrates on the symbols of science, on its language and statements, rather than on events as such. Hypothetico-deductive methodology retains both its simplicity and integrity by attending only to statements; it refers to statements and not to the events as such, which presumably are capable of a more direct cognitive assimilation. Moreover, general laws are idealizations. Lawlike statements are both inaccurate and incomplete as descriptions of particular events to which presumably they apply.

Should the foregoing not be sufficient to reject deductivism, Scriven then mounts his attack on the Hempel–Oppenheim thesis with the following bill of particulars:

1.   It fails to make the crucial logical distinctions between explanations, grounds for explanations, things to be explained, and the description of things.
2.   It is too restrictive . . . [in that it excludes many examples of scientific explanation].
3.   It is too inclusive and admits entirely nonexplanatory schema.
4.   It requires an account of cause, law, and probability which are basically unsound.
5.   It leaves out of account three notions that are in fact essential for an account of scientific explanation: context, judgment, and understanding (Scriven, 1962, p. 196).

Such an unrelenting attack on deductivism should be sufficient to bury it as a significant analysis of explanation; but, in many respects, this schedule of particulars is more contentious than convincing (cf. N10.4). The points Scriven makes here are poignant, but what is not given due emphasis is the fact that hypothetico-deductive explanation is a schema. As such, it is an ideal. Its only straightforward application is in a complete theory.[1] Few sciences, certainly not that of psychology, can offer complete theories without loose constructions and nebulous inference chains. Nevertheless, this fact does not obviate the need for rigorous specifications as concerns adequate explanation. In contrast, what is more distressing is what Brodbeck (1962) has designated the reliance upon "obscurantist" criteria of understanding and intelligibility. These

[1] By "complete theory" is meant one in which *all* relevant variables are accurately specified. Related terms are "closed systems" and perfect knowledge as related to scientific systems. See Bergmann, 1957; Brodbeck, 1962.

have their roots more in intuition and the feel for conceptual context than in logical analysis. Critique of deductivism is warranted, to be sure; it should prompt our care and our caution to achieve logically adequate explanations. But it does not disqualify the deductivist thesis. Intelligibility is secured by logical analysis more than it is by impressionistic reference to "understanding." The deductivist thesis subsumes the ideal of complete theories. As such, it is programmatic as well as prescriptive. Were the case otherwise, the contemporary stress on the axiomatization of theories would be gratuitous.

## Explanation and Prediction

One of the implications of the Hempel–Oppenheim argument is that explanation and prediction should be symmetric. That is to say, the time context of the event to be explained is irrelevant so far as the criterion of deducibility is concerned. Commenting on their schema of explanation, Hempel and Oppenheim write:

> Let us note here that the same formal analysis, including the four necessary conditions, applies to scientific prediction as well as to explanation. The difference between the two is of pragmatic character. If $E$ is given, i.e., if we know the phenomenon described by $E$ has occurred, and a suitable set of statements $C_1, C_2, \ldots, C_k, L_1, L_2, \ldots, L_r$ is provided afterwards, we speak of an explanation of the phenomenon in question. If the latter statements are given and $E$ is derived prior to the occurrence of the phenomenon it describes, we speak of a prediction. It may be said, therefore, that an explanation is not fully adequate unless its explanans, if taken account of in time, could have served as a basis for predicting the phenomenon under consideration (1948, p. 138).

This is a strong statement and exception has been taken to its thesis (e.g., Scheffler, 1957; Rescher, 1958; Hanson, 1959; Scriven, 1962). For a complete theory, such as the Newtonian model of the solar system was once assumed to be, predictions and postdictions could be made with equal facility, and within the same logical schema (as demonstrated, for example, in the planetarium). However, it is not difficult to find exceptions to this simplistic treatment of prediction. In practice, predictions, however rational, seem to include an element of intuitive gambit in which the predictor commits himself against a background of risk or of chance which is not part of any rational structure of the theory. The uncertainty is a cognitive uncertainty belonging to the predictor; in no way is it part of the formal structure of a theory or other explanans. Furthermore, when we turn to microphysics, we find that quantum phenomena can be deduced *ex post facto* as the logic of explanation requires, but due to the uncertainty factors, they cannot be predicted with the same precision (Hanson, 1959). The specification and overall knowledge of the system is less perfect.

There is a significant difference in the character of the two lines of argument suggested above. The elements of intuitive gambit and cognitive uncertainty, so to speak, represent lacunae in the chain of inference. They betoken the inchoate character of the theoretical system which serves as the logical foundations of inference. As such, they can be overcome by completion of the system of inference, by our having available a theory with complete specification of all variables germane to the events in question. In principle, then, perfect knowledge is possible and prediction would indeed follow the hypothetico-deductive schema. However, the deducible-in-principle outlook is obliterated in the argument as presented by Hanson. The character of predictive statements is uniquely different from *ex post facto* explanations. Predictions necessarily carry with them uncertainty effects due to feedback (interference) in our ascertaining the initial conditions and the state of the system. There is no way to overcome this predicament in quantum physics. Even with perfect knowledge (as allowable within the premises of the theory) we cannot in principle predict with the same precision that we can explain events after the fact.

Since the status of the uncertainty principle is still being debated, perhaps one should be cautious in accepting this latter argument as dogma. But there can be little question that gaining knowledge of the state of a system to be predicted is uniquely different from hypothesizing what the state of the system has been in order for certain phenomena to obtain. For example, a neurophysiological explanation of behavior might be such as to assert that if the state of the system could be represented by $S_1, S_2, \ldots, S_j$, then we could infer $E_r$ as a description of the actual behavior. The explanation is hypothetical. No interference effects (e.g., scalpel cuts, electrode implants) have been introduced to affect the states signified by $S_1, S_2, \ldots, S_j$. It is clearly different in the case of prediction. In order to predict behavior, or rather, to predict its description $E$, we must empirically ascertain the state of the system. Thus not only do we need statements of the order $S_1, S_2, \ldots, S_j$, but we will require additional statements of the character $S_k, S_l, \ldots$ which specify the effects that gaining knowledge of the system will have on the system. In principle, it might be possible to build perfect predictive theories incorporating the interference effects but the theory and chain of deductive inference would differ in this respect from those of explanation: they would include interference variables for which there is neither place nor need in explanation.

Even admitting this line of argument, the deductivist may wish to assert that his thesis of the symmetry of prediction and explanation is inviolate. Both explanation and prediction adopt the same schema of deduction. How the initial conditions are determined is irrelevant to his inquiry. He is interested only in the fact that from $C$-statements and

*L*-statements (Hempel–Oppenheim) he can deduce *E* statements descriptive either of past or of future phenomena. This line of argument can only be pursued at the risk of suppressing vital methodological distinctions. In principle, we might think both psychology and mechanics are capable of complete specification of variables and perfect knowledge. Nevertheless, the class of predictions includes a set of variables not included in the class of hypothetico-deductive explanations. Predictions involve interference variables which need not be, and usually are not, included in explanations.

Mention should also be made here of the troublesome reflexive aspects of certain classes of predictions. In complete systems with perfect knowledge, specification of the values of *all* variables will, through the deductive chain, yield a statement exhaustively descriptive of the event to be predicted or explained. But what of systems wherein the statement $E_r$ itself becomes a value of a significant variable in the state of the system, thereby yielding a different *E*, say $E_s$, and different state of the system, then a different $E_t$, and so on *ad infinitum?* This is the familiar problem of reflexive predictions (Merton, 1957; Buck, 1963) wherein the prediction itself serves to enhance or to mitigate the event predicted. Witness, for example, the effect that a precision prediction of the stock market might have on the subsequent behaviors of investors.

This problem is too involved to pursue here. There can be little doubt, however, that it suggests difficulties for the behavioral scientist, not met, say, by the macrophysicist. Reflexive predictions can be shown to be trouble free in this context only if they can be incorporated into what have been designated complete theories.

Yet all this is a rather fruitless debate. There is no question but that scientists and nonscientists alike proceed differently in making predictions and in producing explanations. If taken seriously, the task of prediction is the more difficult. In explanation, all the data, all the information, is before the person; but in prediction this is not the case, the events are yet to happen (cf. N10.5).

## Nondeducible Events

Our third and final question in the critique of deducibility is: Are there any events or classes of events which in principle are nondeducible? Three lines of argument can be entertained as proposing affirmative responses to the question. They will occupy us for the remainder of this chapter. One, statistical laws refer to probabilistic relations between classes of events. No inference can be made concerning individual events. Therefore, no derivation, no explanation (or prediction) in terms of statements about individual events is possible. Two, events occur with putatively emergent properties. What distinguishes emergent from nonemergent properties is their nonpredictable character at the time of their emergence. And three, all individual events are unique. Classification is undertaken as a matter of procedural convenience. One does not suffer from this loss of specificity in the physical (or other nomothetic) sciences, but in psychology and other personalistic sciences the loss is fatal, so it is argued, both to understanding and to prediction. Statements about unique individuals are not deducible from general laws.

(1) *Statistical explanation.*     When describing individual events, we must always think in terms of assigning a property or a set of properties to some particular. Either the particular is to be assigned a given property in the catalog of all properties or it is not. A two-value logic applies. Aside from some subjectivist treatments (see Chapter 13), probability relationships and predicates are always thought to apply to collectives. Thus statistical explanation within the deductive schema permits our deriving statistical laws and statements of relative frequencies but it does not permit us to deduce whether or not a given particular (event) within the collective will have a given property.

As stated here, the argument is quite correct. Our concern need only be as to whether on such grounds the deductivist schema is disqualified as the basis of explanation. At the outset, we should note there is no questioning our not being able to explain or to predict individual events on the basis of laws that are predominantly statistical. Consider the behavior of the die described in the preceding chapter. The die has some propensity to respond, which we have called a disposition. The laws describing that disposition are probabilistic ones. Suppose for all such dice the probability of throwing an even number is twice that of throwing an odd. Thus if some given die is a member of this class of dice, it will fall even with a probability of two-thirds. Translated into the collectivist's language, this means that out of the class of many such tosses, our expectations are that two-thirds of them will be even. But note that neither the property of being even nor the property of being odd is excluded by this lawlike description. Thus, following the deductivist schema, regardless of what the outcome is, it is "explainable" by the same set of laws. Explanations of individual events would therefore lose the precision we expect. In fact, there is no precision in dealing with individual events; that is just the point.

This example is, of course, a trivial one. We could better have taken as our example choice behavior and some stochastic model of learning. Theorems derivable within the model are expressed in terms of probability of response. In the dichotomous choice situation, say, both response $R$ and response $\sim R$ are covered by the theorems of response. Yet which of these two responses is to occur on a specific trial is neither to be predicted nor explained.

This is a poignant criticism and it needs to be taken seriously (see, for example, Hempel, 1962). However, it is fatal to the deductivist point of view only if we assume that science must predict and explain individual events. A law is nonetheless a law because it expresses a probability relationship rather than some categorical assignment of a property. And a prediction is nonetheless a prediction even though it asserts only that some proportion $p$ of all events will have the property. But what is more important, the schema of the argument is the same both in complete systems with perfect knowledge and which permit prediction of particular events, and in relatively incomplete systems with imperfect knowledge and which incorporate probability and uncertainty into their predictions. An analysis of the application of such stochastic models shows that they fit the deductivist schema. From statements of initial conditions and statistical laws, one derives statements about classes or collectives of response. It is of interest to note that among the few attempts at axiomatization of psychological theory is that concerning a statistical learning theory (Estes and Suppes, 1959). Successful axiomatization assures us that the deductivist schema of explanation will hold (cf. N10.6).

(2) *Emergent events.*     Another class of occurrences which is presumed to be problematical for the deductivist schema of explanation is that of emergent events. The concept of emergence is difficult to define and examples of emergent events which carry ontological pedigree over and above the mere symptoms of novelty are all but impossible to verify. Let us be somewhat lenient in our specifications then and define as emergent any event whose occurrence is not deducible within any extant theory. By definition then, emergent events are indeed problematical for those who stress the indispensability of deduction in matters of scientific explanation.

We can, however, be somewhat more explicit. We can focus upon two alternatives allowable within the scope of this definition. One, we may speak of emergent properties within the language of science, such that statements of emergent properties are not derivable within the science from any of the statements of the properties of known particulars. And two, we may speak of emergent properties precipitated, as it were, in the emitive process of creative, cosmic, hormic, or other type of emergent evolution. In the first case, the issues of emergence are primarily epistemological; in the second case, they have ontological significance.

Consider the first of these. From a corpus of theory and fact, all known properties of events can be represented in the set of all predicates, $\{P_1, P_2, \ldots, P_n\}$. An emergent event is then one to which we must assign some new property or predicate, $P_{n+1}$, which is neither deducible or otherwise assignable within the corpus of the science. The ingredient of unpredictability presumably signifies a genuine emergent novelty. A classic presentation of this line of argument can be found in Broad's *Mind and Its Place in Nature* (1925), where he argues that our knowledge of the properties of constituents in chemical compounds may not be sufficient for us to predict the properties of the compound events. Thus he writes:

> The characteristic behavior of common salt cannot be deduced from the most complete knowledge of the properties of Sodium in isolation, or of Chlorine in isolation, or of other compounds of Sodium, such as Sodium-Sulphate; or of other compounds of Chlorine such as Silver-Chloride (p. 59).

After similar examples from chemistry, he goes on to say,

> . . . in abstract terms the emergent theory asserts that there are certain wholes, composed (say) of constituents A, B, and C in relation R to each other; that all wholes composed of constituents of the same kind as A, B, and C in relations of the same kind as R have certain characteristic properties; that A, B, and C are capable of occurring in other kinds of complex where the relation is not the same kind as R; and that the characteristic properties of the whole R (A,B,C) cannot, even in theory, be deduced from the complete knowledge of the properties A, B, and C in isolation or in other wholes which are not of the form R (A,B,C) (p. 61).

We may supplement Broad's examples from chemistry with the following two. If we allow the unreal assumption of an extant science prior to the origins of life, we could hardly have predicted the origins of life from properties of the pre-viable carbons. Or, apropos of the Ladd–Franklin theory of color vision, we could hardly have predicted the qualities of red and green prior to the emergence of the red-green receptors, any more than we could now predict the qualities, say, of ultraviolet were an ultraviolet visual receptor to emerge. Our examples here do not distinguish between properties and qualities of experience. This is a fact we shall have to keep in mind as we examine the response to Broad's argument.

Two lines of argument have, I think, proved all but fatal to Broad's treatment of emergence as an attack on deductive explanation. One, Nagel (1961), has stressed that scientific explanation always concerns the derivation of statements and never the events as such.[2] Thus, for a deductive schema to be adequate to the task of explanation, it must contain statements of all events and properties to be explained within the theory. This is a truism. If some novel property were "emergent," then indeed, if there were no expression for it, if some statement describing or even naming it were not part of the language of the science, that property could neither be predicted nor explained. But in this case the

[2] The present discussion of emergence owes a great deal to the reading of Nagel.

concept of emergence tends to be a trivial one. It merely implies that the science is immature and relatively incomplete. One would then have only to extend the set of predicates and the set of propositions to include statements about the novel property. Explanation of the "emergent" event might then be achieved within the familiar deductivist schema. Suppose, for example, that of some species of primitive organisms the only known properties of response in its native environment were reflexive ones. And suppose further that now under some radical alteration of their environment individuals of the species were observed to display emergent properties of learning. Obviously our theory of these organisms would have to be expanded to include learned response in the set of all response properties. Explanation is not ruled out by emergence of new response properties. Indeed, it becomes imperative to explain the emergent properties through a modification of the theory. As Nagel states the argument:

> Accordingly, all descriptive explanations occurring in a statement that is allegedly deducible from the theory must also occur among the expressions used to formulate the theory or the assumptions adjoined to the theory when it is applied to specialized circumstances. Thus a statement like "Water is translucent" cannot indeed be deduced from any set of statements about hydrogen and oxygen which do not contain the expressions 'water' and 'translucent'; but this impossibility derives entirely from purely formal considerations and is relative to the special set of statements adopted as premises in the case under consideration.
>
> It is clear, therefore, that to say of a given property that it is an "emergent" is to attribute to it a character which the property may possess relative to one theory or body of assumptions but may not possess relative to some other theory. Accordingly, the doctrine of emergence (in the sense now under discussion) must be understood as stating certain *logical* facts about formal relations between statements rather than any experimental or even "metaphysical" facts about some allegedly "inherent" traits of *properties* of objects (1961, p. 369).

A second and equally convincing line of argument has been proposed by Kurt Grelling (an early positivist and victim of Nazi tyranny). Taken at face value there is an inconsistency implicit within Broad's type of part-whole argument. In effect, that argument asserts that properties of the emergent whole cannot be predicted from our knowledge of the properties of the constituent parts. It is short-sighted to assert that properties of the whole are unpredictable from knowledge of properties of the parts, for an exhaustive denumeration of the properties of the parts include all those combinatorial potentialities which are reified (i.e., emerge) when such parts combine to form wholes.

It should be noted that Broad (1925) himself protects against this argument by deliberately excluding the properties of potential combination in the emergent from the set of properties attributable to the constituents. But this is not an allowable safeguard. It spares the doctrine of emergence by keeping the constituents in epistemic isolation. It succeeds only in restricting the discussion to that class of emergent situations where extant theory is insufficiently explicit to permit derivation of the emergent properties of the events. As the quotation from Nagel intimates, emergence in these terms reflects only a logical limitation.

Earlier it was asserted that one must distinguish between properties of objects and those qualities which we regard as the contents of consciousness. Broad's argument has sometimes been interpreted as saying, for example, that from all the properties of hydrogen and oxygen, we cannot infer those combinatorial properties of water such as its translucence and taste, which are qualities of our perceptual experience. This is a mistaken application. Be that as it may, it is quite in order to say that qualities of our subjective experience are never strictly deducible from statements about physical events. It is one of the recurrent themes of logical empiricism that qualia, as it were, are given. They are not deducible or otherwise explainable. The only way it would make sense to incorporate them into the schema of explanation would be to replace them by statements such as those reflecting postulates of psychophysical parallelism. Following this tack, we would not, of course, concern ourselves with qualia, as such. In one of the earliest discussions of emergence, Pepper (1926) discounts all doctrines of emergence which concern themselves with epiphenomena rather than with physical events subject to public and lawful description. It is the nature of epiphenomena to be unexplainable. That is why they, in their pristine isolation, are not the proper subject matter of science.

The foregoing discussion has treated emergence primarily as a problem in epistemology. What if we were to treat it as a doctrine of ontological significance? According to this latter thesis, the universe of laws and relations is itself the subject of ontogenesis, forever developing new "habit patterns," ever building on the fund of its childhood, always emerging into yet another adulthood. Thus the changing, evolving, emerging universe. This theme has been the subject of literature and science alike. It is to be found in the prefaces and plays of Bernard Shaw, in the writings of the biologists C. L. Morgan and J. B. S. Haldane, in the philosophical writings of Alexander, Bergson, Boodin, and Whitehead. It is the subject of debate and counterdebate in modern physical cosmology. It is an enticing doctrine, it appeals to the Heraclitean mystique. Yet, two observations can be made at the outset. One, there is no reliable means of testing this doctrine. And two, nothing in the doctrine precludes our adopting hypothetico-deductive methodology as the instrument of understanding.

Consider first the matter of verifying the hypothesis of cosmic emergence. In order to attest to genuine emergent properties in the universe, we must be able to distinguish such properties from those which are merely novel and from those which by virtue of our epistemological limitations are merely unpredictable. In an article on "The Status of Emergence," Henle (1942) addresses himself specifically to this problem. First, he notes that unpredictability cannot serve as the critical property of emergence, ". . . predictability, far from being a mere predicate, is at least a tetradic relation and we must say, not that quality A is predictable, but rather that quality A is predictable by person B on evidence C with degree of assurance D" (p. 489). Thus, "any characteristic past, present, or future, not related to a given body of evidence would be unpredictable on that evidence." However, novel events, such as the accidental discovery of a new planet, and inadequate theories both imply unpredictability without at the same time implying emergence. Novelty clearly exists, but whereas emergence entails novelty and unpredictability, the latter do not entail emergence. Henle then maintains that a formal definition of emergence requires, (1) that the emergent event must be logically novel, in the sense of its being unpredictable within extant theory; and (2) that it be not merely a spatio-temporal accident, such as the discovery of the new planet. Seemingly such criteria could be applied to the evaluation of novel events. However, the issue of "ontological versus epistemological significance" is left hanging. The ultimate analysis is logical. Emergence is judged in the context of theory and theories are evaluated in terms of their comprehensiveness and simplicity. But logical simplicity relates to the language of science. It possesses no substantive, hence no ontological, significance. Cosmic emergence cannot be conclusively verified.

Be that as it may, even were we to grant the possibility of cosmic evolution, i.e., a dynamic cosmogony, we might wonder whether there would be efficacious alternatives to scientific explanation. To be sure, Bergsonian intuitionism has been proposed as an alternative (cf. N10.7). But then we must enter a different realm of knowledge wherein language can play no part. For example, Bergson (1911) writes, "We do not *think* real time. But we *live* in it because life transcends intellect." Transcendence thus removes the object, the process, from the realm of explanation and thereby accomplishes its own irrelevance for discussions like the present one. However, what is sometimes overlooked is that Bergson was, himself, an astute analyst of abstractive science. His cognizance of the role of invention and representational devices was the source of the sympathetic bonds that existed between him and James and the pragmatists. As such, the rigors of scientific explanation were not to be discounted within the realm of scientific understanding itself. If one were committed to the language of science, then what limited discussion of emergence would be at all possible must be accomplished within the syntax and limitations of that language.

We may visualize two situations in which it might be appropriate to use the language of emergence. Our concern is to show that in neither case is the deductive schema of explanation rendered inapplicable to the task of bringing emergent phenomena within its purview. First, suppose we grant the evolution of the terrestrial universe from the primeval to the complex. This evolutionary process signals the emergence of ever more complex structures out of primeval substance. Thus, for example, in Oparin's conception of the origin of life (1938), primitive life forms (emergents) evolved when the impact of cosmic radiation on primeval carbides instigated a chain of events eventuating in the production of self-duplicating organic compounds. Each event in the chain might be re-garded as emergent in that new substances with new properties came into production where there had been no such substances before. In this context it is little more than a quibble to debate whether emergence is an episte-mological or an ontological hypothesis. In either case, novel events have to be incorporated into a science which at each epoch of emergence could not be sufficiently complete to explain the emergence of the new properties. Awaiting its emergent fund of knowledge, science would have to be retrospective. Still its explanatory function would be achieved deductively and would be expanded as the ingress of emergent properties made it imperative to enlarge the fund of basic predicates.

The second situation is more dramatic. Suppose the universe were such that it could be understood only as a succession of epochs. Not only would we have to contend with emergent properties but with ever-changing laws as well. Engaging as this possibility might be in the realm of science fiction, it is difficult to see how its possibility would in any way alter the scientific enterprise. Laws, to begin with, express relations between variables that designate properties or other classifying character-istics. Thus if one of the variables were time, a law might express change in some property as a function of time. At some higher-order level of complexity, we might find that the function expressed in the law is itself a function of time. We might have a succession of epochs, $E_j$, $E_k$, . . . , $E_n$, . . . such that each epoch contained a unique law over some distinguishable or otherwise enduring classification of phenomena. Under the circumstances we would hardly have any alternative but to proceed as we do under the assumption of a constant universe. We would look for some law descriptive of the epochal changes (i.e., a law of epochs), and make that law the instrument of explanation and prediction. Should no orderly progression of epochal change be in evidence or should assump-tions of the constancy of "nature" not be applicable (as, for example, a random change in universal constants), then our law of epochs would become a stochastic law, incorporating the properties of randomness.

In summary, then, a defense of the deductivist schema of explana-tion is maintained against the proposals and arguments of emergence.

The deductivist, as we so style our partisan here, does not on any grounds rule out novelty. Nor does he ever claim that theories are even approximately complete, sufficiently so that novel phenomena are invariably predictable in advance of the actual occurrence of the emergent properties. Nor does he necessarily rule out on any grounds the possibility of ontologically significant doctrines of emergence. What he does claim is that there is no alternative but to formulate his explanations in terms of laws and formal theories. The critique of scientific explanation often involves discussions of how science is actually done. Doubtless intuition has played a role. The history of science has shown that scientific thinking has been at times haphazard and irrationalistic. But eventually we seek simplified formulations, a tidying up of scientific thinking, not just in the domain of experimental confirmation but also in that of logical analysis and clarification. On these grounds discussions of the methodology of deductivism and schemata of explanation will never lose their relevance. To think otherwise is to retreat into irrationalism, against which the scientific revolution has been the obdurate and incessant countertheme.

(3) *Idiographic versus nomothetic descriptions.*    The third argument is not so much an attack on deductivism as it is an effort to show that explanation is not the only means to understanding. One understands not alone by explanation, he also apprehends meaning directly through a meticulous description of the event-complex as a unique historical phenomenon. Indeed in history, psychology, and political science, direct knowledge by description is indispensable to understanding.

The issue is frequently drawn on the distinction between *nomothetic* and *idiographic* descriptions. Nomothetic descriptions involve statements of general laws, principles of inference, and the language of classes applying to many particulars, whereas idiographic descriptions involve statements explicitly describing the individual as a unique phenomenon in some spatio-temporal section. In scientific explanation understanding is achieved by our utilizing nomothetic statements as tools of description and inference. But inference is always from one class symbol to another. Therefore, in such context, an individual event assigned class membership can be known only by the attribution to it of the defining general property. This obliterates its individuality. And, we are told, it is this individuality which we are concerned to understand. Nomothetic devices may function well for the physical sciences where historical origins and individuality can be ignored, but this is not the case for history and psychology where the unique nonrepeatable history of the event to be understood renders all but the crudest of class identifications impossible.

The alternative, of course, is idiographic description. However, it is not always clear in the arguments whether idiographic understanding is a special kind of intuitive, nonlinguistic understanding, *per se,* or whether it designates a special kind of nonlogical inference. If it is the former, we need hardly concern ourselves with it in a treatise on explanation. Intuitive understanding, if it is beyond the pale of language and its class structure, could neither be communicable nor an instrument of explanation: "Whereof one cannot speak, he must be silent." On the other hand, if it is the latter, then the idiographic approach to knowledge results in a state of understanding which follows from this special kind of nonlogical inference. In this case, we would not have to keep our silence; and the understanding, if it were shared by several observers, might become the instrument of explanation. At any rate, from awareness and the idiographic description of an event complex, $E_1 \ldots E_n$, and some nonlogical instrument of inference, $I_f$, we could infer, predict, understand, comprehend, or otherwise intuit the state of affairs which is the object of curiosity. What that "nonlogical instrument" is, is of course, the crucial item. It cannot be any kind of analogy, for that would throw "idiographic inference" back in the clutches of abstraction, nomothetics, and the class struggle. That is why appeals to *empathy* and to *verstehende* remain so unconvincing as tools of inference; they show their kinship with analogy. As in the cases of identification and projection they reveal their psychological origins as cognitive supports. Experientially derived, they implicitly afford us general principles of inference that we as individuals bring to focus upon individual events.

There can be little question but that some subconsciously processed fund of experience serves us in our individual worlds as the nonformalized instruments of inference. In brief, this is the heart of the doctrine of apperception. Any unique event sequence is meaningful to us to the extent we can assimilate it to the complex system of cognitive schemata. There is, however, an alternative to the empirical origins of the schemata. It renders the doctrines of idiographic intuition and *verstehende* somewhat more poignant than they would otherwise be within ordinary psychological analysis. According to Windelband (1921), to whom the nomothetic–idiographic distinction is due, perceptual schemata are *a priori.* Like the Kantian categories and the transcendental aesthetic, they are the indispensable agents for the reification of experience. Consequently, to attend to the unique event as it happens, to understand it, is to know that that experience *must* be ordered, *must* occur, in just the way it does. Not only do we experience A and B, but in experiencing A and B, we know that B must have the relations (e.g., cause–effect) to A that it does.

Now the Kantian argument for cognitive predispositions has always been an enticing one. However, in spite of some dissent (Michotte, 1963), empiricist psychologists remain unconvinced. They remain good Humeans and make of intuition and apperception nothing that cannot be accounted for in terms of the person's processing information by his experientially derived perceptual categories. Nevertheless, a number of psychologists, primarily personologists, have held out for a special license for idiographic descriptions. Influenced by the writings of philosophers like Dilthey, Windelband, and Rickert, they see in idiographic descriptions an instrument of knowledge different from and compensatory to the nomothetic formula of general theories. In an early paper, Klein (1932) lists four types of understanding: (1) a structural continuity type (e.g., diagrams and models); (2) a functional unit type (e.g., cybernetics, Deutsch, 1960; Gregory, 1961); (3) an implicative type (e.g., by *modus ponens*); and (4) empathetic understanding (as in idiographic description). Of these, the first three fit our schema of scientific explanation. The latter is unique. But doubtless it is Allport (1937) who has placed the greatest emphasis on the idiographic study of personality. Faculty psychology, typologies, trait profiles, attitude scaling, all of these bring with them the suppression of what is unique to the person as an individual. And in a different theoretical setting, Lewin (1935, 1936) has emphasized the individual as being best pictured as a unique field construct of personal and environmental variables, in which his unique genotype can be understood only by probing behind the nomothetic aspects of the phenotype.

For a time, much of this sounded like a radical thesis, almost a rejection of the familiar principles of scientific description and explanation. On closer inspection, however, (see, for example, Skaggs, 1945, and Allport's reply, 1946) it has appeared that the issues are not at all clearly drawn. Both idiographic and nomothetic methods of description and understanding are essential. One is to supplement the other. Thus Allport writes: "Where my view is 'unorthodox' is in my contention that psychological science (and I mean here the total course of psychological inquiry) cannot stop with common traits, factors, IQ's, and like nomothetic dimensions, but must admit additional methods and theories to handle the organic interrelation of the artificialized variables with which nomothetic science deals, and must represent better than it has the personalized coloring of these variables in the individual life" (1946, p. 133). And what constitutes the idiographic personalized coloring of the descriptive variables? It is Lewin who points up the issue which both friend and foe of idiography have come to regard as significant. He writes:

> Even if all the laws of psychology were known, one could make a prediction about the behavior of a man only if in addition to the laws the special nature of the particular situation were known . . . [A task] of equal importance and inseparably connected with the determination of laws, involves the task of representing concrete situations in such a way that the actual event can be derived from them according to the principles which are given in the general laws (Lewin, 1936, p. 11).

Even granting that Lewin's psychology should stand apart in its own right, the issue as drawn seems not to be so critical after all. If by the meticulous descriptions of idiographic methods (e.g., Allport's case study and personal documents) one seeks only to refine the concrete situation so as to apply principles of valid inference, there can be little quarrel. This is precisely what the physical scientist, the biologist, and any other nomethetic methodologist would agree to.

It is also interesting to note that this is the issue at stake in the arguments of statistical versus clinical prediction (Meehl, 1954; Sarbin, 1944). The issue of the validity of method aside (nomothetics apparently has the edge), clinical intuition is nothing if it is not the application of general rules of inference to highly specific classes of events arrived at through the clinician's careful inspection and evaluation of personal data (cf. N10.8).

## RETROSPECT

We may close out this chapter in the same tone with which it was opened. Discussions of scientific explanation are not very reassuring. Although we can give fairly explicit analyses of explanation (as in the writings of Hempel or as in the even more impressively formal constructions of Braithwaite, 1953), few dissertations which pass for explanation in the sciences satisfy the ideal form. At best deductive explanations are reserved for relatively simple, strictly determined systems which are characterized by completeness and perfect knowledge. There are, to be sure, no such systems in psychology. Furthermore, there can be little question but that hunch, wistful hypothesizing, and other intuitive gambits play a large part in filling the lacunae of our deductive schemata. That is why the explicit examples in treatises on the logic of explanation often seem so trivial.

In addition there is always the specter of imperfect knowledge. It is not only that many of our laws are statistical, or that all laws are nomothetic in character (we can learn to live with abstractions), but as Scriven has ceaselessly pointed out, even descriptions of the particular phenomenon are subject to the ambiguities of abstraction. Every particular statement, $Sx$, is such that some property $S$ is assigned to some particular, $x$. Yet properties, it must be emphasized, are not particulars. To assign a property is to assign a class membership. And classes are abstractions, wherein the name of the class imposes just that ambiguity we must invariably face in our letting symbols represent particular phenomena.

Be that as it may, it is defeatist to reject the ideal format of deducibility on the grounds that symbolic representations do violence to unique events, whatever they may be. A more ameliorative attitude, for example, has been adopted by Körner (1964) in an attempt to incorporate imperfect descriptions into the deductivist schema (cf. N10.9). Körner argues that the deductive schema is a presumptive bridge spanning our descriptions of events. The statements about events are essentially ambiguous. Even the two-valued logic of predicates fails us. Still, science has no alternative but the idealization of its chain of inference. And the presumptive bridge between the language of fact and the ideal language of the deductive schema must be established if we are to systematize knowledge.

As a final note, it seems singularly fruitless to stress the inadequacies of formal logic and formal explanation as applied to scientific endeavor when the only alternative, it would appear, is to embrace those kinds of *verstehende* which presumably come with the analysis of common usage and the direct contemplation of causal nexus. Knowledgeable intuitionists from Bergson to Marcel have never tired of telling us that there is another more direct understanding than that of abstractive science. No doubt there is. But it is the kind of understanding one should honestly suffer in silence!

# NOTES

### NOTE 10.1

Leo Postman opened the issue of the circularity of the law of effect in his article "The History and Present Status of the Law of Effect" (1947). Should we fail to define reinforcement and effect independently of learned response then we run the danger of defining the law of effect in terms of response which itself is defined in terms of effect. Examining Postman's comments and others as well, Meehl (1950) has maintained that the charge of circularity is to be avoided if we can in fact define effect and reinforcement independently of response or habit increment. First, Meehl distinguishes between circularity in definition of a term and circularity in proof. A definition is circular if the definiens includes the definiendum among its set of predicates (i.e., if we define $X$ in terms of $Y$ where $Y$ includes $X$ in its meaning). A proof is circular if in establishing the validity of a proposition $P$, $P$ itself is included in the set of premises of the argument. He then argues that in neither sense need the law of effect be circular. Rather than defining a reinforcer as that which strengthens a response, we define it independently, say, as a stimulus related to drive, to satisfaction, or to expectancy. Then the law of effect states that responses emitted in the presence of such stimuli will be strengthened. But the law of effect does not entail our defining response just in terms of those reinforcing stimuli. The search for those reinforcers is empirical. The assumption is that the class of reinforcers will have the property of being "trans-situational." That is to say, a given reinforcer will be effective in many different response situations wherein the classes of response are defined independently of the applicability of the law of effect.

From the conventionalist point of view (Schlick, Ryle, Toulmin) laws are thought to hold for just those classes of events for which they are indeed found to hold. This would seem to imply circularity of a most insidious kind. However, the argument here begins with the question: Are laws true? Of course they are—for just those cases, for those classes of events, for which they are found to be true descriptions. But this renders trivial the meaning of truth evaluation. A law cannot help but be true. What we do not know is its truth range. Thus a law is a good "inference ticket" and a good explainer to the extent it functions to extend the range of its application. The initial statement of the law, however, is made independently of our knowledge of its range. In effect, what we discover from the application of a law is that what holds for one class of events also holds for another. This is what we mean by extending the range of a law. It is also implicit in lower-level explanation.

In brief, we may avoid circularity in our statement of the law of effect, if we define reinforcers and response strength independently of one another. Although the law may be a conventionalistic formula, there is nothing in that formulation which foretells the range of its application.

## NOTE 10.2

Many writers have stressed the role of the familiar in explanation (see e.g., Campbell, 1920, 1921; Hospers, 1946). What is accepted as familiar is a general principle or law which has the status of an unexplained explainer. For most of us, the law of gravitation is an unexplained explainer, even perhaps the law of reinforcement (e.g., for Skinner). It explains but is unexplained. Should one counter that such laws themselves need explanation, he is proposing a legitimate problem. The law needs then to be explained as a deductive consequence of other principles and laws that may constitute a theory. However, the indispensable element of all explanation is the set of first principles which themselves are unexplained. The predicament of explanatory assumptions is that no explanation is complete. One can never explain the particular event and simultaneously all the assumptions, laws, principles, etc., which are the logical components of the explicans. The regress in explanation often stops with the familiar. It is a decision dictated by cognitive appeal and is thereby psychologically arbitrary.

## NOTE 10.3

The rudiments of hypothetico-deductive methodology can be found in the works of Mill, Whewell, and Jevons. However, in recent times the argument was taken up by the positivists Feigl (1949) and Carnap (1936). Substantial accounts are given by Popper in *The Logic of Scientific Discovery,* by Braithwaite in his *Scientific Explanation,* and by Nagel in his *The Structure of Science.* Hempel has been a consistent proponent of deductivism in all of the sciences, deterministic and stochastic, physical and historical (1942, 1948, 1962, 1963). Hull's statement of hypothetico-deductive methodology (1943, Chapter I) has been influential in psychology.

As used in the present chapter deductivism refers to the hypothetico-deductive schema of explanation. Debates over deductivism versus inductivism which one finds in the literature do not refer precisely to the issues of explanation and prediction as discussed in the text. Rather, at stake is the matter of the origin and precedence of hypotheses in empirical contexts. Inductivism tends to stress the priority of data and experience; deductivism (Popper, 1935), the priority of hypotheses. See for example, Kotarbiński (1962) for a discussion and defense of inductivism. For a recent defense of deductivism see Brodbeck (1962).

## NOTE 10.4

For a clear and incisive (and sometimes acid) defense of deductivism against its critics see Brodbeck's article, "Explanation, Prediction, and 'Imperfect' Knowledge" (1962). Responding primarily to arguments of Scriven, Brodbeck makes the following points:

(1)   Stress upon the analysis of common usage reflects a rejection of formal logic. The understanding one gets from such analysis cannot be made explicit. Meaning and understanding of scientific inference require the rigors of syntactical and semantical analysis. As a result votaries of common usage lay emphasis upon subjective rather than objective aspects of scientific knowledge.

(2)   A requisite of explanations and predictions is that they be certain. That is to say from a set of premises some one prediction or explanation should be reached and not another. We justify our explanations by reaching certain conclusions. "Either an explanation is deductive or else it does not justify what it is said to explain" (p. 239).

(3)   Factors of uncertainty and imperfect knowledge do not obviate deductive models of explanation. Uncertainty effects can be described in statistical laws. In such a case an explanation would refer to a class of events not to some particular. Statistical explanations may not enable us to derive statements about singular events but they do follow the deductive schema all the same.

(4)   Belief that "cause" is unanalyzable and therefore basic in our understanding (Scriven) ignores the fact that the foundations of justification rest in logic. Causal imputation is not independent of laws. Explanation is by laws, not by "causes."

(5)   Presentation of nonpredictive historical explanation as the paradigm for explanation is grossly misleading. If history either implicitly or explicitly utilizes laws or rules of inference, then its explanation can be for-

malized in the deductivist schema. Historians may be able to explain where they cannot predict but "historical" explanation is like all scientific explanation; if it is to warrant the credentials of justification, it must be deductivist in nature.

(6)   Inference is a matter of language and logic. One cannot infer one object or state of affairs from another. Analysis of common usage reveals no principles of inference not formalizable in logic.

## NOTE 10.5

A relatively concise summary of the argument against the Hempel–Oppenheim symmetry between explanation and prediction can be found in Scheffler (1957). He would differentiate between prediction and explanation on the following grounds:

(1)   We explain (i.e., deduce) laws but we predict events; abstractions such as laws are not predicted.

(2)   Predictions can be false but explanations cannot be.

(3)   Predictions can be made without sufficient rational support, explanation cannot be.

(4)   Predictions do not explain actual occurrences.

(5)   And, of course, predictions are of the future, explanations are of the past.

It should be noted that no one denies that predictions, actual or in principle, are nondifferentiable from explanation. The important question is whether scientific explanation and scientific prediction have similar logical structure. It is on this question that the Hempel–Oppenheim thesis should be evaluated.

The distinction between events, as such, and the language of science wherein explanation takes place is a significant one (as noted in N10.4). Scriven (1962) has made much of this distinction in his own critique. It is difficult to see, however, that predictions always deal with events, *per se*. What they do involve, of course, are statements about particular events occurring in stipulated space–time coordinates. Expressed predictions like explanations involve language, albeit they may be singular statements. It is not at all clear what it would mean to say that we predict the event as such rather than a statement which is the description of an event.

Argument based on the distinction between events and statements has further ramifications. Toulmin (1953), Ryle (1949), and the Wittgensteinians in general have maintained that statements and logic are one thing; events and phenomena are quite another. We do not deduce events, only statements about events. As such, deduction and logical relationships are not part of the event world. Events do not obey logic, they do not have logical structure, only thinking about events can be endowed with the properties of rational structure. Borrowing from the conventionalist treatments of law by Schlick (1938) and by Ramsey (1931), both Ryle (1949) and Kneale (1949) treat laws not as structures inherent in events, but as inference tickets, as pragmatic devices for finding one's way in the world.

Brodbeck (1962) is critical of this tack not on grounds that we can speak of events without concerning ourselves with statements about events, but on grounds that language and logic reflect the structure of the events themselves. She maintains that language and explanation do in fact indicate to us what is ontologically fundamental in the world.

At first glance it may appear that there is not much to choose between in this argument. Brodbeck, however, expresses the fear that a purely pragmatic evaluation of the role of language demeans the significance of language and logic for ontology. The significance of logic is underplayed in favor of obscurantist insights and understanding which are presumed to emerge in the meticulous analysis not of logic but of common usage.

**NOTE 10.6**

As a statistical example of lower-level explanation (*modus ponens*) we have:

$$(x)\ Sx \supset [P(x \in R) = p]$$
$$Sx_i$$
$$\therefore P(x_i \in R) = p,$$
$$P(x_i \in \sim R) = 1 - p$$

The first premise is a statement of the statistical law. The second premise asserts that the particular $x_i$ has the property S. The conclusion states that the probability that $x_i$ has the property $R$ is $p$. But this is an elliptical statement. Ruling out subjectivist notions of probability, as we shall do here, the interpretation of $p$ is only in terms of a relative frequency applying to the class of all $x$'s. A given $x$, $x_i$, either possesses the property $R$ or it does not, but regardless of which property, the event would have to be covered by the same statistical law. It is this fact that renders statistical explanations imprecise when applied to individual events. Only when we treat the class of many such particulars do we achieve precision of statement in statistical explanation.

Clear presentations of statistical explanation can be found in articles by Hempel (1962) and Rescher (1963). In the former work, Hempel offers the appropriate modification of his earlier views on explanation. In the latter work, Rescher addresses himself to the subject of stochastic processes and Markov chains. For strictly deterministic laws, if a particular $x$ is in state $S_i$ at time $t$, then it can be inferred that it will be in state $S_j$ at time $t + \Delta t$. But for stochastic laws, if $x$ is in state $S_i$ at time $t$, it can only be inferred that $x$ will be in state $S_j \lor \ldots \lor S_k \ldots \lor S_n$ with probabilities $p_j \ldots p_k \ldots p_n$ where $\Sigma p_k = 1$. Assuming successive states for the system, then the transitional probabilities can be represented by a square matrix. Only if the nonzero elements in the matrix are 1.0 will the discrete state system be deterministic. If the system is deterministic then explanation is straightforward and the given sequence of events is strictly deducible. If it is nondeterministic, then any event sequence with $0 < p < 1$ is deducible. Consequently precision of interpretation for stochastic processes is achievable over the class of many trials.

Rescher points out, however, that statistical explanations may fail to contribute much to scientific understanding. Systematization and rational models rather than explanation are required. Needless to say, however, rigorous deductive models are essential to the task.


## NOTE 10.7

The writings of Henri Bergson remain of interest both to psychologist and to philosopher of science. With the possible exception of the popular *Creative Evolution,* the best introduction to his writings is the brief *An Introduction to Metaphysics.* Here one finds crisp and literate statements of his critique of analytic consciousness and of his pragmatic philosophy of science. Bergson came to his views by way of the continental revolt against rationalism and empiricism. But rather than reject science, he delegated to it the instrumentalist role of concretizing, analyzing, and abstracting experience. Hence science was to be regarded as a tool both to apperception and to action. In this, he was a pragmatist. Compare, for example, his "to label an object with a certain concept is to mark in precise terms the kind of action or attitude the object should suggest to us" (1913, p. 35) with Charles Peirce's: "Consider what effects, that might conceivably have practical bearings, we conceive the object of our conception to have. Then our conception of these effects is the whole of our conception of the object" (1878, p. 31).

In the overview, Bergson's philosophy is cosmological. The central thesis is Heraclitean. Duration is the nonanalyzable core of all experience and of all existence. Duration is the ceaseless, noncrystallizable process of fluid states merging one into another. Duration implies mobility throughout; no durational event can be given spatio-temporal coordinates. Abstraction is the means by which we precipitate events from the unanalyzable fluid, and intuition is the means by which we synthesize the multiplicity of states and the unity of consciousness. In the philosophy of life, as against that of knowledge, inner duration is the continuous life of memory which prolongs the past into the present.

One must distinguish between metaphysical knowledge which we know by intuition and symbolic or conceptual knowledge which we know by analysis. Thus the fundamental distinction:

> By intuition is meant the kind of *intellectual sympathy* by which one places oneself within an object in order to coincide with what is unique in it and consequently inexpressible. Analysis on the contrary is the operation which reduces the object to elements already known, that is, to elements common both to it and to other objects (1913, p. 6).

Now it is important to note that Bergson does not dismiss science and retreat into irrationalism. Rather one brings intuition to focus on the same experience that we symbolize and conceptualize within the language of science. Intuition is synthetic. It gives us direct access to the flux and connectedness of what in scientific descriptions are cinematographic reports and presentations. Bergson, quite naturally, is sympathetic to Kant. But he will have nothing of categories and absolute time and space schemata. For him the transcendental schemata are dynamic. They reify all change, and through intuition, they afford the individual his direct access to duration and metaphysical knowledge.

The Bergsonian metaphysics is obscure, to be sure; few philosophers of science care to take it at all seriously. Yet it is of interest to note that some of our contemporaries, disenchanted as they are by the deductivist amplification of Humean skepticism, have sought for something like intuitionism to give to causal relations a seal of ontological approval (e.g., Scriven, 1962; Kneale, 1949).

Bergson himself stressed that scientific analysis is abstractive. It is instrumental in prediction and scientific understanding, but it does not aid intuition. Both the antinomies of philosophy (e.g., Zeno's paradoxes) and bad metaphysics stem from our making ontological claims for scientific concepts. Science analyzes, it cannot construct. It detaches the object of experience from its surrounds, it fractionizes, it crystallizes. The thing in duration succumbs to analysis, symbolization, abstraction. It can never be reconstructed. Abstractive symbols are not component parts but only partial experiences. Applying his skepticism to introspective psychology, Bergson, like James, discounts any ontological basis for the ego-concept:

> On the level at which the psychologist places himself, and on which he must place himself, the 'ego' is only a sign by which a primitive, and moreover very confused, intuition which has furnished the psychologist with his subject matter is recalled; it is only a word, and the error here lies in believing that while remaining on the same level we can find behind the word a thing (1913, p. 26).

**NOTE 10.8**

The importance of idiographic method is perhaps even more significant when we consider history. The poverty of historicism as a nomothetic discipline (Popper, 1957) being what it is, historical epochs are even more unique, if that is possible, than the lives of individuals. Efforts to classify them are singularly Procrustean. Be that as it may, Hempel (1942) and Nagel (1952, 1961) among the empiricists continue to insist that classical procedures of scientific explanation can be applied to the understanding of historical events. History holds no special problems not also to be met, say, in astronomy, paleontology, meteorology, and psychology.

Mention should be made of Sellars' fine paper "The Language of Theories" (1961). Critical of overly formalized accounts of scientific explanation like those of Hempel and Braithwaite, Sellars maintains that what is significant about a scientific explanation is not that it is an adequate covering device for the deduction of laws and events, but that it explains why events conform, in so far as they do conform, to the appropriate laws. If we were given to pinning labels, we would have to say that Sellars is a semantic realist. That is to say, he believes that theoretical terms take their meaning in the context of the observational framework and are not mere reductions or logical constructions out of sense data. Granting theoretical terms surplus meanings and a potential for reification through observation, then the fact of deducibility carries with it the realization that it was just this postulate, this theoretical term, which made the deduction of the event to be explained possible. There is, of course, no need to introduce intuition, *verstehende,* or other obscure agents of understanding to achieve the insight Sellars prescribes. But it is interesting that hypotheses do provide such insights over and above the fact that they are the logical intermediaries of confirmed deductions.

## NOTE 10.9

In his article "Deductive Unification and Idealization" Körner (1964) opts for a moderate Humeanism in which deductive schemata serve to order rather than to structure (modify in a constructual sense) experience. He argues, however, that a deductive schema is not a mere ordering of experience but is an idealization as well.

Körner schematizes hypothetico-deductive method by

$$(b_1 \text{ and } T) \mathrel{\underset{L}{\mid\!\!-}} b_2$$

where '$b_1$' and '$b_2$' designate basic propositions; '$T$', a theory; '$\mathrel{\underset{L}{\mid\!\!-}}$' deducibility within a logic $L$ comprising two-valued logic, quantification theory, theory of equality, and the theory of real numbers. Predicates of $T$ are either empirical or nonempirical, whereas the predicates of $b$ are empirical only. Extension and modification of the theory can be achieved by adding to its logical terms and by predicating additional substantive terms for the field of empirical inquiry. Application of the schema imposes the following restrictions on $T$.

(1)    The mathematical notion of continuity is an idealization of actual measurement.
(2)    The empirical notion of equality is not the same as logical and mathematical equality; e.g., perceptual equalities do not always obey the law of transitivity.
(3)    The schema embraces two-valued logic whereas many other schemata with different logics are possible.

The originality of Körner's analysis concentrates on item (3). It is worth giving in some detail. Speaking of "resemblance classes" and "resemblance predicates," he notes that some classes are exact whereas others are inexact. Thus for any formal theory, its class structure represents an ideal. It is superimposed upon empirical predicates. In classical two-valued logic: if $x$ is an individual and $P$ is a predicate, then in assigning predicate or class membership, we have "$x \in P$" or "$x \in \sim P$". But with indefiniteness of individuals, so far as resemblance predicates are concerned, one should have another category for propositions, say, "$x \overset{\epsilon}{\in} P$" which asserts that $x$ is a neutral or indeterminate candidate for $P$. Here Körner adopts certain ideas of Kleene (*Introduction to Metamathematics,* §64) rather than the three-valued logic of Lukasiewicz. Neutrality in predicate assignment is to be stressed rather than uncertainty.

We are still to operate within the dichotomous class structure $P$ and $\sim P$; but rather than just two truth values 't' and 'f' for true and false, we introduce a third symbol '*' which designates neutrality as concerns assigning $P$. Körner proceeds to develop truth tables for the usual logical operations only now incorporating the neutrality value, and also to extend the schema so as to include quantification operations. The argument is too detailed to include in this note, but Körner then proceeds to show that a modified two-valued logic cannot serve as an instrument for deducing neutral statements. $[p \cdot (p \supset q)] \supset q$ is a correct inference in *modus ponens*. However, if any of the premises were neutral, then an inference is possible only if we treat such premises as true. Thus an idealization is always implicit in our adopting the two-valued convention of logic, when in fact the neutral value might well be included.

The argument is an ingenious one. Inexact predicates must be replaced by exact ones. Against the backdrop of neutrality this forced exactness represents an idealization. Strictly speaking, it is false to assert identity between the basic propositions of a theory and the empirical propositions of which they are the idealizations. We need, therefore, the expression '$b \approx e$' for '$b$ is an idealization of $e$'. Then for

$$(b_1 + T) \mid_{\overline{L}} b_2$$

we have

$$[e_1 \approx b_1 \; (b_1 + T) \mid_{\overline{L}} b_2; \; b_2 \approx e_2]$$

where the $e_1$ and $e_2$ are not deducible from $b_1$ and $b_2$, but $e_1 \approx b_1$ and $b_2 \approx e_2$ are expressions of the presumptive idealization of explanation and prediction. In summary: (1) the entire bracketed proposition, from $e_1$ to $e_2$, is the statement of an empirical proposition employing as an idealization a logical bridge between its parts; (2) one does not, strictly speaking, disconfirm a theory, but rather the whole empirical proposition $[e_1 \ldots e_2]$; (3) scientific propositions such as $[e_1 \ldots e_2]$ differ from ordinary propositions only in terms of their logical structure. They are part idealization. Like all such propositions, scientific explanations are idealizations.

# CHAPTER 11

# Reductionism: I

THE VOCABULARY of reductionism has been a popular one in logic, philosophy, and science; and for this reason, it has often lacked precision in its use. The idea of reduction is, of course, an elementary one. Linguistically, a statement or set of statements, $\{S_R\}$, is reducible to another set of statements, $\{S_r\}$, if the latter can be substituted for the former without contradiction and without loss of content,[1] and if the latter is in some sense more basic than the former. This attempt at a definition is itself not very precise. It is not intended to be. Initially all that is required is some statement which, by and large, covers the many reductive activities of philosophers and scientists.

Generally then, we recognize as reductive any activity wherein the person seeks to substitute for one set of assertions another set whose members are more basic than those of the original. Thus, in philosophy, the theses of phenomenalism and physicalism are both reductive. In phenomenalism, every statement about objects purports to be reducible to statements about sense data. In physicalism, all significant statements, which are not strictly logical statements, are reducible to statements in the physical thing-language. On the other hand, in logic, a symposium on reductionism may be the occasion to debate whether all of arithmetic can be reduced to the language of classes, or whether reductionism is simply the possibility of analysis (Thomson, Warnock, Braithwaite, 1952). The thesis of extensionality, which we found to express the analytic paradigm of logical atomism, is, of course, reductionist. The truth of every molecular proposition reduces to the truth functions of its atomic constituents. Modern empiricism, from its inception with Locke, Berkeley, and Hume, has been reductive in its epistemology. And now-

---

[1] "Without loss of content" requires merely that no subset of $\{S_R\}$ is without a substitutable subset in $\{S_r\}$.

adays the argument between nominalism and realism is debated on reductionist grounds.

"Nominalism versus realism"—this is one of the oldest acts to be performed in the reductionist arena. The question to be debated here is: Are there universal laws, entities, or transcendent hypotheses which are subsistent reals independent of, and not merely reducible to, our conventions in classifying particulars? Realists from the time of Plato have vouched for universals which, in their intension, transcend any finite set of particulars. This is the heart of Platonic doctrine of Ideas. Nominalists, on the other hand, maintain that all generalizations, all abstractions, so to speak, are reductive conventions. There are no capitalized Universals, no enduring Laws; there are only convenient classifications of particular events. This is an interesting issue, not because scientists or philosophers still debate the transcendental doctrines of ideal prototypes, but because it touches upon such basic conceptions as number, law, and inductive inference. Nominalists are necessarily finitistic. For them, the universal quantifier "all" can never reach into the unsampled universe. Their defense of scientific inference must inevitably be postulational and conventional. Although it is not necessary that it be so, empiricists have inclined toward nominalism.

## TWO MEANINGS OF REDUCTIONISM

Our concern is with reductionism as it applies to science, specifically to psychology. The issues are no different for psychology than they are for other sciences, but for psychology they are perhaps more poignant and more timely. Let us begin by distinguishing between reduction as it applies to individual concepts and reduction as it applies to aggregates of concepts such as in a theory or a science itself.

### Constructual Reduction

By constructual reduction is meant the reduction of some term (construct) that is not assumed to designate a specific object with existential status to a set of statements about objects that do have such status. The word 'object' here can be misleading, but it is important to recognize that the existential status of an object derives from its being empirically real and not inferred. Specifically, in psychology, 'construct' refers either to terms in the language of theory, or to terms requiring what is commonly called an operational definition.

Before turning to the use of constructs in psychology, it would be well to review briefly the concept of a logical construction as dating from Russell (1917, 1918) and Carnap (1928). Initially logical constructions were treated as constructions out of sense data. The primitives, i.e., the basic data statements, referred to sense data; and the problem of reductionism was essentially phenomenalistic. The important feature of such constructions is that their meaning is purely contextual. A logical construct does not refer to any identifiable thing as such, nor to any set of things as such. Rather it refers to some set of things upon which some conventional construction is imposed. Russell himself was very explicit that logical constructions were not indubitable entities like sense data. Nor should one make the mistake of inferring existential status for such constructs. Hence the occasion for his "supreme maxim in scientific philosophizing . . .": "Wherever possible, logical constructions are to be substituted for inferred entities" (1917, p. 155). We need to keep this admonition in mind in our discussions of theoretical terms.

As the language of physicalism began to supplant that of phenomenalism, the definition of logical constructions was loosened so as to incorporate basic observation statements as the language of the reductive primitives (e.g., Carnap, 1928; Pap, 1949). However, the status of logical constructs remained the same; they were to be regarded as symbols whose explicit meaning reduced to specific operations performed on the set of basic data. Thus, the "median response," which is the variable plotted, say, in experiments concerning subjective estimates of loudness (Stevens, 1956), is a logical construction. There is, of course, no response as such, no phenomenon we can point to as *the* median response. The value which obtains for our logical construct derives from our performing certain explicit operations upon a set of response data which are empirically basic. When Skinner defines drive in terms of a deprivation schedule or in terms of behavioral variability (1938, 1953), he is treating motivation as a logical construction. And when Hull postulates habit strength as a function of the number of reinforcements, he, likewise, is treating habit strength as a logical construction (cf. N11.1). It is important to note that in all of these examples one cannot point to any thing or set of things by which we can either ostensively or even explicitly define the construct. Nevertheless, the construct is meaningless without its empirical content. It is a content, however, which is subject to a set of constructional operations (cf. N11.2).

For the psychologist, the issues of constructual reduction obtrude when he considers the empirical status of his mediating variables. We have previously differentiated among types of mediating variables (Chapter 8). In the present context, we note that intervening variables are very like logical constructions, reductive and without existential status (in the phenomenalistic sense), whereas hypothetical constructs are not strictly reducible, carry surplus meaning with them, and may in fact pretend to potential existential status. The issue, as we shall see, devolves on whether intervening variables can do the job theory construction requires. Such variables are clean and tidy and are reassuring to radical empiricists like Skinner. Nevertheless, one may need something more substantive than a logical construct to implement S–R psychology; and in so needing, he may plead cause to invert the well-known Russellian maxim. In its place he writes, "Wherever possible advance your theory by the introduction of hypothetical constructs." Discussion of this matter will be taken up in a later section.

As for operational definitions and operationism (the "ism") the crusade fortunately has been put to rest. Psychology certainly must share in the responsibility for what Passmore (1957) calls the "embarrassing amateurism" in defense of operationism. What took on the aspects of a new metaphysic with the publication of Bridgman's *Logic of Modern Physics* was at a slightly earlier date proclaimed by Eddington (1920) as the seed for his neo-Kantian metaphysics. Actually, there is little that purportedly is original in operationism which cannot be found in the writings of all empiricists since Locke. Even Francis Bacon could write of "operative physics" (*Novum Organum*). What is more important is that operationism itself has succumbed to open-textured interpretations. Operations may only partially interpret some concept, thereby leaving the meaning of the concept open. For example, drives, attitudes, reactive potentials, etc., may be operationally measured, but there remains a thingness to what is measured that is not entirely exhausted by an operational description. Nowadays, operationism, if given a heeding at all, is discussed simply as the subject of empirical procedures. After two decades of critical analysis, the proscriptive role cut out for operationism has been abandoned (cf. N11.3).

## Theoretic Reduction

By theoretic reduction is meant the reduction of the postulates, laws, hypotheses of one theory to those of another. Since the emphasis is on reduction, one assumes that the reducing science is in some sense more basic than the reduced science. Hence a "simplification" in the theoretical explanation of events is achieved by the reduction, whereby at the same time this reduction fulfills all the requirements of an explanation. The laws of the reduced science are thereby explained by the laws of the reducing science.

Before proceeding to a discussion of the formal requirements of complete reduction let us note some rather obvious implications of this reductive thesis. First, a hierarchy of sciences is assumed with respect to the inclusiveness and explanatory scope of scientific theories. Hierarchies such as those proposed by Auguste Comte (mathematics, physics, biology, psychology, sociology) are suggestive but misleading because mathematics is there ranked among the empirical sciences. One notes, however, that we often do speak of reducing biology to physics (biophysics), psychology to biology (psychobiology), and sociology to psychology (social psychology as a real socio-psychology). We do not, however, speak meaningfully of reducing physics to biology, or of reducing biology to psychology. There seems to be an ordering natural to our reductive efforts. Second, reduction seems to imply the assumption of a unity of science. If in the hierarchy any one science programmatically reduces to the next lower science, then ultimately all sciences reduce to the basic science—presumably to physics. This is not an unreasonable assumption for the reductionist, although it has often been thrown up as a scarecrow against reductive efforts. Why, it is asked, not teach our sociologists physics to begin with? The reasonable reply is that neither the hierarchical nor the reductive schema precludes our developing at every level of science concepts which are unique to the specific science. It can be argued, however, that the imperative for theoretic reduction comes into play primarily when questions between alternative conceptualizations within a given science need to be resolved. And third, the precautionary note needs to be sounded. In our sanguine espousals of reductive sciences there may be unwarranted pretentions to logical rigor, as if we were dealing with sciences more highly formalized than they actually are. The formalization of physics is impressive though incomplete. The biological and social sciences are in their infancies. Therefore, we may be premature in speaking out for theoretic reduction.

Although one may speak sanguinely of theoretic reduction, actual instances of reducing one science to another are somewhat rare. Sometimes what purports to be a reduction is no more than the development of a theory itself. For example, we hear of Newton's reduction of Kepler's laws of planetary behavior, or we may hear of reducing Mendel's laws of heredity (with their assumption of dominant and recessive characteristics) to a theory of genes. In both examples, however, basic phenomenological laws are found to be deducible within a developing theory. It is more a case of achieving a scientific explanation through development of a theory than one exemplary of reduction (cf. N11.4). The classic example, however, is the reduction of thermodynamics to statistical mechanics. Before the reduction, thermodynamics was a rather loose compilation of gas laws, thermal principles, and laws of conservation and entropy. As a phenomenological science, thermodynamics developed without definite commitments as to the nature of a gas. The relevant variables were temperature, pressure, volume, energy. By assuming a gas to be composed of perfectly elastic molecules behaving according to the laws of Newtonian mechanics, and by making certain statistical assumptions about the distribution and momenta of the molecules, one is able, for example, to deduce the Boyle–Charles law and the second law of thermodynamics (which states that for closed systems the tendency is for entropy to increase).

The physicist proceeds here by assigning an average velocity and mass to the $N$ molecules in a given volume of gas. By assuming the correspondence of pressure and the product of density and square of the velocity of the particles $(p = dv^2/3)$, he is able to make valid inferences concerning manometrically measured pressure. Likewise, by assuming the proportionality of temperature and the mean kinetic energy of the particles $(T = mv^2/3k)$, he is able to infer thermometric temperature. More specifically, he is able to show that conditions which would influence the density and momenta of the particles are the conditions which affect measured pressure and temperature of the aggregate of particles. Derivation of the second law of thermodynamics (Gibbs and Boltzmann) in probabilistic terms leads one to expect the increasing homogenization of phase cells differing as to their kinetic energy. Entropy is converted from a deterministic law into a statistical one by the appropriate reduction in statistical mechanics.

What makes this reduction remarkable is its success in deriving phenomenological laws of gases from a set of postulates about the microstructure of the gas, indeed, in bringing these laws into the manifold of mechanics itself. The significance of the role of microstructure in explaining phenomenological laws should not be overlooked by the psychologist.

## FORMAL REQUIREMENTS OF REDUCTION

Requirements for constructual reduction are simple ones. The reduction is achieved by explicit definitions, by operational definitions, by specific sets of biconditional reduction sentences. Either they are conventional equivalences or they represent constructual operations on a finite set of observational primitives. With the reduction of one theory to another we need, however, to go into greater detail.

Woodger in biology (1952) and Nagel in the physical sciences (1949, 1961) have given us the most explicit statements of reduction. Differences between them are minor ones and the account to be given here follows them in all essentials. We note initially that a formal reduction of one science to another calls for the axiomatization of each of the theories. Thus, let us assume that two sciences or theories that stand in reductive relationship are fully axiomatized so that all sentences are either postulates, laws, correspondence rules, or observation statements, and all theorems of the science are provable within its formal structure. Terms of the language are either logical terms, terms of particulars, or terms of properties or characteristics. Let $T_1$ be the primary or reducing science; let $T_2$ be the secondary or reduced science. Let us follow Nagel in speaking of a science rather than a theory, for a given science such as psychology will not only contain statements unique unto itself (e.g., sensation) but also statements in the language of physics (e.g., descriptions of physical stimulus intensity). Thus the language of physics may be common to both psychology and physiology. Let the functors (i.e., predicative expressions) of $T_1$ and $T_2$ be as follows:

$$T_1 = a,b,c, \ldots ,A,B,C, \ldots$$
$$T_2 = a,b,c, \ldots ,A,B,C, \ldots ,G,H, \ldots$$

where $a,b,c$, are functors borrowed from other sciences and are common to both $T_1$ and $T_2$ (and other sciences as well); $A,B,C$, are common to $T_1$ and $T_2$; and $G,H, \ldots$ are functors unique to $T_2$. Then for the complete reduction of $T_2$ to $T_1$ the following requirements must be fulfilled:

1.   The vocabulary of $T_1$ is a subset of $T_2$, i.e., all functors and primitives of $T_1$ are also members of $T_2$. One might call this the principle of simplification since the reducing science necessarily must have fewer primitives and functors than has the reduced science.

2.   Every expression $G$ in $T_2$ not in the vocabulary of $T_1$ must satisfy the biconditional

$$(x)G_x \equiv P_x,$$
where $x \in P \equiv ( \ldots ,x,a,b,c, \ldots ,A,B,C, \ldots )$.

That is to say, every unshared statement in $T_2$ but not in $T_1$ must be constructible from functors of $T_1$. Furthermore, the biconditionals must be well established theorems of $T_2$. (Nagel calls this the *principle of connectibility*.)

3.   All expressions (postulates and functors) of $T_2$ not shared by $T_1$ must be reducible to expressions in $T_1$ by virtue of the above biconditionals (Nagel calls this the principle of *derivability*).

Fulfillment of these requirements assures us of an effective reduction. All laws and theoretical constructions of the reduced science are then expressible in the language of the reducing science.

The crucial requirement is (2): all theoretical expressions in $T_2$ must connect with expressions in $T_1$. Nagel's choice of 'connect' here is well considered. A word like 'derive' would be restrictive. The biconditional, $G_x \equiv P_x$, serves as a theorem to be established in one of three ways. One, such a biconditional may express the logical equivalence of synonymity. For example, a conditioned eyelid response might be regarded as equivalent to a set of responses in the appropriate efferents of neurophysiology. Two, the connection may be empirically established. For example, an expression of anger may be correlated with an increase in adrenalin content of the blood. Or three, the biconditional may be postulated as a convention connecting two expressions. For example, drive might be equated to reduction of blood sugar to some specified percentage of a "normal" level.

This last possibility differs from the other two in the sense that it involves an element of fiat and convention not contained in the former. That is, one might proceed preferentially and choose only theoretical terms in the secondary science which are indeed translatable in terms of the primary language. But as Woodger points out this is a Procrustean reducibility. We proceed by prior commitment to stay within the range of the primary science, when in fact the autonomous development of the secondary science may have resulted in a vocabulary unique to it. Reductionism in this case would be coercive and Woodger prefers to regard the matter as one of "interpretability" (of $T_2$ in $T_1$) rather than of reducibility (cf. N11.5).

## REDUCTIONISM IN PSYCHOLOGY

The preceding discussion has been the groundwork for what follows. I will not attempt to assess the extent either of the successes or the failures in reducing the laws and theories of psychology to those of physiology. The failures have been many, the successes few. Psychology started out its experimental incarnation as a discipline prone to physiological explanations. Psychophysics, of course, invites this kind of emphasis. But Titchener defected from physiologism, as did even Watson. Furthermore, subsequent concentration upon phenomenology and behavioral studies encouraged the development of unique psychological languages, even though phenomenologists like Köhler and behaviorists like Lashley still preferred the reductive language of physiology.

One suspects, however, that in their wistful moments psychologists invariably come to think of physiology as the ultimate in explanation. Learning, memory, perception; all of these are very close indeed to organic functioning. If physiology is to be ignored, it is to be so only for methodological reasons. Yet even where pragmatic ingenuity is to prevail, such as in personality and in learning theory, it is suspected that new developments in neurophysiology will result in our modifying purely psychological conceptions. The old arguments over functional and organic disorders in psychopathology have to be rephrased. One does not say that aberrant function can be studied in a purely psychological language. If reduction is not required, certainly a joint psychological, physiological language is.

Still the arguments go on. We hear the calls to neurophysiology. We also hear that psychology suffers from the accidents of its stimulus–response, reflex-oriented vocabulary; physiological reference is clearly dispensable. Much of the debate would be avoided if we took Woodger's counsel (cf. N11.5): in order to meet the requirements of reduction, the relevant sciences must be axiomatized. Neither psychology nor physiology is sufficiently systematic so as to be axiomatizable. But not all of the debate can be avoided. Vocabulary and the conceptual framework do determine the direction of the psychological efforts. It is not just that we may cavalierly issue promissory notes on some future psycho-physiology; but the language of learning theory predisposes us now to thinking in terms of physiological equivalencies.

### *Methodological* versus *Metaphysical Reductionism*

Before taking the issues of reductionism directly to psychology, it is necessary to make another distinction. We should be careful to distinguish between methodological and metaphysical commitments to reductionism. By *methodological reductionism* is meant the arbitrary decision, for whatever purpose, to confine the language of one's science to expressions which at least in principle are reducible to the language of a reducing science. For psychology this would mean restricting its theoretical constructs to terms reducible in principle to the language of physiology. The emphasis is one of methodological predilection (Hebb, 1949, 1955, 1959; Krech, 1950, 1951; Morgan, 1959). Of all the languages open to psychology that of physiology seems most promising, most disposed to implementing the complete interpretation of its mediating variables. It is acknowledged that purely psychological constructions of memory trace, cognitive structure, and drive can be invented and exploited to the exclusion of any other class of constructions. However, it is felt that evils of semantic diversification can be avoided only by restricting theoretical constructs to hypotheses reducible to the language of physiology. The subject matters of psychology are varied and complex. Theoretical psychologists suffer from the lack of one theorist understanding or utilizing the language of another theorist. Psychology needs a common theoretical language, and physiology is the language all can understand and use. The case is similar to that for methodological behaviorism. There, mental phenomena and consciousness are not denied. The language of private data is avoided in favor of the physicalistic language which is anchored in public observation and public report (Lashley, 1923). Communicational and observational agreement is achieved, perhaps at the expense of restricting the field of study.

In contrast, *metaphysical reductionism* is, in one sense, a stronger principle. It asserts that for psychology ultimately all questions of theory are to be resolved by physiological reductionism. That is to say, all arguments, crucial tests, and so on, concerning the nature of hypothetical constructs eventually are to be settled by reducing them to the microstructural components of physiology. Just as we foresaw in Chapter 9 that cybernetics is to be regarded as the bare prospectus for neurophysiological construction, the language of psychology will be refined through the history of successful reductive analysis and construction. This compares with a metaphysical behaviorism which assumes that all sentences in the mental language are really translatable into sentences in the physicalistic language; the language presumably of pure mental content is meaningless.

This distinction in philosophical types of reductionism is the source of much confusion. The most important misconception.is to interpret metaphysical reductionism as a dogmatic defense of, nay, a call to, physiologizing. More likely, it is methodological reductionism which is the more dogmatic. The latter precludes all but physiological speculation on methodological grounds alone. Metaphysical reductionism only speaks of ultimate reductions and ultimate objectives. All black-box phenomenologists can, if pressed, embrace this type of reductionism, as can all pragmatists and inventive instrumentalists. As metaphysical reductionists their only firm commitment is that ultimately theoretical constructs will be interpretable in the reducing discipline, and *that no logical barriers stand in the way to the reduction of psychology to physiology*. It does not mean that psychology should give up its unique conceptions and theorizing as a macrobehavioral discipline.

## Reductionism and Hull's Behavior Theory

Before turning to the objections to reductionism (Chapter 12) it may be well to have in mind what a program for reduction might be like. Consider for example, the theory of Clark Hull. It comes as close to an axiomatized macrotheory as psychology can boast. Hull (1943, 1951, 1952) presents a hypothetico-deductive system which starting with certain unspecified and undefined primitive terms is then structured according to its sets of definitions, postulates, and theorems. Empirical support derives from the theorems which are tested by virtue of coordinating rules. In order to establish the reducibility (in principle) of Hull's system, we would have to ascertain whether all functors in the system are derivable from functors in the physiological language (which we assume to be a subset of Hull's behavioral language). According to the requirements of connectibility and derivability, $(x)G_x \equiv P_x$ means that any functor $G$ in Hull's theory must be reducible to a sentence in the neurophysiological language, i.e., constructed of functors admissible to that language. Reducibility would be precluded only if there were some sentence $G_x$ in Hull's theory such that for all sentences $P_i x$ in the language of neurophysiology, $\sim (G_x \equiv P_i x)$ (where $P_i x$ is a possible molecular sentence in the language of physiology).

Without laboring the reductive program point by point, I think it is safe to assume that such a program is in principle possible. Hull's own language is often quasi-physiological. Although he does not presume to offer a neurophysiological theory of learning, he makes clear his belief that neurophysiology is the basis of a molecular explanation of molar events. It is only the nascent state of physiology which prevents the psychologist from going directly to molecular explanations (cf. N11.6).

It is, of course, one thing to issue promissory notes on reduction and quite another to square the accounts. For the present, all we can assess is the possibility of a reduction and what purpose, if any, a reductive program might serve. In his final formulation of his system (*A Behavior System*, 1952) Hull first presents seventeen postulates and as many corollaries. Assuming a glossary of terms and some rather poorly specified correspondence rules, he then utilizes the greater part of his monograph to deduce 132 theorems, each of which can be thought of as a behavioral hypothesis. A successful reduction of Hull's system would then mean that the lawlike statements concerning molar behavior, as set down in the theorems, would be deducible from, hence explainable by, a successful reduction of the postulates to the language of neurophysiology. As this statement stands, however, it makes no pretense of distinguishing significant from trivial reductions. A significant reduction, it must be emphasized, brings to a science explanatory enrichment which otherwise it would not have.

Suppose, for example, the simplest of behavioral sciences—one which is exhausted by a finite set of stimulus–response laws $R_i = f(S_j)$ without intervening concepts of any kind. If the language of this science contains only $S$ and $R$ terms, then any reduction of these terms to the language of neurophysiology would be trivial providing substitution of language is all that is achieved by the reduction. It would be quite a different matter, however, if mediating variables were introduced in the neurophysiological language such that the set of behavioral laws could be deduced from postulates not contained in the simple behavioral system. The behavioral laws would then be bound together in a way not found in the S–R behavioral science as such.

If we go a step further and introduce into the behavioral science intervening variables that are strictly interpretable (i.e., constructible) in stimulus and response terms (i.e., in the observation language), the situation is complicated but it is not altered in any significant way. Suppose, for example, that our laws are now of the form $R_i = f(S_j, IV_k)$ where any IV is itself a function of a set of stimulus variables. This might be the case if IV were a specification of motivation in terms of hours of food deprivation. Our behavioral function is a more complex one now, but it is still substantially an expression of S–R law without theoretical complications. The law now incorporates the facts of a maintenance schedule in the set of independent variables. And again, if we were to reduce all terms in the $R$, $S$, and IV language to neurophysiology, the reduction would be a trivial one, unless, of course, it carried with it some explanatory surplus not contained in a terminological transliteration, as such. This is simply a restatement of the argument in Chapter 10, in which a distinc-

tion was made between levels of explanation, i.e., between lawful explanation of individual events and theoretical explanation of the laws themselves. A reduction of the statements of one science to those of another
is significant only if higher-order explanation is achieved by the reduction.

Proceeding now to Hull's postulates, we note that some deal with
stimulus variables (postulates 1,2,3,6,7,10,11,12), some deal with response variables (postulates 1,3,14,15,) and some deal with mediating
variables (postulates 3,4,5,6,7,8,9,10,11,12,13,14,15,16,17). The overlap here is considerable and a reductive roll-call over the postulates would
not be particularly rewarding. What we should note is that all stimulus
constructs are amenable to reduction whether the stimulus term refers
to a segment of the environment or to intra-organismic functions. The
physicalistic environmental language is, of course, common both to the
psychological and physiological languages. And any description of a stimulus as an intra-organismic mediator is obviously reducible in principle to
neurophysiology. A similar analysis holds for response terms, whether
they refer to molar acts, response latencies, or response amplitudes.
However, it is the mediating variables that are of particular interest.
If they are in fact intervening variables, then like all logical constructions, their status is truth functional. Consequently, their reduction can be
rather trivial. If, however, they are hypothetical constructs, carrying with
them the implications of hypothesis about some mediating state not
subject to a finite truth extension over a set of observables, then the
question of neurophysiological reducibility is a pressing one. An important caution here! One must be careful to note the difference in our
two senses of reducibility. He must distinguish between the constructual
reducibility of the intervening variable as a logical construction and the
theoretic reducibility of the hypothetical construct where existential foundations are to be secured in a lower order scientific discipline.

The major mediating variables of Hull's system are habit strength
($_sH_R$), reaction potential ($_sE_R$), inhibition ($I_R$, $_sI_R$), oscillation of reaction potential ($_sO_R$), and reaction threshold ($_sL_R$). To this list add
the conditional factors of drive ($D$), stimulus intensity dynamism ($V$),
and incentive motivation ($K$). Of these, habit strength and reaction potential play the most important roles in the chain of behavioral deductions.
Now according to Postulate 4, habit strength is defined by an equation of the form

$$_sH_R = 1 - 10^{-aN},$$

where $a$ is some empirically determined constant and $N$ is the number of
reinforcements from a base of zero reaction potential. Assuming that a
reinforcement trial is observationally unambiguous, then $_sH_R$ is clearly
an intervening variable. Its reduction would be trivial, as the matter

stands. Reaction potential is a somewhat different matter. According to Postulate 8,

$$_sE_R = D \times V \times K \times {_sH_R},$$

where $D$, $V$, and $K$ are determined by hours of deprivation, stimulus intensity, and quantity of incentive, respectively. Values of these latter variables are determined by observation. Therefore, $_sE_R$ would pass as an intervening variable if it carried no additional implications of existential substrata. However, it is not clear that $_sE_R$ is intended as a mere calculational convention. Postulates 14,15,16 also specify $_sE_R$ as functions of reaction latency (14), reaction amplitude (15), and number of trials to extinction (16). And other approaches have given different quantifications of $_sE_R$ in terms of starting latencies and running times (Zeaman, 1949), and in terms of reinforcements and trials to extinction (Yamaguchi, 1951). Thus, rather than a single definitional estimate of $_sE_R$, we have several convergent estimations of $_sE_R$ as if this reaction potential were a state of the organism to be inferred, observed, and measured. Although one may choose to play strict definitional and operational games, it is not clear that this is what is intended by Hull and by his students. From Hull's earlier postulation of habit strength (1943), one suspects that even $_sH_R$ is regarded as being something more than a convention. We sense that effects of reinforcement and trial repetition bring about changes in the structure of the organism which are what $_sH_R$ *intends* to measure. In other words, $_sH_R$ is not just a convenient invention, but is semantically tied to a state of the organism which we might better regard as a habit *structure* predisposing the increased probabilities of certain response patterns.

The ontological status of Hullian constructs has been the subject of conjecture and debate. In their classic differentiation between types of mediating variables, MacCorquodale and Meehl (1948) placed $_sH_R$ in the fold of intervening variables. Hull's 1952 revision of the postulates would appear to reinforce that opinion. On the other hand, Koch (1954) and Rozeboom (1956) would, by virtue of Hull's own presentiments, assign $_sH_R$ the status of an hypothetical construct—the surplus meaning, though not requiring neurophysiological content, certainly leaning in that direction. In spite of the authority of MacCorquodale and Meehl, the latter recourse seems the safer one. None of the mediating variables seems to stand as a pristine convention. When we introduce the inhibition variables ($I_R$, $_sI_R$) and the oscillation factor[2] ($_sO_R$), which are clearly more speculative, then there seems little point in holding out for the purely conventionalistic status of any of the mediating variables. No doubt it is safer to mean by the construct no more

[2] Together, these compose the Hullian analogues of the epicycles and equants of ancient astronomy.

than a set of definitive operations. In the early stages of theory construction, this strategy is likely to obviate unnecessary and fruitless arguments concerning ontology, which neurophysiology, in its present state, is in no position to arbitrate. But eventually the constructions come to mean more than a set of operations. That is to say, $_sH_R$ and $_sE_R$ have a different semantic status than has a logical construction (such as a "median response," or an "index of efficiency"). They point to something whose postulated ramifications are not exhausted by the set of values we can assign to a definitive equation. The 132 theorems of *A Behavior System* are given without proof. It is indeed doubtful whether they could be proven by the set of postulates and corollaries interpretable strictly as conventions.

What then is the reductive status of Hull's behavior system? We have skirted the answer, but the answer seems quite straightforward. Were all of the mediating variables to be considered intervening variables, then a reduction of Hull's behavioral descriptions would be possible by transliterating stimulus and response terms into equivalent sets of environmental and afferent and efferent statements. This being achieved, the reduction would, however, only be a trivial one. But if, as our own conjecture leads us to think, the mediating variables are hypothetical constructs with surplus meaning, then it seems that psychologically and methodologically the most fruitful recourse is that of reductivism. As Rozeboom (1956) argues, there is nothing logically compelling about the proposal to reduce hypothetical constructs to the neurophysiological substrata. However, he does not provide an alternative heuristic for the exploitation of the surplus meaning of a given construct. Pure pragmatics will not work, for invention itself is tied to preconception. To think otherwise is to think one can engage in the fruits of deductive argument without attending to and justifying the premises of the deductive system.

The difficulty in giving an out-and-out affirmative answer to the reductionist hypothesis is that, as it stands, Hull's behavior system is not sufficiently formalized to permit the direct application of the criteria of reduction. However, in an examination of Hull's theory we meet no logical barriers to reduction, and Hull's own linguistic biases would seem to place the genesis of the mediating variables in the microrecesses of neurophysiology (cf. N11.7).

## DEFENSE OF REDUCTIONISM

It is now possible to pull together some diverse threads of the argument in behalf of reductionism. Some points of the preceding discussion will be restated. These will be followed by a statement of the criterion of reducibility for selecting among alternative theoretical constructions.

(1) Metaphysical reductionism implies that all questions as to the nature and status of mediating variables in psychology will be answered by reducing those variables to neurophysiology. If such mediators are indeed intervening variables, then that reduction can be trivial. However, if such mediators are hypothetical constructs with surplus meaning, then the existential status of such constructs is to be found in the reducing science. This thesis of reductionism does not entail that psychology should proceed immediately to neurophysiology any more than it entails that genetics should proceed immediately to biochemistry. Nor does it hold out the promise that reductions will be easily forthcoming, or that they will offer any particularly effective program or a plan for the development of the science in question. As shall be argued, acceptance of reductionism means to adopt a metaphysical position as to how certain questions arising over the tenability of alternative theoretical constructions are to be resolved.

(2) Reductionism does not entail our rejecting systemic developments of a secondary science in its own language and independently of the primary or reducing science. On the other hand, the difficulties of successful reduction should not be used as an argument against "premature" theory construction in the secondary science. One must keep in mind the promise of ultimate interpretations of theoretical terms in the language of the reducing science. In this context, it is appropriate to say that reduction is the source of some ontological direction.

(3) The argument for indifference, convention, or pragmatism as concerns the existential status of mediating variables is suspect. Mediators mediate between stimulus and response events, each of which is amenable to reductive analysis. This fact necessarily places mediation between two reducible environmental-organismic states. Consequently, as MacCorquodale and Meehl (1948) suggest, questions of the physical locale of the mediators become relevant. One's empirical commitments may be in jeopardy if he were to hold out for the purely conventional interpretation of a construct where, in fact, existential anchoring in functors of a higher-order science is possible (cf. N11.8). If, as several writers have intimated, the distinction between intervening variables and hypothetical constructs is a pseudo-issue (Marx, 1951; Bergmann, 1954; Madden, 1961), that is to say, if intervening variables also gain surplus meaning in their application, then their reduction would be neither trivial nor irrelevant. For then the prospect of reduction would provide the most fruitful heuristic to their amplification within the theory.

(4) As a final point, let us consider reducibility as a criterion for selecting among alternative theoretical constructions. In Chapter 10 several criteria were suggested for selecting among alternative scientific hypotheses. Among them was the criterion of reducibility. (a) First sub-

sume a hierarchy of sciences $T_j, \ldots, T_s \ldots, T_z$ such that any given science in the hierarchy contains all of the functors of the preceding science plus some set of functors not found in the preceding science (except possibly by means of reduction sentences). (*b*) For a given science, $T_s$, assume two or more alternative theories, $T_{s1}, T_{s2}, \ldots$ agreeing as to some finite set of predictions but differing as to their hypothetical terms $H_{1i}, \ldots, H_{2j}, \ldots$. Assume further that no set of experiments has led indirectly to the confirmation or disconfirmation of one over another of these hypotheses. The criterion of reducibility then asserts that that hypothesis which can be formally derived from the functors of the higher-order science is to be preferred to that hypothesis which cannot be so derived.[3] It is obvious that this criterion of reducibility is more easily stated than applied. Any successful reduction requires the formalization of both the primary and secondary sciences. Considering the state of personology, for example, there is little prospect of formalization sufficient to allow our reducing the constructs of personality to physiology. It is not surprising then that theories of personality carry with them the spirit of the option (Berenda, 1957), where conversion is likely to play a more significant role in selecting from among alternative constructions then any penetrative sense of realism. To be sure, the personologist has little reason to be impressed with the thesis of reductionism.

In learning theory the matter is somewhat different. The theories are often quasi-formal. The categories of stimulus–response and mediating variables predispose our thinking in terms of physical locus. Furthermore, theories of learning have much in common as to first principles. For the most part, they differ only as to how the response repertory is strengthened and secured. Consider the issue of reinforcement. This is where the formal systems of Hull, Guthrie, Tolman, for example, make their stand. When the language of reinforcement is stripped of its personalistic overtones (as if reinforcing agents were gremlins soldering circuits together) what is involved is a question of schematic layout. Is the input–output system sufficient unto itself to establish S–R connections by virtue of some mechanism of contiguity, or must we include some mechanism of reinforcement with possible feedback complications? And what is the role of drive in learning? There is good reason to believe that these issues (along with those of latent learning, presensory conditioning, exploratory behavior, and secondary reinforcement) will be resolved by more explicit models of neurophysiology rather than by more refined behavioral studies.

[3] The language of levels and orders is sometimes confusing. By *higher* orders and *higher* levels I shall mean the more inclusive generalization or explanation. Thus the primary science (the reducing science) is higher-order than the secondary science (the reduced science). Assuming reducibility for psychology then psychology is lower-order than physiology. And microphysics would presumably be the highest-order of the empirical sciences.

Doubtless motivational variables will prove significant, as even contiguity theorists will agree. But whether reinforcement itself warrants an agency of its own in the system, or whether it is a very general term to cover a myriad of selectivity processes, is a question likely only to receive its answer in neurophysiology (cf. N11.9).

# NOTES

## NOTE 11.1

In Hull's *A Behavior System* Postulate 4 defines habit strength initially in terms of the number of equally spaced reinforced trials. Thus for habit strength

$$_sH_R = 1 - 10^{-0.0305N},$$

where $N$ is the total number of reinforcements. In Postulate 5 primary motivation or drive $(D)$ is defined as a function of enhancing $(D')$ and inanition $(\epsilon)$ components both of which are functions of hours of deprivation $(h)$.

$$D = D' \times \epsilon$$
$$D' = 37.824 \times 10^{-27.496 \frac{1}{h}} + 4.001$$
$$\epsilon = 1 - 0.00001045 \ h^{2.486}$$

The exactness of the constants should not be disconcerting; as the definitions stand both habit strength and drive are logical constructions, that is, intervening variables. As concepts, their operational status is assured since $N$ and $h$ are both observational variables.

Skinner is somewhat less explicit but it is clear that he, too, favors operational interpretations of drive:

> In measuring strength of drive we are in reality only measuring strength of behavior. A complete account of the latter is to be obtained from an examination of the operations that are found to affect it. The 'drive' is a hypothetical state interpolated between operation and behavior and is not actually required in a descriptive system. The concept is useful, however, as a device for expressing the complex relation that obtains between various similarly effective operations and a group of co-varying forms of behavior. The properties assigned to the state are derived from the observations of these relations (Skinner, 1938, p. 368).

Again, in 1953 he writes:

> A drive need not be thought of as mental or physiological. The term is simply a convenient way of referring to the effects of deprivation and satiation and of other operations which alter the probability of behavior in more or less the same way (Skinner, 1953, p. 144).

Skinner makes it clear that drives are not internal stimuli or physiological states or any other substantive states not definable in terms of simple operations.

One finds that the mediating variables of Tolman's theory are also subject to simple reductive analysis. Tolman himself undertakes the operational analysis of demands (Tolman, 1937).

The job of defending the operational status of the intervening variables in several learning theories is often thankless. Although such variables are given operational interpretations they often emerge as possessing surplus meaning in use. This is apparent in the literature on the issue of intervening variables versus hypothetical constructs (Marx, 1951, 1963).

For an examination of the status of Hull's constructs, see Koch (1954).


**NOTE 11.2**


An ostensive definition is denotative and requires exemplification of what is defined. An explicit definition is one involving synonymity in which the thing defined is replaced by its equivalent set of defining properties. Logical constructions and operational definitions resemble explicit definitions. However, a distinction must be made between a defining set of properties, as such, and a set of operations performed on a set of observations. A measure of intelligence may be explicitly defined as a set of responses on a given test. But intelligence may be operationally defined in terms of the test response *and* the arithmetic operations performed on such test performances. In this case, intelligence as operationally defined would be akin to a logical construction without inferred elements. If by intelligence this is all we mean, or if all theoretical terms were like 'specific gravity' with its operational definition (the ratio weight/volume) then there would be no problem of meaning (Hempel, 1958). The theoretical intensions of such terms could be dispensed with. However, this would stultify theory construction. Not all theoretical terms can be defined in terms of an explicit set of observables or in terms of explicit operations performed on a set of observables. Rather, the whole operational enterprise calls for a dispositional setting. We must distinguish between explicit definitions and dispositional terms.

In the following discussion let us take $C$ as some concept, $S$ as a stimulus description, and $R$ as a response description. We need to define $C$. An explicit definition here might be $Cx \equiv Rx$ def. That is to say, the concept $C$ can be attributed to $x$ if, and only if, $x$ is also $R$. But this will not do, for the definition does not prescribe the conditions under which $R$ is to occur. For example, a person may be considered of such and such level of intelligence if he knows the meaning of thirty out of a list of forty words. But by the above definition we would affirm $Cx$ regardless of whether $Rx$ because the subject $x$ had $R$ in his unrehearsed repertory, or because he had gotten hold of a clandestine copy of the list of words and had done some prior rehearsing. Even the most restricted operational definition requires a clear stipulation of the situational setting.

As a second effort let us try a dispositional definition of the form:

$$Cx \equiv (Sx \supset Rx).$$

That is to say, $x$ has the theoretical property $C$ if, and only if, it is the case that if $x$ is $S$ then $x$ is also $R$. Thus, in the above example, $S$ would specify the situational requirements of the test procedure. It is like the example "$x$ is volatile if, and only if, it is the case that if $x$ is exposed to air $x$ loses mass." But this formulation, too, offers serious difficulties. By the definition of material implication $(S \supset R) \equiv \sim(S \cdot \sim R) \equiv [(S \cdot R) \vee (\sim S \cdot R) \vee (\sim S \cdot \sim R)]$. Note that assignment of $C$ could then be justified whenever the test conditions were not imposed. Thus we could attribute $C$ to $x$ regardless of whether he was or was not tested. If tested then $R$ must be true, but if not tested, then either $R$ or $\sim R$.

Because of this difficulty Carnap has proposed an alternative explication of operational reductions which has found rather wide acceptance (cf. Hempel, 1958). By virtue of the "reduction pair"

$$S_1 \supset (R_1 \supset C)$$
$$S_2 \supset (R_2 \supset \sim C)$$

one is able to derive the bilateral reduction sentence for $C$, namely

$$Sx \supset (Cx \equiv Rx)$$

by equating $S_2$ to $S_1$ and $R_2$ to $\sim R_1$. Thus, for example, given an anxiety scale under specified conditions then a score above a given critical level means the person is assigned what we conceptualize as a critical anxiety factor.

The discussion of Carnapian reduction sentences is more complicated than I have shown. The simplified test conditionals, with $(S_2 = S_1)$ and $(R_2 = \sim R_1)$, need not hold for reduction pairs; in which case the reduction pairs may serve to define experimental conditions for assigning a new predicate, $C$, to objects in terms of the familiar experimental predicates $S_1$, $S_2$, $R_1$, $R_2$. In such a case, the truth of the reduction pair (equivalent to $\sim(S_1R_1 \cdot S_2R_2)$ ) is synthetic. However, as treated above the bilateral reduction sentence is conventional and analytic. This derives from the fact that the cut between $R$ and $\sim R$ is in some sense arbitrary. But note that $Sx \supset (Cx \equiv Rx)$ is not equivalent to the explicit definition $SxRx \equiv Cx$. Logically, all that we can infer from an operational definition is what a measurement should be under given test conditions in order for the defined concept to apply. The implication for inferring $Cx$ from $Rx$ does not rule out other conjunctions of $S_i$ and $R_i$. It is the very nature of operational definitions that they be open textured. Not only does the definitive biconditional hold, i.e.,

$$S_1x \supset (Cx \equiv R_1x)$$

but also

$$S_2x \supset (Cx \equiv R_2x)$$
$$\vdots \qquad \vdots$$
$$S_nx \supset (Cx \equiv R_nx)$$

where the range of the concept $C$ covers many test result conditionals, and where $S_2, \ldots, S_n, \ldots$ and $R_2, \ldots, R_n, \ldots$ represent events different from those in the initial operational setting. It is the openness of this range which leads one to seek some higher-order binding factor over the range of application of *C*. Thus, for example, should *C* be an "anxiety factor," we might be led to extend the range of the factor by endowing it with presumptively existential properties which would enable us to deduce other sets of *S–R* values for appropriate biconditional reduction sentences. Initially, of course, *C* is measured operationally. But it is only partially interpreted. Its extension is then determined by empirical test of purportedly alternative operations. Thus, as Carnap suggests, electric current can be measured by a deflection of a magnetic needle, by a quantity of silver separated out of solution, by heat produced in a conductor, etc. Temperature can be measured by an expansion of mercury or by electrical resistance, etc. And anxiety might be measured by blood chemistry, by activity of the reticular arousal system, as well as by an anxiety scale. As I shall argue, the concept itself carries the inchoate conception of its own extension. Strict operational reduction of a concept does not exhaust its entire meaning.

For discussions of the issues mentioned here see Carnap (1936, 1937); Koch (1941); Feigl (1945); Hempel (1954, 1958); Pap (1949, 1962).

## NOTE 11.3

The manifesto of operationism (or operationalism) has undoubtedly been P. W. Bridgman's *The Logic of Modern Physics* (1927). Although his thinking on operational definition dates from 1914, he makes no claim to originality. As the gospel crystallized into a dubious orthodoxy, Bridgman himself came to regret his role as expositor:

> I feel that I have created a Frankenstein which has certainly gotten away from me. I abhor the word *operationalism* or *operationism*, which seems to imply a dogma, or at least a thesis of some kind. The thing I have envisaged is too simple to be so dignified by so pretentious a name; rather, it is an attitude or point of view generated by continued practice of operational analysis (1954, 79, p. 224).

After two notable symposia (*Psychological Review*, 1945; *Scientific Monthly*, 1954), the dogmatic overtones of operationism tended to soften. Except for its logical interest, the subject eventually came to assume its proper role as a footnote to empirical procedure.

Etiologically, it is interesting that Bridgman's operationism was occasioned by the radical innovations introduced by the special theory of relativity. Newtonian concepts of absolute space and time had so prevailed that scientist and philosopher alike had come to take their empirical and absolute character for granted. However, speculations concerning events as measured from rapidly moving frames of reference necessitated our treating the idea of simultaneity as relativistic. Nor was Bridgman the only person to see the operational significance of the new physics. Eddington, in *Space, Time, and Gravitation* (1920), writes:

> Counting appears to be an absolute operation. But it seems to me that other physical measures are on a different footing. Any physical quantity, such as length, mass, force, etc., which is not pure number, can only be defined as the result arrived at by conducting a physical experiment ac-

cording to specified rules. So I cannot conceive of any "length" in nature independent of a definition of the way of measuring length. And, if there is, we may disregard it in physics, because it is beyond the range of experiment (p. 8).

The piece is spoken by the relativist in dialogue with an orthodox physicist and a mathematician. As one of the first people to expound on the philosophical significance of relativity, Eddington became a thorough-going operationist. But more uniquely, he elevated his pointer-reading operationism to the status of an idealistic ontology. His thinking, it is claimed, is neo-Kantian. Knowledge of the external world can only be mediated by consciousness and its operational play upon its sense data (Eddington, 1920, 1928, 1939).

Not all operationists will be embarrassed by this kinship to Kant. The contemporary "Italian operational school" draws its inspiration from Bridgman and from Hugo Dingler, the prolix neo-Kantian of the early part of the twentieth century (Ceccato, 1952). The argument from Dingler is interesting, for it brings operationism closer to metaphysics than votaries are prone to admit. The basis of Dingler's operationism is gnoseology, the problem of reification of the known out of the unknown. This was a matter of some mystery to the Greeks, for the unknown always provides the reservoir of potentiality. Dingler, however, was concerned with establishing the univocality of something's becoming known. He sought semantic constancy, as it were, by imposing a dictionary of operations on the knowing process. Thus univocality in the reification of the potential was the key idea in Dingler's operationism.

The Italian operationists tend to withdraw from these metaphysical commitments to the unknown. If the process of becoming aware of a reality "does not take place between a known and an unknown, it nevertheless takes place between a proposed definition and a semantical obligation." Although this process of operational reification translates into the unfortunate neologism "awarening" (*consapevolizzazione*) it designates an important epistemological attack—what one might call the operational invasion of the unknown. The contextual combination of apprisal and material or thing apprised through operation is called the "provenience" of the operational invasion. If we let the more metaphysical volatilia evaporate, what then remains is that substance of the operational predicament which has provided people such as Feigl (1945) and Hempel (1954) with material for their critiques of operationism. According to the latter, the operational invasion is always guided by something not fully conceptualized in the operational definition. Operationism must fulfill what Ceccato calls the semantical obligation.

We have discussed operationism without benefit of a definition of it. It is fitting that Bridgman be heard: "In general, we mean by any concept nothing more than a set of operations; *the concept is synonymous with the corresponding set of operations*" (1927, p. 5). However, it is just this strict equating of a concept to a set of operations which has proved the shortcoming of the dogma. Few, if any, theoretical concepts are synonymous with an explicit set of operations.

For some early espousals of operationism see McGeoch (1936, 1937), Tolman (1936, 1937), Boring (1936), Kantor (1938), S. S. Stevens (1935a, 1935b), Bergmann and Spence (1941), and C. C. Pratt (1939).

**NOTE 11.4**

The Newtonian synthesis of planetary laws and mechanics is one of the supreme achievements in the history of science. The saga is interesting not alone for Newton's creation of celestial mechanics but also for the example of Kepler's travails in arriving at the laws of planetary motion. Kepler was the phenomenologist, so to speak; Newton, the reductionist theory builder.

The story of Kepler is one of dogged but rewarding persistence. Formulation of his first two laws alone required in years the number of days he predicted the task would take. With respect to his "discovery" of both the first and third laws, he compares Truth to the lascivious maiden of Virgil "who surrenders unexpectedly to her pursuer when he has already given up hope" (Koestler, 1959). The first two laws derived from his efforts to describe the orbit of Mars—a task assigned to him by Tycho Brahe. As was known from antiquity, the revolutionary motion of planets in their orbits was not uniform; hence, the invention of epicycles and eccentrics such that appearances of non-uniform motion could be accounted for in terms of uniform motion in circular orbits. Despite his otherwise mystical inclinations, Kepler ruthlessly cast aside the old face-saving geometrical devices. In keeping unconsciously, at least, to the precept of parsimony, he tried to simplify assumptions as to the nature of both the orbit and planetary motion. This was difficult to do. The simplest of assumptions, a circular orbit and uniform motion, obviously would not suffice. Thus by combining principles of equal sweep in equal time with the assumption of the eccentric locus for the sun, and by trying first circular, then ovoid, and finally elliptical orbits, Kepler was able to arrive at the great planetary laws.

*First law:* The orbit of the planet is an ellipse with the sun located at one of its two foci.

*Second law:* The planet moves in nonuniform motion about the sun so that the radius of the planet with respect to the sun sweeps out equal areas in equal increments of time.

The third law came later, after extensive trial-and-error search for a cosmic principle interrelating all the planetary orbits.

*Third law:* The relation of the period of revolution of a planet to its mean orbital radius is such that the ratio of the square of the time to the cube of the radius is constant for all planets ($k = T^2/r^3$).

Kepler left planetary astronomy with three acceptable laws but no theory. Newton's reduction of the Keplerian laws derived from his own three laws of motion, the law of gravitation, and certain other basic assumptions. On the basis of such assumptions, Newton considered masses to attract one another; for the purpose of calculations, all mass was to be regarded as located at a center of gravity. Thus estimates concerning the diameter of the earth and the orbital radius of the moon could be utilized as the base for his computations concerning the mutual attraction of the two bodies.

Newton's laws of motion are as follows:

*First law:* The principle of inertia and conservation of motion.

*Second law:* The force acting upon a body is proportional to its change in momentum ($mv$), and determines the direction in which the change in momentum occurs. From this the familiar $F = ma$.

*Third law:* Conservation of action: action and reaction are opposite and equal.

*Law of gravitation:* Gravitational force between two objects is equal to the product of the masses of the two objects divided by the square of the distance separating their centers of gravity: $F = Gm_1m_2/r^2$, with $G$ the gravitational constant being contingent upon units of mass, length, and time.

Newton could show that Kepler's first law was derivable from a gravitational force effective as the inverse of the square of the distance between the planet and the sun. Kepler's second law requires that an effective force must be directed toward the sun. The most graphic deduction is that of the continuous gravitational pull of the moon toward the earth as it maintains its constant tangential motion. A combination of the tangential (inertial) and gravitational forces results in the bodies following an elliptical orbit in periodic but nonuniform velocity. What is remarkable is that the system of celestial mechanics is sufficient to deduce hypotheses about the behavior of any planetary system—just as, for example, it is successfully used to predict (or explain) the behavior of Halley's comet.

A question we might wish to raise is this: Is the achievement of Newton a "reduction" or an "explanation"? Was there a prior theory for Newton to exploit? Debate would be fruitless. Actually there were poorly formed "theories" before Newton gave the world his *Principia*. Though no one took him seriously, Kepler himself was sure that the cosmic principle of the five regular solids would somehow allow these solids to hold all the orbits of the planets within their concentric shells. The phenomenological laws of the planetary universe were to be explained by Pythagoreanism. Newton did, of course, succeed in reducing the phenomenological laws of planetary behavior to the language of mechanics. In subjecting celestial phenomena to the language of mechanics, he did achieve both a reduction and an explanation. The reduction itself was the occasion for building a science of mechanics.

## NOTE 11.5

Woodger, who is a pioneer in axiomatics for the life sciences (1929, 1937, 1952), is himself critical of reducing psychology to physiology. Neither of the two disciplines have been axiomatized, neither are particularly mature. With respect to reduction in general, he writes:

> Strictly speaking, we can only fruitfully discuss such relations between theories when both have been axiomatized, but, outside mathematics, this condition is never satisfied. Hence the futility of much of the discussion about whether theory $T_{(2)}$ is reducible to theory $T_{(1)}$ 'in principle.' Such questions cannot be settled by discussions of that kind but *only by actually carrying out the reduction,* and this is not done and cannot be done until the theories have been axiomatized (1952, p. 271).

Woodger, who is not at all reluctant to recommend anthropomorphism to us when we are speaking of man, prefers that we develop a person language for an interpersonal theory of behavior. We cannot wait upon the development of the primary discipline to which behavioral theory is to be reduced.

> I ask whether it is good empiricism and good science to postpone the study of persons until you have completed a behavior theory, founded on the study of white rats and robots, in the hope that you will then be able to deduce the statements descriptive of persons from the postulates at which you arrived from your experiments on rats? The behaviorist programme is a long-term policy. We do not know whether it will ever be completed. It would surely be foolish to reject a theory which is expressed in the person language and refuse to try to extend and improve it simply on the ground it cannot be translated into the physical language (1952, p. 309).

The most that could be achieved is for psychology to be interpreted in terms of physiology. But even that is prohibitively restrictive. According to Woodger, the theory of persons cannot wait upon the development of physiology; it must develop its own language and without concern for reduction.

Additional discussions of formal requirements of reduction can be found in Bergmann (1957) and in Kemeny and Oppenheim (1956). The latter is a discussion and extension of the Nagel–Woodger treatments.


## NOTE 11.6

Hull's language has often been suggestive of a physiological bias (e.g., stimulus trace, afferent interaction, and his early discussion of drive in terms of tissue deprivations and needs). However, over the decade of his three theoretical books, he makes it clear that molar descriptions concern gross responses of the organism as apart from the molecular physiology. In the *Principles of Behavior* he wrote:

> It is conceivable that the elaboration of a systematic science of behavior at a molar level may aid in the development of an adequate neurophysiology and thus lead in the end to a truly molecular theory of behavior firmly based on physiology (1943, p. 20).

Almost a decade later he was to reaffirm that belief in the *Essentials of Behavior:*

> Now while this molar or non-physiological approach presumably permits a much less perfect behavioral science than will someday be possible with a full knowledge of neurophysiology, it does give us a great deal of understanding of behavior. . . . Meanwhile in the case these postulates stand up under logical utilization, they may serve as a suggestive lead to neurophysiologists in their empirical investigations, and ultimately to a higher integration of gross molar behavior and neurophysiology (1951, p. 6).

Here Hull alludes to a point that has been made by critics of classical reductionism (Feyerabend, 1962; Sellars, 1961; Feigl, 1961; Scriven, 1958). A reducing science is seldom so mature or so formalistically complete that a reduction is straightforwardly achievable. Rather the secondary science itself generalizes and modifies the concepts in the reducing science which are requisite for the reductive undertaking.

Other Hullians (Spence, 1956; Kendler, 1952) have emphasized the nonphysiological basis of behavior theory. However, neither would preclude reductionism on logical grounds.


## NOTE 11.7

Since formalization and axiomatization of the primary and the secondary science is propaedeutic to reduction, discussions of actual reduction are premature. Rather we should focus upon prospective reduction as the means of resolving theoretical issues, especially those concerning mediating processes. However, the task of defending reductionism on this prospective basis is simplified when the given theory of behavior has been the object of formal analysis. Hence attempts to formalize theories of learning are of considerable interest. Consider the following:

(1) Hull's postulational system is frequently offered as the example par excellence of formal behavior theory. Yet, its very lack of formal rigor has made it subject to hypercritical attacks on that account (Koch, 1954). However, in a little-referred-to paper of F. B. Fitch ond Gladys Barry (1950), the authors treat Hull's theory to a rigorous formal analysis. In spite of the brevity of the paper, the analysis is too long to give in detail; but the following points should give the flavor of the argument.

The complete formalization is composed of thirteen definitions and five axioms with their corollaries. The definitions cover the following terms, each of which plays a significant role in the postulates of Hull:

D1.  Stimulus events.
D2.  Response events.
D3.  Time of occurrence or time stretch of such events.
D4.  Initial time for dating onset of neural functioning.
D5.  Tendency in a stimulus-response pair ($_sH_R$ at time $t$).
D6.  Increment in tendency (acquisition).
D7.  Stimulus similarity.
D8.  Response similarity.
D9.  Function for amount of drive.
D10.  Goal gradient function (important in drive reduction).
D11.  Function for effective drive reduction.
D12.  Function for dependence of increment of tendency.
D13.  Constant of proportionality between increment of tendency and effective drop in drive.

Although no consistent effort is made to tie these definitions to neurophysiological substrates, it is obvious that each can serve as a hypothesis for neurophysiological explorations. The axioms of the analysis cover the following items:

A1.  The state of habit strength at any given time.
A2.  Increment of habit strength as a function of stimulus similarity, response similarity, latency of response, and a function expressed in A3.
A3.  Effective drop in drive as an integrable function over time of goal gradient and average rate of drive reduction.
A4.1–A4.5.  The equation of increment of habit strength with partial derivatives for each of the independent variables as listed in A2.
A5.1–A5.6.  Goal gradient as function of drive reduction.

It is a comparatively simple matter to apply the criteria of reduction to this set of definitions and axioms. We can assume that the physicalistic language is common to both psychology and neurophysiology (hence all statements about the environment, time, space, etc., are admissible). The salient terms for reduction are then stimulus, response, and drive reduction. Since every stimulus and every response is a truth functional extension over afferent and efferent components, then drive reduction alone becomes the crucial concept. Thus, we may argue that a reduction of Hullian psychology is possible if drive can be describable in predicates admissible to the neurophysiological language. This latter condition can only be satisfied by empirical research. However, in light of recent advances concerning motivation and activation, achievement of the empirically reductive equivalences between drive and neurophysiological process seems quite possible. The promise of reductive achievement is perhaps not so remote as some critics have inclined to think (e.g., Bergmann, 1953).

(2) In a somewhat less ascetic vein, Voeks (1950) has undertaken the formalization of Guthrie's theory of learning. She proceeds from postulates and definitions to the deduction of a set of theorems, each of which expresses an hypothesis with behavioral implications. In brief the postulates (or principles) are as follows:

P1.  Principle of association.
P2.  Principle of postremity (a refinement on recency).
P3.  Principle of response probability (as a monotonically increasing function of number of stimulus cues).
P4.  Principle of a dynamic stimulus situation.

The definitions cover the following:

D1.  Stimulus.
D2.  Cue (an unconditioned or previously conditioned stimulus).
D3.  Response.
D4.  Conditioned response.
D5.  Indirect conditioned response to a stimulus pattern.
D6.  Postreme response.
D7.  Incompatible response.
D8.  Learning.

Because of the absence of mediating constructs (maintaining stimuli are not conspicuous in Voek's formalization), Guthrie's theory has not offered the challenge to reduction that Hull's theory has. Still the language of stimulus and response is certainly conducive to reduction, and simple conditioning and association models of learning, of all psychological models, have been most amenable to reductive analysis. As for response probability being a function of stimulus cue, this principle, essential both to the contiguity theory of Guthrie and to the statistical learning theory of Estes, is well modeled, so to speak, by the neurophysiological schematics of Milner (1957) and Rosenblatt (1958). Both the Mark II of Milner and the Perceptron of Rosenblatt account for a stochastic cuing process in terms of mediating cell assemblies which augment the probability of response.

To be sure, a Guthrian need not be concerned with neurophysiology, but there is nothing in the formal analysis of the principles and laws of learning which militates against a reductionist claim.

(3) A third major theory of learning to be treated to formalization is that of Tolman. Tolman's own presentations of his sign gestalt or expectancy theory were admittedly informal and "programmatic" (e.g., 1932, 1934, 1948). Moreover, because of his emphasis upon cognitive processes and purposive behavior, he himself has been accused of mentalism, of leaving his subjects "buried in thought" (Guthrie, 1935). With an avowed preference for a re-inforcement principle, MacCorquodale and Meehl (1953, 1954) have at-tempted a formalization of expectancy theory. Noting among other things that the data language of Tolman and his students is ambiguous, that not all of their behavioral hypotheses can be derived from the expectancy construct, and that the language of expectancy has a mentalistic, intentional intonation, these writers prescribe a set of postulates which place the constructs of expectancy theory on firm behavioral and physicalistic foundations. The last item of their criticism is especially worthy of comment. As we shall see in the following chapter, the thesis of intentionality has frequently been offered as a barrier both to logical behaviorism and to reductionism. Since Brentano, it has been generally recognized that a mental act involves an element of "aboutness." Propositions expressing intentional events have a unique structure. There is the object of regard, judgment, thinking, etc., and there is the intentional act of regarding, judging, thinking, etc., which has a logical status different from that of the physical object. Strictly interpreted then, cognitive statements with intentional aspects are not themselves "truth functions of their components." To escape this predicament and to assure that all intentionalistic terms or de-scriptions are translatable into the data language, MacCorquodale and Meehl formulate postulates of expectancy in terms of stimulus and response.

A brief paraphrase of the postulates follows. What is missing from the condensation are the details of the characteristic curves of growth, strength in-crement, etc. The unit of analysis is the expectancy unit $(S_1R_1S_2)$ in which $S_1$ is the elicitor stimulus situation, $R_1$ is the response elicited, and $S_2$ is the ex-pectandum or stimulus situation associated with goals and ends.

P1.    *Mnemonization:* Growth of $(S_1R_1S_2)$ is a function of the valence of $S_2$ and the probability that $S_2$ follows from $S_1R_1$.

P2.    *Extinction:* Expectancy strength of $S_2$ on $S_1R_1$ diminishes as a function of decrease in its probability on $S_1R_1$ from some prior rate.

P3.   *Primary generalization:* Other elicitors (S*) of $R_1$ and $S_2$ events will receive expectancy strength from $(S_1R_1S_2)$ as a function of the similarity between S* and $S_1$.

P4.   *Inference:* The temporal contiguity of $S_2S*$ given an expectancy $(S_1R_1S_2)$ yields an increment of strength to a new expectancy $(S_1R_1S*)$.

P5.   *Generalized inference:* If $S*S_2$ occur in temporal contiguity, wherein $S_2$ is inferrable from $S'_2$ in the expectancy of $S_1R_1S'_2$, then that contiguity will produce an increment of strength in $(S_1R_1S*)$.

P6.   *Secondary cathexis:* Contiguity of S* and $S_2$ when S* has valence produces an increment of strength in the absolute valence of $S_2$ (analogous to secondary reinforcement).

P7.   *Induced elicitor cathexis:* Acquisition of valence by an expectandum $S_2$ induces valence in the elicitor $S_1$.

P8.   *Confirmed elicitor cathexis:* Confirmation of an expectancy when $S_2$ has a valence produces an increment in the cathexis of $S_1$ (reinforcement of $S_1$).

P9.   *Valence:* The valence of a stimulus S* is a multiplicative function of the need D and the cathexis C*.

P10.  *Need strength:* Need strength is a temporal function of deprivation since a prior satiation.

P11.  *Cathexis:* Cathexis of S* is an increasing function of the number of contiguities of it and the consummatory response.

P12.  *Activation:* Reaction potential $_SE_R$ of response $R_1$ in presence of $S_1$ is a multiplicative function of the strength of $(S_1R_1S_2)$ and the valence of $S_2$.

Some important terms remain undefined (e.g., consummatory response), but care is taken by the authors to define stimulus and response as classes of afferent and efferent events. Note should be taken that MacCorquodale and Meehl present their set of postulates only as a provisional and "nonsufficient" attempt at formalization. However, it is significant that they are able to deduce confirmed hypotheses from the domain of latent learning, and that they bring together certain principles of reinforcement and expectancy theories.

The authors' own preference (1954) is for a system of implicit definitions wherein the meanings of the constructs are uniquely contingent upon the whole system of postulates and grow, so to speak, with the accretions to the system. Although no attempt is made at reduction itself (the language of physiology "will be fine when we can get it") they prefer hypothetical constructs, with their openness of meaning, over allegedly "direct, operational definitions." "Stimulus" and "response" are terms in the peripheral language to be sure; but "mnemonization," "inference," and "cathexis," are terms for the centralistic locale. And so, also, for the language of strengthening, increment, and extinction. Responding to an article by Kendler (1952) (in which he argues that the issue of what is learned is a pseudo-issue, and that all we seek in our constructions is to amplify upon lawful behavioral relationships), MacCorquodale and Meehl (1953) declare it both fruitful and empirically legitimate to speculate on the mediating process. In fact, such speculation is regarded as essential in the long run. No one denies that the brain and nervous system mediate behavioral process. We may speak as if our constructs are no more than strict logical constructions out of the data language, but such constructs become reified if for no other reason than that the empiricist is more comfortable in palpable than in abstractive locales. Since reductive and nonreductive psychologists admit the need for mediating variables, the question of physical locus is relevant. If it were presumed not, it would be like asserting that the request for the existential credentials of mediating constructs is inappropriate where, in fact, such credentials are in principle obtainable.

In summary, formalization facilitates reductive analysis. Formalization brings into sharp relief the constructs mediating the ontologically basic language of stimulus and response. In the reductive framework, such constructs become the hypothesis of neurophysiology. Making good on the promise of reductionism, however slow that process may be, will eventually decide which constructs will stand and how they will be modified.

## NOTE 11.8

In this context it is interesting to consider what the conventionalistic tactics of the parapsychologist might be. Should he argue strictly from observables, as the extrasensory psychologist often does, than any mediators would be fair pragmatic support of a theory that accounts for the paranormal behaviors. What is distressing here is the denial by many parapsychologists that one can seek a neurophysiological reduction of paranormal behavior. Yet such reductionism is just what some radical behaviorists consider as irrelevant. It is perhaps ironic that Skinner, a nonreductionist and a critic of extrasensory experiments (1948), cannot base his critique of parapsychology upon the reductionist's claim that the physical locale for the stimulus–response rubric be an intact neurophysiological continuum.

## NOTE 11.9

The last decade has seen a growing interest in building models for the deduction of behavioral phenomena. Deutsch (1960), for example, gives a schematic model that is compatible with Hull and the principle of reinforcement and that is amenable to reduction. In fact, Deutsch visualizes the psychologist as blocking out in schematic form hypotheses for the neurophysiologist to explore.

> The psychologist can, by inference from the behavior of the system, suggest hypotheses which the physiologist, helped by knowing what types of phenomena to look for, can then confirm by direct observation. On the other hand, the physiologist's observations, the significance of which may be obscure to him, can suggest to the psychologists the type of hypotheses which could account for certain behavior, and this he can go on to test by making behavioral predictions. In this way the psychologist and the

physiologist can work together, the psychologist relieved of the necessity of physiological speculation and the neurophysiologist presented with actual hypotheses he can test (Deutsch, 1960, p. 173).

According to him, then, his schematic should provide the neurophysiologist with testable hypotheses concerning structure and function. Details of the model are provided in Figure 11.1. The mechanics of this basic behavioral

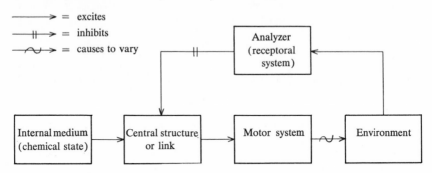

**Figure 11.1**    Diagram to illustrate suggested mechanism of need (from J. A. Deutsch, *The Structural Basis of Behavior.* Cambridge: Cambridge University Press, 1960).

unit or link can best be presented in Deutsch's own words:

> The system which has been postulated can be described in five propositions. There are five elements in it, related to each other in three different ways. The elements will be called an analyzer (a receptoral system), a link, a motor (or effector) organization, an environment, a feature of the internal environment. The three kinds of relation are activating; switching-off; causing to vary. The elements are related to form the unit in the following way:
> 1. The primary link is set into activity by a feature of the internal environment.
> 2. When the primary link is active it indirectly activates the motor organization.
> 3. The activity in the motor organization causes the environment to vary.
> 4. A particular variation in the environment activates the analyzer.
> 5. The activated analyzer switches off the link. Most of these relations will not be all or none, but more or less in nature (1960, pp. 33–34).

Note that this "need"-oriented system provides no place for a construct of need as such. The internal (subcortical) activating system is itself sensitive to various kinds of physiological deficits. Motor activity (behavioral hypotheses, as it were) continues until a particular response and environmental variation evokes stimulus input (the analyzer) which in turn effects cessation of the activating link. Any sequential act will involve a series of units such as in Figure 11.1, each with its link. The underlying deficit serves as an activator of the sequential set of links until it too is eventually terminated by the analyzer of some consummatory response. But the activity of each link is terminated by the elicitation of its own analyzer; thus the cessation of one link allows activation of the next link in the series and those two links will become connected. Thus far, the linkage series is explanatory of any unlearned sequence of behavior (e.g., it coincides nicely with Tinbergen's sequential analysis of instinct; 1951). Additional principles are required for explaining contiguity and frequency effects in learning. Deutsch finds that he can derive hypotheses concerning the phenomena of reinforcement, latent learning, exploration, extinction, self-stimulation (see Gallistel, 1964) without hypostatizing drive and need. At each point he is conscious of the possibility of translating his schematic into neurophysiological hypotheses.

Deutsch's model is only one among many which draw support from recent discoveries concerning the activating and alerting functions of the subcortical reticular system. Berlyne's theory of exploratory behavior (1960) presents a conjectural exploitation of the limited data of arousal. Subcortical nuclei both facilitate and inhibit activity of the cortex. Thus they serve both to alert the cortex for processing specific sensory inputs and to inhibit other areas that might offer cortical competition. In combination they mediate the selectivity of attention and efficient response. There is, however, an optimal state of arousal. Overarousal may result in fixations and compulsive behavior; underarousal may result in disorientation. Both states in their extremity result in relatively inefficient behavior. Drive states are activators; in other words, they serve to stimulate the arousal state. In presence of such drive, the "consummatory behavior," itself, results in deactivation. Intensive and novel stimuli also serve to activate and to arouse. One might think then that boredom and the absence of stimulation would mean low arousal and that curiosity is the manifestation of a search for arousal (Hebb), but Berlyne disagrees. Rather, he suggests, boredom means high arousal and high activation level. Under the circumstances, novel stimulation is sought. To some extent competing arousals will inhibit one another. But what is more important is that the increased arousal due to curiosity in an explorable situation is relieved (i.e., diminished) by exploration, by familiarization, and by recognition. In affective terms, arousal is pleasurable up to a certain level; beyond the optimal level, it becomes unpleasant and instigates behaviors directed, in the end, toward reducing arousal. Berlyne has some interesting speculations to present concerning behavior in the face of uncertainty, but where his system is most fruitful is in the deduction of the learning that takes place in the absence of ostensible reinforcements.

Perhaps the best known of the behavior models to incorporate hypotheses of arousal is that of Hebb (1949, 1955). Its most distinctive innovation is that of postulating mechanisms for establishing order, stability, and habit out of assemblages of randomly organized components. Instead of presenting complex sets of prepotent reflex structures (there may be these, of course), the cortex offers myriads of randomly firing associative and processing cells which adventitiously become associated with specific sensory inputs. Association takes place between the input mosaic and some particular set of processing components that happen to be firing at the moment of input. Input is, of course, projected to specific areas of the cortex, but just what cells participate in processing a perceptual configuration are selected according to the coincidence of input and the random firing of the processing cells. This "cell assembly," so to speak, is built up as a processing manifold through cell modification and growth. Such processing manifolds can either be transient or lasting. Associative processes of stimulus and stimulus and of stimulus and response are implemented by phase sequences in which contiguously active cell assemblies are connected at the level of neural function.

The original model was hardly more than a prolegomenon to a future system. Certain objections arose in conjunction with Hebb's limited neural postulates. For example, learning would occur much too rapidly, and there would apparently be no deterrent to a cataclysmic recruitment of cell firing. Drawing upon the works of Eccles (1953), Lorente de Nó (1949), and others, Milner (1957) modified the cell assembly mechanism so as to overcome these objections. Furthermore he proposed specific subcortical arousal mechanisms to accommodate motivational and learning effects. To Hebb's original set of neural postulates (temporal summation, synaptic strengthening, refractoriness, neural fatigue), Milner added postulates of collaterally induced inhibition and cell priming. Establishment and strengthening of cell assemblages is occasioned not only by the coincidences of cell firings but also by the fact that the firing of any long axone neurone induces inhibitory effects at the synapses of adjacent inactive cells. Collateral branchings of such long axone cells fire short axone cells which in turn inhibit synaptic transmission of adjacent transmitters. Cell assemblies thus become self-protective and self-sustaining under steady input. Once the assemblies are secured their phase sequences are established, as Hebb had postulated.

In addition, Milner was more explicit as to the role of the subcortical (reticular) arousal system. The postulate of priming states that any subthreshold stimulation of a cell leaves that cell primed for subsequent firing. Thus, one assembly primed by previously active assemblies can be excited by fractional complements of the original stimulus (witness, for example, the effectiveness of cues and redintegration in learning). But priming also renders the cortical cells (i.e., those associatively linked to active cell assemblies) susceptible to arousal. Let the arousal centers become active either from cortical input or by receptors sensitive to deficit; these centers in turn activate the cortex so as to increase the rate of random firing of the cortical cells. However, because some cells are primed they are more likely to be firing at the incidence of a stimulus input than any random sampling of cells. Associative strengthening is thereby predisposed.

Motivational level affects learning in two ways: (1) by eliciting cortical activity and response, and (2) subsequently by affecting the rate of learning. The effects are not independent of one another. Since arousal varies with motivation level, more cortical cells will be active and available for the coincident firing underlying the formation and association of the cell assemblies. Moreover, the effects of reinforcement, reward, and satiation are such as momentarily to reduce the level of arousal. This in turn decreases the availability of cells and cell assemblies for the associative processes essential to learning.

None of the mentioned systems presents actual physiological models of learning processes. That is, none deals with a point-by-point, process-by-process, mapping of neuroanatomical units. At most they block in hypothetical components which serve as the blue prints for conceptual nervous systems. It is for the neurophysiologist to implement the function of components with his own explorations and findings. Nevertheless, the above theories do differ in a significant way from learning theories such as that of Hull, Tolman, and Guthrie. The hypothetical constructs refer to possible microstructures of the mediators and are not alone conjecturable from molar behavioral events.

Speculations in modeling conceptual nervous systems are extensive. They vary from studies of cybernetics and automata to actual neurophysiological models. F. H. George (1961) presents a fairly comprehensive review of the literature of cybernetics and adjacent disciplines. With respect to brain functions, D. A. Sholl (1956) offers a very readable survey of some of the statistical aspects of cerebral organization. There are two notable symposia on brain functions and integrative processes: Delafresnaye (1954) and Jeffress (1951), and another symposium edited by Delafresnaye (1961) on brain mechanisms and learning.

More elaborate conceptual nervous systems are to be found in Rosenblatt (1958); Pribram (1960); and Galanter, Miller, and Pribram (1960). One should, of course, not overlook the classic works of Hebb (1949, 1955).

Advances in biochemistry already suggest that reduction can be carried a step further. Presently one finds impressive hypotheses on how stimulus inputs may modulate changes in the structure of DNA and RNA molecules of nerve cells such that unique structure of the molecules may code the response potentials of the cell or may affect the resonance properties of cell response (Landauer, 1964). Reviews relating biochemistry to memory and learning are to be found in Morrell (1961), John (1961), Thomas (1962), and Gaito and Zavala (1964).

The intention here is not to give a survey of the literature in psychobiology but only to indicate that it is a fairly rich one. Speculations concerning future reductions of psychology are not as idle as they have appeared to some. The advances are perhaps sufficient to make the criterion of reducibility a useful one for evaluating the theoretical terms of psychology.

# CHAPTER 12

# Reductionism: II

IN SPITE of the dramatic developments in the domain of psychobiology, reductionism has not been a particularly popular doctrine within psychology itself. Occasionally calls come for psychologists to formulate their explanatory systems in neurophysiology (e.g., MacCorquodale and Meehl, 1948; Krech, 1950; Hebb, 1955), but for the most part, the psychophysiology is done by physiologists, engineers, and biophysicists rather than psychologists. On the contrary, psychologists have frequently demurred as concerns the value of neurologizing. One can, of course, understand the objections to a premature neurophysiology; it is likely to interfere with explicit treatment of data and lawful description of behavior (cf. N12.1). Yet the objections continue when the arguments on grounds of prematurity no longer seem quite so trenchant.

For the psychologist objections to reductionism can be grouped into two categories: methodological and phenomenological. The former of these includes policies and procedural commitments as to the subject matter and theory of psychology. As such, no crucial logical issues prohibitive of reduction are involved. The issue of the logical impossibility of reductionism is, however, raised with respect to the phenomenological aspects of psychology. Here, the personalistic and cognitive languages purportedly offer difficulties not encountered in a purely physicalistic language. We will not be concerned here with objections based solely on the preference for remaining in the behavioral language on grounds that much remains to be done of a descriptive and exploratory nature. One cannot quarrel with such a decision. As Sellars (1956) and Bergmann (1957) have pointed out, reductionism as an article of faith in the absence of a well-structured secondary science (psychology) is a trivial thesis. At this stage of the science much remains to be done in the behavioral language as such. Hull, Tolman, and Spence all might agree to some such statement of the situation. None objects to the ultimate possibility of neurophysiological explanations. And, though individually preferring the behavioral language, none has made the disavowal of reductionism a commanding statement in his scientific credo—even though their respective procedural preferences may have been interpreted as such.

At the outset it should be noted that the point of view expressed in this chapter is that there are no logical barriers, and perhaps no technological ones, to reductionism in psychology and that all explanations of behavior can in principle be reduced to the language of neurophysiology.

## METHODOLOGICAL OBJECTIONS

In general, when the qualifier "methodological" is found in the philosophy of science it has been used to designate a point of view calling for firm procedural commitments. Though such commitments are not logically entailed and may often arise only for the lack of metaphysical support for one over another procedure, they are binding all the same. They do indeed become part of a working credo. As a rule, then, methodological decisions are made when issues are raised for which no straightforward answers are forthcoming. Such was the case, for example, when Lashley (1923) sought to disallow consciousness as a suitable subject matter for psychology. With respect to a methodological (nonreductive) behaviorism, the argument is somewhat analogous. Reliance upon neurophysiology is unwarranted, untested, or too restrictive. Under the circumstances, a strict operational behaviorism is considered essential to psychology. Intervening variables with strict behavioral interpretability are preferred to hypothetical constructs. This, the nature of our "hypothetical" terms, seems to be the focal issue and the one to which we want eventually to turn. But first, some preliminaries.

### Reductionism and Psychology

When the psychologist speaks of reduction he means, of course, the reduction of psychology to physiology, or more precisely, to neurophysiology. If he is unfamiliar with the formal requirements for reduction, as he is likely to be, he is inclined to espouse some article of faith such as "no psychosis without neurosis," only substituting "behavior" for "psychosis" as more befits the proper subject matter of psychology. Whether any science in its history has exemplified the paradigm of formal reduction is for the present immaterial. Neither the language of psychology nor that of physiology is so rigorously developed that conjointly they permit the reduction of the statements of one science into the statements of the other. Nor is there any immediate prospect of this being achieved. What we do have are some rather impressionistic, at best, schematic accounts of how the concepts of one science can be related to those of the other.

Note that I say related and not reduced. This is simply a precaution to avoid the implication that the reducing science in this case is either a finished or a mature science standing independently of the reduced science. Both neurophysiology and psychology are relatively immature sciences. Their relationship has been a symbiotic one. The concepts of one science have been instrumental to the development of the concepts of the other. Rather than a neurophysiology offering a tidy system of finished concepts for the deduction of certain laws of psychology, we find one in which the concepts are subjected to substantial revisions in order that they may be adopted as an explanatory basis of psychology. Nowhere, perhaps, is this more clear than in the study of memory functions. Early neurophysiology was reflex oriented. The functional unit of the central nervous system was the reflex arc, with the accompanying processes of synaptic growth and neurobiotaxis. These conceptions fit well into the traditions of associationism, and in time they became the neurophysiological model for Thorndikean stimuli–response psychology. But the subsequent investigations of people like Bartlett, Lashley, Köhler, and Hebb soon made it obvious that the functional unit of memory had to be more complex than the reflex arc. Consequently, we find conceptions of reverberating circuits emerging to complicate the synaptic picture. Similar examples can be found in the area of perception. The phenomena of afterimages, of perceptual constancies, of perceptual generalization have served both to stimulate and to guide neurophysiologists in their work. Contrariwise recent work on the subcortical centers of the brain, particularly the reticular formation, has led to the rediscovery of consciousness and the language of awareness (Delafresnaye, 1954).

## Two Types of Reduction

One needs, however, to look more closely at the meaning of reductionism for the psychologist. I have said that for the most part reductionism means the reduction of psychology to neurophysiology. But this is a restricted usage; for one could speak of the reduction of theoretical terms without necessarily implying that the theoretical terms are reduced to terms in the neurophysiological language. In the philosophical literature, one finds reductionism discussed in at least two contexts. In the context of what in the last chapter was called constructual reduction, one speaks of reducing theoretical terms to a set of observation statements, or, for the phenomenalist, to a set of statements about sense data. This is reductionism as discussed by the phenomenalists, by the physicalists, by the logical atomists, and critically by people like Quine (1953) and Barker (1957). In the second context, that of theoretic reduction, one speaks of reducing one theory to another. Such would be the case in reducing psychology to neurophysiology, or in reducing genetics to biochemistry. This is the treatment of reductionism that appears to predominate in the philosophy of science (e.g., Nagel, 1949, 1961; Woodger, 1952; Kemeny and Oppenheim, 1956). It should be apparent that the two treatments of reductionism are not mutually exclusive. On the other hand, they do not mutually entail one another. This is quite clear in the reductive accounts of psychology. One can, for example, be a strict reductionist so far as concerns his theoretical terms, yet not believe that it is either necessary or desirable that psychology make reductive use of neurophysiology. Such a view is explicitly defended by B. F. Skinner (1938, 1950) and by Spence (1956). There are other psychologists who defend psychology as a neurophysiologically reducible discipline yet would suggest that the theoretical concepts be treated as inferred entities rather than as logical constructions deriving from strict behavioral data reduction. MacCorquodale and Meehl (1948) and Hebb (1949) defend this type of argument, as do perhaps most psychologists who believe in the neurophysiological foundations of psychology. At first glance, this appears paradoxical. People who are reductionist in the constructual sense may be nonreductionist in the theoretic sense. Witness, for example, Skinner and Tolman. On the other hand, people who are reductionist in the theoretic sense may not be strictly so in the constructual sense. There is no logical difficulty here, however, and any sense of paradox disappears when we examine the possibility of reducing the theoretical constructs of systems such as those of Skinner or Tolman to neurophysiological terms. The preference of, say, a Skinnerian for a radical nonphysiological behaviorism is just that, a preference. Indeed there is nothing to prevent him from reducing either his observational or his theoretical terms to an inclusive language of neurophysiology (i.e., to the physical language and the language of neurophysiology, as such).

## Hypothetical Concepts and Reductionism

There have been several occasions to refer to the distinction between intervening variables and hypothetical constructs, as proposed by MacCorquodale and Meehl (1948). Whether this distinction holds for the physical sciences may be open to some debate; but doubtless it has proved useful in psychology for distinguishing those people who want stringent operational reductions with no element of surmise from those who wish to include the element of surmise as a promise of constructual reification. For example, in the systems by Skinner and Tolman, different as they are, the variables mediating between stimulus and response are really translations of statements of observable events. That is to say, they are anchored either to the stimulus complex of events or to the response complex. Regardless of which anchorage, the translation is achieved at no cost of empirical uncertainty. There is no open texture implicit in the translation, no surplus of meaning which appeals either to the fictionalists or to the reductionists opting for the promise of a more explicit translation of their theoretical terms.

Our concern here should be to recognize that psychologies that insist upon using intervening variables as mediating between stimulus and response are readily adaptable to reductive translations ("psychologies" rather than "theories," for in this context Skinner appears to be correct in his insisting that stimulus–response psychology, which utilizes only intervening variables as its theoretical terms, can be lawful but it is not theoretical). (Cf. N12.2.)

## The Case for Reductionism

Now the radical behaviorist prescribes just those conditions for behavioral analysis which have led philosophers such as Bergmann (1954) to assert the triviality of the reductive thesis. In other words, the radical behaviorist prescribes a linguistic range which assures the possibility of neurophysiological reduction. Bergmann does not spell out the argument, but it is a simple matter to do so. Since neuronal activity is an all-or-none affair, it is amenable to analysis within the truth functional paradigm of logical atomism. Note that the inclusive physiological language includes statements about the physical world as well as those concerning the properties and activities of organic systems. The physiological language will, of course, contain statements of laws and of theoretical terms, but that need not concern us here. It will be sufficient to show that any statement admissible to radical behaviorism is translatable into a statement in the neurophysiological language.

Let us first consider response. We may define response as any anatomical displacement occurring over some specified increment of time. (It is doubtful that any treatment of response would lead to the rejection of this broad definition.) In turn we may then define organismic behavior as some complex of responses. We may then justify neurophysiological reduction by the following argument. Every anatomical displacement is mediated by the motor-efferent system of the organism. Thus each possible response and each behavior is describable as a molecular proposition whose truth value is a function of the truth conditions of each and every atomic proposition corresponding with each and every motor unit in the organismic system. Each response is specified at any given instant of time when we know which motor units are contracting at what instant of time. Since response is defined as occurring over some increment of time, then some particular response will be equivalent to a molecular proposition which sums over the neuronal instants for the increment of response time. In general, behaviors are not so anatomically refined as responses. But the crudeness of behavioral descriptions such as that of bar pressing, turning toward a goal, etc., offers no difficulty. For, in what is a one–many relation of responses to behavior, any given behavior can be represented by a class of many molecular propositions each expressing concatenations of responses.

Thus so long as behavior is the appropriate subject matter of psychology, all response states and behavioral descriptions are expressible in the language of neurophysiology. However, one notes that stimuli are also involved. But this is not problematic. Descriptions of the physical stimulus are coadmissible to our two languages (e.g., to psychology and physiology). We need only describe the stimulus as an afferent function of the organism. Since every possible stimulus is some kind of input and every input is coded in terms of afferent activity (ruling out extrasensory inputs), then every possible state of stimulation is expressible as a truth function concerning the response of each and every afferent cell. In principle, then, both stimulus and response are reducible to neurophysiological states.

Note that nothing has been said of mediating variables. All that has been asserted is that the observables, the data of behavior, of stimulus–response, and of the ecological setting, are expressible in the neurophysiological language. What can we now say of the mediating variables? If such are intervening variables, that is to say, if they are logical constructions, then there is no element of such variables which is not reducible to the inclusive language of neurophysiology. On the other hand, if the mediating variables are hypothetical constructs, then regardless of what may be their inferred neurophysiological status they cannot be strictly reduced to a set of statements in the neurophysiological language. That is, there is an unspecified set of predicates which schematize the open texture or the heuristic possibilities of the construct. An expectation may be that research will lead us to a closing up of the texture of the construct, but the state of neurophysiological knowledge being what it is for the present, all that can be offered is a promise. But the radical behaviorist's proscription of all hypothetical constructs ensures the possibility of complete neurophysiological reduction! There is just a touch of irony here. For in what passes as learning theory, Skinner and Tolman have been among the most persistent opponents of neurologizing psychology. Yet their equally persistent espousal of intervening variables over hypothetical constructs assures us that their own "theories" of psychology are reducible to neurophysiology.

The first point to be made then is that radical behaviorism (under which include Tolman as well as Skinner) has no argument against reducing psychology to neurophysiology other than that of a vocabulary preference. Indeed the insistence upon intervening variables, operational definitions, and the observational language guarantees the reduction of psychology against either logical or technological difficulties.

But now what of open-textured theories in which the theoretical terms are only partially interpreted? It has been argued effectively that theories which utilize only intervening variables, which insist upon the strict operational reduction of their theoretical terms, are heuristically sterile. Innovations, other than *ad hoc* ones to accommodate deviant events, are apt to be wanting. Moreover, the level of explanation provided by laws without theoretical synthesis is lower than that provided by a synthetic theory. That much is granted by behavioral theoreticians. But, on the other hand, it is the despair over reducing the inventions of theoretical psychology to neurophysiology which has led some people to embrace instrumentalism, or rather to take instrumentalism and turn it into the boast of fictionalism. Let us consider a sampling of opinion here.

Berenda (1957) has made a plea for peace among personologists on the ground that all personality theories enjoy equal veridical status providing, of course, all account for behavior. His plea was made to clinical psychologists, and the need for modifying aberrant behavior being as pressing as it is, perhaps the gambit of pragmatism is understandable.

Setting his argument on such background statements as one "must give up the preconception that physics is engaged in revealing the ultimate nature of some real objective world behind the world of phenomena," and "theories do not give us pictures or laws of an absolute reality but (as John Dewey emphasized) are merely the tools or instruments created by brilliant minds to deal more or less adequately with some selected aspects of observable phenomena," Berenda goes on to assert:

> A scientific system need not try to provide us with a *unique* theory of phenomena, nor need its abstract concepts be visualizable in terms of concrete or mechanistic imagery, nor need the theory be quantitative. More than one theory of personality or of therapy could be used by the clinician, and possibly the abstract terminology of various theories (all "verified") could be shown to be equivalent. Which of such theories the clinician uses may be a matter of personal preference, congenial to his own temperament. We can only seek to construct some self-consistent system of abstractions or concepts that, as simply as possible, logically organizes a given area of phenomena in the field of human behavior. More than one such system is possible (1957, p. 727).

This is a clear and unguarded statement of an instrumentalistic position. For reasons stated in Chapter 11, exception must be taken to the language of "temperament" and "personal preference."

But let us now turn to the area of learning theory, not so pressed, as it were, by the demands of behavioral crises. Consider the following quotations. Responding to the question of "What is learned?" Kendler writes:

> I am convinced that the selection of any theoretical model, be it physiological or phenomenological, or for that matter, physical, mechanical or statistical, is in the last analysis a decision having *no truth character*.

That is, in spite of the fact that the choice of a model may, and usually does, influence both experimentation and theorizing, *the choice itself* cannot be evaluated as being right or wrong. It is a matter purely of personal taste (1952, p. 276; Kendler's italics).

Then speaking of the temptation to reify constructs, he writes:

This reification in turn is due to the failure to distinguish sharply and consistently between the operational meaning of intervening variables and the intuitive properties ascribed to these concepts. If we conceive the intervening variables as being an economical device by which experimental variables are ordered in relation to behavior variables, then this confusion will not arise. The basic difference between such intervening variables as "habit" and "cognitive map" can be specified only in terms of their stated relationships to the observed variables, not in terms of the connotations they arouse (p. 276).

And writing specifically to the question of reductionism, Kessen and Kimble assert:

Our version of the purely psychological psychologist is the scientist who erects his theory and develops his concepts so the deduced theorems can be confirmed or disproved by observations of behavior. This we demand of him *and nothing more.* The symbols he uses for theoretical manipulation may have any flavor he likes—neurological, physical, sociological, aesthetic—but such a psychologist is not required to specify locus or 'real' nature in his theory so long as concepts mediate the prediction of behavior. . . . Nor is the pure psychologist inhibited in the range of constructs he may choose. He can invent concepts to the limit of his ingenuity and vocabulary. . . . We must repeat that the mere claim that a theory is neurological does precisely nothing to give it greater authority than a "purely psychological" approach (1952, p. 264).

Now it is interesting that both Kendler and Kessen and Kimble have adopted the metaphor of taste, as if the anterooms to the laboratory are to become scientific kitchens. There is substantial defense of Kendler's essay. As a spokesman for Hullian theory, he makes a plea for operational reduction of theoretical terms. Realization of this program would result in the conditional refinements of the S–R laws, but not in a theory in the philosophical sense. A putative theory including only completely interpreted terms and including no provisions for reduction to a more basic science could provide no explanation of the laws of behavior. Indeed, no particular explanatory purpose is served by translating behavioral laws into the language of neurophysiology unless the laws as translated are then deducible from a set of postulates in the neurophysiological language. Kendler is not clear as to what he wants of his theory. At times he appears to require that it have some higher-level explanatory power—in which case he would have to augment his theory with hypothetical constructs. And in that case, the critique on behalf of reductionism would be germane.

For Kessen and Kimble the case is more clear-cut. They are thinking of theories whose theoretical terms, sentences, and transformation rules permit the deduction of behavioral laws. Why then their emphasis upon the extreme pragmatic approach? It is true, as they intimate, that one does not validate the theoretical antecedents in a confirmatory experiment. However, one does not generally argue that since a true hypothesis implies all antecedents, then all antecedents are equally plausible. It is also true that the abstract nature of models in microphysics and the impalpable character of some of the theoretical terms lend themselves to conventionalistic considerations. In physics there are both logical and technological factors complicating the experimental accessibility of theoretical entities (cf. N12.3). But this is not the case in psychology where the theoretical terms designate such constructs as motivation, habit, memory. There are, as yet, no clearly stipulated logical strictures upon tying the hypotheticals directly to a dictionary. Thus when psychologists argue the example of physics as to the abstract character of the hypotheticals, they do so without specifying how it is that the example of psychology is like that of physics. Fictionalism, even at the despair of reifying hypothetical constructs, seems cavalier. That the psychologist should introduce his hypothetical constructs as convenient fictions when neither logic nor technology would preclude his formulating them within the scope of neurophysiology would be to renege on his empirical commitments.

There is, however, a more serious objection to an uncritical instrumentalism. It concerns questions of the psychology of invention. How do we, in fact, undertake the invention and renovation of our theoretical concepts? What are the crutches of insight into their open texture? One might answer, "Models." But let us be more specific.

In order to find answers to the questions of invention, we must labor the distinction between intervening variables and hypothetical constructs. Previously it was suggested that a strict interpretation of an intervening variable restricts its generalizability. For example, in Skinner's operant conditioning, the variable of motivation level enables us to select an appropriate law of extinction. But the law incorporating the variable is not itself generalizable except through an empirical search. The point can be made clearer, perhaps, if we consider a treatment of intelligence, $Q$. Let $Q$ be an intervening variable mediating between stimulus and response. Its status as an intervening variable is assured by our defining it operationally either by explicit definition or by reduction sentences. In either case, the measure of $Q$ is a matter of test performance, and a strict interpretation of $Q$ is such that if the test conditions and a given level of $Q$ then by implication we infer a given level of performance (i.e., $SxQx \supset Rx$ from $Sx \supset (Qx \equiv Rx)$). But, of course, not even the most radical of empiricists wants to be so restricted in the application of $Q$ to the test performance. Rather he seeks to generalize his predictions to a class of S–R laws contingent upon $Q$. That is, he seeks the class of generalizations $\{(x)(S_ixQx \supset R_jx)\}$, where $i$ and $j$ range over all appropriate values of $S$ and $R$, including, of course, those necessary for defining $Q$. But then how does he establish this expanded class of generalizations? Either his search is random or it is guided by the endowment of $Q$ with surplus meaning. With but rare exceptions, it proves to be the latter alternative. It is the surplus meaning of $Q$ which serves as the basis for explaining why $i$ and $j$ have the range they do. For example, if $Q$ meant *only* what it measures on test performance, then any generalizability would be adventitious. On the other hand, suppose that $Q$ designates a set of properties of the central nervous system. By postulating what these properties are, not only would we be able to deduce the test behavior but also the range of stimulus–response relations for which $Q$ serves as mediator. Moreover, our freedom to postulate indicates that that range itself is left open (cf. N12.6).

This much of the analysis is straightforward and finds expression in most critiques of operationism. But as this analysis stands, it is not critical of instrumentalism as such. Difficulties arise only when we consider the relative heuristic potentialities of different kinds of hypothetical terms. Presumably instrumentalism, with an unlimited field for speculation, lacks principles of inherent guidance which we expect from a reductive discipline. How, in fact, do we modify our theoretical terms? Surely our conceptual improvisations are not merely matters of aesthetics or taste. More than likely, heuristic potentiality is latent within the theoretical term itself. It is the language of the science itself which prompts the model and, in turn, the family of hypotheses which that model provides. The reason for this is not hard to find. In psychology, for example, the language of perceptual and behavioral description has from its inception been interlarded with the language of physiology. Witness the formative work of Helmholtz, Fechner, Müller, and Wundt. Thus the direction of explanation is all but mandatory. Psychology's linguistic involvements being what they are, neurophysiology then serves as the basis of its microstructure.[1]

Because of these linguistic predilections, the argument in behalf of aesthetic enterprise seems suspect. The built-in guidance is missing. One

---

[1] J. R. Kantor points this out effectively and disapprovingly in his *Problems of Physiological Psychology* (1947). In this work, he rejects tradition and calls for the introduction of a new vocabulary of interbehavioral descriptions. Whether such a vocabulary escapes the traditional S–R language is subject to doubt. However, his argument that our present language makes neurophysiological reduction unavoidable is convincing.

cannot enhance what he sentimentally calls the "elegance" of his theory by aesthetic innovations except that such contrivances are somehow simplifying and basic. So long as one considers models that are not purely mathematical (and that, it appears, is what Kessen and Kimble have in mind), the model ought to possess reasonable analogy. That is, a theory would suffer less from the strains of improvisation, and would be less susceptible to becoming a quaint paragraph in the history of the subject, if it should seek reduction in another theory that is more basic in the sense that the latter theory includes a formalization of terms and concepts appropriated by the former. Observe here psychology's appropriation of the language of stimulus–response itself, of 'inputs' and 'outputs,' of 'afferents' and 'efferents,' of 'sensory' and 'motor.' No stimulus–response psychology, no behaviorism does without these analogues. Some of the confusion over defining stimulus and behavior could be obviated by a reduction of these terms to the components that are neurophysiological and to those that entail statements concerning the social and physical environments. The plea for aesthetic license, on the other hand, is reminiscent of the episode with epicycles. The analogues within psychology are drive and inhibition. One can adduce almost any kind of behavior with these two mediating constructs, just as one can manufacture almost any celestial motion with some appropriate machinery of epicycles and eccentrics. Indeed, many S–R psychologies incorporate inhibition and facilitation into their theoretical structures. But these are also concepts in neurophysiology with substantial observational interpretation (cf. N12.4). Since for the psychologist there is a proven analogy involved here, and since he is not engaged arbitrarily in appropriating vocabulary, he is exposing himself to subsequent embarrassment if he does not take pains to bind his terms to their usage in the primary science.

## PHENOMENOLOGICAL OBJECTIONS

Thus far we have contended only with arguments that maintain that reductionism is unwarranted, or untested, or restrictive. Calling for procedural agreements, these contentions take a pragmatic turn, but they are not compelling. Turning to a different line of attack, what about arguments that would rule out reductionism on logical grounds? All such arguments can be classified as "phenomenological." Furthermore, they can be separated into those which involve psychological problems of meaning and those which are purely phenomenalistic. The former of these two classes of argument can be further divided according to their embracing either behavioral or mentalistic phenomenology. Thus, in outline, the argument considers:

(1)  Phenomenological objection:
     *a.*  for behavioral phenomenology
     *b.*  for intentionalistic phenomenology
(2)  Phenomenalism and the mental language

Each of these items will be considered in turn.

### Behavioral Phenomenology

Behavioral phenomenology (Koffka, MacLeod, Snygg and Combs, Krech and Crutchfield, Tolman, Brunswik, Lewin) is based on the premise that the individual's response to his environment reflects a unique cognitive structuring of his behavioral world. Accordingly, the world, which we can undertake to describe objectively, has for the individual a unique meaning determined by his values, attitudes, memory, as well as by the structural functions of his sensory-perceptual apparatus. Thus behavioral descriptions entail descriptions of the environment, but it is a personalized social environment. An accurate behavioral description must therefore report on the functional interaction between the person and his ecology. From this point of view, it has been argued that a reduction of psychology to physiology is impossible on the grounds that phenomenological descriptions require a nomenclature for which the language of neurophysiology offers no translation. It is not just the absence of vocabulary that offers a problem; presumably there is a logical barrier to our translating functional world-organism descriptions into the physicalistic language of physiology (Jessor, 1958).

Now this appears to be an incorrect presumption. Descriptions of the physical environment can, of course, always be included within the set of initial and boundary conditions which are stated for the neurophysiological description. There is no point of logic why statements describing the behavioral (psychological) environment cannot also be included in the set of all statements to be reduced to neurophysiology. The difference is one of reference, not of logic as Jessor, for example, has maintained. For neurophysiology, statements about the extradermal physical environment are found in the set of statements about initial conditions (e.g., statements of the specific physical energies capable of eliciting the sensory response), whereas the statements about the psychological environment either are inferred from behavior or are taken to be those of constructs implicitly reified as neurophysiological processes. We may conjecture with Krech (1950) that the only adequate explanation of behavioral phenomenology will be that which offers a neurophysiological reduction of the cognitive structure; to be explicit, that which explains the functional relationship between the proximal and distal stimuli. The fact that one set of environmental statements involves extradermal descriptions and the other set of environmental statements involves intradermal descriptions may constitute a difference of reference, but it does not constitute a point of logic against the possibility of reductionism (cf. N12.5).

What is needed, and what with but rare exceptions is missing from phenomenological accounts of behavior, is some set of schemata for describing that diversity of S–R relations which ascribe to a particular organism its apparent uniqueness. In its place, we often substitute highly personalized postulates of the cognitive agent that are suggestive of a ghost in the chain of hypotheticals. However, Mario Bunge (1963, 1964) has constructed a set of schemata for the concrete representation of S–R systems within a phenomenological rubric. Assuming that stimuli are either constant, sudden, or periodic, and assuming that the transmitting system containing such unspecified hypothetical subsystems as memory, heredity, etc., is either perfect, amplifying, or damping, he is able to derive dependent integral equations (Bergmann's "process functions") descriptive of unique response classes. Furthermore, complex organisms can be represented as multichannel transmitters, with the application of scattering matrix theory yielding the response equations. It is interesting that Bunge calls his approach "phenomenological." His black boxes give concrete descriptions of responses without specifying the structure of the box itself. And it is interesting also that he calls his own schematization "superficial," useful perhaps in behavioral science "where mechanisms are not sought either because of an anachronistic methodological conviction, or because the grapes are still sour" (1963, p. 357). Needless to say, his black-box analysis of phenomenology does not run into any logical difficulties in describing the data of input and output. All that is missing are the details of the black box, and those details neurophysiology could presumably provide.

## Intentionalistic Phenomenology

There is another side to phenomenology, the mentalistic one. It turns upon the distinction between intentional and nonintentional events. An intentional event is a mental act involving a mental content. What sets it off from nonintentional events or objects is the fact that it is ontologically imbedded in a context of active aboutness. A thought is a thought *about* something, a belief is a belief *about* something, a fear is a fear *of* something, etc. The logical status of such acts is unique. The meaning of an intentional event is neither conventional nor factual. It contains both the mental content of the intended experience and the thinking, believing, or hoping about it. Thus in order to seek, establish, or know the referents of intentional terms, we must enter the realm of privileged access. Needless to say, the contexts of aboutness do not surround nonintentional events. Physical objects, for example, are sufficient unto themselves.

This thesis is more poignantly stated for the case of an intentional act. The latter is a mental activity culminating in a decision which at the behavioral level is the occasion for some behavior selected from a set of behavioral options. In the language of intention, then, this activity underlies the motive for the particular decision. But the actual behavior reflecting that decision requires a different type of description, and as such, is reducible to physicalistic terms. On the other hand, the phrase 'wanting to go to the movie' designates an intentional act in which the wanting is *about* going to the movie but which itself is not an objectively describable act. The two languages are quite different. One is mentalistic and intentional, the other is physicalistic and nonintentional, with neither a logical nor an empirical bridge between the two. If one now wishes to maintain that psychology should concern itself with motivational explanation in the intentional language, and that this would distinguish it logically from the physical sciences, then, to be sure, the idea of reduction would be incompatible with our understanding of psychology and physiology (Peters, 1958; Winch, 1958).

This argument is not convincing. Doubtless, Brentano's distinction between intentional and nonintentional events is a trenchant one. It helps to elaborate mentalistic doctrine. But just as in other arguments for the uniqueness of mental events, acknowledgment of such events does not preclude the development of a science in which the difficulties of reduction across kinds are circumvented. Brodbeck (1963), for example, has argued that intentional meanings can, for reductive purposes, be treated as equivalent to psychological meanings. In behavioral phenomenology these latter meanings are given dispositional interpretations. An object $O$ means $P$ to $S$ if $S$ behaves in such and such a way. According to her, then, the intentional meanings of mental events are reflected in decisions, and such decisions are psychologically interesting only if they are accompanied by responses appropriate to the decision. Thus intentional meanings are also given dispositional interpretations. However, it is necessary to remember that behavioral dispositions are not causally connected with intentions. Causation belongs alone to the physical language. There is, therefore, a conventional commitment to be found in the decision to treat intentional meanings as dispositional. But it would seem that this is a reasonable commitment, at least as reasonable as postulates of parallelism. The clues to intentional meaning are such as wanting and believing. These are least refractory when we treat them as dispositions to act.

As in other mentalistic arguments this one testifying to the uniqueness of intentional events asks too much of reductive science. It condemns efforts at scientific explanation on grounds that we cannot provide a logical basis for the transmutation of the "mental" into the "physical," and vice versa. However, the issues suggested here are more easily pursued in terms of the raw data and contents of mental experience. How are we to handle the mind–body problem within the reductive framework?

## The "Mental" and the "Physical"

No attempt will be made here to review in any systematic way the many tactics for dealing with the mind–body problem. One might, for example, adopt the tactic of methodological behaviorism. Then without further ado he could dispense with the mental language and proceed to his behavioral analyses. There should, however, be some reasoned defense of his Procrustean bias. It is not sufficient to point out that introspectionism and phenomenology have led to sterile preoccupations with hypotheses about publicly unverifiable inner experiences, as the early behaviorists were inclined to do. There is always the question as to whether some significant thing is left out of the account of experience by our censoring it of its offensive mentalistic predicates.

The problem was attacked by the empiricists themselves at a more sophisticated level than that undertaken by the behaviorists. Questions such as "Is there a mental language?" "If so, to what does the mental language refer?" "What are the unique features of a mental language?" have to be answered. (It is significant that mentalistic language has never been successfully suppressed either in psychology or psychoneurology.) For a while the English analysts were preoccupied with problems of "other minds." For example, in a long series of papers (*Other Minds,* 1952), Wisdom argued that there is a feature about reports of private experience, the immediacy of one's own sense data, and self-analysis that is different from statements in the physical language. One cannot point to what he experiences as his own sense data in the way he can point to physical objects. When observer A speaks of his own experience, the language has a different semantic structure than it does when he calls observer B's attention to the data, say, of behavior. Nevertheless, one cannot deny significance to the mental language on that account.

This issue was followed by two others: the problem of a private language and questions concerning the significance of any so-called mental language. In his posthumous *Philosophical Investigations* (1953), Wittgenstein asks if any reliable means exists for learning a private language; i.e., a semantically rigorous language about the data of one's consciousness. Noting that learning a language involves "referring-to" in which the reference must be reliably held over a time span, Wittgenstein concludes that one cannot refer to, say, a particular pain in the way he can refer to the objects in a cupboard. There is no temporally sustained check on correct usage. In his *Concept of Mind* (1949), Ryle, on the other hand, questions even the intentions of the so-called mental language. Analyzing a number of traditional mentalistic statements (concerning will, emotion, etc.,) he concludes that they are really disposition-like statements whose correct analysis reveals them to designate behavioral events. Thus Ryle maintains that mental language only pretends to a special status, and that adequate translations in the behavioral language are substitutable for the mental statements.

Now none of these critical treatments of the mental (or private reference) language in any way represents an effective denial of mental events.[2] We need hardly try to say what a mental event is. It is simply given. What Tolman has called the raw feels of experience are indubitable. The important questions are: Can a significant mental language be developed? And can the predicates of such a language be incorporated into the language of psychology through reductive reference?

## Identical Reference Hypothesis

In the discussion that follows our attention shall be confined to the hypothesis of the identical reference of sets of mental and physical events. Such an hypothesis has an inherent plausibility to psychologists and physiologists. It has been held explicitly by Mach (1897), by W. Köhler (1947), Place (1956), Smart (1959, 1963), but especially by Feigl (1958). Simply stated, it asserts that there is a point of common reference for mental and the corresponding physical events and the description of such compresent events converges upon that point of reference. It shall be assumed, one, that no proscriptively monistic solution of the mind–body problem is acceptable, and two, that the contemporary languages of psychology and physiology give a certain relevance to questions of mind–body reduction which early behaviorists found it convenient to deny. We shall want first in the discussion to examine the question of what constitutes an adequate explanation of mental events; and second, through a consideration of Feigl's ideas we shall want to examine questions concerning the adequacy of a mental language. Remarks which follow express the belief that the reduction of the mental to the physical is contingent upon our treating mental terms as dispositional.

First, then, what constitutes an explanation of mental events? If one considers this question a meaningful one, he is likely to respond with some of the familiar statements on the mind–body problem. He may espouse theses of epiphenomenalism, or psychophysical parallelism, or even interactionism. But such theses are merely relational in character; apparently they do not present formal explanations of mental events, as such. On the other hand, he may recognize in the question a request for deducing

---

[2] In a review of *The Concept of Mind,* Hanson (1952) mentions that Ryle's analysis is one of what we mean by statements in the putative mental language and is not an examination of what, if anything, there is for a possible mental language to refer to. Quite a different matter from that of metaphysical behaviorism.

statements about mental events from some set of statements which are, in an explanatory hierarchy, judged to be more basic.[3] Thus he may proceed in one of two ways. One, he may seek to deduce statements about mental events from the application of relevant psychophysical and psychoneurological laws. But, even though this may meet the minimal formal requirements of explanation, it is not likely to prove very satisfactory. I, for example, unmollified by my Cartesian training, may be looking for someone to explain how it is that consciousness, the redness of the rose, pain, redolence, and the taste of honey, can be produced by the responses of congeries of nerve cells. It is the failure in just this "meaningful" quest that has prompted neurologists to proclaim ignorance as to why neural terminus or specific energies should spell the difference, say, between seeing red and feeling that peculiar piquance of a sneeze. In these circumstances I am not likely to be satisfied with the information that the striate cortex and the reticular formation have roles to play. Black boxes do not provide the kind of explanations I might seem to want.

Two, our respondent may offer us a theoretical model and a higher level of explanation. Consider now a model of a neuronal network which on the basis of its assumptions shows that output excitation is proportional to the log of its input excitation. From such a model we could deduce the Weber–Fechner law on the relation between sensation and physical stimuli. Or consider an ingenious mechanical analogue suggested by Howells (1954). He found that ordinary laboratory scales discriminate just detectable differences among weights according to the Weber ratio, $k = \Delta w / w;$ i.e., the constant ratio between the increment of detectably different weight and a base weight. Thus, he could construct a friction model for the perceptual discrimination of weights. In either case, the theory might enable us to deduce the Fechnerian laws of psychophysics. Does the successful deduction of psychophysical laws then provide us with an explanation of consciousness? Formally, yes, if by consciousness we mean a person's reporting his subjective judgments. But again this may not satisfy the querist. What he wants to know is how any set of physical events, biolectrical, biochemical, or mechanical, can produce the raw data of consciousness. Nothing less than the details of transmutation apparently will satisfy him.

In all of this our intransigent querist appears to be asking the impossible. No so-called explanation satisfying the logical requirement of explanation is going to satisfy him. He is mixing his categories. Ryle was not the first to call our attention to category mistakes and ghosts in the machine (cf. N12.7). In an article published in 1933 and prophetically

[3] One cannot rule out the attempt to explain mental events in purely mentalistic terms, but the prospect is unlikely; for if one retains his allegiance to the idiom of phenomenalism, he is not likely to regard the raw data of awareness as requiring explanation.

titled "The Ghostly Tradition and Descriptive Categories of Psychology," H. B. English attributed difficulties in the mind–body problem to the fact that psychological events and physiological events are abstractions of a fundamental process occurring in an anatomical locus. Like Mach before him, he argued that one cannot explain how two constructions of the same process interact or how they reduce one to the other. The request for such explanations is apparently a meaningless one.

Here, it would appear wise to join the skeptics. To ask of an explanation of mental phenomena that it be other than a formal one (e.g., a deduction from a psychophysical law) is to commit a category mistake. It is almost, but not quite, like asking the phenomenalist to explain what is given and indubitable by means of logical constructions (physiological terms) which are themselves based upon those givens. Still, there is a sense in which dual descriptions of the same process may satisfy our demands for an explanation. Mental concepts are ambiguous. Therefore, if we adopt an hypothesis of the identity of reference, and if we achieve a systematic development of the concepts of neurophysiology then we can, in a way, achieve an understanding of our mental concepts.

Feigl has doubtless been the most persistent advocate of this identity hypothesis (1950, 1958, 1961). According to him, qualitatively different sources of evidence converge upon the same fact. Thus he contends "that the designata of the mentalistic language are identical with the descripta of the behavioristic language and both are identical with the designata of the neurophysiological language." He goes on to say that "the factual reference of some of the terms in each of these different languages (or vocabularies) may be the same, while only their evidential bases differ" (1950, p. 623).

The factual reference is the world event. The evidential bases for this event are expressed in our introspective reports, and in our behavioral and neurophysiological descriptions. The three descriptions, being compresent to the event, are not deducible from one another but share a common variance with the event through manifest intercorrelations. Therefore, it is the establishment and confirmation of such correlations that accomplishes the reduction of psychology to physiology. There are two assumptions to be met here. One, what Feigl calls the systemic identities must be empirically ascertained; and two, the mental language must be sufficiently pure and sufficiently precise so that it brings to the systemic analysis the unique contents which we attribute to mental events. Otherwise, we would not be in contact with the problem of mind and consciousness. Meeting the first assumption is contingent upon meeting the second; so it is to the latter that we should direct our attention.

Now reductionism is possible within this schema if for every relevant event $E$ there are subsets of descriptions in the mental, the behavioral, and the neurophysiological languages that can be intercorrelated. In this context the language of behavior and that of neurophysiology have not been problematic in the way that the language of pure phenomena has been. It is not a question of whether there are raw-feels (the methodological behaviorist does not dispute this) but rather a question of whether what can be asserted in the mental language can be said less equivocally (or inferred) within the behavioral and neurophysiological languages. I say, "less equivocally" because there is question as to the meaning of purely phenomenal statements.

This is not the place to review the arduous explorations of "other minds" and "private languages." However, it is essential to seek some commitment as to what kinds of statements are to be included in the mental language. What, if any, is the contribution of raw-feel statements to the compresent descriptions of the referent–event? The answer to this question is usually, "None!"—that is to say, manageable statements in the mental language are regarded as being translatable into the more semantically precise statements in the behavioral language.

To explore what may, or may not be, an obvious point, let us look at a simple experiment in the study of tolerance of pain. The experimental subject in the presence of a group of his peers is subjected to electric shock. From an initial subliminal intensity, the voltage is increased until the shock becomes "unbearable." According to Feigl, the complete description of this event-complex would involve statements from the mental, behavioral, and neurophysiological languages, and, of course, from the physical language. Again, only the statements in the mental language will be problematic.

Provisionally, we may grant raw-feels without our necessarily acknowledging that we can talk meaningfully about them. In order to describe them let us say that from the initial absence of feeling there emerges the phenomenal sequence, "a pleasant tickling, a prickling, an unpleasant vibrato, a jolting, an unbearable convulsive-like seizure of the member." The fact that we have mixed phenomenal and behavioral descriptions is unfortunate. But what other linguistic recourse is there? Perhaps we should invent a terminology. We could use words such as "tickle," "prickle," "stickle," etc., but this is not the problem. The question is, after we have invented the terminology, can it have any significance other than that deriving from its contaminative translation into the behavioral language?

Initially it should be made clear that by a mental language which suppresses behavioral reports, reference is not being made to the language of psychophysics. Statements of psychophysical relations are reports of discriminations and judgments made in the presence of physical stimuli. They can be given a strict operational interpretation, in which case they would make no reference to the raw-feels with which we are presently concerned (Bergmann and Spence, 1944; Stevens, 1939). But what of "prickles" and "stickles"? Are they comparable in any way? For example, are they matters of degree, or are they pointillist variates in the multifarious set of raw-feels? It is tempting to say that pains, as such, are not matters of degree. A convulsive jolt is just as unique and *interesting* in its raw-feel way as a tickle. What makes one pleasant and the other unbearable are the behavioral and physiological co-respondencies. If we could succeed at pure introspection with an accompanying suppression of the behavioral and physiological concomitants, we might achieve that mythical demeanor of the purified existentialist, oblivious to everything but the sublime kaleidoscope of qualia. But, of course, we cannot suppress the behavioral and physiological variables, otherwise we would have different qualia, and *a fortiori* different events.

The difficulty arises from our trying to establish qualitative relations among our raw-feels. It is not a case of "this pain next to that pain" but of "Is this pain greater (more painful) than that pain?" What is the meaning of, "This pain is unbearable, the other is not"? And what of the statement, "$S_1$ can stand more pain than $S_2$ can"? It is not difficult for us to translate these statements into the behavioral and neurophysiological languages. Pain is "unbearable" when specified verbal and withdrawal responses occur, and when the significant complex of nociceptive reflexes occurs. On the other hand, it is much more difficult for us to translate these statements into a purely mental language. And I suspect that it is not just a case of our being tongue-tied because of the behavioral contamination of our language. It may be that the person does not know and cannot identify the purely phenomenal state of unbearable pain. He can writhe *with* pain, withdraw *from* painful stimuli, and even cry out for the anaesthetic *because of* pain, but the putative fact of that unbearable pain is implied by the behavior and reflexive response of the organism, not by the raw-feel as such.

This is familiar behavioristic terrain. However, it is important to emphasize that dispositional analyses of mental terms do not obviate the semantic pretensions such terms have for relating to possibly genuine nondispositional mental contents. In other words, there may be something more to the translation of a mental term than the set of its dispositional predicates. But what that something more is, is not a subject matter for science; indeed, it cannot be described at all.

Feigl's analysis fails us then in the way contemporary psychology fails us; it cannot say what cannot be said. Disappointment arises over the fact that the promise of a "true" psychophysics or "true" psychophysiology reduces to a behavioral-physics or a behavioral-physiology wherein the behavior is that which occurs in the context of a person's attending to his own awareness. Such disappointment is inevitable, but then one cannot very well complain that a science has limitations on the grounds it fails to do what cannot be done. Just as psychology earlier at Titchener's behest was unable to avoid the stimulus-error, so now at the mentalists' behest it cannot avoid the response-error. Sperry (1952), for example, has made a very good case for treating perception as a perceptual-motor complex, in which the two components are as inseparable as stimulus and stimulus object. (See also Langfeld, 1931; MacKay, 1956; Broadbent, 1958.) Psychologically, the argument is all but clinched by the facts of motor feedback. Perception involves sensory input, a scansion function, motor response, and an afferent feedback. Not only is a perception of some object complex, but it contains information not found in the primary or the secondary qualities of the object.

In way of summary, let us look in on a serious poker game about to reach a climactic moment. Our hero has overcommitted himself, and the stakes are high. It is too costly for him to stay and too costly for him to get out. Moreover, he holds three cards of a royal flush. He discards, draws two cards, and peeks! Behold, he has filled out his royal flush! Now! He must contain his joy. His winning is assured. He must draw out the bets. He cannot smile; he cannot frown; he cannot blink, blanch, or blush. Far better now if he were to show no signs at all. Pulse and blood pressure? He must control these, too. His opponents are sensitive detectors. They watch the pupils of his eyes, the color of his cheeks, the artery along the temple. Safest then to suspend all propensities. What then of our player's feelings? There are those who would contend that our player would have no feeling at all, no exuberance, no joy, none of the exaltation which comes to the poker table on wings of the sure-thing principle. But then, feelings cannot be ruled out, not on logical grounds at least. How, then, would he, and how would we, describe those feelings?

Suppose at this moment of our subject's expressionless transport, we were to pluck him from the table and take him into the laboratory. Since expression is now denied him, we can as well dispense with all his motor apparatus, all his efferents, save, perhaps, those of speech. We must allow him to speak to us of his feelings. Nor need we deprive him of all his sensory inputs, for we need to interrogate him. "What is your joy like now?" we ask. "Has there been any change? Is it just like the joy you feel when you dance for it, clap your hands and swoon?" Suppose our subject, X, answers, "There has been no change." Then, of course, we understand him, for we can substitute within our psychophysical descriptions the dispositional predicates appropriate to that joy. Moreover, we understand his feeling by analogy, for 'joy now' designates one of those feelings which is accompanied by the class of behaviors we label 'joyful.' But suppose he says, "No, joy is not the same; there is some ineluctable remainder that is pure feeling." Can he help make the meaning of this residual feeling clear to us? I think not; we have been deprived of the source of analogy. Will some kind of cerebrograph help? Again, the answer is negative. There is no suitable analogy, for the brain recording which we get from him is like no other picture with which we are familiar. The efferent system is dormant. We can test our own use of feeling-words by matching behavioral descriptions and cerebrograms; therein the source of Feigl's psychophysical correlations. However, no such testing can occur where behavioral descriptions are denied and the cerebrograms necessarily are disparate.

As a matter of concern, then, we may ask: what contribution does the mental language make to the elucidation of the compresent event? If it carries nothing but the burden of behavioral paraphrase, why then insist upon the mentalistic dimensions of the event? Now, it is obvious that identity theorists such as Feigl want to acknowledge the unique content of consciousness itself. Mental content is not merely embedded in the disposition to act. Dispositions are not at all the mental content itself. There is a psychic residue, as it were, that participates in the event. Physiology, behavior, and mental content are inseparable. Together their components comprise the event.

What troubles the reflective behaviorist here is the absence of any specification as to what the contribution of the mental language might be. What can a nondispositional language add to the description of a person's experiencing and responding. It is not that our psychologist would deny consciousness. Even radical behaviorists have given up quoting William James (1904) out of context. Nor is it just that the semantics of mental statements are problematic in the way methodological behaviorists have found them to be (Lashley, 1923). Rather it is also the case that statements about mental contents fail to add useful information to the description of the compresent event. What is significant are the facts of sensory discrimination as such, not the unique qualities of mental contents. We could replace some present set of primary qualities with an entirely different set, and it would, I surmise, not make a jot of difference. That is to say, it is inconsequential, if not accidental, that we see the chromaticized world through the conscious media of blue, green, red, and yellow rather than, say, sweet, sour, bitter, and salty. This could presume to be a radical thesis. What it suggests is that speculations about cerebroscopes and the contents of other minds are quite beside the point. One person's red could be another person's salt and there would be no detectable perceptual difference. Both persons would see the world as they do see it—I am tempted to say, as the world is. For what is important are (1) the structure and sensitivity of the receptor and (2) the central processing of input into invariant perceptual patterns. So long as there are structures, i.e., cell aggregates to process the input, they would be sufficient to effect a perceptual structure (cf. N12.8). The particular code of conscious qualia may be intrinsically interesting, but it is secondary to the fact that some code should exist (cf. N12.9).

# NOTES

## NOTE 12.1

To take a sampling of opinion over the years: J. B. Watson writes, "We need in psychology all the available facts neurologists can give us, but we can very well leave out of consideration those ingenious puzzle pictures that compose the action of the central nervous system with a series of pipes and valves, sponges, electric switchboards, and the like" (1929, p. 19). He then goes on to assert that "physiologist qua physiologist" operates at the molecular level and is not concerned with behavior. It is for the psychologist to define his own problems, techniques, and language at the molar level.

Concerning human learning McGeoch writes:

> It seems futile to define learning in terms of hypothetical factors such as neural charges, tensions, or the logical properties of total fields. These factors may conceivably aid interpretation, but they do not at present define learning. A definition must keep as clear as possible of theory and as close as possible to the facts, and to the conditions and operations by which they are obtained. A definition which can be given no specific meaning in terms of performable operations is not a satisfactory experimentalist's definition. An operational definition is implied in what critical experimenters do and write. It is implied here in saying that by learning is meant the phenomena of the learning curves and of the learning experiments in general (1936, p. 110).

Doubtless Spence speaks for a large group of contemporary psychologists, when, in comparing his own formulations to those of Hull, he writes:

> A second matter in which Hull and I differed, although the difference was one of degree, was the extent to which, after defining a hypothetical intervening variable in purely quantitative terms as a mathematical function of some experimental variable, further neurophysiological specifications should be made. Hull was particularly prone to add further specifications suggesting the possible locus, structure, or functioning in the nervous system of these constructs. His justification always was that such conjectures provided experimental hints to physiologically oriented psychologists interested in making such coordinations of our knowledge.
>
> Now my interest in the integration of knowledge from different fields would, I think, make me one of the last to deny the potential value of such attempts. However, I would insist that the added physiological concepts introduced by the psychologist should be significant ones, by which I mean they should be concepts that appear in the network of physiological laws. Unless such is the case, one does little more than add a physiological name. Moreover, there is no little danger that such physiological notions will mislead or at least distract from the significant aspects of the mathematical portion of the theory. Indeed there is probably no better instance of this than that provided by Hull's concept of habit strength ($H$). After defining habit strength as a mathematical function of the present stimulus and antecedent environmental conditions, Hull then identifies it further with the notion of a receptor–effector connection in the nervous system (Hull, 1943).

Just what the *beneficial* "surplus meanings" accrued to the mathe-matical concept of habit as a result of this added physiological connota-tion has never been made clear to me. That it did provide for additional meanings is amply shown by the extent to which critics used them to characterize the whole story as based on an outmoded conception of the nervous system, or, worse still, to deride it as a mechanistic, telephone-switchboard theory of behavior. . . . Let me hasten to add here that I am not advocating that behavior scientists eschew all physiological concepts. That all behavior has physiological correlates seems as certain to me as anything I know. Hence, I should not hesitate to employ fruitful physio-logical concepts whenever I thought they might help. At the present state of development they are not, in my opinion, very useful (1956, p. 55).


## NOTE 12.2

This point bears upon the heuristic potentialities of theoretical behaviorism as against those of the radical behaviorisms of Skinner and Tolman. Consider Skinner's treatment of motivation and reinforcement which, in theoretical systems such as that of Hull and Deutsch (1960), are mediating variables. For Skinner, reinforcement is a response-anchored variable reducible to changes in the rate of response with respect to time. Motivation is a stimulus-anchored variable reducible to manipulations and changes of the subject's environment. Thus hunger motivation is completely describable in terms of deprivation schedule. What there is to be said about the subject's hunger is exhausted by an explicit statement of its food intake, eating habits, weight status, etc. Consider first, the role of motivation as a mediating variable. A strict S–R psychology would be one for which there is a set of S–R laws such that for the appropriate stimulus conditions one could predict the subsequent response. One explanation of this behavior would then be in the familiar form of *modus ponens*, which from $Sx$ and $(x)(Sx \supset Rx)$ one concludes $Rx$. Sup-pose, however, we are now to include mediating variables that are anchored at the stimulus end. What we are achieving by this refinement is a more limit-ing specification of the stimulus variables. Although Skinner would like to emphasize the mediating variables and utilize objects in the physical world merely as stimulus cues, the whole physical stimulus–deprivation schedule complex composes the stimulus description. We do not have a theoretical de-scription of behavior here; we have only a lawful one. Skinner is quite justified in his antitheoretical bias. Indeed he has no need for theory. Any manipula-tion of motivational factors results simply in his prescribing different laws for different stimulus conditions. There is, for example, no recognized need for explaining *why* the probability of a response increases with increased motiva-tion. (Such an explanation might derive, for example, from a deduction of the events at the neurophysiological level.) That it does occur is a sufficient ex-planation of the events. One can, I think, evaluate Skinner's treatment of pri-mary and secondary reinforcement in the same way. All explanation is of the type wherein the behavior is deduced as an application of a law. The range of behaviors explainable is, of course, confined to the range of empirically derived laws.

**NOTE 12.3**

As is well known, the study of microphenomena in quantum physics has evoked puzzles and predicaments not encountered in classical deterministic mechanics. One cannot study the microstructure of the atom without using a probe to elicit information concerning such structure. With particles as small as the electron, any detector, even one as small as the photon, has sufficient energy to affect the state of the electron. If we pinpoint the electron with high energy, short-wavelength "illumination," we give it such a kick that we alter its momentum in a significant way. On the other hand, if we mitigate this effect by reducing the energy and increasing the wavelength of the illuminative probe, we can conceivably get an accurate measure of the momentum of the electron but because of the minuteness of the electron relative to the wavelength of the light source, the illuminative agent is diffracted so as to leave the "picture" record of the position of the electron uncertain. Such is the predicament of the uncertainty principle as visualized in the Gedanken experiment.

The derivation of the uncertainty relationships can be demonstrated by reference to Figure 12.1.

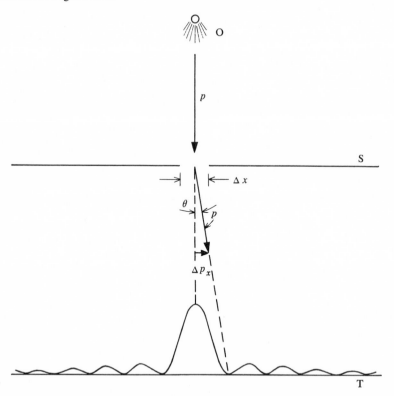

**Figure 12.1**    Illustration of the uncertainty of momentum for a particle which has passed through a single slit (from R. T. Weidner and R. L. Sells. *Elementary Modern Physics.* Boston, Allyn & Bacon, 1960).

In this set-up, T is a scintillation screen, S is a screen with slit comparable in dimensions to those of a diffraction grating, and O is the source of illumination. Now visualize a source at O, emitting electrons with momentum, $p$. The curve at T is the probability density of the electron shower arriving at T and indicates the nature of the diffraction pattern. The momentum, $p$, is a function of the wavelength of the electron, $p = h/\lambda$, (with $\lambda$, the wavelength, and $h$, Planck's constant). The uncertainty of the momentum in the $x$ direction is then expressed by

$$\Delta p_x \geq p \sin \theta. \tag{1}$$

According to the diffraction pattern, $\theta$, the angle giving the first nodal point on the probability density, is

$$\sin \theta = \pm \frac{\lambda}{\Delta x}. \tag{2}$$

Substituting for $p$ and $\sin \theta$ in (1), we then get the uncertainty relation

$$\Delta p_x \Delta x \geq h, \tag{3}$$

namely, the product of the uncertainties of the momentum and position components is at least as great as Planck's constant. Note that we can decrease $\Delta p_x$, the uncertainty in momentum, by increasing $\Delta x$, since $\sin \theta$ in (2) is an inverse function of $\Delta x$. But we can only know $p$ with certainty by taking $\Delta x$ infinitely large. Hence, the familiar difficulty; should we determine the momentum of a particle with certainty, we would be completely uncertain as to the position (since it could be anywhere within $\Delta x$). And, *mutatis mutandis*, similarly for position and momentum (cf. Weidner and Sells, 1960, pp. 150–157).

Now the interesting thing here is that the premises upon which the argument is based permit no exceptions. Granting such premises, and many others that constitute the foundations of classical quantum mechanics, von Neumann (1932) has offered a proof that the system within its formal framework provides no exception to the uncertainty principle.

What is the significance of this for the psychologist? Arguing from the effect of the probe and the principle of complementarity, Bohr himself sees an analogy for psychology (Bohr, 1950). One cannot probe the brain without altering, or even destroying, the functioning tissue. Perhaps so, but it does not follow that we need probe every cell of the nervous system in order to get the prerequisite information. Recent microtechniques in electrode plants are exquisitely refined and are sufficient for us to gain information concerning the functioning of single cells. The neurologist can infer from his limited observations to complex functions. There are no logical barriers to his explicit inference. But this *is* the case in the quantum effects. It is not only technically impossible, it is logically inconsistent to make statements about a determinate system of microstructures with completely specified positions and momenta. This is so at least so far as quantum mechanics now formally stands.

This last sentence must be added because that formal system of quantum mechanics is being challenged. The issues are too complex to go into here, but doubtless they present one of the most significant problems in all of contemporary philosophy of science. The attack upon the indeterministic foundations of quantum physics is led by the physicists Bohm and Vigier and by the philosopher Feyerabend. Discussion of the issues by these three people can be found in Körner (editor), *Observation and Interpretation in the Philosophy of Physics*. The so-called Copenhagen Interpretation of the implicit character of indeterminancy is held in effect by von Neumann, by Bohr, Heisenberg, Born, and Dirac, and by the philosopher Hanson (1958, 1963). Papers and discussion by Feyerabend and Hanson can also be found in Feigl and Maxwell (editors), *Current Issues in the Philosophy of Science*.

## NOTE 12.4

In this context it is worth pausing over the concept of inhibition. Inhibition is explicitly defined within Hull's S–R psychology. And it finds implicit expression in the psychoanalytic concepts of repression and the superego. In neither case does it reduce to neurophysiology. But note what Kessen and Kimble (1952) have to say in this context. Responding to an argument of Krech in behalf of a field theory of brain function, they express the popular pragmatic riposte ". . . the concept of the superego has as sound possibilities for the integration of behavior as the concept of brain fields or dynamic systems." I think not, and for the reason that the concept of inhibition as inherited from neurophysiology carries with it greater generalizability than is found in its unique contextual interpretation in psychodynamics. This comment applies both to Hull and to psychoanalysis but let us confine our attention to the concept of the superego.

According to psychoanalytic theory, the superego is a theoretical construct from which we deduce that certain classes of response are inhibited; that is, the superego stands as a kind of mediator or filter through which certain responses are processed while others are blocked. There is no effort here to interpret the hypothetical construct in neurophysiological terms, rather the properties intended by the construct are translated into the control system incorporating the introjected rules and values of the person's world. From this and other theoretical assumptions we can deduce that an anxiety state will implement certain inhibitory blockages of what otherwise might be an habitual or a rational response. The story is familiar, and indeed, very satisfying to people who wish to dramatize those personalized samplings of behavior we call maladjustment. But it is not difficult to find a more generalizable treatment of inhibition within the precincts of neurophysiology. Consider, for example, a Hebblike model of brain function in which responses are mediated by means of cell assemblies. In its nonactivated state, the system may exhibit sporadic firing of its components in which the units of synaptic inhibition are summative and the response random. Any input into the system effects a synchrony of neuronal response within the assembly and the assembly in turn instruments the response. Thus the assembly is a process element in the S–R system. Now synchronization of the neuronal responses results in a summative increase in inhibitory potential, in other words, in an increase of the threshold for subsequent response. Allowing for both synaptic and neuronal recovery, we can deduce normal function under periods of sustained input. But what if the input reaches a chronic state, such as it does in states of anxiety. Then it is not difficult to see that the inhibitory resistance reaches a critical level wherein the so-called normal processing of response is itself inhibited. From this neurophysiological model not only can we deduce the dramatic disruptions of behavior that we find in some psychopathology but we can also predict behaviors not initially predictable by psychoanalytic theory. For example, any sustained input, say attention inordinately enforced, will result in the inhibition of response. This is a hypothesis that has been confirmed in experiments on mental fatigue (Karsten, 1928), periodic blocking in sustained routine tasks (Bills, 1931; Broadbent, 1958), and can account for various types of panic inhibitions (Hebb, 1959). Hebb's treatment of a more elaborate theory enables him to deduce behavioral disorganization under conditions of sensory deprivation.

The point of this note should be obvious. It is a kind of testimonial on behalf of neurophysiological reduction. One could, of course, opt for more; say, for a logic of discovery. But that does not seem to be forthcoming (Hanson, 1958). As it is, the language of psychology is rooted in that of physiology. It offers us terms of stimulus–response, sensation–perception, emotion, and intelligence, all of which carry a mixed pedigree in psychology and physiology. One can, of course, appropriate any language he chooses for his theoretical terms. Both repression and mental fatigue might be suggested by the facts and hypotheses of neural inhibition, and the neurophysiological hypotheses serve only as a manner of speaking and nothing else. But without a genuine reductive support, an integration of the two concepts under a common construct might very well be missing. That is to say, if a formal reduction were not applied, the two theoretical terms would remain isolated without the significant reductive bridge. The substance of the foregoing argument is that reductionism is preferable to instrumentalism. It could as well be phrased in terms of the existential status of theoretical concepts but this is not required. Psychology carries with it systemic bias, and because of this it will find its most fruitful source of hypotheses within the reducing science.

## NOTE 12.5

It is not clear to me why a preference for phenomenological descriptions should be conceived as the basis for a logical objection to reductionism. Although, to be sure, the Gestalt psychologists distinguished clearly between physical and behavioral languages, they did not regard the languages as being logically incompatible. Witness the importance given to Wertheimer's doctrine of isomorphism. Even Koffka (1935, p. 61), perhaps the least physiologically minded member of the Gestalt triumvirate, could accept physiology as the locale for mediation between the behavioral and geographic environments.

Now if one is to establish the logical incompatibility of two languages, he must show that biconditional translations are impossible by virtue of the limitations implicit in the domains of the two languages, e.g., as between the language of one science and that of the putative reducer. However, one must be careful to distinguish between limitations due to the incipient state of a language and those that are matters of logic. For example, suppose we were to have a science of consciousness and were to note the emergence of a new, unique property of experience, such as seeing infrared. According to the emergentist's case against hypothetico-deductive explanation (Broad, 1925), one cannot deduce the new experience from what he knows of physiology; hence, the new experience is uniquely nonreducible. But only at that time! Nothing precludes enrichment of the language of physiology sufficient to give reductive cover to the emergent phenomena.

However, the purpose of this aside is to take note of a more serious possibility of logical incompatibility as between scientific languages. If we visualize the neurophysiological mechanism as functionally describable in the language of the computer system, e.g., a digital system, then certain theorems relating to completeness and computability within computer systems turn up difficulties for reducing certain problem-solving behaviors of human computers to the language of mechanical computers. The argument turns on one of the most significant of the theorems proved by Gödel. In paraphrase: assuming some formal (computer) system $L$ to be consistent, then that system is necessarily incomplete; more specifically, there is some proposition in $L$ such that it can be shown to be true (by our resorting to a metasystem) but which cannot be proved in $L$. It is the parenthetical phrase "by our resorting to a meta-system" that is particularly significant. Gödel, a human computer of the highest excellence, has the option of an ingenious recourse which is denied the extant computer, bound as the latter presumably is by its formal language, $L$. That is, Gödel was able to prove the incompleteness of his primary computer logic by going outside that logic. And this the computer cannot do.

It is this getting outside one's logical system in order to assess the system itself that would appear to be denied any explicitly constructible computer system. This, at least, is the argument of Nagel and Newman (1958) who were among the first to communicate the significance of Gödel's work to the nonspecialist. In this (what Smart (1963) calls "the argument from Gödel") they have been supported by Kemeny (1959), J. R. Lucas (1961), and Bronowski (1966), among others. But there has been a strong counterargu-ment stemming from important work on the character of computability within conceivable computer systems (see, for example, Putnam, 1960; Scriven, 1960; George, 1961; Smart, 1963). It *is* conceivable that we can build a com-puter that will prove Gödel's theorem of incompleteness. Thus the machine can be said to simulate Gödel. But not quite. What Gödel revealed is that *any* system $L$ (however we may complicate it by adding axioms and supplementary logics) will be incomplete. That is to say, we may establish a new system $L'$, including $L$ *and* the metasystem, sufficient to prove the incompleteness of $L$. And we may build a computer to implement that $L'$ (thus simulating Gödel). However, that extant computer will not function to determine its own incom-pleteness. This counterargument poses something of a paradox. Although on a complete set of instructions (as given in Gödel's proof) we can build a com-puter to compute a given result (i.e., Gödel's theorem), we cannot at the same time build a computer that can apply that significant result to itself. To be more concise, although we can build a computer to simulate *any* given act of ratiocination of which the human computer is capable, we cannot build a computer that will simulate *all* acts of which the human computer is capable.

The argument can be poignantly stated as the problem of simulation. Are there any behaviors of organisms which are nonsimulable? If indeed there are nonsimulable behaviors and if we assume that, functionally, neurophysiology is a computer language, then it should follow that some behavior, some aspect of psychology, is not reducible to neurophysiology.

It should be helpful here to introduce the idea of a Turing machine as a vehicle for talking about machines, their capabilities and limitations. (See Turing, 1937; George, 1961; Kemeny, 1954; Putnam, 1960; Hawkins, 1964; and for technical accounts, Kleene, 1952 and Davis, 1958.) A Turing machine is a conceptual (rather than hardware) machine with the following components. There is a tape, possibly of infinite length, which is divided into squares. There is also a scanner that can inspect some given square at some instant of time in the machine's operation. In addition the machine possesses a writing element such that it can either write a symbol from a finite alphabet on the tape, or it can erase any symbol in the square that is being scanned. Furthermore, the machine contains a driving element that can effect one of the following options: it can move the tape one square to the right of the square presently scanned, it can move the tape one square to the left, or it can leave the tape as is, any option being implemented upon its receiving instructions from the machine program. This, in effect, instructs the machine as to which square the machine should scan. Finally, there is a machine program which is instrumented by a finite set of internal configurations (logical states) such that the scanned symbol *and* the internal configuration form a couplet which dictates the next operation of the machine. A Turing machine is then fully described by a machine table for which every couplet of scanned symbol and internal configuration, there results an instruction as to tape scansion and printing. A machine table thus determines a set of "instantaneous descriptions" (a description of the tape and some internal configuration at a given time) such that from its initial state the machine continues to run through a sequence of instantaneous states with one of two eventualities: either the machine reaches a stopping state, in which case there is no continuing instruction, or the machine runs forever. Should the machine, on the former eventuality, reach a terminal instantaneous description, then a solution to the computer problem is reached, and it can be read from the finite record of the tape. Should no such terminal state be conceivable, then the problem which the machine undertakes to compute is unsolvable.

Proofs within the theory of Turing machines belong to the technology of metalogic. However, the following results are to be noted. (1) A problem of computation is computable (provable) if one can prove that the machine eventually will reach a terminal state; otherwise it is noncomputable. (2) Any algorithm of computation, any systematic proof, can be programmed into some Turing machine. (3) Any given Turing machine can be incorporated into a universal Turing machine; thus any problem that can be computed by some machine can be computed by a universal Turing machine. And (4), in support of Gödel, it can be shown that for some simple Turing machine there is a halting problem (i.e., the problem as to whether a terminal state will be reached) which itself is unsolvable.

Von Neumann (1951) has pointed out the significance of the universal Turing machine. Such a machine, incorporating a finite set of instructions, can compute any problem for which the computational procedure can be made explicit. Another related and (to the issue of reductionism) significant proposition is that due to McCulloch and Pitts (1943). They establish that any logical function, any computation that can be described in a finite set of words, can be realized by a system of neural networks functioning on digital lines.

The substance of the arguments of Turing, von Neumann, and McCulloch and Pitts is that if one can describe completely the processes and linkages of a problem-solving behavior, then it is possible, at least in principle, to build a machine that can simulate that behavior. Let us now see how the argument from Gödel fares.

We now formulate the argument along somewhat different lines which are more amenable to the issue of simulation as such. Is there any behavior of which the human computer is capable which cannot be simulated? The consensus seems to be: "Not if we can fully describe the actual computation." Visualize now a game, in which the human computer $H$ is to compute against a putative simulator $S$. The purpose of the game is for $S$ to simulate $H$ and for $H$ to outwit $S$ such that on the basis of telephonic response cues, $H$ is to provide an intelligent observer a cue which clearly distinguishes his response from that of $S$. (This is a version of Turing's game of imitation; Turing, 1950.)

Should $S$ properly simulate $H$, then presumably the observer would not be able to distinguish the two. We may as a matter of definition say that $S$ simulates $H$ if and only if on equivalent sets of inputs we obtain equivalent sets of output from $H$ and $S$. By equivalent sets we mean that for a set of statements $\{E_H\}$ describing the input for $H$ there is a biconditional translation into the set of statements $\{E_S\}$ describing the input for $S$. Thus

$$\{E_H\} \equiv \{E_S\}$$

symbolizes the input equivalence. Similarly for the response or output sets,

$$\{R_H\} \equiv \{R_S\}.$$

Then we define equivalence such that $H$ and $S$ are equivalent if and only if

$$\left\langle \{E_H\}, H \right\rangle \rightarrow \{R_H\}$$

$$\left\langle \{E_S\}, S \right\rangle \rightarrow \{R_S\}$$

and $\qquad \{E_H\} \equiv \{E_S\} \qquad$ and $\qquad \{R_H\} \equiv \{R_S\}.$

Now, generally, $S$ simulates $H$ if two requirements are met: (1) *substitution,* and (2) *inclusion.* Substitution implies that wherever $<\{E_H\}, H>$ occurs as an occasion to predict some $\{R_H\}$, we can *substitute* some $<\{E_S\}, S> \rightarrow \{R_S\}$ and infer $\{R_H\}$ from $\{R_S\}$. Inclusion stipulates that there is no set $\{R_H\}$ such that we cannot establish $\{R_S\}$ by translation (substitution), nor subsequently is there any $\{R_H\}$ without an equivalent $\{R_S\}$.

We now propose the game of the *mischievous self*. The behavior to be described belongs to the class of all behaviors and hence is a behavior to be simulated. Our human computer $H$ assumes there is some machine $S$ such that $S$ simulates $H$; it is then the purpose of $H$ to outwit $S$. Now $H$ easily outwits $S$ by the strategy of being mischievous. $H$ builds a machine, $M_S$, which is a replica of $S$. He assumes $M_S$ will indicate to him, $H$, what he ought to do. But then he, $H$, will do something else—thus assuring invalidation of any computation by $M_S$.

One's initial response is that $H$ is taking an unfair advantage of $S$ and $M_S$ through introducing a time lag. And, to be sure, $H$ is. But note that *H's behavior is among the class of all behaviors to be simulated.*

One alternative for us, now, is to impose our requirements of equivalence upon the argument. When $H$ insists on a time lag before committing himself to the mischievous response he is, in fact, supplementing $\{E_H\}$ with $\{E_{\Delta H}\}$; that is, he is acting at time $t_0 + \Delta t$ rather than at $t_0$. Thus we have

$$\left\langle \{E_H, E_{\Delta H}\}, H \right\rangle \to R_H$$

$$\left\langle \{E_{M_S}\}, M_S \right\rangle \to R_{M_S}.$$

Since the inputs are now not equivalent, then $\{R_H\}$ and $\{R_{M_S}\}$ understandably are not equivalent. A better simulation triple would then be $<\{E_{M_S}, E_{\Delta M_S}\}, M_S>$ where $\{E_{\Delta M_S}\} \equiv \{E_{\Delta H}\}$. However reasonable this tactic appears to be, it will not work. $H$ now takes his cue from the new simulator and then again imposing the time lag, he does something nonequivalent to what $M_S$ computes. The game now becomes regressive with the following schema:

$$\begin{array}{lcl}
H_0, R_{H_0} & \longleftrightarrow & M_0, R_{M_0} \\
H_1, R_{H_1} & \longleftrightarrow & M_1, R_{M_1} \\
\vdots & & \vdots \\
H_{n-1}, R_{H_{n-1}} & \longleftrightarrow & M_{n-1}, R_{M_{n-1}} \\
H_n, R_{H_n} & &
\end{array}$$

Here $H_i, R_{H_i}$ is a couplet indicating that the human computer $H$ at stage $i$ makes the response $R_{H_i}$. Each horizontal double arrow establishes the putative simulation of $H$ by $M_S$. The diagonal arrow indicates the actual play, as it were, i.e., the programmed state and response of the mischievous $H$.

Now you may not like the rules of the game. You may indeed demand that $H$ and $M_S$ respond simultaneously. (It is not clear this would save simulation against the mischief, since $H$ may, prior to any time $t_j$, ascertain what $M_S$ would compute at $t_j$.) However, the rules are explicit. Any $H$ can follow them; and for any $M_S$, the response of $M_S$ can be controverted no matter how faithful a simulator we attempt to construct. Accepting this paradigm for the game, we cannot build the simulator which $H$ cannot controvert. The result of this game is that $H$'s behavior cannot be simulated by any simulator, $M_S$, *which we seek to enter in H's game.*

(Suppose we were to enter $H$'s nervous system as $M_S$; $H$ would still controvert it. Although we may grant "no psychosis without neurosis," $H$ can, because of the time lag, do something different at $t_0 + \Delta t$ than he does at $t_0$.)

There is, however, a better alternative. We can attempt to simulate the above game such that now we have $S$ interacting with $M_S$, where $S$ is the simulator of $H$ and $M_S$ is the putative simulator of $S$. Moreover since $S$ and $M_S$ are both machines, we can make one the replica of the other. Now this is a rather more interesting situation. And again the game develops:

$$
\begin{array}{ll}
S_0, R_{S_0} \longleftrightarrow & M_{S_0}, R_{M_{S_0}} \\
S_1, R_{S_1} \longleftrightarrow & M_{S_1}, R_{M_{S_1}} \\
\quad \vdots & \quad \vdots \\
S_{n-1}, R_{S_{n-1}} \longleftrightarrow & M_{S_{n-1}}, R_{M_{S_{n-1}}} \\
S_n, R_n &
\end{array}
$$

Here $S$ simulates $H$'s behavior in the previous game. $S$ plays the mischievous game against its replica, and the play of $S$ cannot be simulated by any $M_S$ that *we enter in this game.*

Thus it would appear there is something of a paradox in simulation. The rules of this mischievous game stipulate those conditions which render it impossible that any *extant* simulator can simulate the behavior of the mischievous self. On the other hand, it is possible to conceive a mechanical simulator, $S$, that can simulate the behavior of the mischievous self.

In my opinion this "paradox" is not incompatible with the results of the theory of Turing machines. Although it is possible to imagine a game in which $H$ can outwit the machine which would simulate him, once we detail the game, then we can simulate *that* game. We can indeed simulate the game of the mischievous self, the game of outwitting, of controverting, the best-conceived simulator. It would appear that there is no logical barrier to the kind of simulation which is implicit in reductionism.

There is, however, a melancholy afterthought. Suppose we put a boundary on our computer resources; for example, on the tape resource of a Turing machine or on the program resource of any computer. Then we may visualize the ultimate machine $S_z$ and its putative simulator $M_{S_z}$. The play of the game for $S_z$ then regresses to

$$
\begin{array}{ll}
S_{z-1}, R_{S_{z-1}} \longleftrightarrow & M_{S_{z-1}}, R_{M_{S_{z-1}}} \\
S_z, R_{S_z} \longleftrightarrow & M_{S_z}, R_{M_{S_z}} \\
S_z, R_{S_z} \longleftrightarrow & M_{S_z}, R_{M_{S_z}} \\
\quad \vdots & \quad \vdots
\end{array}
$$

and $M_{S_z}$ now simulates $S_z$. In a word, $S_z$ cannot contradict itself. But for $H$ the situation is conceivably different:

$$H_{z-1}, R_{H_{z-1}} \longleftrightarrow M_{z-1}, R_{M_{z-1}}$$

$$H_z, R_{H_z} \longleftrightarrow M_z, R_{M_z}$$

$$H_{z+1}, R_{H_{z+1}} \longleftrightarrow M_z, R_{M_z}$$

$$H_{z+1}, R_{H_{z+1}} \qquad \vdots \qquad \vdots$$

And there is *no* point at which $H$ cannot controvert its putative simulator.

I am not at all sure that the argument for the boundedness of computer resources is an allowable one. However, for the moment, I find it enticing to consider the possibility that in the long run it is the machine that turns up moral. Ultimately the machine must do what it ought to do. To man alone, we assign the possibility of caprice.

**NOTE 12.6**

The argument in behalf of reductive guidance is akin to what Rozeboom (1961) has called "ontological induction." He gives a rigorous formulation to some of the issues adumbrated in the text. However, the gist of his argument can be given here in less formal exposition.

Just as according to the Russellian theory of types we have particulars, classes of particulars, classes of classes of particulars, and so on, so in empirical science we have laws, laws about laws, laws about laws about laws, and so on. Beginning with laws as empirically ascertained, we proceed to theories (which, in a sense, are laws about laws), to reductions (which are, in a sense, laws about theories), etc. The problem for ontological induction is that of proceeding from lower-order hypotheses to higher-order ones.

The question of ontological induction is one of how we proceed, say, from simple laws of behavior to the synthesis of a set of laws all belonging to a family of laws according to the synthetic principle. A strict allegiance to the empiricistic principle would mean that the synthesis of a law of laws would be haphazard. Indeed, if the radical empiricist is as serious about eschewing theory as he claims, then he cannot in conscience direct his experimentation via the synthetic principle implicit in ontological induction. For example, after having obtained a law of extinction, he could not systematically explore the higher-order relation of extinction and schedule of reinforcement, except that experience or a hunch leads him to anticipate some relevant interdependence. But, whether it is the comparative naïveté of experience or a neurophysiological model is logically irrelevant. The fact is, a premise operates to guide the search for new relationships.

Now the search for information is seldom random. Even if accidental experience is the source of hypothesis, one finds himself leaning toward one source rather than toward another. It is this epistemic leaning, so to speak, which becomes the instrument of ontological induction. Consider the case of the relation of extinction to schedule of reinforcement. A simple law of extinction may describe the response function from the point of terminal reinforcement. Why then, from the statement of this law as formulated upon a schedule of regular reinforcement, should we proceed to explore the effects of partial reinforcement upon extinction? The accidents of discovery, serendipity, may play a role, but more than likely our hypotheses about the processes of reinforcement afford us a basis for generalizing to related phenomena. A theory of partial reinforcement which systematically integrates extinction over the entire range of reinforcement schedules (e.g., Deutsch, 1960) may come along after the facts are in. This is quite often the case. But the collation of related laws itself reflects a principle of implicit systematic bias which only a theory can render explicit.

Following a hierarchy of types of laws, Rozeboom starts with some sample dispositional concepts and proceeds to structural variables (the parameters of a dependent-independent variable function) and then to still higher-order variables of structural covariation. Each level represents an ontological jump. Each tells us something of the "structure" of events. It is, however, the higher level of integration that is ontologically more interesting. Here we seek the element of communality among laws and their structural variables. By virtue of the covariation of one set of structural variables (say, that of reinforcement) with another set (say, that of extinction) we seek the principle of communality. Thus by a triangulation of the communal variables, we arrive at hypotheses signifying a higher-order structure.


## NOTE 12.7

Ryle attacks the concept of mind analytically as mistaken doctrine. The doctrine follows the mentalist tradition of placing a "ghost in the machine." The mistake, a category mistake, deals with confusing statements belonging to different logical types. Ryle first notes that the "official doctrine" incorporates "Descartes' myth," namely, a dualism of mental and physical. One is "inner"; the other "outer." Even as metaphors they allude to distinctly different classes of things. Each has its own laws, its own existence status.

> But the actual transactions between the episodes of the private history and those of the public history remain mysterious, since by definition they can belong to neither series. They could not be reported among the happenings described in a person's autobiography of his inner life, but nor could they be reported among those described in someone else's biography of that person's overt career. They can be inspected neither by introspection nor by laboratory experiment. They are the theoretical shuttle-cocks which are forever being bandied from the physiologist back to the psychologist and from the psychologist back to the physiologist (1949, pp. 12–13).

And moreover, the conundrum is carried forth to infest the contemporary problems in psychology and philosophy.

Secondly, Ryle points to what he labels 'category mistakes.' Category mistakes are made by people who treat concepts belonging to different logical types as if they belong to the same logical type. He demonstrates this mistake by a number of forest-for-the-trees type confusions. For example, a person can see the buildings, offices, and members of a university but he cannot see the university as such; or the foreigner can see the members of a cricket team, and even (what is more amazing) understand the rules of the game, but he cannot see the element of team spirit. It is the old problem of wanting to assign to a logical construction the same kind of existential status that one assigns to objects upon which the logical construction is based—like saying there is the response of subject A, the response of subject B, the response of subject C, *and* the average response of the three.

Ryle then maintains that variants of the myth of Descartes, and the materialist and idealist counterstrategies for dissipating the myth by monistic reductions, are all examples of category mistakes. All assume that the predicates assigned to mind and those assigned to matter are of the same logical type. Since, Ryle maintains, the two classes of predicates belong to different types, then the doctrine of interaction and reduction are pseudo-doctrines occasioned by linguistic confusion. One can attempt a language of sense data, he can also (as Russell does) speak of logical constructions which are operational extensions of those sense data; but he cannot speak of causal relations, or of any relations but logical ones, between the two without indulging in a category mistake.

## NOTE 12.8

One might ask, "What does it mean to say that there is a psychic residuum that is not reducible to a dispositional language, that there are raw-feels, redness now, pain, sour, and putridness that have subsistent qualities not in any way translatable into dispositional terms?" This is an interesting question. For although we think we understand it when it is asked (i.e., we think we understand the intention of the question), we fail utterly to conceive what might constitute its adequate answer. We have all played games with fictive cerebroscopes ("Your red may be like my green"), but even these fantasies fail to convince. For, if we were to switch brains around, we would not alter the extent of public agreement; and if we were to use the peephole of the cerebroscope just to have a peek and compare, we could not circumvent the logical difficulty of the peeking observer's looking at S's sensorium through the mediation of his own nervous system and sensorium, whereas S himself has but direct access to that same sensorium.

These are interesting puzzles, and it is surprising more thought has not been given to their difficulties and possible outcomes. Psychologists, for example, can provide us with some relevant though perhaps less dramatic analogy from the laboratory of perception. Stratton (1897), I. Kohler (1955, 1962), and J. G. Taylor (1962), among others, have carried out experiments on inverting, reversing, and otherwise distorting visual fields. What is remarkable is how adaptable the perceptual system is. After a period of disorientation, and readjustment, the perceptual calculator reconverts the data back into a stable, familiar perceptual surround. It is as if we were to affix some kind of

color converters to the eyes such that every hue is converted to its complementary hue. After some initial discomfort over seeing the grass as red and
the sky as yellow, we would in time adjust to seeing normal turf and the usual
pleasant skies. Whether we would ever see the red as green is a question
difficult to answer. But no doubt a person with such converters would learn
anew to recognize "green" grass and his "blue" skies; and in time he would
learn to adjust his vocabulary such that his red is green, his yellow is blue.

Aha, but now we may remove the converters. Our subject is confused
again. Green, our actual green, does not look green to him. It is at this moment
that it is of interest to speculate about how the world is in the eyes of another.
But only in passing, it would appear. From the experiments on inverted vision
we would expect that the readjustment to normal vision comes about rapidly
and the subject again sees the world as others see it.

Inverting devices need not be peripheral to the nervous system. Suppose
some demon inserted such devices at the portals of the sensorium. Then indeed
my red might be like your green. But only a test would show this, and because learning to see is a protracted process and because we all adjust to a
public language of perception no such test is possible. What I wish to maintain
here is that conceivably we could have inverted vision as between two observers but we would never know it. Moreover, if there were inverted vision—
or even inverted modalities—it could not make any practicable difference in
our perception. For that reason I would suggest that the debates over other-
minds, private access, and the impossibility of private language are, with the
exception of placing logical restrictions upon some types of discourse, largely
gratuitous.

The issue can be carried even further. Suppose you learn that in an
autopsy on Mr. S, his brain had been hooked up in an unusual manner. The
optic tracts were found to terminate in an area normally reserved for taste,
whereas the gustatory tracts ended in the occipital center. By the usual anatomical inference Mr. S should have tasted with his eyes and seen with his
tongue. Let us see. Was the autopsy performed because, while living, Mr. S
showed aberrant perception, or simply because his body had been bequeathed
to medical school for the routine cadaverous dissections? I commit myself by
suggesting it was the latter case; which is to say, that it came purely as a surprise that the brain of S had been wired incorrectly. Since this case is a hypothetical one, let us bring Mr. S back to life and submit him to the ritual of
a Gedanken experiment. First, the following facts. Mr. S has normal 20–20
vision. He is not color blind, has excellent depth perception, and in every way
has shown normal vision. In addition he appears to have normal gustation.
He can discriminate salty, sweet, sour, and bitter, is reported to have a fine
palate for vintage wine, and suffers the usual palatary deficit when afflicted
with a head cold. Second, let us assume Mr. S actually "tastes" his way down
the labyrinthian paths he takes and actually "visualizes" his way through the
arts of savory. I say assume, because it would really make no difference how
Mr. S, or any of us, is hooked up providing sufficient cerebral cells are allotted
to the task of processing sensory input. The crux of this argument is: not only
is it not important to question whether one man's red is like another man's
green, but it is equally unimportant that one man's vision might be like another

man's taste. That this should be the case is suggested by the following experiment.

Mr. S is placed in a reclining chair at the side of our study table. He is given a pencil and requested to draw what appears to him when his left eye is open and his right eye closed. Mr. S is a skilled draftsman and what emerges is a sketch very much like that which Ernst Mach drew for his book *Analysis of Sensations*. It shows the frame of the eye, the side of the nose, the vest, trousers, shoes, and off into the detail of the room. And he does this, mind you, with the sense modality—our sense modality—of taste. Mr. S sees as well as you or I. But where our rods give rise to achromatic figure and ground, his give rise to a figure-ground complex of, let us say, salty tastes. Where our cones give rise to the spectrum of the rainbow, his give rise to a similar rainbow—or should I say the same rainbow—in a sensory complex of bitter, sweet, salty and sour. He can thread a needle and he can walk a tight-rope, such is the fineness of his discrimination. Every movement before his eyes plays upon his retina, the shifting patterning of figure upon ground, the constancies, the chromatic complexes: all of these are processed to become his visual images in terms of sweet and sour, bitter and salty. And no one, I submit, could ever tell the difference.

This fantasy has several implications that appear to be compatible with some contemporary speculations upon brain functioning. One, it may make little difference where the sensory tract ends within the cerebral cortex, providing there are sufficient cells to process information and providing the scansion functions of the diencephalon are not disrupted. Two, a significant factor in perceptual discrimination is the peripheral apparatus with its specific responsivities to different types of stimuli. And three, learning is indispensible for establishing the "public" foundations of the experienced world.

The first point appears to be supported by the recent statistically flavored speculations in neurophysiology and neuroanatomy (e.g., Pitts and McCulloch, 1947; Hebb, 1949; Milner, 1957; Rosenblatt, 1958; Sholl, 1956; Uttley, 1954; Hayek, 1952). Neither the doctrines of specific energies nor specific connections seem particularly significant for the neural processes in perceptual organization. Rather we have equipotential systems with random interconnections and initial randomness of function. With experience and its sensory impress, facilitative and inhibitory growth processes occur to create the anatomical units of perception (e.g., of equivalence classes, pattern templates, recognition classes, etc.). Thus plasticity of structure and function is stressed rather than specificity and inflexibility. There is, of course, some specificity of structure. The receptors have their unique structures and the sensory modalities have their specific projection areas; but returning to the world of fiction, if a switching of sensory tracks were to be achieved in the prenatal organization, and were we somehow to compensate for differences in cell availability in the respective projection areas, then it might very well be that a tasting viewer would see the world as any other viewer does. Behaviorally at least we might very well be unable to detect the difference.

The second point stresses the importance of the peripheral apparatus. It is the structure of the eye, its resolving power and complexity of the input matrix which is significant, as much if not more than the particular aspect of the sensory quality, as such. The eye of the tasting viewer performs like the eye of any other viewer. It responds differentially to chromatic and achromatic stimulation. It has the same distribution of rods and cones, the same thresholds, the same convergence toward common optic pathways. The only difference is that the input data are decoded in dimensions of taste rather than what we are prone to preempt for vision. Mr. S as tasting-viewer (and viewing-taster), just as any other viewer, experiences the world that the peripheral sensory apparatus (with sufficient central processing units) makes possible. It is the structure of experience which is important not the content. Alternatively, for Mr. S it makes little difference what qualities accompany taste. So long as food substances in solution differentially evoke the gustatory nerves, that and differential processing at the cortical level implement the gustatory aspects of taste. It is purely accidental, and immaterial, that lemonade tastes sour and a little bit sweet rather than, say, yellow and a little bit blue.

Finally, the third implication stresses the significance of learning. The work of Senden (1932) and Riesen (1947) has shown that vision comes slowly to the newly seeing subject. The puzzle Molyneux proposed to Locke has been answered. Not only can the subject who gains his sight after congenital blindness not distinguish the cube from the sphere, he even has to learn to see what it is he is supposed to judge. The infant does not see a world of objects and detail when it opens its eyes. The world emerges only very slowly, partly by association with other sensory inputs, partly by the complex of integrations behind constancy phenomena, but not the least of all, by the public context in which he learns what is to be an object and how it shall be symbolized.

What has been given here is just the outline of highly speculative aberrations. One would indeed have to know more about these tasting-viewers. But two hypotheses emerge from these speculations which I find it hard to resist. One, it would be impossible to detect such aberrant perceivers as tasting-viewers (a riposte to all that has been fantasied?). And two, since cerebroscopic inspection appears technically impossible and since experiments on inverted vision indicate that discrepancies in perceived context are not lasting and occur primarily at the moment of inversion, those protracted deliberations on private access and the content of other minds seem to be singularly pointless. Insofar as individuals make compatible perceptual judgments, they see the same world. By "sameness" I mean there is no evidence that perceptual processing results in the reification of discrepant worlds under standard conditions of observation. However, there is stronger suggestion of "sameness" than that we obtain simply from perceptual agreements. It is tied to the facts of peripheral stimulation. What is important is the fact that the eye, as the complex receptor it is, is responsive to differences in wavelength and intensity of light. The relevant facts are the number, distribution, and response characteristics of the rods and cones. The facts of neuronal summation and convergence of the tracts may also be significant. But what is not particularly significant are those unique qualities of experience which emerge in the perceptual processing. Should any one of us through intervention of a perceptual demon suddenly become a tasting-viewer, we should no doubt suffer some temporary disorganization, but in a relatively short time the perceived world would come back into focus and "look" pretty much as it always had. The facts of sameness of the world thus derive from the attributes and dimensions of the physical stimuli and from the response characteristics of the particular receptors. The world would be different to different observers only if it presented different faces to each of them. This might be the case if light varied in wavelength for observer $S_j$ but not for observer $S_k$. It might also be the case if $S_j$ had the normal complement of rods and cones but $S_k$ had only rods. In the latter case $S_k$ would only be a partial detector. But even then, the two would agree as to the facts mediated by the rods. And they would not disagree as to color. It would only be that $S_k$ is blind to some characteristics of the stimulus to which $S_j$ responds.

Consider now a nation of tasting-viewers, viewing-tasters, smelling-touchers, touching-smellers. (Our case would be simplified if there were as many primary tactual qualities as there are olfactory qualities but this condition is not necessary.) They could be from another planet, if you wish, but it would obviate some irrelevant matters if we were to keep them here on earth, looking in all respects like the rest of us except for certain anatomical details of their brains. We may ask: will such a group have a different picture of the world? Will they make a different construction of the world based on a different set of properties? Only a moment's reflection prompts a "no" answer to both questions. How would they visualize the world? In three dimensions, of course. Doubtless, they would embrace coordinate geometry and differential equations; and doubtless they would consider "vision" the most important of the descriptive senses. Newtonian mechanics would be as real as it would be to "normal" viewers. Mass, force, acceleration, momentum, all of these would derive from their conceptualizing the data of sensory input. That an object "smells" solid and "smells" heavy, as it were, is quite immaterial to the fact that the object is perceived as being solid and as being heavy. Thus perception results from the fact that the sensory apparatus is responsive to certain properties of the physical world. So long as the individual can discriminate among his sensory cues to the extent he does as a normal perceiver, then it makes no difference as to how (as to content or qualia) those sensory data are processed. The chiaroscuro in nuance of saltiness will be the "same" as it is in black and white. That is to say, there will be no conceivable difference in the complex descriptions as given by tasting-viewer and normal viewer. The physical descriptions will be invariant. They will be invariant so long as we maintain sensory differentiation and discriminability. Thus, it is essential that we have qualities and degrees among the sensory components of perceptual content. But how these qualities differ, or what they are, or that they should be as they are, are not questions of concern for science. Nor, I suspect, should they be of concern to philosophy.

In resumé then, the hypothesis of the irrelevance of the unique contents of perception leads me to the following conclusions: (1) assertions concerning the private, unique, and irreducible character of conscious events are meaningless in that neither they nor their contradictions (e.g., your red may not be my red) have conceivable consequences either for science or for ordinary language. (2) The distinction between primary and secondary qualities of experience is largely irrelevant. Quality differentiation among stimuli is the

perceptual counterpart of sensory detectability of the physical stimulus variables. That such stimulus variables are detected is important; the uniqueness of
the perceptual quality in sensory decoding is not. (3) The nondispositional
properties of perception, the residue of consciousness, is but an artifact of
discrimination. Things that are physically different are judged to be different,
just as the figure is different from the ground. What is significant is that
a differentiation is made, and not that it should be blue against green rather
than sweet against salty. A color or a taste is not something one describes.
And a tasting-viewer points as well as a "normal" viewer. That is all he needs
to do and really all he understands about the uniqueness of what he sees!


## NOTE 12.9

Bibliographic addendum: Skinner's antitheoretical, antireductive bias finds expression in his Presidential address to the Midwestern Psychological Association (1950). For a critical assessment of this point of view, see Feigl
(1951), and Scriven (1956).

Bergmann (1953, 1954, 1957) also expresses objections to reductionism on methodological grounds. He distinguishes between process laws
with significant historical variables (as in psychology) and process laws without
them (as in physics). Although the form of the equations expressing the
laws may differ (integro-differential as against differential equations), this
need not constitute an objection to reductionism as such.

Woodger (1929), who has made one of the classic statements on the
formal requirements of reductionism, objects to reductionism in biology on
grounds that mechanical principles cannot adequately explain hierarchies of
levels of organization in living organisms. He objects to reductionism in psychology on the grounds that the person language of psychology with its
cognitive, affective, personalistic overtones cannot be translated into the language of some higher-order disciplines.

# PART III

# Probability and Inference

# CHAPTER 13

# Meaning of Probability

WHATEVER THE DIVERSITY of tactics in scientific empiricism, its various strategems are those of finding support for the assertions of science. Logic, to be sure, plays a preeminent role. It constitutes the rational structure of our knowledge. Yet knowledge is distinguished also for its empirical content. The assertions of science express propositions concerning the nature of events and concerning processes underlying those events, as such processes are spelled out in the hypotheses of our theories. Such assertions are meaningful only if there exists some means, some strategy, for evaluating their truth status—hence the importance of the verification principle of meaning. A statement is meaningful only if there exists some means for evaluating the truth of the proposition that it asserts. In Part I of this work, we examined in some detail the difficulties that this principle faces. In the chapters that follow, we shall be concerned primarily with those statements of science which have the status of general propositions. We shall be concerned with establishing support for those statements of science whose extension covers a greater range of events than the sample of data constituting the empirical component of the support.

For the present then, let us consider that our skepticism concerning simple empirical statements (data reports, existential statements, reports of pointer readings, and so on) is resolved. It is to be assumed that we have at our disposal reliable data reports. The question initially to be considered is, How do we utilize and process finite sets of data in support of general propositions? How do we find support for general propositions which for all practical purposes are to be prefaced by a universal quantifier? This is the problem of induction.

Typically, our defense of induction is based upon statistical methodology. We make assumptions concerning the nature of our data, we adopt a statistical model based on some theory of probability, and then, on the premises of the data and the model, we propose some decision procedure for evaluating the plausibility of an experimental hypothesis. Such, in fact, is the schema of the Neyman–Pearson strategy of inductive behavior which has until recently come to dominate statistical decision in nearly all of the sciences.

One has a data model of his universe in which certain parameters of the distribution are specified as the hypothesis of the model. Different classes of events over the entire range of events are judged for this model to be more or less "probable." If one assigns to a critical region the classes of events judged arbitrarily to be improbable, then he has the basis for the following decision rule: should an actual data sample be such as to warrant inclusion in the class of improbable events (i.e., the critical region) then the hypothesis that stipulates that inclusion is to be rejected; on the other hand, should the sample be such as to warrant inclusion in the complementary class of probable events, then the hypothesis is to be accepted. In a word, the support for our decision rests in our stipulating what is probable or improbable on the basis of some hypothesis. The overall strategy is hypothetico-deductive in character. We postulate certain parameters for our universe. If the parameters hold, then we can derive an expected distribution of data points. Should our actual experimental data depart, in the probability sense, from our expectations then we reject the hypothesis upon which our experiment was made. Such a decision is straightforward. It coincides with the deductive strategy of disconfirmation (Popper, 1959) and with all the semantic advantages appertaining thereto. But what if the data are probable on the hypothesis? The experiment then supports the hypothesis. There are, however, other hypotheses which these same data may be found to support. The truth status of the hypothesis is left open. Even though our decision procedure commands us to accept the hypothesis, we do so only with misgivings that other hypotheses may also be plausible. At most the hypothesis we test and find acceptable may itself be judged plausible; yet plausibility may not be the substance we empiricists should like to take as the foundations of positive knowledge.

There are many problems now for our statistical empiricist. The actual decision possibility is more complicated than has been so far indicated, even for the Neyman–Pearson theory of inductive behavior. Decisions involve costs and prior investments in hypotheses. Particularly troublesome is our pursuit of support for a specific hypothesis which is *a priori* derived within some scientific theory. The hypothesis is specific, yet our decision is couched in the imprecise language of tenability or plausibility where the status of the hypothesis itself is left in considerable doubt. We should like to be treated to strong confirmation. The discovery of Neptune made possible by Leverrier's and Adams' calculations is part of the confirmational lore of science, as was the verification that light rays are subject to the effects of gravitational fields. We should like to think that as our own scientific theories become more formally sophisticated, we should be able to derive incisive hypotheses reducing to explicit sets of data expectations.

Unfortunately, the strategy of the null hypothesis and the significance test focuses much too conveniently on rejection rules, disconfirmation, and long-run results rather than on unqualified support of specific hypotheses. It is for this reason that increasing attention is being given to the revival of Bayesian inference procedures wherein degree of belief or degree of support can be assigned to specific hypotheses on the basis of the evidence. The support here is the support of confirmation rather than that of disconfirmation.

Now it should be noted that the language of probability is common to all of our inductive procedures. We arrive at our inductive decisions with the uncertainty as specified in our probabilistic language. However, the meaning of this language differs according to whether we adopt the Neyman–Pearson or the Bayesian strategies. In the one case, probability is assigned to decisions about hypotheses, whereas in the latter case, we are attributing probability to some truth status of an hypothesis itself. Probability theory offers us the foundations of inductive inference, but the kind of inference we engage in is reflected in the meaning we wish to assign to the concept of probability itself.

We shall restrict ourselves then to a discussion of induction as it is manifest in probability theory and statistical decision procedures (cf. N13.1). First, it will be necessary briefly to review the formal character of probability theory. Such theory constitutes the syntactical system of inference. And then we shall turn our attention to the definitions and alternative conceptions of probability. The problems here allude to the semantic aspects of the language of probability. These matters are discussed in the present chapter. Following this, we shall wish to review alternative strategies for decision. One might suspect that this fills out the threefold aspect of semeiotic, and indeed it does. But it should be noted that defense of statistical decision procedures rests upon more than pragmatics. The problem of meaning is at stake. One cannot divorce the kind of statistical procedures he proposes as the basis of inductive support from the fundamental problems in the meaning of probability. These matters will occupy us in Chapter 14. Finally, in Chapter 15, we shall address ourselves briefly to one of the most recalcitrant problems in the history of philosophy, that of justifying induction.

## FORMALIZATION OF PROBABILITY THEORY

The formalization of probability theory must be regarded as essential to the assessment of its consistency and completeness. As such, a successful axiomatization only assures us that, as a formal system of logical infer-ence, the theory does not lead to contradictory assertions in the abstract language and it does provide means for answers to all questions that can, within the formal language, be considered as meaningful statements about its permissible entities (i.e., random variables). We shall not be concerned with giving a complete account of formal probability systems. It is, how-ever, to be noted that the paradoxes of probability (e.g., Bertrand's para-dox, the Petersburg paradox) are problematic only in the semantic interpretation of probability theory, and not in the syntax as such. Para-doxes of alternative estimates of probability and of infinite cost wagers (cf. N13.2) do not arise for the formalist. He assumes that a probability is a real number within specified limits and subject to explicit manipula-tions. And paradoxes, should they be found, must be attributed to the interpretation of the abstract system rather than to some inherent incon-sistency of the formal system itself.

As in other axiomatic systems the formalization of probability theory begins with a set of definitions relating the entities of the abstract system to entities in the theory (cf. N13.3). Then, on the basis of a set of axioms and the rules which the abstract system provides (i.e., set theory), one proceeds to derive the fundamental theorems of the theory (cf. N13.4). The entities of the formal system, the variables and the parameters, are now purely abstract, and efforts to tie such entities to semantic concepts (interpreted entities) in the theory may, and often do, lead to avoidable confusions—avoidable, that is, if one remains within the formal language as such. Thus, in the formal system of probability, the probability vari-able, $P(A)$, may not be defined other than to indicate that it takes real values between 0 and 1. No effort is made to relate $P$ to counts of equally likely events, relative frequencies, or degrees of belief.

This property of formal systems is, of course, well understood. But perhaps nowhere in probability theory is it so apposite as it is in considera-tion of mathematical laws of large numbers. These laws, all of which say essentially the same thing, have played an important role in the justifica-tion of induction. They propose that any variable that is itself a function of a series of random variables converges toward a constant as the num-ber of elements in the series approaches infinity, and the probability that the difference between that variable and the constant is less than some arbitrarily small real number tends to 1 as the number of elements in the series tends to infinity. If we were to interpret this statement in terms of empirical sampling, where the elements in the series are sampling en-tities, it would appear that the larger the sample the closer the statistical variable is to a parameter descriptive of the universe. In fact, such an interpretation is known as the empirical law of large numbers. It is im-portant, however, to distinguish between the mathematical and the em-pirical laws of large numbers. The former is formally correct; it is therefore indubitable. What the latter proposes is that our empirical sampling entities will be conformal with entities in the abstract law. This is a hypothesis and is, of course, subject to critical scrutiny.

Although the conjecture of the empirical law of large numbers does indeed seem intuitively to be a justifiable one, there are several difficulties that come immediately to attention. Infinite sampling is meaningless—a mathematician who would reach infinity by means of an endless sampling of successors would get nowhere in his effort to understand the concept. Furthermore, it is not clear what the empirical counterpart of a parameter is. True means, for example, are fictions we live with because as working empiricists we are gentlemanly enough not to question what others might term our essential myths about families of random events. At times we are hard pressed, therefore, to relate by correspondence rules terms in the abstract language to terms in the observation language, or even to terms in the theoretic language. But regardless of the difficulties and the embarrassments, we shall find that all systems of inductive support such as we know them in statistical methodology seek to tailor their concepts and their inference rules to consistent sets of axioms and theorems in abstract probability theory. For, in the consideration of the formalized theory of probability, we need only be concerned whether theorems in the theory follow rigorously from a set of definitions and postulates.

## MEANING OF PROBABILITY

Development and formalization of probability theory can proceed without regard to the problem of defining probability as such. According to the mathematical theory, probability is simply defined as a variable taking real values within a specified range. Still it would be quite misleading to proceed on the assumption that semantic aspects of the term probability have never been a consideration in the development of the theory. As is well known the mathematical development followed upon an interest in the analysis of gambling games (for example, by Cardano, Fermat, Pascal, James Bernoulli, and Laplace). It is also apparent that there has always been a need for a language of corrigible belief and partial conviction. The development of probability theory as a formal discipline provided us with sophisticated tools for the logico-empirical support of partial belief in the areas of inductive conjecture and behavior.

From the beginning then, we observe that the language of probability has applied to two domains of discourse. One is where the probability has epistemic properties and applies directly to the state of mind of a person holding specified beliefs. Here the language of probability conveys to us that a person holds a belief that something may or may not happen, that something is more likely to happen than not to happen, that it is likely not to happen, and so on. What distinguishes the belief from apodictic knowledge is the essential qualification of possible error—not in the rational chain of inference, but in the realization that what any proposition asserts may, as a subject of that partial conviction, be in error (cf. N13.5). The other domain of discourse is that wherein the language of probability asserts properties about classes of events, about objects whether they are artifacts, propositions, or beliefs themselves. Having specified a class of objects, and this itself may be a subjective convention, the predicates of the probability language apply to subclass membership within a larger class. Here we may speak of the probability of outcomes of random devices, or of long-run frequencies of events in protracted sampling.

It is natural for us to assume that in objective treatments of probability numbers can be assigned: counts can be made in such a way as to be conformal with the real values the probability variable is to take. It is not so easy to assume that degrees of belief or of partial (nonapodictic) conviction can be as easily assessed in the domain of real numbers. Numbers, of course, can arbitrarily be assigned to any belief, any state of mind, if you so choose. The problem is, first, to make these assignments conformal with the mathematical theory of probability, and then to make them compatible with our empiricistic requirements for assigning meaning to all nonlogical predicates.

In pursuing these matters, one soon discovers one of the pleasant ironies of the debate over the proper definition of probability. On the one hand, any strict attempt to objectify the meaning of probability results in our having to make so many subjective judgments and to adopt so many conventions in the tasks of enumeration that the claims for objectivity are all but insincere (de Finnetti, 1937). On the other hand, if we are to assure ourselves that subjective probabilities are to meet the requirements of consistency and coherence, that is, for such probabilities to constitute the rational support of partial belief, we must seek some kind of objective justification which refers these beliefs to the world such beliefs are about (von Wright, 1962).

## Necessitarian, or Classical, Definition

The definitive statement is that of Laplace (1796).

> The theory of chance consists in reducing all the events of the same kind to a certain number of cases equally possible, that is to say, to such as we may be equally undecided about in regard to their existence, and in determining the number of cases favorable to the event whose probability is sought. The ratio of this number to that of all the cases possible is the measure of this probability, which is thus simply a fraction whose numerator is the number of favorable cases and whose denominator is the number of all the cases possible (1951, p. 6).

For the most part, this definition of probability has been regarded an objectivist one. It is assumed that there are universes of events that can be partitioned into equally likely classes of events; that, for example, if a cubelike object has six symmetrical faces, it is to be regarded equally likely that after an uncontrolled roll of the object, it will come to rest on any one or another of its six faces. Although this definition finds wide application, and especially in those cases where combinatorial enumeration is called for, it is faced with several serious difficulties.

One, how do we support the assumption of equally likely classes within a true partition of some universe. It has been objected that the argument for equally likely classes already subsumes an understanding of probability, the definition of which is in question (cf. N13.6). That is not so much to the point as the matter that the premise is taken as presumptive of the properties of real objects. The assumption of symmetry, as this is often called, has achieved its significance almost as a function of our technology (cf. N13.7). As we have become more expert in the manufacture of artifacts and also in our classificatory analyses, we have succeeded in establishing a wide range of applications where the classical probability concept would appear to be appropriate. But, then, the idea of the equally possible events reduces to the search for the equally frequent, and it would therefore be the idea of frequency which would be fundamental to any definition of probability.

Two, granting the above, then it would appear that a partition of a universe into equally likely classes is as much a subjective as an objective matter. The partition into equally likely classes is always determined by such outcomes as support the subjective judgment. This is necessarily restrictive. It precludes application of probability to those "chance" events wherein there is no means of prior conjecture as to what a class composition should be: for example, the probability of someone's being named Smith. But what is more to the point is the subjective character of the judgment supporting equally likely partitions. In the one case, the partition may merely be intuitive, "that is to say, to such as we may be equally undecided about. . . ." Thus principles of indifference have been invoked to support intuition: if there is no reason sufficient for favoring the occurrence of one event class over another, then the two event classes are equally likely (cf. N13.8). In the second case, the partition may be artificial and adventitious; presumably any domain can be partitioned into equally likely classes with sufficient ingenuity. For example, suppose we find that the male–female schema does not constitute an equally likely partition of Homo sapiens. Then, even working on the basis of sex, we might reclassify some members of the universe such that the frequency of males *and* females with a set of properties $\{X_i\}$ is equal to that of males *and* females with the set of properties $\{X_j\}$. People addicted to artifacts, such as dice and roulette wheels, might be inclined to subsume some natural partition of the domain of occurrences into equally likely sets, but this is an error. At most, we proceed from a state of ignorance which is subjective, or we seek applications of our conventions of equally likely partitions by improvising those situations in which the assumption appears to be useful.

A third line of criticism of the classical view of probability fixes upon the paradoxes of its applications. In the writer's mind, at least, the paradoxes appear to be less destructive than is often assumed (cf. N13.2). Paradoxes of probability estimates (e.g., Bertrand) are overcome by explicit instructions as to how a partition of some sample space is to be undertaken. The Petersburg paradox of the infinite expectation wager can be overcome by the adoption of a simple stopping rule. Such criticisms stem from taking the classical notion of probability as too general or taking it as indication of some underlying structure of real words. If we realize that the notion of equally likely partitions is adopted as a premise in the strategy of methodological ignorance, then, as in other methodological commitments, we will also realize its subjective and conventional rather than ontological character.

## Frequency Definition

There are some applications of the language of probability to the world of events wherein enumeration over equally likely classes cannot be undertaken. In such cases partitions of the event space are arbitrary; if we have no means for the prior assessment of the events in this partition, then obviously we are reduced to some empirical procedure for obtaining sample frequencies. Longevity probabilities are of this type. If we would assign a probability to life expectancy for any given age group, we have no recourse but to go to actuarial tables and project what we find there for the given age group. If we would assign a probability to the chances of the long shot's winning in any horse race, we would have to undertake an extensive survey of past races and project that result. Even where it is possible easily to categorize events into natural classes, the assumption of equal likelihood often fails us. Thus, in perhaps the first published example of statistical decision, Arbuthnot (1710) rejected the hypothesis that the equal likelihood of male and female births was part of the Divine plan, on the grounds that the actual frequencies did not support such an hypothesis (cf. N9.3). Even at this early date, we observe that a distinction is to be made between ideal probability estimates based on some principle of indifference and actual empirical frequencies.

There were other reasons for looking to sampling and frequency counts rather than alone to prior analysis of the event space. The notion of expectation, which is so important to the gambler, makes little sense except that one takes into consideration wagers, or other such behaviors, over the long run. What early gamblers required were rational means for anticipating what the long-run results might be. If the partition of an event space into equally possible classes proved both feasible and fruitful, one could hardly take exception; but where such partitions were not possible, more strictly empirical methods were required. Even the classical estimates were subject to check, the equally possible partitions being no more than calculational devices for our anticipating how the long-run frequencies might trend. Also, one should not overlook the need to suppose equally possible partitions on the basis of empirical frequency counts. Although much intuitive support has been marshaled in justification of the principle of equally likely classes (the principles of symmetry, indifference, insufficient reason, etc.), it is still apparent that the ultimate justification of this simplifying assumption must be empirical. Two classes of events are equally likely only if the frequencies with which their respective members are selected are equal in the long run for some sampling procedure.

This last statement is a bit obscure, since the terms 'selection', 'random', and 'sampling' are left undefined. But that is the way with equally possible events or event classes—what is equally likely often reduces to what is equally frequent (Venn, 1866; cf. N13.9).

A discussion of a frequency interpretation of probability needs to focus upon four points: (1) probability is a matter of relative frequency under some selection procedure, (2) the probability $p$ as a generalized property is some limit toward which the relative frequency converges, (3) probability applies either to a set of events or to a set of statements about events, and (4) a probability statement has no significance as concerns the occurrence or nonoccurrence of an individual event.

(1) Probability is a matter of relative frequency. Let us assume some sampling procedure for selecting events. Designate that procedure how you will, with the elements in the sample space, $N(A)$, constituting a series. Some of the elements in $N(A)$ may possess a property $B$ and some may not. Therefore, the probability that an event in the selection procedure $A$ will also possess the property $B$ is $N(AB)/N(A)$. To be explicit, we write

$$P(AB \mid A) = \frac{N(AB)}{N(A)}.$$

This reduces to $P(B \mid A)$, and when the sampling procedure is understood, this reduces simply to $P(B)$. It should be emphasized, however, that no statement of probability as a relative frequency is complete without its specifying what the sample domain is in terms of a selection procedure (cf. N13.10). All probability is in this way conditional; probability applies to any set of events that can be described as random variables, regardless of whether such events, or subsets of them, satisfy the conditions of equal likeliness. Under these conditions, probability is to be regarded as an empirical, i.e., strictly operational, concept; it is *a posteriori* rather than *a priori*, and it is applicable to any domain of events for which a sampling procedure can be specified.

(2) The probability, *p*, as the property of an incompletely surveyed class is a limit toward which the relative frequency converges. As one often begs for an intuitive understanding of equal possibility, so might he ask for an intuitive understanding of the concept of convergence toward a limit. The larger the sample, the more reliable it is as a vehicle of inference. We need hardly justify the assertion that the more information we have somehow the more confidence we place in a generalization appropriate to the domain from which the information is acquired. These statements are, of course, impressionistic ones. Explicit accounts of the principle of convergence date from the writings of Venn (1866), Boole (1854), and Peirce (1878). More recent accounts are due to the one-time colleagues, R. von Mises (1957) and Reichenbach (1938, 1949; cf. N13.11). Assume some domain of experience, some event space, such that events in the domain constitute a sequence, $x_1, x_2, \ldots, x_n, \ldots$ Assume further that for some property $\phi$ it is possible to ascertain whether for any *x, x* has the property $\phi$; thus, if '$\phi$' is a class name, we ascertain $x \in \phi$, or $x \in \sim\phi$. Then the probability $x \in \phi$ is the limit of the relative frequency of those instances in the sampled sequence $x_1, x_2, \ldots, x_n$ possessing the property $\phi$ with respect to all such instances whether possessing $\phi$ or $\sim\phi$, the extent of convergence toward that limit being a function of *N*, the number of elements sampled from the event space.

The salient idea here is that of limit. It is not difficult to formulate a formal definition of a limit, but it is not so easy to interpret a limit of a frequency which is itself a matter of empirical observations. Mathematically, a sequence $a_n = a_1, a_2, \ldots, a_n, n \to \infty$, has the limit *a* (i.e., $\lim a_n = a, n \to \infty$) if corresponding to some positive $\epsilon$, however small, there is some integer *N* such that $|a - a_n| < \epsilon$ for all $n > N$. Any function of a continuous variable *x* has a limit *a* if, and only if, as *x* tends to infinity, there is, corresponding to each positive number $\epsilon$, however small, some positive number *k* such that $|f(x) - a| < \epsilon$ for $|x| > k$. (Courant, 1937). Mathematical functions that are asymptotic and at the same time convergent exemplify such limiting properties. But now what can we say for the relative frequencies

$$p_f = \lim_{n \to \infty} \frac{x_f}{n} \, ?$$

Since these frequencies are contingent upon a sampling of events and are not strictly determinate items in an abstract sequence, we have no assurance that $p_f$ over any finite stretch might not diverge rather than converge so far as concerns the limit.

One might retort that experience teaches us that the principle of convergence holds. When people (e.g., Weldon, Hudleson) have taken the trouble to sample random events over large numbers of trials, the results appear to converge toward a reasonable expectation. There is, to be sure, a touch of plausibility to this line of support; but there are serious objections to it. For one thing, we are attempting to defend an empirical principle by recourse to empirical support. And this inevitably sets the circular trap of our attempting to justify induction on the grounds it appears to have worked in the past. We have no assurance that convergence will continue over the long run in the sample sequence, only a specious confidence which itself is supported by our fiducial commitments. Equally distressing is the fact that whereas it is often possible to determine what the limit is for some arithmetic series, $A_n$, it is not possible to do so for the probability $p$, toward which $p_f$ "condenses." That is to say, we take as an act of faith that $p_f$ converges toward $p$, but there is in many cases no means for prior assessment of what $p$ should be. We are always, it would appear, chasing a will-o'-the-wisp. We presume $p_f$ zeros in on $p$, but we do not know; for whereas $p$ is a property of an abstract infinite sequence, $p_f$ itself is a summary over empirical observations.

This latter predicament has led writers in the theory of probability to take refuge in mathematical laws of large numbers, and in principles of inverse inference. Indeed, if the world were describable in just the terms provided by the formal laws of large numbers, there would be no problem. In general, if the term $p_f$ is assumed to be a random variable in a formal system, then it can be shown that the following principle holds:

$$P(|\ p_f - p\ | < \epsilon) \rightarrow 1 \qquad \text{as } n \rightarrow \infty.$$

That is to say, the probability that the absolute difference between $p_f$ and $p$ is less than some arbitrarily small value approaches 1 as $n$, of $x_f/n$, approaches infinity (cf. N13.11). From this we can, in turn, infer the proximity of $p$ to $p_f$ rather than that of $p_f$ to $p$. Mathematical laws of large numbers show that the principle of convergence over a sequence holds for random variables of the formal system, and holds within the formal language of probability theory. Empirical laws of large numbers are quite another thing. Such laws propose that relative frequencies in actual empirical sampling are in fact describable in the formal language provided by the mathematical law.

But how do we justify the empirical law? How can we be sure that an empirical sequence of sampling events is conformal with the properties of the formal system? We can approach these problems only by making additional assumptions of the very kind that we are led to question. Laws of large numbers may offer formal models for empirical sampling, but the question of deciding whether the model is an appropriate one is itself a matter of sampling and empirical support of the kind that makes assumptions such as that of laws of large numbers (cf. N13.12).

The principle of inverse inference, on the other hand, indicates that if the law of large numbers holds, then we should be able to make an explicit inference to the value of the parameter $p$ on the basis solely of knowledge appropriate to the determination of $p_f$. In other words, we should be able to make an inference from sample to universe. This principle forms the support of our popular procedures of statistical inference. Granting that our random variables should be distributed as prescribed about the parameter (the expected value), and granting that our probability functions are appropriate descriptions of a world of experience, then we may justify our inferences concerning parameters on the assumption of the formal model.

(3) Probability applies either to a set of events or to a set of statements about events. In order to explicate probabilistic statements about singular events, it is necessary to distinguish between a sequence over an event space and a sequence over a propositional space. For every event in the sequence $[e_1, e_2, e_3, \ldots]$ we may substitute a proposition so as to constitute the sequence $[P_1, P_2, P_3, \ldots]$ in which the truth values of $P_1$, $P_2$, $P_3, \ldots$ are assessed by reference to the corresponding elements $e_1$, $e_2$, $e_3, \ldots$ Thus if $[e_i]$ constitutes a sequence of outcomes in tossing a die, $[P_i]$ might constitute a sequence in which every proposition in the sequence asserts the outcome is an ace. A truth analysis of the sequence $[P_1, P_2, P_3, \ldots, P_n]$ (i.e., the relative frequency of true propositions) would then give the probability of throwing an ace either in the empirical language of events as such, or in the propositional language. Reichenbach made this "identity of conception" important for his theory of induction. George Boole clarified the distinction in one of the early treatments of the frequency principle.

> . . . there is another form under which all questions in the theory of probabilities may be viewed; and this form consists in substituting for *events* the propositions which assert those events have occurred, or will occur; and viewing the element of numerical probability as having reference to the *truth* of those *propositions*, not to the *occurrence* of the *events* concerning which they make assertion. Thus, instead of considering the numerical fraction $p$ as expressing the probability of the occurrence of an event $E$, let it be viewed as representing the probability of the truth of the proposition $X$, which asserts that the event $E$ will occur (1854, p. 247).

(4) A probability statement has no significance as concerns the occurrence or nonoccurrence of an individual event. Observe that in both the event and the propositional series, the probability relation is applica-

ble to classes of elements in the series and not to individual elements as such. Thus we speak of the probability of throwing an ace with a die if it is understood that by 'the probability of throwing an ace with a die' we are not assigning any property to any specific toss. On any given toss, the die will show its ace-up face or it will not. The given outcome does not share any of the properties of a probability.

Now this well-known feature of frequency treatments of probability has been thought to constitute a serious objection to the frequency principle. In part this objection rides on our failure to appreciate the distinction between an event that is some particular to which we can assign class membership and an event which is the generic name for a class composed of many individuals. Thus the 'probability of throwing *an* ace with the die' can be an ambiguous statement. In part the objection rides on the feeling that decisions based on probabilities are singular acts, and that somehow a probability or probable inference must be related to some specific unrepeated action. If a person appreciates the distinction between an event as an individual occurrence and an event as a class name, then it is true for him that he cannot apply his probabilities (as frequencies) to events of the first type. If he would insist that individual occurrences are uncertain and that some language like that of probability must be sought for describing or even for acting upon that uncertainty, then either he must follow the frequentists in adopting a collectivist transliteration of such probabilities or he must, as the subjectivists do, seek a different, more personal, foundation for probability theory.

The issues can be clearly stated for the psychologist. A counselor is to consult with a student as to the advisability of pursuing a career in medicine. Among the data he reports are those of a predictive test. Say the student falls below some suggested cutting score for student admission. How does the counselor advise the student? as client centered? or as group centered? What significance does the test result have for this student, if the probabilities stipulated by the test norms apply only to a collective? Or consider the case of some experimentalist who runs a significance test on a hypothesis derived from a theory. He adopts a decision policy which allows him to accept or reject (or perhaps remain non-committal about) that hypothesis, the decision being contingent upon the evidence. His decision involves a singular act; but the justification of his action is a probabilistic one. Suppose the evidence is such that it leads him to reject the hypothesis with a Type I risk (probability of rejecting the hypothesis, given the hypothesis is true) of 0.01. Presumably the action of our experimentalist is more rational than that of some intuitionist who decides to reject (or accept) the hypothesis without benefit of evidence. But is it? Or rather we should ask, how is the experimentalist to defend an action applying specifically to a unique event when the rationale for that action is interpretable only in terms of the collective.

Perhaps nowhere is the issue more piquantly stated than in Peirce's red-black option for felicity or woe.

> An individual inference must be either true or false, and can show no effect of probability; and therefore, in reference to a single case considered in itself, probability can have no meaning. Yet if a man had to choose between drawing a card from a pack containing twenty-five red cards and a black one, or from a pack containing twenty-five black cards and a red one, and if the drawing of a red card were destined to transport him to eternal felicity, and that of a black one to consign him to everlasting woe, it would be folly to deny that he ought to prefer the pack containing the larger proportion of red cards, although, from the nature of the risk, it could not be repeated. It is not easy to reconcile this with our analysis of the conception of chance. But suppose he should choose the red pack, and should draw the wrong card, what consolation would he have? He might say that he had acted in accordance with reason, but that would only show that his reason was absolutely worthless. And if he should choose the right card, how could he regard it as anything but a happy accident? He could not say that if he had drawn from the other pack, he might have drawn the wrong one . . . (1878, p. 160).

In effect, Peirce says it makes no difference which pack of cards our man chooses. Since so far as he is concerned he is the only person to be granted the option, no justification of choosing one over the other deck can be made on a strictly probabilistic basis. Yet, it would appear to us to be folly for our man of destiny not to prefer the red deck. How does Peirce respond to this predicament? In the double meaning of the term, he is a pure "collectivist."

> It seems to me that we are driven to this, that logicality inexorably requires that our interests shall *not* be limited. They must not stop at our own fate, but must embrace the whole community. This community, again, must not be limited but must extend to all races of beings with whom we can come into immediate or mediate intellectual relation. It must reach, however vaguely, beyond this geological epoch, beyond all bounds. He who would not sacrifice his own soul to save the whole world, is, as it seems to me, illogical in all his inferences, collectively. Logic is rooted in the social principle. To be logical, men should not be selfish . . . (1878, p. 162).

And writing specifically to the man who must make the choice between decks.

> The man whom we have supposed as having to draw from the two packs, who if he is not a logician will draw from the red pack from mere habit, will see, if he is logician enough, that he cannot be logical so long as he is concerned only with his own fate, but that that man who should

care equally for what was to happen in all possible cases of the sort
could act logically, and would draw from the pack with the most red
cards, and thus, though incapable himself of such sublimity, our logician
would imitate the effect of that man's courage in order to share his
logicality (1878, p. 163).

According to Peirce then, the answer is clear: where probability is involved (and where in gaining diagnostic information is probability not
involved?) all counseling ought to be group centered. The counselee should
not be concerned with whether or not a diagnostic measure is, or will be,
a correct predictor of his own level of achievement. He should only be
concerned that his decision be consonant with the collective wisdom. And
the experimentalist, bent on defending his own thesis by the fiat of his
critical significance test, would be less guilty if he were concerned not
so much with his own special scientific pleadings as he was with the method
and brotherhood of all the sciences. For myself, as experimenter, it is not
that "this evidence" supports "my hypothesis" but that, acting in accordance with probable inference and decision procedures, I have contracted
to share in the sublimity and logic of collective undertakings. Under these
circumstances, the restrictions of the frequency principle of probability
stipulate that probable inferences are logically coherent only so long as
they apply to collectives.

*Criticisms of the frequency interpretation.* Doubtless the most
serious critique of the frequency theory of probability has been undertaken by contemporary subjectivists who would extend matters of personal belief and uncertainty to domains for which collectives cannot conveniently be provided. To such critique, we turn presently. If one chooses
to use the language of probability in a more or less flexible manner that
prerogative is always open. One need then only to distinguish types of
probability (e.g., Carnap, 1950). Thus there is one line of criticism in
which the argument appears purely to be of a linguistic character. For
one reason or another, it is thought that the collectivist notion of probability is unnecessarily restrictive. "Probably it will rain today, therefore,
I shall stay home and tend to my chores." I am not concerned with long-
run calculations, nor any brotherhood of decision-makers in the toils of
the weatherman's collective. I want some language to express my uncertainty, and such that I may take some positive action in accordance with
it. The frequency theorist, of course, denies that it is appropriate to interpret expectations in terms of singular decisions, therefore, his language
of probability is restrictive.

Now frequency theorists are first of all empiricists. They would not
deny our right to make sense of the probable beliefs upon which we make
our particular decisions; but they would deny that probability, as limiting

frequency, is in any way coherent with a unique decision whose logic is interpreted independently of collective action. Doubtless we have some kind of intuitive feeling for saying things in the physical sciences for which, unfortunately, there is no set of acceptable predicates in the physical language. Such has been the status of putative causal properties and relations. We do, of course, have elliptical modes of expression which for the most part translate the causal property into a set of relational (e.g., contiguity) empirical predicates. And so it is for the frequentist with respect to probability statements. Speaking of the probability of individual events is an elliptical mode of speaking in the same way that a causal language might be. It is really not a criticism of the frequency principle if, in its denying the applicability of probability to individual events, it is denying what quite properly does not belong to those events.

There is, however, a point upon which the empirical pretensions of the frequency principle seem wanting. It is not at all coincidental that logical empiricists have inclined toward a frequency interpretation of probability. Such an interpretation emphasizes observation and sampling. But what of limiting frequencies and probabilities as limits based on fictive notions of infinite sampling? A relative frequency is one thing; a limit projected on a finite sampling is quite another. On the one hand, probability as relative frequency is strictly reducible to observations or to terms and statements in the observation language; on the other hand, no such reductions are possible for probabilities which are limits.

Another difficulty arises in the support of the principle of convergence. The principle of convergence is expressible in terms of the *empirical* law of large numbers. Its support, if it is not purely conjectural, often comes from the assumption of a mathematical law of large numbers. These assumptions, however, are subject to test. And the only method that we as probabilists are inclined to accept is that which assumes that any discrepancies between an empirical sequence and a mathematical law of large numbers constitute a sequence of random events subject to interpretation in terms of assumed laws of large numbers. Indeed, empirical laws of large numbers would hardly be laws at all should they be deprived of the support of our mathematical models. Suppose we were to toss a coin and find after a large number of tosses that "heads" shows with a frequency of 0.75. Fair enough for the empiricist; he would conjecture that the limiting frequency will be somewhere within $\epsilon$ units of 0.75. But what stops him from getting a run of tails so that after a large set of additional trials, the relative frequency converges toward zero? Why assume any limiting frequency to begin with. It is obvious that we do make nonempirical assumptions. Either we assume uniformity and thereby an appropriate mathematical model, or, like Reichenbach, we proceed in desperation that if anything will work our methods of inference will, and if nothing will work, then to be sure nothing is lost.

## Personalistic, or Subjectivist, Definition

We have seen that there are difficulties inherent within both the necessitarian and the frequency definitions of probability. The one is rather too limited, restricted as it is to ideal worlds with neat, denumerably symmetrical properties. The other, in spite of its brisk operational integrity, leaves us uncomfortable in the face of the infinite collectives which are the subject of scientific generalization. To complicate the matter, we are inclined to attribute predicates in the probability language to individual events. Thus, in the matter of making personal decisions, we hardly need instruction from Cicero and Bishop Butler to recognize that "probability is the guide to life." We act as if something is probably true or is probably false, likely to occur, or likely not to occur, and so on. Were we strict necessitarians, our guidance for making personal decisions in unique contexts would degenerate into an analysis of the symmetrical properties of presumptive worlds. Or, were we frequentists, we would have to apologize for speaking elliptically—not as if some individual act or decision were subject to accurate description in the probability language, but rather that our specific act belongs to a class of many such acts in which the probability stipulates the relative frequency of the property assignment within the class. Yet what is more distressing is the fact that there appear to be many occasions for adopting the familiar language of probability when there seems to be no means at all for explicating the meanings of our probabilistically tainted predicates.

Such is frequently the case when we speak of our beliefs, our judgments, and our presumptions short of conviction. We know what it is to take census over the symmetrical possibilities of an event outcome when this activity is possible. We know what it is to observe events over a stretch of occurrences and thence to make our tallies. Indeed this is what we prefer to do when these alternatives are ones that we can exploit. But what of those situations in which we find it appropriate to say: "It is improbable that there will be a recession"; "Very likely, Mr. Simpson will decide not to run"; "It seems very improbable to me that the psychoanalytic theory of repression is true"; and so on?

It is easy to see that the language of probability lacks precision. Providing we are proscriptive, we can be fairly explicit about the meaning of probability. Yet we utilize the language of probability to speak vaguely on matters of belief and judgment. Here probability may attest to little more than the intensity of feeling which accompanies our forced conjectures in the face of ignorance. Perhaps we should not be disturbed by this looseness in usage. The language of probability is not the first to run the gamut of imprecision. Even in statistics, terms like 'consistency,' 'reliability,' and 'sufficiency' have their explicit technical meanings and yet also belong to the domains of ordinary discourse. There is no difficulty for us if we understand the intent and context of usage. Still, 'probability' is somewhat different from these other terms. Even in its ordinary usage, such as "Probably it will rain," we find there is need to give an incisive explication of the term, as if in its application to matters of belief and judgment, we have after all its most singular, if not all inclusive, extension. At least this is what many people holding to a personalistic interpretation of probability would like to maintain.

Two questions arise. Can we give a rigorous formulation of personal probability comparable to that of our other two treatments? (That is, can we assign probability values to beliefs on the presumption that our degree of belief corresponds with the probability of the truth of what is asserted in the belief?) Can we extend the language of this putatively well-formalized concept probability to such situations as are problematic to alternative conceptions? The answers to both questions appear to be affirmative. What remains to puzzle out is to what extent the personalistic interpretation of probability will enrich the language of science and broaden our tools of inference.

Consider the first question. So long as theories of subjective probability embrace the mathematical theory of probability, as indeed they do, formal rigor is assured for the syntax of the theory. As we have seen, axiomatic treatments of probability make no assumptions on how the measure of probability is to be assigned. The formal theory of probability remains the same for all interpretations, necessitarian, frequency, or personalistic. What is required, however, is that the measure of the probability variable be both *consistent* and *coherent*. *Consistency* generally is a requirement imposed upon logical systems. It stipulates that within the given system it should be impossible that both $A$ and $\sim A$ be inferred from the same set of postulates. Among the characteristics of consistent systems is that of transitivity. If $a > b$ and $b > c$, then $a > c$. As applied to interpretations in the probability language the problem assumes pragmatic aspects. Assignment of the probability measure should indeed conform to the requirements of consistency. If we were to determine by some means that $a$ is more probable than $b$, and that $b$ is more probable than $c$, then indeed $a$ should be regarded more probable than $c$. We should also expect that the maximum probability would correspond to entailment, a minimum degree of probability to logical impossibility and that intermediate degrees of probability apply to the region of logical uncertainty in a way such as not to violate any of the characteristics of logically consistent systems. As a result, the applied probabilist turns to the requirement of *coherence*. He seeks to establish measures such that a consistent system of betting could be undertaken on the basis of those measures. This implies that a person making bets calculated on the odds as derived from such measures does not bet in such a way that he is sure to lose. For example, if the bettor's use of his probability measure violates the assumption of transitivity then a "cunning" adversary could make book against him in a way that assures a loss (Ramsey, 1931; cf. N13.13).

Although the consistency–coherence requirements apply to all probability interpretations (cf. N13.14), it is in the matter of assigning personal probabilities that we find the greatest challenge. Personal probabilities are based on belief and judgment; and, in retrospect, our systems of belief are notoriously "inconsistent" and irrational. It is not surprising then that efforts to systematize personal probability have been called systems of rational belief. These are normative systems that prescribe how we ought to act, or how we ought to make book, if we are to be consistent and coherent. The task before the personalist, therefore, seems obvious. He must establish the conditions of judgment and the procedures such that a coherent set of probabilities will be forthcoming.

At the outset, we should note that there is nothing in subjective probability which need be incompatible with the results of the necessitarian or frequency treatments. For those cases where symmetrical partitions of the event space do in fact seem justified, or for those cases where relative frequencies diverge from some conspicuous model of symmetrical properties, a coherent system of estimating personal probabilities should yield corresponding results. The rational person operating on the assumptions of personal probability would indeed act on the classical or on the frequency measures of probability when it is appropriate to do so. But what of those situations in which neither symmetric partitions nor frequencies will provide a probability measure? In such cases, we must turn to behavior in the face of options; we must examine the risks one might wish to assume against rewards that are conditional on some outcome.

Let us consider a simplified version of Ramsey's prospectus (1926) for subjective probability. In order to measure belief, we visualize the person responding to options involving goods, the gain of which is deemed a measurable "good" and loss of which is deemed a measurable "bad." The gain here is contingent upon the correctness of the belief and the loss is contingent upon incorrectness of the belief. Since this reduces to a problem in expectation, a measure of the probability of belief can be derived from weighing the magnitudes of gains or losses one would risk in combination against a sure reimbursement (or loss). For example, suppose one were offered the option of a dollar in any event, or $X$ dollars if a coin comes up heads and zero dollars if it comes up tails. Which option our subject chooses should be contingent upon the value $X$ and the probability, $p,$ that he assigns to his belief in the occurrence of heads. The crucial point for determining probability comes at the point of indifference in which $Xp,$ the subjective expectation, just balances the sure gain. Then our subject would be rational and coherent providing in all such options his probability scale would lead him to choose the risk option whenever $Xp$ exceeds the sure gain, but otherwise to choose the sure thing.

Suppose S believes that the coin is biased and assigns a degree of belief $S(p) = 0.75$ to the proposition the coin will turn up heads. Then if we were to offer him one dollar as a sure thing against $X$ dollars if the coin turns up heads, he should, consistent with his belief, accept the risk option for all $X$ if $X > 1.33$; otherwise he should take the sure thing. Suppose now we were to offer him an altogether different option: one dollar for sure; or $Y$ dollars if two tails in two throws, otherwise nothing. Then by virtue of the probability calculus and a coherent set of personal probabilities S would choose the risk option only if $(1-p)^2 Y > 1$; i.e., only if $Y$ exceeded \$16. Should he take the risk if the offered $Y$, say, were only \$10, then his behavior would not be consistent within the operations of the calculus; nor would it be coherent. Some other player, with the same beliefs, could systematically better the expected gains of S, and were S to pay the fair price of one dollar for the pleasure of playing the game, he would in the long run end up with a loss.

In the above, we have assumed the subjective probability $S(p)$ without going through the mechanics of determining the measure. Granting the rationale of expectation, and for the moment at least, discounting the marginal utility of money gains, it would be a simple matter to calculate $S(p)$ on the event E by virtue of taking $K$ dollars as the sure-thing gain and then adjusting the risk gain, $X$, until the subject is indifferent between taking the $K$ dollars for sure and opting for $X$ dollars contingent upon the occurrence of E. Suppose, for example, $K$ is one dollar and our subject becomes indifferent as to taking the one dollar outright or opting for a gain of three dollars contingent upon the event E: heads on the toss of a somewhat irregular coin. Then, $S(p) \times 3 = 1$ indicates to us that our subject estimates $S(p) = \frac{1}{3}$ (cf. N13.15).

It is obvious that in such games as the above, we want to check the reasonableness of belief and personal probability against the long run of outcomes. In this case, personal probability implicitly assumes the rationale of the frequency principle (von Wright, 1962), and it is difficult to see how a personalist would proceed differently from a frequentist, or assuming symmetrical events, from a necessitarian.

The critical test arises, however, when one must make decisions in the absence of any opportunity to evaluate expected payoff in the long run. If there is only to be a single payoff based on the outcome of a single trial, then personal probabilities must be reasonably assigned over all possible outcomes of that single trial. One would wager, for example, that a theory is true or it is false, that the troops will come by land or by sea or by air or not at all, that the coming vote will result in a victory, a stalemate, or a defeat for the proposed coalition, and so on. There is no external check upon these personal probabilities, only an internal consistency as reflected in the coherence of the set of probability estimates. It is sometimes asserted that subjective probability is suspect because it is subject to whim. There being no external check upon expectation and payoff, there is no means of establishing reliability among the probability estimates. This, however, is misleading and it can be in error. Consistency is implicit within the given individual's set of probability measures, not as between two individuals who differ, say, as to the amounts of information that are available to their respective selves, nor as between probability estimates of the same individual when he has available different sets of information. The defense of rational belief is based upon the possibility of a consistent and coherent system of beliefs for a given individual under a state of mind (available information) for a specified slice of time. Attempts to formalize subjective probability (Ramsey, 1926; de Finetti, 1937; Koopmans, 1940a,b; Good, 1950; Savage, 1954) have all undertaken to define the conditions sufficient to assure possible coherence among personal degrees of belief for the given point in time (cf. N13.16).

Still, it is a matter of disturbance that a subjective estimate of probability is not uniquely determined and is contingent upon the state of one's mind (cf. N13.17). One can for a given point in time have a consistent and a coherent set of beliefs and personal probabilities and yet suffer heavily at any game of wagers with nature. For example, he might assume he was playing his game of craps with fair dice, develop a coherent set of beliefs on the pattern of classical probability, only to find that he was a consistent loser because the dice were loaded. Coherent systems of personal probability are hardly enough. One needs constantly to check the actual payoff on prediction with the events themselves. It is true that personal probability almost more than any other kind is subject to revision on the basis of information. As we become more sophisticated and gain new information, we change our probability estimates; but the information is invariably of a *general* nature indicating to us that the class of events to which we are predicting has been reconstituted on the basis of that information. We alter our probability estimates because the character of the sampling domain, as we now know it, has been altered.

It might well be argued that where coherence in personal beliefs is assured, personalistic treatments of probability add little, aside from the unique formal dress, to what is already known from necessitarian and frequentist treatments. And even where we are inclined to boast that personal probability touches the domain of unique events, i.e., assigning the probability to a unique cause or a unique effect, we visualize refining our estimates by means of an empirical verification of long-run expectation.

Were this the extent of contention among the personalists, it is unlikely that subjective probability would warrant the attention it is receiving. There is one area, however, in which personalistic probability substantially departs from our other notions. That is the area of decision. We now address ourselves briefly to the second of two questions stated earlier. Can we extend personalistic probability to cover situations that are clearly problematic to alternative conceptions?

Our now-traditional decision procedures as exemplified in various forms of the significance test are, by and large, based on the frequency principle of probability. As a result, we can assign probabilities neither to parameters about some ideal domain of data points, nor to any theory. We are in effect forever bound by the indecisiveness of hypothetico-deductive strategy. Whereas disconfirmation of a hypothesis or theory may be direct, support and confirmation is indirect and tentative. We may only say that an hypothesis is plausible on the data, it is tenable, it has not been disconfirmed. We cannot say that it is true, or that it is probably true, or that it is held with a degree of belief measured by the probability $p$.

Some of the very earliest efforts to formalize inductive support of decision, however, have been based on assigning probabilities in this taboo domain of discourse. Simple manipulations of the product rule in probability theory lead to Bayes' theorem whereby we may ultimately derive probabilities of causes, hypotheses, and theories on given evidence. For a discrete set of hypotheses, $\{H_i\}$, or set of theories, Bayes' rule yields

$$P(H_k \mid E) = \frac{P(H_k)\ P(E \mid H_k)}{\sum_{i=1}^{n} P(H_i)\ P(E \mid H_i)}$$

From the prior probabilities $\{P(H_i)\}$ and the likelihoods $\{P(E \mid H_i)\}$ we can indeed determine the posterior probability $P(H_k \mid E)$ for the given $H_k$. As was well-known even in Bayes' time, the matter of assigning prior probabilities is problematic. However, should the difficulties be circumvented, or at least in some way mitigated, then Bayes' rule may indeed be a useful foundation for deciding among alternative hypotheses.

Contemporary personalists do not now prescribe for us general means for assessing personal probabilities corresponding to members of the set $\{P(H_i)\}$; but they do stipulate conditions for a coherent body of beliefs about such a set, and as a consequence they prescribe the conditions in which it is possible to speak meaningfully of *a priori* and *a posteriori* probabilities. The ultimate defense of personalistic probability rests its utility for supporting inductive decision. It affords a strategy of decision different from that of our classical decision procedures and in some respects more incisive. But this, in part, is the subject matter of the succeeding chapter. It is only in the context of statistical decision that we may fully appreciate the current fruitfulness of personalistic conceptions of probability.

## Some Other Views

It is not easy to fit all the many treatments of probability into either a two- or threefold mold. First of all there is the threefold grouping: the necessitarian (or classical), frequency, and personalistic interpretations. Second, there is the twofold grouping as between objectivist and subjectivist interpretations. Here the necessitarian interpretation is classified as objectivist even though the properties of symmetrical partitions are as much a logical matter as they are empirical. However, since the symmetry of equally likely classes is presumed to be inherent in the universe of events rather than in a state of mind, this classical view of probability is to be regarded objectivistic. Still there is another class of interpretations that fits none of these rubrics. They are termed logical definitions of probability on the grounds that probability expresses a logical relation between propositions rather than a relation between events, classes of events, partitions, and so on.

## Probability as a Logical Relation

*Keynes.* "The terms *certain* and *probable* describe various degrees of rational belief about a proposition which different amounts of knowledge authorize us to entertain. All propositions are true or false, but the knowledge we have of them depends on our circumstances . . ." (Keynes; 1921, p. 3). According to Keynes, probability is a logical relation between propositions that serve as premises and propositions that assert conclusions based upon those premises. Let $h$ be a proposition that asserts our "direct knowledge," let $a$ be a proposition that asserts hypotheses or conclusions which are matters of "indirect knowledge." Then for $a \mid h = \alpha$ we have the proposition $h$ justifies the conclusion $a$ with a degree of rational belief equal to $\alpha$.

The idea of a probability relation corresponds with that of rational belief. As Keynes observes, this formulation has subjective overtones. Since we cannot assert the belief in any proposition independent of premises or knowledge, then all probabilities, all beliefs, are conditional on knowledge or evidence. However, Keynes also hastens to point out that probability is not "subject to human caprice." Once the facts are given, as stipulated in $h$, then the probability of $a \mid h$ is strictly and objectively determined, if it is at all determinable.

Assuming $\alpha$ as a measure of $a \mid h$, not all degrees of rational belief are measurable. For a logically valid argument in which $a$ is a theorem from a set of sufficient premises, $h$, we should assign the value 1 to $\alpha$; if $a$ is a contradiction on $h$, we should assign the value 0, as within the formal probability theory. But what of intermediate degrees of belief? The proposition $a$ must either be true or false. The probability then expresses the degree of belief that we may have that $a$ is in fact true.

For all valid logical arguments, the probability is 1 or, allowing for the possibility of error in reasoning, very nearly 1. For arguments in which $0 < \alpha < 1$, we will regard the premises, $h$, as not sufficiently complete either to infer $a$ or $\sim a$ with certainty. According to Keynes, only in a few relatively restricted applications of this inductive procedure is it possible to assign values to $\alpha$. In some cases, it is possible to make comparisons between two probabilities, such that in spite of our inability to assign absolute magnitudes to the probabilities, we may order them along a continuum of uncertainty. In matters of forecast and prediction, of evaluating the truth of hypotheses about past events and counterfactual conditionals, no probability measure is possible.

Keynes is somewhat more conservative than frequentists or personalists.[1] He would restrict probability measure to that domain of experience in which it is possible to apply the principle of symmetry. Here Keynes addresses himself to the principle of indifference. "The Principle of Indifference asserts that if there is no *known* reason for predicating of our subject one rather than another of several alternatives, then relatively to such knowledge the assertions of each of these alternatives have an *equal* probability" (1921, p. 42). Since uncritical application of this principle leads to the paradoxes of the equal probability of complementary propositions (e.g., cf. N13.8), Keynes proposes a more rigorous formulation of equally likely alternatives. The selection of the set of alternatives should be such that "there must be no known reason for preferring one of a set of alternatives to any other." Judgments of indifference are to be made on the grounds that for no two equally likely alternatives, $x \mid h$ and $y \mid h$, is it possible to find additional conditions $h_i$ such that $x \mid h, h_i$, and $x \mid h$ are not equal. In such cases, $h_i$ is judged *irrelevant* to the degree of belief $x \mid h$. We are also to make sure that our analysis of possibility is what later personalists were to regard as "fine." That is, the partition of possibility should be such that no alternative in the set of basic alternatives could be further divisible into elements "similar in kind." Thus conditions of *irrelevance* of evidence and *indivisibility* of alternatives should enable us to utilize a principle of indifference while avoiding the paradoxes that trapped early users of the principle.

Generally, where we may use the classical interpretation of probability, we may rephrase it in the language of the relation between propositions. However, Keynes' treatise of probability has never been widely adopted as a foundation for inference or statistical decision. Its primary renown perhaps stems from its application in one of the unique

---

[1] Had Keynes treated probability as a relation between propositional functions, $\phi(a) \mid \psi(a)$, rather than between propositions as such (Russell, 1948, p. 397), he might conceivably have incorporated a frequency principle into the measure of probability. As the argument stands, he cannot.

defenses of induction (see Chapter 15). If the principle of indifference can be applied to the possibility of the hypotheses of theories, then regardless of our inability to assign measurable *a priori* probabilities, we can show that any confirmatory evidence enhances the probability of the theory.

*Jeffreys' theory.*      Both Jeffreys' theory (1939, 1957) and that of Keynes can be classified as formal treatments of rational belief. Both place emphasis upon Bayes' theorem as a rule of inference. But whereas Keynes is inclined to apply his theory as a justification of induction even where measurable probabilities are not forthcoming, Jeffreys restricts his more axiomatic approach to those situations in which reliable estimates of probability are obtainable.

For Jeffreys, probability is "a valid primitive idea for expressing the degree of confidence that we may reasonably have in a proposition" (1939, p. 15). Like Keynes, he believes that it is meaningless to assign a probability to a proposition or an hypothesis as such. Probability can only be determined against a background of information available at a given moment. This does not mean that probability is a subjective notion; it is objective in that any two individuals having available the same evidence and following the same rules will arrive at the same degree of belief, $P(p \mid q)$. Jeffreys goes to considerable pains to show that probability, as he visualizes it, conforms with the addition theorem and the product rule. Probabilities are additive over finite spaces and the product rule leads to ramification in Bayes' theorem. This latter theorem yields the principle of inverse probability.

$$P(H \mid eE) \propto P(H \mid E) \, P(e \mid EH)$$

with $H$, $e$, and $E$ being the hypothesis, the new evidence, and the extant prior evidence, respectively. That is to say, the probability of the hypothesis on the new and old evidence is proportional to the prior probability of the hypothesis and the likelihood of the new evidence.

This is the fundamental principle of Jeffreys' treatment of inductive inference. We should note, first of all, that it is Bayesian. However, Jeffreys' utilization and defense of Bayesian inference is objectivistic rather than subjectivistic. The prior probabilities of hypotheses are, as it were, objectively determined by one's applying the principle of indifference to a set of hypotheses given a state of knowledge at a particular time. Speculation concerning the range of potential hypotheses is contingent upon background information. Therefore, it is possible to specify a range of potential hypotheses which can be partitioned by the principle of indifference into equally likely alternatives. Moreover, it makes little difference what initial probabilities one assigns to hypotheses.[2] Successive confirmatory experiments will give support to one over another of the hypotheses by virtue of its posterior probability approaching 1 (Jeffreys, 1955; Wrinch and Jeffreys, 1921). Jeffreys is not reluctant to let our ignorance dictate the principle of indifference. "To say that probabilities are equal is a precise way of saying that we have no ground for choosing between alternatives. . . . To take prior probabilities different in the advance of observational reason for doing so would be an expression of sheer prejudice" (1939, p. 34). Later we find Jeffreys observing: "The idea that there is an inconsistency on assigning probabilities on no evidence is based on the confusion between a statement of logical relations and one of the constitution of the world" (1955, p. 276).

It is not quite appropriate to speak of our "assigning probabilities on no evidence." This is a second point worthy of note. Since all probabilities are relational, then all prior probabilities are assigned on the basis of extant knowledge. Jeffreys is careful to distinguish between *prior* probabilities and *a priori* probabilities. The assignment of the prior probability is made on a given body of extant evidence and prior to additional experimental evidence. Assignment of an *a priori* probability would have to be made independently of any evidence whatsoever. The principle of inverse probability expresses a relation between posterior and prior, between final and initial probabilities, and not any relation involving purely intuitive assignments of probability.

Finally, it should be noted that as in most of Bayesian procedures, decision concerning the posterior evaluation of an hypothesis will be a function largely of the likelihood measure, $P(e \mid EH)$. Thus support for decision is to be found in likelihood tests rather than in the classical significance tests.


## Credibility: Russell

The notion of credibility has frequently figured into the theory of probability and inference. It is not a new idea since it belongs to the family of ideas associated with degrees of belief appropriate to the rational man. Bertrand Russell, for example, feels that credibility is an essential complement to the concepts of probability.

> I think, therefore, that everything we feel inclined to believe has a "degree of doubtfulness," or inversely, a "degree of credibility." Some-

[2] A more general postulate is that of simplicity. "The set of all possible forms of scientific laws is finite or enumerable, and their initial probabilities form the terms of a convergent series of sum 1" (Jeffreys; 1957, p. 36). The principle of indifference and of equiprobability need not apply. It is sufficient that an ordering of initial probabilities of hypotheses be possible on the assumption that the simpler hypothesis is the more probable.

times it is connected with mathematical probability, sometimes not; it is a wider and vaguer conception. It is not, however, purely subjective. There is a cognate subjective conception, namely, the degree of conviction that a man feels about any of his beliefs, but "credibility," as I mean it, is objective in the sense that it is the degree of credence that a *rational* man will give (1948, p. 359).

For Russell, mathematical probability as applied to statistics and inference has to do with classes. Degree of credibility differs in that it is assigned to single propositions which may concern unique hypotheses or events. It differs from subjective probability in that there may very well be a difference between credibility and "subjective conviction." Indeed, just as Ward Edwards (1954, 1962) has reported, such differences are the subject of experimental investigation. Credibility should be the guide to life, not probability as such, and certainly not subjective conviction as untutored by principles of rational judgment.

Degrees of credibility are conferred by argument, by data, by personal belief. How can we evaluate them? Can we assign a quantitative measure to them? Russell answers outright, only when mathematical probability is relevant to the relation as between propositional classes. He feels this is "clear to common sense." One only needs to assume that each proposition in the argument of the propositional function possesses equal credibility. Thus relative frequency is a measure of credibility, providing principles of indifference or place selection (not mentioned by Russell in this context) hold over the range of the argument.

Not all credibilities are measurable, however. Even demonstrable inference is subject to error. The conclusion of the argument is held only with more or less certainty contingent on the length, difficulty, and clearness of the argument itself. Only by making great simplifying assumptions might we assign probabilities to the validity of the argument. Russell lists several applications of credibility where measurement is in doubt. One, we cannot assign probability to the truth of a general proposition. There is a difference between the syllogism "Most $A$ are $B$; this is an $A$; therefore, this $A$ is probably $B$" and "Probably all $A$ are $B$; this is an $A$; therefore, this $A$ is probably $B$." Russell, like many others, finds it doubtful that we can assign measures of credibility to the latter argument. Two, even the datum, that upon which we assign truth status to the proposition, is subject to doubt and thus to credibility. We do not know for sure whether our datum is a true one or whether we are being deceived by illusion, legerdemain, or hallucination. Defining "datum" as "a proposition which has some degree of rational credibility on its own account," Russell maintains that unmeasurable uncertainty creeps into the argument which is due to (1) faint perception, e.g., nondiscriminable differences, (2) uncertain memory, and (3) dim awareness of logical connection. And three, subjective certainty, based as it is on a psychological sense of conviction, is subject to doubt. The function of knowledge is to reduce the discrepancy between credibility and subjective degrees of belief. "Perfect rationality consists, not in believing what is true, but in attaching to every proposition a degree of belief corresponding to its degree of credibility" (1948, p. 415).

In the end Russell tends to be traditional, for he does not experiment with systems for bringing these degrees of belief into the purview of formal probability theory.

# NOTES

## NOTE 13.1

1.  Here induction and inductive inference refer to the logical elaboration of a set of premises some of which are statements in the observation language. The conclusion of such an inference is an hypothesis that translates into the language of either actual or potential observation. The hypothesis must be logically compatible with the premises. It should be emphasized that the logic of inductive logic is deductive logic, no more, no less. But it is the application of logic to statements in the observation language which gives to inductive inference its unique character. There is another point to consider. Customarily the premises of a deductive argument are either postulates or axioms or are propositions to which we can assign an apodictic truth value. In much of inductive inference, the case is different. The premises and postulates of the argument are often of a probabilistic nature; hence, the conclusions are also of a probabilistic nature. What we infer is a proposition that asserts that something is probably the case.

The proposition asserting a probability relation is deductively certain, it follows from a valid argument. But the proposition asserting the probability relation asserts that the relation holds only with the relative frequency, the expectancy, or the degree of belief as indicated by the probability predicate. Deductively, we may arrive at the proposition $P(\alpha\beta \mid \beta) = q$ by straightforward manipulations in the theory of probability, but for any given specimen possessing the property $\beta$, we cannot say with any certainty whether it will or will not have the property $\alpha$. The conclusions of inductive inference carry with them the uncertainty implicit in their probability predicates; the conclusions of a deductive argument are not at all uncertain. Another point of emphasis here is to say that with respect to the uncertainty of inductive conclusions we are concerned with the semantic interpretation of the proposition, whereas with respect to deductive conclusions we are only concerned with their conformity to syntactical rules.

2.  Not all of the usages of 'induction' are restricted to matters of empiricistic inference. An excellent review of the treatments of induction is to be

found in William Kneale's *Probability and Induction*. First, Kneale distinguishes among three types of induction which admit of no uncertainty and must be set aside from inductive inference as we think of it in scientific empiricism.

a. *Summative induction* (Aristotle's *Prior Analytics*) proceeds by the *complete* inspection and enumeration of a finite set of events. A generalization over a restricted set of events follows from the application of the syllogism to this finite enumeration. For example, $x$, $y$, and $z$ all possess the property $\phi$; $x$, $y$, and $z$ are all the members in the class $C$; therefore, all members of $C$ have the property $\phi$. This is a universal statement but it is restricted to the finite class $C$. Such statements of restricted universality seem straightforward enough. In fact, summative induction is easily extended to include probabilistic generalizations on relative frequency counts in finite classes. The only difficulties arise in our making sure of the count and making sure that all the events in the class have in fact been inspected. Not only do we need to know that $\phi x$, $\phi y$, and $\phi z$ but also that $x$, $y$, and $z$ are *all* the members in the class $C$.

b. In the case of *intuitive induction* (Aristotle's *Posterior Analytics*) one pleads for the establishment of unrestricted universal truths on the basis of finite sampling. We know something by intuitive induction if from a single observation we can know indubitably that some necessary relation holds. Examples of such universal statements would be "all colored things are extended" (the basis of Locke's primary qualities), "every event must have a cause," "there are no dimensionless objects." Presumably such statements are known indubitably because of the inconceivability of their being false. Experience alone does not tell us such statements are true; their truth is known as an act of intuition. Critics of this kind of intuitionism (e.g., Carnap) are likely to maintain that such truths are matters of linguistic convention; to deny the truth of such statements is to reject certain of our rules of well-constructed sentences. Kneale himself removes this type of "induction" from the allowable domain of induction by distinguishing between "principles of modality" and "matters of fact." Being colored and being nonextended are known to be incompatible modalities, and they are known to be incompatible without our referring to facts as such.

c. *Mathematical induction* is based on the recursive properties of certain types of proof. Suppose some formula $A_n$ to be a true theorem in the elementary theory of numbers (e.g., $A_n = n(n+1)/2$ as the sum of $n$ terms in the series $1 + 2 + 3 + \cdots + n$). We assume that $A_n$ is true for the integer $n$ in the series of its applications. Then if we can show that $A$ holds for $n+1$ if it holds for $n$, and if it is established that it holds for $n = 1$, then it follows that it holds for the entire range of integers however large. By mathematical induction, we may establish unrestricted universal truths as applied to the domain of numbers. The character of the proof and support, however, is purely deductive. As Kneale points out, the definition of number itself is recursive, i.e., it is based on the concept of succession. Therefore, mathematical induction simply reflects the abstract properties with which we endow number.

All of the above treatments of induction are such that their respective inductive procedures lead to necessary truths. What of inductive inference as we apply it as an instrument of scientific knowledge? Here the propositions in question are unrestricted generalizations, but the domain of application covers the whole of possible experience. Not only must the generalization be logically correct, but it must be empirically correct in that it is a true statement concerning matters of fact.

*d.* By *ampliative induction,* Kneale means to include those examples of scientific inference whereby we make predictions of the future, or make estimates concerning generalizations appropriate to unlimited domains of experience. This is the type of induction with which we are primarily concerned in this chapter. From the time of Bacon on, it becomes a focal point of epistemology. We watch its growth from Bacon's method of induction by elimination (essentially the strategy of disconfirmation) to John Stuart Mill's famous methods of experimental inquiry, finally to the development of modern statistical inference and decision. Only in its ampliative resources does induction become problematic. In the case of summative, intuitive, and mathematical induction, the validity of the inference is demonstrable. This is not so in the case of ampliative induction; for, although inductive inferences concerning an extant body of fact can be checked, no such checks can be made, nor can any proofs be given, for propositions about unlimited domains of experience which encompass the future.

References on philosophical, nonstatistical treatments of ampliative induction are too numerous to give in detail, but the following are mentioned:

Classic treatments:
  F. Bacon, *Novum Organum*
  J. S. Mill, *A System of Logic*
A modern treatment after the pattern of Mill's methods of inquiry can be found in
  J. O. Wisdom, *Foundations of Inference in Natural Science* (1952)

## NOTE 13.2

1.  Bertrand's paradox is often presented in critiques of the classical or necessitarian treatment of probability. If a given artifact or thing to be modeled can be analyzed so as to yield a set of equally likely outcomes, then the probability is the ratio of counts between the outcomes having a given property and the total number of outcomes. Suppose now our problem is this. A chord is to be drawn at random to cut a circle. What is the probability that the chord will be longer than the side of an equilateral triangle inscribed within the circle? The paradox is that there are three answers, one-fourth, one-third, and one-half, each of which is defensible.

*a.* A chord is determined by any two points on the circumference of the circle. Since the first of the two points can be taken anywhere, strike the point and inscribe an equilateral triangle so that one of its vertices coincides with that point. The random event that now determines the line is any point on the circumference of the circle. Assuming a symmetrical distribution of points, then one-third of the points determine chords longer than one side of an inscribed equilateral triangle. In Figure 13.1, let A be the initial point. Then any point on the arc BC gives a chord longer than the side $\overline{AC} = \overline{AB}$.

   b.   Any chord can be constructed as perpendicular to a radius of the circle which the chord cuts, and that chord is then bisected by that radius (from a theorem of plane geometry). It can be easily proved that the chord that is the side of the inscribed equilateral triangle bisects and is bisected by the radius perpendicular to it. Therefore, the probability of constructing a chord in this fashion which is longer than the side of an equilateral triangle is one-half. In Figure 13.1, any chord constructed perpendicular to the radius ED will be longer than AC providing the point for intersection is taken in the segment EF.

   c.   Similarly, take any point at random within the larger circle; draw a radius through the point and construct a chord perpendicular to the radius at the point. Since only points within the circle of radius $\overline{EF}$ yield chords longer than the side of an inscribed equilateral triangle, the probability is the

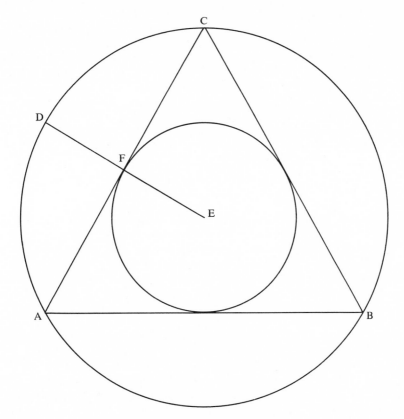

**Figure 13.1**  Bertrand's Paradox.

ratio of the smaller to the larger circle. Since the areas of the two circles vary as the squares of the radii, the probability is one-fourth.

Bertrand's three estimates of $p$ stand as a paradox only if we fail to specify how the actual sampling and construction of the chord is to be undertaken. Once we specify that chord is to be determined by points selected at random from the circumference of the circle, then one and only one value $p$ is possible on the assumption of an equally dense distribution of points along that circumference. And in similar fashion determinations for other methods of construction yield their respective solutions.

Another paradox along a similar line is von Mises' problem of the watered wine (1957, p. 77). Wine is to be diluted with a volume of water randomly chosen so as to exceed the amount of wine but not to exceed twice the amount of wine. Thus the ratio of water to wine is somewhere between 1 to 1 and 2 to 1. Assuming an equal density of points on this continuum, the probability is 0.50 that the ratio is between 1 and $\frac{3}{2}$ to 1. But consider instead the inverse ratio of wine to water. The range of the ratios is now between 1 to 1 and 1 to 2 with the probability being 0.50 that the ratio is between half the distance 1 to 1 and $\frac{1}{2}$ to 1. Thus the probability is 0.50 that the wine/water ratio is less than $\frac{3}{4}$. Now a wine/water ratio of $\frac{3}{4}$ is equal to a water/wine ratio of $\frac{4}{3}$. Thus if we compute on the basis initially of a water/wine ratio, we obtain the $p = 0.50$ that ratio of water to wine is between 1 and $\frac{3}{2}$; whereas if we compute on the basis initially of a wine/water ratio and then convert, we obtain $p = 0.50$ that the ratio of water to wine is between 1 and $\frac{4}{3}$.

Here, as in the Bertrand paradox, insufficient attention is given to the problem of constructing the sample space to which the principle of equally probable events applies. Our problem is to dilute the wine randomly with as much as up to twice its volume in water. First, fill a cup of wine, pour it into the decanter. Now fill the cup with water, likewise pour it into the decanter. We are now ready for the random component. It is equally probable that we add less than one-half cup of water or that we add more than one-half cup. Now, regardless of whether we take the water/wine ratio or the wine/water ratio our computations are based on the probability of 0.50 of their being between 1 and 1.5 cups of water in this mixture. The water/wine ratio is 1.5 to 1; the wine/water ratio 1 to 1.5. Converting the latter ratio to the water/wine ratio obviously removes the paradox. Von Mises failed to distinguish clearly what was the random variable; he took the ranges of ratios as his random varibles when he should simply have taken the volume of water as the random variable.

2. The Petersburg paradox is based on the assumption that no gamble is worth an infinite amount of risk, for there is always the possibility of a loss no matter how high the probability of a win, if $p < 1$. Consider the following wager. A person tosses a coin until he gets a head. If the head occurs on the first toss, he wins two dollars; if on the second, he wins four dollars; if on the third, he wins eight dollars, . . . , if on the $n$th toss, he wins $2^n$ dollars. The game ends as soon as he tosses a head. The player is then assured of some winnings contingent upon what trial it is that he tosses his

first head. The question is: how much should he pay for the privilege of playing the game? According to classical probability theory, the fair price is equal to the expectation, where the latter is equal to the product of the probability of winning times the prize. Since one may win on any trial $i$, $i = 1, 2, 3, \ldots, n, \ldots$, then the total expectation of the game is the sum of the expectations over all possibilities of winning (by the addition theorem of probability). Thus

$$E_T = \sum_{r=1}^{\infty} E_r = \sum_{r=1}^{\infty} p^r 2^r = 1 + 1 + \cdots + 1 + \cdots .$$

That is to say, we should pay an infinite amount of money as the fair price of the game.

The paradox is occasioned by our extending classical probability to games with infinite expectation. If we limit such games, then the paradox is circumvented. A simple way to make the Petersburg game a fair one is to adopt a stopping rule; namely, if the game goes to $N$ tosses without a head, the player receives nothing. Under such rules it is possible to compute a fair price for the game without doing violence to our ideas of expectation (cf. Feller, 1950).

## NOTE 13.3

In this and the following note, a brief outline of the formalization of the theory of probability is given.

The following table of interpreted set theoretic expressions is, except for minor notational changes, taken from Kolmogorov (1950, p. 5).

| *Set theory* | *Random events (probability theory)* |
|---|---|
| 1. $AB = 0$ | 1. Events $A$ and $B$ are incompatible (i.e., mutually exclusive). |
| 2. $AB \ldots N = 0$ | 2. Events $A, B, \ldots, N$ are incompatible; i.e., at least two events out of $A, B, \ldots, N$ are incompatible. |
| 3. $AB \ldots N = X$ | 3. $X$ is the event defined by the simultaneous occurrence (conjunction) of $A, B, \ldots,$ and $N$. |
| 4. $A \cup B \cup \ldots \cup N = Y$ | 4. $Y$ is the event defined by the occurrence of at least one of the events $A, B, \ldots,$ or $N$. |
| 5. $\sim A$ | 5. Any event that occurs when $A$ does not occur and is necessarily incompatible with $A$. |

| Set theory | Random events (probability theory) |
|---|---|
| 6.  $A = 0$ | 6.  Event $A$ is impossible. |
| 7.  $A = S$ (where $S$ is the set of all possible sets) | 7.  Event $A$ must occur. |
| 8.  The system $\mathcal{U}$ of sets $A_1, A_2, \ldots, A_n$ forms a decomposition (partition) of $S$ if $A_1 + A_2 + \cdots + A_n = S$ for nonintersecting sets of $A_i$. | 8.  For any experiment $\mathcal{U}$ there exists the set of all possible mutually exclusive outcomes. |
| 9.  $B \subset A$: $B$ is a subset of $A$. | 9.  The occurrence of event $A$ necessarily follows from the occurrence of $B$. |

In order to clarify the distinction between points and sets and between particular events and classes of events, it is well to indicate that $S$ is the collection of all elements, all points out of which the set structure is composed, whereas $\mathcal{F}$ (a "field") is a set of some subset compositions out of the elements of $S$. As applied to the language of logical atomism, the distinction in the set theoretic language makes it possible to distinguish between explicit molecular extensions of atomic facts and classes of such occurrences which define a general proposition. To indicate that there is a field of partitions of all elements in $S$ is to suggest that there are alternate classificatory schemata for the events in a finite world.

A concise treatment of the Kolmogorov axiomatization of the probability over finite probability spaces is to be found in Suppes (1957; pp. 274–290).

## NOTE 13.4

Such a set of axioms is provided in Kolmogorov's classic monograph, *Foundations of the Theory of Probability*. We have already been exposed to the Kolmogorov axioms in the effort to provide a formal model and calculus for a theory of random dice behavior (Chapter 9). Let me now provide a fuller resumé.

*Set theory.* The axiomatization of probability theory begins with definitions relating the language of random events and the language of set theory. By assigning to any specific event occurrence a point in the event space of set theory, we may subject the event as translated to the operations of set theory, e.g., class inclusion, union, intersection, impossibility, incompatibility, necessity, and so on. Thus any statement about the disjunction, conjunction, impossibility, and so on, of random events finds equivalent expression in the abstract language of set theory (cf. N13.3). Moreover, just as one distinguishes between an event as a particular molecular constellation of atomic occurrences and an event that is expressed as a general proposition (see page 193) so does one distinguish in set theory between a point and a set which includes the point. Once we establish the correspondence of the set entities with the occurrences of random events, all that is required is that we introduce some convention by which we assign to sets $A$, $B$, . . . , probabilities $P(A)$, $P(B)$ . . . which take real values between 0 and 1. But note, neither in the formal definitions nor in the formal set of axioms is the notion of probability defined other than by assigning some $P(A_i)$ a real value within those limits.

*Kolmogorov axioms.* Let $S$ be the universe of elements $e_1$, $e_2$, . . . , $e_n$ out of which all possible sets can be constructed. Then out of these elements can be constructed a field $\mathcal{F}$, i.e., a set of subsets on $S$, such that the elements of $\mathcal{F}$ are random events. The concept of a field or family of sets may appear superfluous to the domain of all primitive elements $e_i$, but this is essential for making explicit the possibility of alternative partitions of the sample space into alternative classes of random events. The axioms are as follows:

A1.   $\mathcal{F}$ is a field of sets on $S$

A2.   $\mathcal{F}$ contains $S$ in its family of sets

A3.   To each set $A$ in $\mathcal{F}$ is assigned a nonnegative real number, i.e., $P(A) \geq 0$, with $P(A)$ being the probability of $A$.

A4.   $P(S) = 1$, i.e., the probability of some element or some set of elements on $S$ is equal to 1.

A5.   If $AB = 0$ then $P(A \cup B) = P(A) + P(B)$; i.e., if $A$ and $B$ are incompatible, then the probability of $A$ or $B$ is equal to the sum of the probabilities assigned to these classes.

From these axioms, one may establish that for some given probability space, i.e., some given partition, $S_k$, and $A \subset S_k$ then

$$P(A) + P(\sim A) = 1$$

and for the null set

$$P(\sim S_k) = 0.$$

*Product theorem.* The so-called multiplication theorem of elementary probability theory follows not from the axioms above but from the definition of conditional events. If '$A \mid B$' reads "$A$ under the condition $B$" or "$A$ given $B$" then the conditional probability of $A \mid B$ is defined as

$$P(A \mid B) = \frac{P(AB)}{P(B)} \tag{1}$$

for $P(A) > 0$. From this directly follows the generalized multiplication theorem

$$P(AB) = P(B)\, P(A \mid B) \tag{2}$$

and for $P(B \mid A)$,

$$P(AB) = P(A)\, P(B \mid A). \tag{3}$$

Two events $A$ and $B$ are defined as being independent if

$$P(AB) = P(A) \cdot P(B),$$

that is to say if, $P(B) = P(B \mid A)$ and $P(A) = P(A \mid B)$.

*Bayes' theorem.* One of the most basic theorems in all the history of inductive inference is that of Bayes. On the basis of (2) and (3), and simply stated, it is

$$P(B \mid A) = \frac{P(A) \; P(A \mid B)}{P(A)} \tag{4}$$

Thus, with the appropriate information, we may determine the probability of one set of events conditional on another from the probability of the latter conditional on the former. Suppose we know that $S$ can be partioned into the following finite sets of sampling domains: $S_1, S_2, \ldots, S_j \ldots S_m$, such that each $S_j$ contains all of the primitive elements of $S$ but is partitioned according to its own unique set composition. Suppose to each of these possible domains, we assign the partition $\{E_1, E_2, \ldots, E_i, \ldots, E_n\}$ such that $P(E_i \mid S_1) \neq P(E_i \mid S_2) \neq \cdots \neq P(E_i \mid S_m)$. Then if we can assign values to all conditional probabilities, $P(E_i \mid S_j)$, and to all probabilities, $P(S_j)$, we can on any given $E$ assess the probability of any given $S_k$.

$$P(S_k \mid E) = \frac{P(S_k) \; P(E \mid S_k)}{\sum_{j=1}^{m} P(S_j) \; P(E \mid S_j)} \; . \tag{5}$$

If, as Charles Peirce mused, universes were as plentiful as blackberries and therein could we assign probability values to $S_1, S_2, \ldots, S_m$, then indeed this theorem would have become one of the major crutches of inductive inference. Translating into the language of evidence, we can improve upon our *a priori* conjecture of some $S_k$ by comparing it with the posterior probability of $S_k$ conditional on the evidence $E$. However, arguments over the possibility of assigning probability values to any $S_j$ are, for the present, quite beside the point. Bayes' theorem is easily proved within the axiomatized foundations of probability.

*Random variables.* Thus far we have only been concerned with finite probability spaces where enumeration is possible. In order now to extend probability theory to infinite spaces and to continuous variables, one needs an axiom of continuity and the notion of a random variable. Although Kolmogorov's argument is too complex to go into here, the basic ideas will help to make the extension of the theory to continuous variables at least a plausible one.

Assume a series of sets over some probability field such that $A_1 \supset A_2 \supset \cdots \supset A_n \supset \cdots$ (i.e. every succeeding set is included in the just prior set). The axiom of continuity then asserts

A6.    For the decreasing sequence of sets $A$

$$A_1 \supset A_2 \supset \cdots A_n \supset \cdots \text{ on the field } \mathcal{F}:$$

if the product of the sets

$$A_1 A_2 \cdots A_n \cdots = 0 \quad \text{as } n \to \infty,$$

then

$$n \lim_{n \to \infty} P(A_n) = 0.$$

This axiom permits us to extend a general theorem of inclusion to continuous variables; namely, if $A \subset A_s$ where $A_s$ is a sum of independent sets, then $P(A) \leq P(A_s)$ however fine the set structure.

We may now extend the set theoretic structure of probability to the notion of a random variable. Let $a$ be some real number. Then if $x$ itself is some real value such that $x$ can be constructed from the set of basic elements of $S$, and if the set of all $\{x < a\}$, for all $x$ constructed of those basic elements, is itself a member of some probability field $\mathfrak{F}$, then $x$ is a random variable.

*Mathematical expectation.* The idea of mathematical expectation is fundamental to all probability theory. Although expectation intones a subjective state of mind, it should not be so interpreted in the abstract theory. There, mathematical expectation is arbitrarily defined as a constant over a set of random variables. For finite probability fields

$$E(x) = \sum_{i}^{n} x_i \cdot P(x_i), \tag{1}$$

where $i$ runs the range of all possible sets. For infinite probability fields

$$E(x) = \int_s x P(x) \, dx. \tag{2}$$

When applied to familiar probability spaces (1) yields $E(x) = np$ for the binomial situation and (2) yields $E(x) = \mu$ for the distribution of normal variates. In the abstract theory of probability it should be noted that $np$ and $\mu$ (or their equivalent expressions) are constants and require no interpretation in fictional universes of palpable events.

*Laws of large numbers.* If it can be established that each of a finite set of variables $x_1, x_2 \ldots x_n$ is a random variable then some $X = f(x_1, x_2, \ldots, x_n)$ will itself be a random variable over a probability field. The essential idea of laws of large numbers is that of convergence. Some operation $S$ over the sequence $x_1, x_2, \ldots, x_n, \ldots$, converges if for any two values of the operation, $S_n$ and $S_m$, $n > m$ in the series, there is an $N$ such that the absolute difference $|S_n - S_m|$ can be made as small as we wish providing only that $m > N$ (Courant 1937, p. 367). This is the formal support of our intuitive ideas that there is some constant $K$ toward which some arithmetic operation on a set of variables, $\{x_1, x_2, \ldots, x_n, \ldots\}$, converges and such that as $n \to \infty$, there is no difference between $S_n$ and $K$. As concerns the probability of convergence we may say $S_n$ on $(x_1, x_2, \ldots, x_n)$ "converges in probability" (Kolmogorov) if for $\epsilon > 0$ there exists an $N$ such that $n > m > N$ and

$$P(|S_n - S_m| > \epsilon) < \epsilon.$$

The proof of various laws of large numbers rests in demonstrating that the property of convergence holds for the abstract worlds of random variables.

Since $S_m$ and $S_n$ are themselves random variables, we may define the expectation of $S$ as $E(S_n) = K$ for $n \to \infty$. Thus, if the property of probable convergence holds as above, it is reasonable to assume that convergence of $S_n$ on $E(S_n)$ for $n \to \infty$ is also subject to probabilistic interpretation. One line of support for laws of large numbers expressing such probabilistic convergence is to be found in a well-known theorem by Tchebycheff. In this, the inequality

$$P(|\,S_n - E(S_n)\,| > \epsilon) \leq \frac{\sigma_n^2}{\epsilon} \tag{3}$$

is proved. As in other statements of convergence $\epsilon$ can be made as small as we wish. Since $\sigma_n^2$ is the familiar variance term of the random variable in question and is itself a function of $n$ such that as $n \to \infty$, $\sigma_n^2 \to 0$ then convergence of $S_n$ on $E(S_n)$ is assured by taking $n$ sufficiently large.

More generally, a sequence of variables $S_1, S_2, \ldots, S_n, \ldots$ is said to obey a law of large numbers if it can be shown that

$$P(|\,S_n - \mu\,| \leq \epsilon) \to 1,$$

where the constant $\mu$ is generally the expectation of $S_n$.

An early form of the law of large numbers is to be found in a theorem of Bernoulli where the basic elements in $S$ are in one or another dichotomous classes. Let $x$ be the value of a Bernoullian trial with $x = (0,1)$. Let $S_n$ be the $\sum_i^n x_i$ over $n$ such trials. Then Bernoulli's theorem establishes that the quantity

$$P(|\,S_n - np\,| \geq \epsilon)$$

can be made infinitely small by taking $n$ infinitely large. We assign to $p$ the real value $P(A)$ where $A$ is the set of all $x$ taking the value 1. Simple proof of this theorem can be achieved through utilization of the Tchebycheff inequality (cf. Parzen, 1960; Gnedenko and Khinchin, 1961).

A rigorous axiomatization of elementary probability over finite spaces, and along the line of Kolmogorov, can be found in Suppes (1957). A descent from the highly abstract theory of probability to its more mundane surrounds (but still with the same formal foundations) can be found in Kolmogorov (1963).

## NOTE 13.5

Among the earliest treatments of epistemic probability is that of John Locke. In the *Essay Concerning Human Understanding* (IV. 15.1), Locke defines probability as "the appearance of agreement upon fallible proofs."

> A demonstration is the showing of the agreement or disagreement of two ideas by the intervention of one or more proofs, which have a constant, immutable, and visible connexion with one another; so probability is nothing but the appearance of such an agreement or disagreement by the intervention of proofs, whose connexion is not constant and immutable, or at least is not perceived to be so, and is enough to induce the mind to judge the proposition to be true or false, rather than the contrary (IV. 15.1).

Probability then is descriptive of whatever truth property we can assign to "belief, assent, or opinion."

Commenting upon Locke's treatment of probability, Charles Peirce concurs in the distinction between valid inference (demonstration) and probable inference that is a matter of belief; but he draws attention to the frequency aspects of support. "But, in the long run, there is a real fact which corresponds to the idea of probability, and it is that a given mode of inference sometimes proves successful and sometimes not, and that in a ratio ultimately fixed" (1878; cf. Buchler, editor, 1940, p. 159). Although Locke alluded to testimony, authority, and analogy in support of probable judgment, he was clearly aware that probability is held in "conformity with what is usually observed to happen. . . ."

For a discussion of the Peirce's indebtedness to Locke on a frequentist treatment of probable inference, see Braithwaite (1953, pp. 264–271). The term 'epistemic probability' is here due to Hawkins (1943); elaborating upon the work of Peirce, he distinguishes between "existential" and "epistemic" probability, with a frequency support for each.

## NOTE 13.6

If we restrict our definition to the abstract language of classes and then define probability as a denumerable ratio among equally likely classes, we need only clarify what an equally likely class is. What we have to make explicit is the assumption of symmetry. The language of sampling is inappropriate for abstract systems if by sampling we visualize some operational procedure. We must stay within the abstract system. How may we do this and still stipulate what we mean by an equally possible class? If we assign to the class some abstract property such that each class in the set of all equally possible classes has that property, we are confronted with the need to assign some value, $P_i$ to the class $C_i$, $P_j$ to the class $C_j$, and so on, such that $P_i = P_j = \ldots = P_k$. What then is distressing is the fact whatever the property of $P$, the probability compounded of $P_i$, $P_j, \ldots, P_k$, it does not appear to be differentiable from whatever is the property of $P_i, P_j, \ldots, P_k$. That is to say, any steps we would take to compare any two $P$'s, say $P_i$ and $P_j$ will not differ from the steps we would take to compare two probabilities, say $P_a$ and $P_b$.

## NOTE 13.7

The earliest dice (animal astragali or knuckle-bones) used in divination were far too asymmetrical to have given rise to ideas of equally possible outcomes inherent in the classical definition of probability. Still, among these natural bones, the most regular ones appeared to be sought; and it was obvious from early games that some outcomes were expected more frequently than others (David, 1962). Eventually, conventional dice came to be manufactured. By the time Cardano addressed himself to the analysis of gaming, ideas of equally frequent outcomes and fair risks were fairly well established. If one were to wager rationally, then it should be obvious that symmetric devices are simpler to analyze and to predict than asymmetric ones. However, it would appear that because of the asymmetry of early gambling devices the initial ideas of probability were of a relative frequency rather than necessitarian nature.

As David indicates, the notion of equally probable outcomes was very slow in coming to the analysis of random events. Not only were the early artifacts of gaming and divination asymmetrical but the arts of divination might have had an element of contrived control: "It is just possible that during his training the novitiate was taught to manipulate the fall of the dice, or even the astragali, to achieve a desired result."

## NOTE 13.8

The principle of indifference is easily subject to misinterpretation. A good example is to be found in a recent statistics book. The next person to enter the door, say of the local post office, will either be named 'Smith' or he will not. There are, therefore, two name classes: 'Smith' and 'not-Smith.' We have no prior information as to which class he belongs. By the principle of indifference, the two classes are equally possible. Therefore, the probability that our person is named Smith is one-half! Obviously, we do have some prior information about the differential frequencies in surnames. This is hardly an appropriate application of the principle. But suppose we were to go to a foreign land in which there is no basis for estimating the frequency of name assignments. If we are sure that no present knowledge is sufficient for us to establish that any one property is more likely than another, then, and only then, is the classical notion of probability applicable.

The above argument of dividing the world into that of an existential proposition and its contradictory, and then pleading ignorance of the truth of one or the other proposition and thereby claiming equally probable events is due to Keynes (1921). Of this argument von Mises writes: "It does not occur to him [Keynes] to draw the simple conclusion that if we know nothing about a thing, we cannot say anything about its probability" (1957, p. 75).

It should not be forgotten that the Marquis de Laplace was a strict determinist.

> Given for one instant an intelligence which could comprehend all the forces by which nature is animated and the respective situation of the beings who compose it—an intelligence sufficiently vast to submit these data to analysis—it would embrace in the same formula the movements of the greatest bodies of the universe and those of the lightest atom, for it nothing would be uncertain and the future, as the past, would be present to its eyes (Laplace; 1951, p. 4).

For the intelligence with infinite resources there would be no equally possible classes, no probability applications. All events would be strictly predictable. Therefore, we must assume that probability and the principle of indifference are the tools only of fallible intelligence. But people are more or less intelligent. What is equally likely to one person because of his state of knowledge (i.e., ignorance) may not be to another in light of his own. The principle of indifference, the principle of insufficient reason, as it is sometimes

called, thus remains personalistic rather than objectivistic. There are no procedural rules for applying it as independent of personal judgment.

It would appear that this is a trap laid for any determinist; a necessitarian
view of probability is itself personalistic. The more information the person acquires, the less fallible he becomes and the less likely he is to find his prior
conventions sufficient for supporting equally likely partitions.

An interesting effort to rehabilitate the classical principle of indifference,
can be found in a recent book by Hawkins (1964). Defining probability theory
"as the appropriate discipline for formulating and justifying inferences based
on certain kinds of evidence" (p. 137), Hawkins maintains there is no incompatibility between the principle of determinism and the idea of an objective
probability based on the principle of indifference. The postulate of determinism
asserts; "For every event $E$ there is some set of conditions $C$ such that wherever
conditions $C$ are realized, event $E$ occurs" (p. 145). The postulate of probability asserts: "For every event $E$ and probability $p$ there is some set of
conditions $C^*$ such that whenever conditions $C^*$ are realized, event $E$ has the
probability $p$" (p. 146). Hawkins then distinguishes two applications of
the principle of symmetry. We may attribute symmetry to the properties of the
events themselves, e.g., head and tail surfaces of a coin, the surfaces of a cube,
etc., or we may attribute symmetry to our specification of the dynamical conditions underlying the occurrence of an event. These two senses are, for Hawkins, quite significantly related. Let us assume the principle of determinism
such that if the conditions, $D_1$ or $D_2$, . . . , or $D_k$ occur we could predict with
certainty events of the type $E_1$ or $E_2$, . . . , or $E_k$ respectively. To say that
$E_1$ or $E_2$ . . . or $E_k$ are symmetrical events is then to say that in any actual
specification of the dynamical conditions determining any $E$, it is equally probable whether $D_1$ or $D_2$ . . . or $D_k$ obtains. Symmetry, indifference, and equiprobability are thereby transferred to the sets of conditions determining the
events. One might, of course, argue that we can overcome our limitations in
specifying dynamical conditions and thereby alter the probability of some $E$.
Hawkins would maintain, however, that because of the symmetrical properties
of some physical artifacts and systems, no specification of conditions will
overcome the lack of omniscience sufficient at least for us to say that the
occurrence of the event (collocation of particular and property) on one set of
conditions will be more or less probable than its occurrence on another. As
Hawkins indicates, the principle of indifference is an hypothesis; it is not
a priori certain. It may serve as a postulate for the development of probabilistic physical systems, but it is also subject to empirical tests.

If it seems puzzling that a rigorous determinist should be an equally
rigorous probabilist arguing for the objectivity of chance, we should reflect
upon the cost of information. Suppose from our initial state of knowledge in
predicting according to the principle of indifference, we foresee some new state
of perfect knowledge such that from $D_i$ we can predict $E_i$ and from $D_j$ we can
predict $E_j$ where previously we had regarded $E_i$ and $E_j$ as equally probable.
Hawkins' argument might lead us then to conjecture that in order to get the
information sufficient to specify either $D_i$ or $D_j$ we would introduce enough
uncertainty such that no matter how much knowledge we had, the residual uncertainty would make it equally probable whether $D_i$ or $D_j$ obtained for the

subsequent occurrence of $E$. Speculate, for example, how much knowledge one would need in order to predict the fall of a symmetrical coin. The greater the amount of information that is required and the greater the precision, the less accessible becomes the goal of certainty in prediction. The assumption of physical symmetry implies that the cost of gaining information to establish the nonsymmetry of the events in question is sufficient to introduce noncompensated uncertainties which themselves conceal that nonsymmetry.

The idea of a causal theory of probability making use of classical concepts of enumeration is not of recent vintage. It played a significant role in the early application of Bayes' theorem to the problem of the probability of causes. More recently it has found explicit applications to the probabilistic foundations of dynamical physical systems (Birkhoff and Lewis, 1935; Hopf, 1934, as suggested by Poincaré, 1905; see also Nagel, 1939). Nor, it should be added, were the early Bayesians or Poincaré the first to speak specifically of the probability of causes. Hume's *Treatise* carries a long section (I: III:XII) "Of the probability of causes." However, it should be noted that Hume's conception of the probability of causes is quite different from that of Poincaré and Hawkins. Rather than the probability relating to a sampling of dynamical conditions affecting physical events, it betokens a degree of belief supported by the past association of experiences. Probability is the basis of a less "vivacious" association of ideas than occurs in the case of constant conjunction—and, all the more, is subject to the same skepticism as is appropriate concerning the conjunction of the experiential ideas. Hume distinguished between the probability of chances and the probability of causes, the former being more nearly descriptive of probability as based on the principle of indifference, the latter being more akin to our present conceptions of subjective probability.

## NOTE 13.9

An exception to the argument of the equally possible being the equally frequent is taken by William Kneale in his *Probability and Induction* (1949). Although we may use observations and frequencies as support for our fundamental notions of equally possible events and classes, such support should not be confused with the premises essential to defining probability. Kneale rejects the principle of indifference as supportive of "equipossible" events in favor of more nearly logical principles like that of the "identity of indiscernibles" (Leibniz). Consider every element in a primary or fundamental probability set, $\alpha_1, \alpha_2, \alpha_3, \ldots$ . Then it is possible to specify any particular event in the series of all events having the property assigned to it such that no confusion (i.e., of disjunction) is possible. Such a set would logically constitute the set of equally possible events. Assume another set of events $\beta_1, \beta_2, \beta_3, \ldots$ , each of which according to its own specifications is unique. These too form a primary set. Assume further that any conceivable factor on which we wish to make any $\alpha_i$ or any $\beta_j$ contingent is also a contingent factor for all $\alpha$ and all $\beta$. Then the $P(\alpha,\beta)$, the probability that an event which is $\alpha$ is also $\beta$, is the ratio of the range of $\beta$ to that of $\alpha$. If such ranges are closed and thereby finite (as in typical marbles-and-urns problems) then $P(\alpha,\beta)$ is a simple proposition. The issue of contingent factors is introduced in order logically to make sure that there is nothing in the set of all factors specifying the individual $\alpha_i$ and $\beta_j$ which would make any one more likely selected than the other or make any disjoint subset more likely selected than any other disjoint subset of an equal number of elements.

Kneale, then proposes including both closed and open ranges within his range definition of probability. If the ranges of $\alpha$ and $\beta$ are closed and finite there seems to be no problem to establishing $P(\alpha,\beta)$ as $N(\alpha\beta)/N(\alpha)$. However, if the ranges of $\alpha$ and $\beta$ are infinite, there are obvious difficulties; one cannot enumerate over infinite sets. Facing such difficulties, one can assume subsets of the range $R(\alpha)$, say, $R(\beta)$, $R(\gamma)$, . . . such that for every element $\beta$ included in $R(\alpha)$ there is a one-to-one matching with an element $\gamma$ in $R(\alpha)$ and so on. Then $R(\alpha)$, though infinite, is reducible to a set of subsets each of which is infinite. The number of such subsets may itself be finite, in which case the equally dense subsets become members of a series of elements satisfying the conditions for defining primary sets (namely, no contingent factors are isolable which would make any one class any more likely than another). Such would be the case if the subclass structure were a homogeneous mesh or matrix superimposed over a Venn domain. On the other hand, the number of subsets in $R(\alpha)$ may itself be infinite. It is not clear then how we would proceed except by random sampling as is usually prescribed by frequentists. However, it should be clear that what the frequencies turn up is not essential to a definition of probability as based on ranges with equipossibility structure. One assumes that there is always some specification of events or disjunctive sets of events such that primary equiprobable sets underlie all domains of experience subject to probability anaylsis.

For critical discussions of Kneale's range definition of probability, see Broad (1950), Anscombe (1951). Kneale takes his departure from ideas of von Kries and Wittgenstein.

## NOTE 13.10

Charles Peirce, one of the earliest expositors of the frequency interpretation of probability, is explicit:

> The inference from the premise $A$, to the conclusion $B$, depends as we have seen on the guiding principle, that if a fact of the class $A$ is true, a fact of the class $B$ is true. The probability consists of the fraction whose numerator is the number of times in which both $A$ and $B$ are true, and whose denominator is the total number of times in which $A$ is true, whether $B$ is so or not. Instead of speaking of this as the probability of the inference there is not the slightest objection to calling it the probability that if $A$ happens, $B$ happens. But to speak of the probability of the event $B$, without naming the condition, really has no meaning at all.

As concerns statements of the character '$P(B)$,' Peirce goes on to say:

> It is true that when it is perfectly obvious what condition is meant, the ellipsis may be permitted. But we should avoid contracting the habit of

using language in this way (universal as the habit is), because it gives rise to a vague way of thinking, as if the action of causation might either determine an event to happen or determine it not to happen, or leave it more or less free to happen or not, so as to give rise to an *inherent* chance in regard to its occurrence. It is quite clear to me that some of the worst and most persistent errors in the use of the doctrine of chances have arisen from this vicious mode of expression (1878, p. 159).

The relevance of Peirce's counsel should not be overlooked by critics of classical probability who rely upon paradoxes like that of Bertrand for support. If one includes directions for sampling in the set of conditions, $A$, then the complete specification $P(AB \mid A)$ will not yield the contradictory results we might get from a careless interpretation merely of $P(B)$. See the discussion in N13.2.

## NOTE 13.11

John Venn (*Logic of Chance*, 1866) is often credited with the first explicit treatment of a frequency definition of probability. He, himself, gives prior credit to Leslie Ellis. In many respects, Charles Peirce's early essays on the subject are more notable for their recognition of the difficulties of the notion of relative frequency and for their applying frequentist ideas to the realm of probable inference.

In the "Doctrine of Chances" (1878) Peirce follows John Locke in believing that probability and probable argument are the basis of uncertain belief. However, his unique contribution rests in his insisting that the support of uncertain belief is a frequency matter.

> . . . in the long run, there is a fact which corresponds to the idea of probability, and it is that a given mode of inference sometimes proves successful and sometimes not, and that in a ratio ultimately fixed. As we go on drawing inference after inference of the given kind, during the first ten or hundred cases, the ratio of successes may be expected to show considerable fluctuations; but when we come into the thousands or millions, these fluctuations become less and less; and if we continue long enough, the ratio will approximate toward a fixed limit. We may, therefore, define the probability of a mode of argument as the proportion of cases in which it carries truth with it (1878, p. 159).

And again Peirce writes:

> Probability is a kind of relative number; namely, it is the ratio of the number of arguments of a certain genus which carry truth with them to the total number of arguments of that genus . . . (1878, p. 164).

Richard von Mises (see the popular *Probability, Statistics and Truth,* 1957) begins his discussion of probability by defining first the collective from which sampling is to be undertaken, and then a principle of place selection to satisfy the indispensable assumption of randomness. Since probability for von Mises is an empirical concept, the 'collective' denotes a sequence of events "which differ by certain observable attributes." The collective designates the sample space for which some probability can be assumed to hold. The second important idea concerns that arrangement of all events in the series constituting the collective. This arrangement should be such that no *a priori* procedure of selection can be contrived so as to alter the probability limit toward which a relative frequency condenses. This assures us of what we mean by randomness and independence of events in the collective. No procedure of selection, such as taking every other event in the series, or every one associated with a prime number, or every one following another event of a given type, should alter the value of the limiting frequency for the given collective. Von Mises calls this the "principle of the impossibility of a gambling system." No strategy of betting which is contingent upon any pattern of prior outcomes should alter the limiting frequency, and hence, the expectation of winning. Probability, then, for von Mises entails the following ideas: (1) the collective, (2) selection and the place principle, (3) relative frequency of attribute among elements in a series, and (4) limiting properties of the relative frequency as a function of sample size.

Reichenbach's treatment of probability (1938, 1949) would appear to agree in practical details with that of von Mises. That is, probability is long-run frequency such that the difference between $P_f$ and its limiting value $P$ itself approaches zero as $N$ approaches infinity. At the same time it differs in some important respects. Reichenbach is more explicit as concerns the logical structure of a series; he makes no assumptions relevant to a placement principle. Like Boole and Peirce before him, he notes that the frequency conception of probability is equally applicable to the language of events and the language of propositions. And most uniquely perhaps, he argues that the probability of inference leads to what can be regarded a three-valued system of logic.

Assume a universe of possible experience, all possible propositions to be structured in a series. Assume further that there is some, possibly infinite, subset of the elements of this series the selection of which defines a fundamental sampling procedure. For any element in this series assume that it is possible to ascertain whether or not that element possesses some given property (i.e., belongs to some given class). Probability, then, is simply a logical construction from a finite selection of elements from that series which expresses the relative frequency of elements possessing the given property. Furthermore, as a strategy for induction, it is assumed that for some relative frequency $h_n = m/n$ any prolongation of the series $s > n$ will result in an $h_s$ which will remain within a small interval about $h_n$; i.e., $h_n - \epsilon \leq h_s \leq h_n + \epsilon$.

Although the place selection principle of von Mises might make for a stronger defense of induction and probable inference, it does not form a part of Reichenbach's own defense of induction. Whether or not we can project the relative frequency toward some limiting value holding over all elements in the series, holding over all time, as it were, is itself a matter for verification. Assuming a place principle is simply to assume the problem of induction away. However, assuming that there is a limiting frequency, then procedures of inference based on the frequency conception of probability should lead to success in estimating what the limiting frequency is (or within what limits it resides).

Reichenbach argues for an "identity conception" as between the logical conception of probability dealing with belief and probable inference and the mathematical conception of probability dealing with relative frequency and the formal probability calculus. Probability is a logical construction from some relational system $L(e_1, e_2, e_3, \ldots)$ in which $e_1, e_2, e_3, \ldots$ are elements in the series to which dichotomous truth values can be assigned. However, the elements $e_1, e_2, e_3, \ldots$ can be replaced by a propositional series, $L(p_1, p_2, p_3, \ldots)$, in which elements in the propositional series assert the truth of element in an event series. Thus the truth function of belief and probable inference is operationally reducible to a frequency interpretation.

The identity conception of logical and mathematical probability enables Reichenbach to develop his conception of a three-valued logic as applied to inductive inferences. Although the elements in series $(p_1, p_2, p_3, \ldots)$ are subject to dichotomous truth assessment, the relational system $L(p_1, p_2, p_3, \ldots)$ itself is a logical construction yielding a relative frequency value between 0 and 1. Thus the truth value of the propositional series covers a continuous range of values between false and true. The intermediate values between 0 and 1 constitute the 'weight' we wish to assign to a propositional series. "The concept of weight is, so to say, a fictional property of propositions which we use as an abbreviation of frequency statements" (p. 325). Weights are therefore the support of our "posits" about single events which properly belong to a series. Posits on individual events are wagers of a kind in which the rationality of the wager is interpretable only in terms of long-run frequency.

## NOTE 13.12

There are several forms of laws of large numbers, all of which give formal support to a principle of convergence (v. Mises; 1957). The oldest of these is due to James Bernoulli. Assume that $m$ of $n$ trials with dichotomous outcomes have some property $\phi$ and $n - m$ have no such property. Then for any universe of trials no matter how large there is some parameter $p$ such that the difference between $m/n$ and $p$ can be expressed as a random variable about the expectation $p$. Bernoulli's law of large numbers then, in effect, states that for any $\epsilon$ however small

$$P(|\, m/n - p \,| < \epsilon) \to 1 \qquad \text{as } n \to \infty,$$

or more precisely for any $\epsilon$ and $\eta$ however small, the probability that $|\, m/n - p \,|$ will be less than $\epsilon$ can be made greater than some probability $1 - \eta$ by taking $n$ sufficiently large.

A simple demonstration of this law is available to anyone who is familiar with the binomial expansion and its normal approximation as $n$ becomes large. The random variable $m/n$ has a sampling variability (standard error) equal to $\sqrt{p(1 - p)/n}$. Let the value be $\sigma_p$. Then for any given value of $\eta$, e.g., $\eta = 0.01$, one can determine a $K$ such that

$$P(|\, m/n - p \,| < K\sigma_p = 1 - \eta.$$

Since $\sigma_p$ is inversely proportional to the magnitude of $n$, then $K\sigma_p$ may be made vanishingly small by taking $n$ sufficiently large. At the same time, we may take $\eta$ vanishingly small by taking $K$ sufficiently large. Thus both $K_{\sigma_p}$ and $\eta$ can be rendered vanishingly small by taking $n$ sufficiently large. (This feature of binomial probabilities is well demonstrated by the familiar confidence interval curves of Clopper and Pearson, 1934; the larger the $n$ the narrower the range of $m/n$ about $p$.)

A more conservative principle, yet one from which the Bernoullian law can be derived, is Tchebycheff's inequality. By a procedure of eliminating small values of $x - \mu$ (substitute $m/n - p$), Tchebycheff was able to establish the following:

$$P(|x - \mu| \geq K) \leq \frac{\sigma^2}{K^2}.$$

Thus for binomial (Bernoullian) trials

$$P(|m/n - p| \geq K) \leq \frac{p(1 - p)}{nK^2},$$

and the probability that $|m/n - p|$ will exceed $K$, however small, can be made as small as we wish by taking $n$ sufficiently large.

Critical discussions of laws of large numbers can be found in Braithwaite (1953), von Mises (1957), Kneale (1949), Nagel (1939). Relatively simple derivations of the laws can be found in Braithwaite (1953); Gnedenko and Khinchin (1961), and Weatherburn (1957).

## NOTE 13.13

Writers who have made recent contributions to the study of personal probability (e.g., Ramsey, 1926); de Finetti, 1937; Koopman, 1940a,b; Good, 1950; Savage, 1954, 1962) have all emphasized the consistency–coherence requirement. It is perhaps questionable whether two such concepts are needed but the hyphenation used here is to emphasize the logical and the pragmatic aspects of what generically we might regard the consistency criterion. Should a system of personal probabilities be consistent or otherwise conformal with the formalization of probability theory, then this should be a sufficient condition for coherence. Furthermore it is difficult to see how a system could lead unequivocally to coherent system of wagers and "posits" were we not able to establish its consistency in a formal sense.

It should be obvious that systems of personal probabilities based on ideally partitioned (finite) universes are more amenable to consistency evaluation than are systems superimposed on the possibility of infinite alternatives. It would appear then that the classical view of the probability domain, with its purported partition into symmetrical properties, would thus offer a paradigm for consistent systems. But the paradigm is not required. De Finetti, for example, would argue for the possibility of a consistent system of beliefs independent of objective paradigms and of anything approaching complete knowledge. All that is required of S for him to have a coherent set of beliefs is that it not be possible to bet against S, using S's odds and expectations, such that S is sure to incur a loss (de Finetti, 1937, 1963). It is interesting that although originally (1937) de Finetti wrote independently of any knowledge of Ramsey's earlier essays (published in 1931) both arrived at essentially the same schema for the requirement of coherence.

In addition to the consistency–coherence requirement, de Finetti (1937) imposes the condition of *exchangeability*. This requirement is more appropriate to discussions in the justification of induction, but in brief, events are exchangeable if all nondistinguishable events (except for arrangement and combinatorial constitution) in a given class can be assigned the same probability. De Finetti (1937) utilizes a simple example for demonstrating the above characteristic. Suppose our sampling of experience is describable in terms of $n$ Bernoullian trials in which $r$ out of the $n$ elements have some given property, say a success. Then by combinatorial analysis there are $_nC_r$ possible results for the class. Suppose further that for each of these results (events), we estimate the probability $p_i$, with $i = 1, 2, \ldots, {}_nC_r$. The average probability over the class would then be

$$\bar{p} = \frac{\sum_{}^{nC_r} p_i}{{}_nC_r}.$$

Then, if for any event in the class (in which the class is defined by the property "$r$ successes out of $n$ trials") the probability $p$ is equal to $\bar{p}$, then any and all such events are *exchangeable*.

A bit of reflection will make it obvious why this requirement of exchangeability is so essential to de Finetti's defense of induction. If the judgment of probability or the measure of personal belief were contingent not only upon the event as recognized and described in terms of its class membership but also on its unique construction, then one could not use the *generic* information as the instrument of his inference. For example, suppose from ten tosses of a coin, the person were to make a subjective estimate of the probability of heads. Suppose, moreover, the person gets six heads and four tails. If the conditions of exchangeability were not met then our person might make a different estimate of $p$ if he got heads on the 2nd, 3rd, 5th, 6th, 9th, and 10th tosses, say, than on the 1st, 4th, 5th, 6th, 8th and 9th. This would play havoc with inductive inference and certainly with the application of Bayes' theorem to problems of inference.

## NOTE 13.14

As Bertrand's paradox has shown for the classical treatment of probability, inconsistency can be safeguarded against only if we spell out in detail the partition of our event space and sampling procedure. Conceivably one could determine the probability, $p$, of a randomly drawn chord being longer than the side of the inscribed equilateral triangle and the probability, $q$, of the chord being shorter than the side of the triangle such that $p + q \neq 1$. Such would be the case if we were to determine $p$ and $q$ independently and with different construction instructions for each.

The properties of convergence toward a limiting frequency are presumptive ones established for formal theorems, such as for laws of large numbers, but not in any way for strings of observations as such. Consistency can be assured for the frequency principle of probability only if we endow it with extra-empirical properties such as that of randomness.

## NOTE 13.15

Procedures for estimating the subjective probability $S(p)$ are often more complicated than indicated here. To begin with they may assume that for gains and losses there is an additive schedule of utilities subject to interval scaling. That is to say, it is possible to determine a set of four utilities $\{a, b, c, d\}$ such that the difference between $a$ and $b$ is to be regarded as equal to the difference between $c$ and $d$. Discussions of the assessment and scaling of utilities are beyond the range of the present discussion; however, there is a simple device due to Ramsey (1926) which indicates the general schema. Assume that you have found an event $E$ such that for subjective probabilities $P(E) = P(\sim E) = \frac{1}{2}$. Then our set of utilities $\{a, b, c, d\}$ is properly scaled if it is a matter of indifference to S that he choose between $a$ if $E$ is true or $b$ if $E$ is false, and $c$ if $E$ is true or $d$ if $E$ is false. The search for an $E$ with $S(p) = \frac{1}{2}$ is itself determined by the indifference of S to the option $a$ if $E$ is true or $b$ if $E$ is false, and $b$ if $E$ is true and $a$ if $E$ is false, where it should be noted $a \neq b$.

A more recent but somewhat more restricted treatment of $S(p)$ estimation is to be found in a paper by Davidson and Suppes (1956). Suppose our subject S is to be offered the following schedule of options.

|       | Option 1 | Option 2 |
|-------|----------|----------|
| $E$   | $x$      | $u$      |
| $\sim E$ | $y$   | $v$      |

$x$, $y$, etc., are the gains under the options contingent on the occurrence or non-occurrence of the event $E$. Let $S(E)$ be the subjective probability of $E$ and $S(\sim E) = 1 - S(E)$. Let $\phi(x)$, $\phi(y)$, etc., be the utility functions of $x$, $y$, etc. If the subject S is then indifferent as to the options, we have

$$S(E)\phi(x) + S(\sim E)\phi(y) = S(E)\phi(u) + S(\sim E)\phi(v). \qquad (1)$$

Assume now that for S there is some event $E^*$ such that for every pair $x$, $y$ we have

$$S(E^*)\phi(x) + S(\sim E^*)\phi(y) = S(E^*)\phi(y) + S(\sim E^*)\phi(x). \qquad (2)$$

For any $\phi(x) \neq \phi(y)$ we may infer

$$S(E^*) = S(\sim E^*) = \tfrac{1}{2}. \qquad (3)$$

Now if $E = E^*$, we determine from (1) that

$$\phi(x) + \phi(y) = \phi(u) + \phi(v) \qquad (4)$$

which enables us to determine equality of utility differences. Given now the determination of interval scale of utilities, it is possible to determine $S(E)$

over a finite set of events. Assuming $S(E) + S(\sim E) = 1$, then from (1) we get

$$S(E) = \frac{\phi(v) - \phi(y)}{\phi(v) - \phi(y) + \phi(x) - \phi(u)} . \tag{5}$$

That is to say the subjective probability $S(E)$ is determined solely in terms of assessed utilities assigned to our option paradigm.

There is a large literature in this field. For a sampling of behavioral studies on the measure of subjective probability, see W. Edwards (1954, 1962); G. M. Becker (1962); Davidson, Suppes, and Siegel (1957).

## NOTE 13.16

Brief summaries of two of the several formal treatments of subjective probability are given here.

1.  An early and influential treatment of the subject is that of Bernard Koopman (1940a,b, 1941). Addressing himself to what he calls intuitive probability, he is to analyze "a category of propositions of a nature marked by features neither physical nor mathematical but by their role under the aspect of reason." "Their essential characteristic is their involvement of that species of relation between knower and the known evoked by such terms as probability, liklihood, degree of certainty, as used in the parlance of intuitive thought" (1940b, p. 763).

To the conventional logical rubrics, Koopman adds the relation "not more probable than," symbolized '$\prec$.' Thus by '$a \mid h \prec b \mid k$' Koopman asserts that "$a$ on the presumption of $h$ is no more probable than $b$ on the presumption of $k$." The task is to enunciate a set of axioms and derive a set of theorems sufficient to include this relation within conventional logic and mathematical theory of probability.

First, Koopman offers a set of five axioms, which for the most part are transcriptions of axioms in modern logic (i.e., axioms of verification, implication, reflexivity, transitivity, and antisymmetry). These enable him to utilize the partial ordering properties of $\prec$ in defining the probability relations:

$$a \mid h \approx b \mid k : \text{equiprobability}$$
$$a \mid h < b \mid k : \text{inferior probability}$$
$$a \mid h \parallel b \mid k : \text{incomparability}$$

A second set of four axioms enunciates composition and decomposition of relations through the transitivity properties of the $\prec$ relation and other properties ("alternative presumption" and "subdivision") which enable us to assert properties (irrelevance and comparison) essential to the idea of ordering.

From this set of axioms, Koopman then proceeds to derive the theorems of the theory of probability. These fall into three groups. The first group includes the theorems on comparison. In these, a probability measure of $a \mid h$ is derived such that $0 < a \mid h < 1$; means are derived for stipulating factors of conditional irrelevance (i.e., a set of factors $\{c_i\}$ such that no factor

$c$ coupled with $h$ alters the order status ($\prec$) of $a \mid h$); and order relations are derived for the disjunction of options.

In the second group are theorems on numerical probability. First, a measure of probability is derived for a finite propositional set, and the intuitive probability $P(a \mid h)$ is shown to be appraisable if the upper and lower limits of its construction in the propositional set are identical. Here, for example, the propositional set might be conformal with the elements in a set of putatively equally likely events. From this base the elementary theorems of probability (conditional probability and disjunction) are derived.

A third group of theorems concerns statistical weight and sequential frequency. The function of this group is to establish the link between the concept of limiting frequency as it is applied to sampling in the physical world and the "intuitive idea of probability." For example, it is proved that for finite sets of elements, in which it is possible to select sets which are equally probable in the intuitive sense, it is also possible to produce an appraisal $P(a \mid h)$ of $a \mid h$ corresponding to a limiting frequency in the objective world.

Koopman maintains that it is not possible to establish partial orderings ($\prec$) initially without assuming other ($\prec$) propositions. That is to say, all such orderings concern prior conditional propositions of the character $a \mid h$:

> . . . we may hazard the view that in principle the authority of the first ($\prec$) proposition does not reside in any general law of probability, logic or experimental science. And the notion presents itself that such primary and irreducible assumptions are grounded on a basis as much of the aesthetics as of the logical order (1940b, p. 774).

It should also be noted that Koopman restricts the application of probability to experimental propositions, where such propositions "may in principle be verified by the performance of a single crucial experiment." Hence he is reluctant to apply probability to a comparison and evaluation of the credibility of theorems. Thus some usages of the term 'probability' are not admissible to interpretation within its intuitive treatment.

2. Another influential work in personal probability is Leonard J. Savage's *The Foundations of Statistics* (1954). Savage's treatment is more extensive than that of Koopman in that it lays out the subjectivist foundations for statistical inference and decision. In his later writings (e.g., 1962, 1964), it is hardly possible to distinguish Savage's presentation of subjective probability from his espousal of Bayesian procedures of inference.

The formal development is too extensive to submit to easy and concise summarization. However, the following points may be noted. We are familiar with the strategies for establishing an ordered and coherent system of preferences. Personal probability thus is to be reduced to the theory whereby probabilities are to be assigned on the basis of consistent decisions in the face of uncertainty. "Subjective probability refers to the opinion of a person as reflected in his real or potential behavior" (1962, p. 11). Simply stated, the formalized system requires that the probability measure be such that

$$P(A \text{ or } B) = P(A) + P(B),$$
$$P(A) \geq 0,$$
$$P(S) = 1, \qquad \text{where } S \text{ is the universal event.}$$

More generally, personal odds derived from betting options are to be such that

$$\frac{P(A)}{P(\sim A)} = \frac{P(A)}{1 - P(A)}.$$

The above relation is obvious as an expression in the mathematical theory of probability. The object for the person is for him to develop a coherent set of beliefs (potential behaviors) such that that relation does indeed hold (Savage, 1962).

The formal development (1954) constitutes a system of postulates and theorems sufficient to establish the above. Savage first establishes the relation of ordering of elements within a set sufficient to cover a set of preferences. This he does by reference to postulates of simple ordering (conforming to the transitive relation) and the "sure-thing principle." A sure thing is one in which some preference as between acts or objects is not altered in any way by the presence either of $B$ or of $\sim B$, i.e., the preference is a sure thing with respect to $B$ if it is not conditional on $B$. Next in the argument, a qualitative personal probability is defined. An event $A$ is not more probable than $B$ ($'A \leq B'$), if for a given preference schedule one would choose to receive the prize contingent upon the occurrence $B$ rather than receiving it contingent upon the occurrence of $A$. Now, if the set of all possible events, $S$, carries a probability measure and also a qualitative probability ordering such that the ordering of the one set of measures can be inferred from the other, then there is agreement between the two. Additional requirements are made to tighten up the correspondence between the probability measure and the qualitative personal probability. There must be a partition of $S$ such that no event of the partition is more probable than a given event. In such case the qualitative personal probability is *fine*. The partition should also be such as to permit the establishment of equivalence relations. In this case the qualitative personal probability will be *tight*.

Whereas Koopman is regarded as a dualist in admitting an objectivist, as well as an intuitive, treatment, Savage is more nearly a monist in holding that other treatments of probability (e.g., the necessitarian) may be useful but only in limited situations for checking the consistency of personal belief. And contrary to many people, Savage believes that all sets of finite additivity have a probability measure. He would not be reluctant, for example, to assign a probability to an historical event.

## NOTE 13.17

Who is subjective and who is objective? Objectivists (necessitarians and frequentists) and subjectivists alike back off from being "subjective" in a pejorative sense of the term. Objectivity is a virtue. Von Wright (1962), a frequentist, argues that Ramsey's treatment of subjective probability presumes that the subject knows what it means to be indifferent. Either indifference is a matter of ignorance or it is a reasoned attitude based upon the person's own objectivist analyses or intuition concerning a class of events. The subjectivists obviously do not wish to contend that the subject judges out of ignorance. On the other hand, de Finetti (1937; Chapter II) has argued effectively that the personalist determination of probability is stringently operational, whereas both the classical and frequentist interpretation suffer for their lack of systematizing the subjectivistic elements implicit in each. For example, the notion of equipossibility and equally likely classes is implemented by subjective judgments. And for the frequentist his inclination to project from observed frequencies to as yet unsampled frequencies, to predict future frequencies, is supported by his subjectivistic presumptions. In fact, it is because of the subjective aspects of traditional conceptions of probability that de Finetti undertakes his own formulations of a subjective probability.

Frequentists especially are reluctant to air their subjectivistic embarrassments. An unpublicized case is that of the debate between one- and two-tail tests in classical significance tests (see Chapter 14). The standard argument asserts that the critical region (the region of improbable events) for rejection of the null hypothesis is to be distributed among the two asymptotic tails of the sampling distribution if there is no replacement hypothesis to be *a priori* deduced from a theory. On the other hand, if there is some replacement hypothesis as derived from some theory, then the experimenter is entitled to concentrate all of the critical region into one or another of the two tails according to direction. But the entitlement to one or another type of test is contingent upon the state of the mind of the experimenter. Conceivably, two experimenters processing the *same* data might arrive at different decisions concerning the null hypothesis, even though they agreed precisely as to what was the appropriate risk. A statistic ($t$, $z$, etc.,) significant for one experimenter may not be for the other.

## NOTE 13.18

Conceivably one can classify probability theorists as monist or dualist. Monists admit to only one meaning of probability and can be frequentists (e.g., von Mises, Reichenbach, Ellis, Boole, Venn, Peirce), necessitarians (Laplace, Kneale, Jeffreys), or personalists (Ramsey, de Finetti, Borel, Savage). Dualists who would, of course, embrace two meanings of probability may disagree as to which of the meanings of probability the two should be. Most dualists wish to attribute a meaning and possibly a measure of probability to confirmation of hypotheses and theories which is different from the legitimate application of probability to the domains of relative frequency (e.g., Carnap, 1950; Nagel). Some would simply distinguish between the necessitarian and frequency interpretations of probability (e.g., Margenau). And some would distinguish between intuitionist and objectivist views, admitting, of course, that both may serve a function (e.g., Koopman). It is claimed by the personalists (especially de Finetti and Savage) that all meanings of probability, all its useful applications, can and should be formalized under the ideas of subjective probability.

There is a very large literature on the meaning of probability. One perhaps could distinguish between the more formal treatments of the problem (e.g., de Finetti, 1937; Koopman, 1940a,b; Good, 1950; Savage, 1954; Jeffreys, 1939); and the more philosophical (e.g., Carnap, 1950; Kneale, 1949; Peirce, 1878; Reichenbach, 1938, 1949; Nagel, 1939). But the distinction is hardly worth maintaining since all probabilistic defenses of induction involve the mathematical theory of probability. One thing that does stand out among the latter group, however, is a preoccupation with the problem of justifying induction.

Good general discussions of the meaning of probability can be found in Nagel, *Principles of the Theory of Probability,* and in a symposium appearing in *Philosophy and Phenomenological Research,* 1945, Vol. 5; 1946, Vol. 6 (contributions by D. Williams, E. Nagel, H. Reichenbach, R. Carnap, H. Margenau, G. Bergmann, F. Kaufmann, and R. von Mises). An excellent critical review of this symposium appears in Koopman (1946).

Shorter discussions are available in Russell (1948); J. O. Wisdom (1952); I. J. Good (1950); E. H. Madden, editor (1960). Critical discussions of the classical and frequency definitions are to be found in Kneale (1949).

An excellent selection of studies relating to personalistic probability can be found in H. E. Kyburg and H. E. Smokler, editors, *Studies in Subjective Probability* (1964).

For a recent probabilistic interpretation of credibility in terms of information theory, see Hawkins (1964).

CHAPTER 14

# *Statistical Inductions*

GENERALIZATIONS are of two generic types: summative and ampliative. A summative generalization is some kind of summary statement over a finite set of observations. As such, it is a logical construction; the finite set of observations is transformed into the generalization by an explicit set of logical operations. In contrast, an ampliative generalization involves not only logical operations over a set of observations but also an inductive bridge not of itself explicated or supported by the data themselves. It is generalizations of this second type which have remained problematic throughout the history of empiricism.

The problem of induction is that of making an inference from a finite set of observations and data to a generalization over an extended set of "data points" not itself the subject of observation. In a sense no induction is possible; there are no indubitable means of getting directly from a finite set of observations to an extended set of measures or quantities that have not been determined, and which, therefore, belong more properly to the imaginary domains of possibility. If we think of our generalization as being a statement of one type and the observation statements as being statements of another type, then there are no means of deriving the one from the other without our making assumptions that are themselves subject to doubt, to verification, to the very query we are seeking to answer. This is the familiar problem of induction, with all its publicized scandal.

There have been several strategies for resolving the problem. The inductive bridge incorporates the principle of uniform nature (J. S. Mill). The inductive bridge might be regarded as a kind of scientific intuition in which the generalization is found to be internally consistent with the complex structure of science (Kneale). The inductive bridge might be a cognitive intuition in which the mind itself is the indubitable processor of the data input (Kant). Or it may be that we are merely playing games. All generalizations are really restricted generalizations; a generalization is not subject to disconfirmation, it is an inference ticket for anticipating

431

specifiable occurrences and events (Ramsey, Schlick). Now what distinguishes all of these tactics, these defenses of inference, is their presumption. There is always a "providing" clause. Given the set of observations and providing certain structures or relations, then a certain type of conclusion is defensible. Yet the element of doubt, of skepticism, always remains. Though the assumptions are necessary to the inductive bridge, they are always subject to critique and possible rejection. So it is with all strategies of induction. It is not so much that David Hume discovered a problem as it was simply the case of his defining the difference between purely deductive arguments for which we can claim certainty and inductive arguments for which we can claim nothing of the kind.

Here at least we can recognize the problems. There is, however, a less codified sense in which the analysis of inductive inference proves to be refractory. When we attempt to analyze what scientists do we find there is no general method, no tidy set of tools by which the investigator moves from his data to general hypothesis. We are hamstrung at the very beginning of our analysis. As we have seen, observation and fact cannot be separated from the conceptual framework within which the investigator operates. He does not make observations and then generalize by means of inductive inference. Rather, he brings to the laboratory and to the world his preconceptions, and then he observes. To speak of objectivity, and of random sampling, let us say, is to propose a naive picture wherein each scientist is hardly more than a technician at loose in a universe of preformed facts. This hardly in any way captures the spirit of scientific investigation. Were it really so, we might continue to prepare our students with Mill's canons of induction and then instruct them to go out in search of a cause.

Indeed, when we analyze what scientists do we discover no general method by which the individual investigator engages in inductive inference. At times a "single" observation may give evidence to his preformed hypothesis, as, for example, in his making an observation during a solar eclipse. At times his hypothesis might emerge without the benefit of any empirical search. Here the hypothesis is worked out in the travails of a "creative" synthesis, in which internal consistence within extant theory is prized over the grubbing for any empirical support. The Galilean revolution in the mathematization of science epitomized this spirit. At times, too, the scientist is intuitionist, not knowing just how the significant insight was gestated from the mixture of theory, fact, and fancy. Only in the humdrum of scientific empiricism, it would appear, do we get down to the academic exercises of establishing the formal foundations of "informative inference."

For the most part, it does not bother the working empiricist that what he takes for granted has in the minds of philosophers, at least, required justification. He is not likely to be distracted with the positivist's self-effacing efforts to find sanction for even the most basic of his data statements, his protocols. Yet when he gives his attention to matters of empirical support, of inference and decision, he is prone to be more so-phisticated, finding for himself prefabricated defenses spelled out in the gospels of his statistical methodology. His defense and justification of inductive inference are statistical in nature. Granting certain models of the world, with their respective calculi, then he can easily formulate rules for accepting one hypothesis over another.

Now there is something salubrious about this statistical climate. Being well-bred to skepticism, yet still prone to dogmatism, the empiricist welcomes the opportunity to ritualize his decision. He never forgets that he operates in a world of uncertainty. Yet the ritual of a calculation and a rule enables him to make decisions—sometimes to make optimal decisions wherein he might maximize his gain, but more often simply to distinguish what is significant, and perhaps worthy of publication, from that which is not significant. He speaks knowingly of errors and makes allowances for them. He adopts policy positions, with all the comfort and caress of optimality. And if he is encouraged ever so slightly, he may speak boastfully of the return of the rational man. And yet, if our contemporary empiricist is pressed, he will soon let you know that all is not quite well. Proneness to simplifying assumptions spoils the game of decision and informative inference. The translation of decision statements leads to semantic obscurities. We have had a preview of this in the discussion of the meaning of probability. The issues there are integral with those of inference and decision. What interpretation we give to probability cannot be separated from our strategies and defenses of inductive inference.

## SOME PRELIMINARIES

Should we review the many applied texts and treatises of the past two decades, we might readily conjecture that statistical methodology is a finished product in which the only ostensible challenge to the writer is that of expository skill. This is especially true of the works written for the behavioral scientist. However, the literature on the foundations of statistics gives us quite another picture. Theoretical statisticians now as never before differ as to their interpretations of probability statements; they differ on the strategies and commitments of decision; and they differ as to what kinds of metaphysical attitudes are appropriate to the creative scientist. In the present chapter we shall be concerned primarily with informal expositions of two approaches to statistical inference: the Neyman–Pearson theory of inductive behavior, and Bayesian procedures of inference and decision. In addition there will be occasions to refer to the fiducial argument of R. A. Fisher, and to the likelihood principle that is common to both of the above theories of inference. Each of these points of view has its devotees. Each has been offered as support for inductive inference. First, however some distinctions and a general rubric for inference.

## Inductive Inference versus Inductive Behavior

According to both Boole and Peirce, a frequency interpretation of probability enables one to establish the equivalence between probabilities about events and the probabilities of statements about those events. Thus to say that the long-run probability of heads in the tossing of a coin is one-half is not different in any important sense from my saying "the probability of my being correct in saying heads for every toss of the coin is one-half." All frequentists are inclined to agree with Boole and Peirce since one statement, the latter, operationally translates into long-run frequencies in the event world. The distinction, however, achieves significance even for the frequentist when we consider statistical inference. Probabilistic statements about parameters, or about hypotheses about parameters, purport to be about the world. That is, there is a certain proneness to treat generalizations probabilistically as if independent of *our* making predictions or *our* expressing degrees of confidence. Providing there is no semantic confusion as to the translation of such confidence statements, then there is no difficulty in linguistic partisans reaching agreement. However, when we make some definite statement about a hypothesis being true (or of a parameter being within a set of limits, as in statistical inference), there seems to be an important difference between attributing probability to an hypothesis which may or may not be true (but must be one or the other) and attributing probability to a statement about the hypothesis. For example, according to the fiducial argument, it is permissible to say that a parameter (i.e., the true generalization) lies within a definite set of limits with a specifiable probability. The properties of probability are assignable to the parameter. On the other hand, Neyman (1938, 1950, 1952)—to whom the present distinction is primarily due—emphasizes that probability applies not to the hypothesis as such but to a *class* of statements each of which asserts the truth of the hypothesis. Neyman contends that only in the long run of making many inferences, each of which is a dogmatic statement about the truth of an hypothesis, can we interpret "inference" in probabilistic terms. But here the emphasis is upon what we *do* in the long run. We commit ourselves to act in certain ways as regards dogmatic pronouncements. The relevant probabilities then are descriptive of our actions and not of a fictional world of the statistician's mind in which parameters are treated as random variables. If I say, "The probability is 0.95 that the true mean of a population lies within $X \pm K$ units," this may sound very much like my saying "The probability of my being correct in saying the true mean lies within $X \pm K$ is 0.95." Yet the translation that Boole and Peirce could insist upon is not readily applied. A true mean of a population, our parameter, is a universal constant. It has different ontological status from that of the statements of hypotheses about it. For Neyman, it is not so much that a distinction is to be made between inductive inference and inductive behavior, as it is that the former reduces to the latter. Probability statements as applied to inference are descriptive of our behavior in making inferences, and not of a truth property of the parameter, nor of the explicit hypothesis that stipulates that the parameter is to be found within clearly specified limits.

The argument for inductive behavior clearly reduces to a frequency interpretation of probability. The argument for fiducial probability concerning parameters leaves the meaning of probability somewhat obscure.

## Inductive Inference and Decision

Closely related to the above distinction is one between inference and decision. At first glance making an inference is like making a decision, but in statistical strategies, at least, there is a difference in emphasis. Inference is, in a sense, less explicit than decision. According to statistical inference we are content to specify a family of hypotheses (about a parameter), each of which is plausible or acceptable as against a family of hypotheses each of which is implausible and hence unacceptable. Decisions to act in accordance with these bits of hypotheses are not made an explicit part of the inductive procedure. Statistical decision, however, commands an explicit acceptance or rejection (or possibly a delay of judgment) of some specific hypothesis. Consequently we must stress the errors of making false decisions, either of acceptance or rejection, and we must assess the risks attending to such errors. Again the emphasis is upon behavior, upon action, error, and consequence rather than upon the hypothesis and the parameter as such. We decide to act as if a hypothesis is true, or as if it is false, whereby the decision procedure is a pragmatic one for manufacturing those limited comparisons which enable us to assess comparative error and risk. It does not particularly concern us that no specific hypothesis (e.g., the null) is ever likely true. Strategies that emphasize the language of inference, on the other hand, incline more toward acceptance ranging over a class of hypotheses, any one of which must be acceptable. Only in rejection of a hypothesis is an explicit decision made.

It is not easy to make simple generalizations on how the statistical strategies stand as concerns the distinctions between inference and behavior, and inference and decision. For the most part they are defended by the traditionalists who follow the Neyman–Pearson theory of statistical induction. Adherents to the frequency interpretation of probability are inclined to adopt strategies of decision and inductive behavior, for that is where their language receives its most explicit interpretation.

## Schema for Probabilistic Inference

Let us now establish in somewhat general terms a schema which though essential to the Neyman–Pearson decision procedure might also prove useful in the discussion of alternative procedures. First we will consider an "event" a generic designation for a class of many occurrences all of which possess some defining property. Now assume an event space over the domain of all possible events such that for any universe specification we visualize a partition with the following properties:

> To each class $\{E_i\}$ within the partition of the universe a probability $p_i$ can be assigned such that $0 \leq p_i \leq 1$.

> The sum of all probabilities over all classes within the partition is 1, i.e., $\Sigma p_i = 1$.

> The probability calculus, as formalized by Kolmogorov, is applicable to establishing the probabilities among the union and disjunction of classes (sets) within the partition.

Assume further that for this partition of the event space different probability assignments are possible, subject to the conditions enunciated above. Call any set of probability assignments a universe specification, the latter to be identified by the parameter $\theta$. Then the family of all such universes, $\{\theta_i\}$, will be known as the parameter space, $\Omega$. This is to indicate that the issue of universe identification is open; the problem of inference is that of doing what we can to make the identification.

Consider now the following tactic. For any given universe, identified by the parameter $\theta_k$, divide the partition of the event space into two complementary classes, $w$ and $\sim w$. Furthermore, adopt a convention such that the probability that any occurrence is a member of $w$ is much less than the complementary probability of the occurrence being a member of $\sim w$; that is, $P(x \in w \mid \theta_k) \ll P(x \in \sim w \mid \theta_k)$. Thus, were we sure that we were sampling the universe identified by $\theta_k$, we might very well be willing to bet that whatever our observation, it would fall within the class $\sim w$ rather than the class $w$. Or after the fact, should we observe that the occurrence $x$ is indeed a member of the class $w$, we might very well be inclined to doubt that $\theta_k$ is the proper identification of our universe.

As it stands, however, the issue of the tactic is not clearly drawn. Consider now two possible universes as identified by $\theta_0$ and $\theta_1$. Furthermore establish the dichotomization $\{w\}$ and $\{\sim w\}$ on the basis of $\theta_0$. Since we are to regard the universes identified by $\theta_0$ and $\theta_1$ as noncoincident, we may conclude that $P(x \in w \mid \theta_1)$ is not equal to $P(x \in w \mid \theta_0)$. Now at least two strategies of decision are open to us. Consider $w$ to be a critical region to our decision. Then, should a sampling observation $x$ fall within the critical region as defined with respect to $\theta_0$ and should $P(x \in w \mid \theta_1)$ be greater than the probability for the critical event $P(x \in w \mid \theta_0)$, then we should choose the hypothesis $\theta_1$ over $\theta_0$. As it stands, of course, this gives an incomplete picture of a two-hypothesis decision procedure. The details of this will be covered in the discussion of the Neyman–Pearson procedures. A second strategy may simply involve our concentrating on the probabilities of the evidence conditional on the two hypotheses. To assign the variable $x$ a class membership is to give it event identification. We then designate the probability of the event conditional on the hypothesis the *likelihood* of the event (sometimes regarded as the likelihood of the hypothesis). Thus $P(x \in w \mid \theta_0)$ and $P(x \in w \mid \theta_1)$ are both likelihoods. Now for any event $E_k$, $P(E_k \mid \theta_0) \neq P(E_k \mid \theta_1)$, a strategy based on the likelihood principle might dictate the decision, that is, choose whichever hypothesis assigns the highest likelihood to the observed event.

The details of these procedures need to be spelled out, but there is a common theme running throughout the two strategies mentioned here. With knowledge of likelihood for any given universe (or of corresponding likelihoods for alternative universes) we judge the plausibility of the hypothesis by virtue of its likelihood. If a hypothetical universe is such as to render an observation "unlikely" and yet the observation obtains, we are inclined to express doubts concerning the hypothesis. On the other hand, if the hypothesis is such as to render the observation "likely" then we are inclined to hold the hypothesis as plausible. 'Doubt' and 'plausibility' are rather imprecise terms expressing little more than attitudes of mind. In the popular statistical literature, the spirit of decision is captured by the terms 'acceptance' and 'rejection'. These are stronger terms. It is in their use that many of the debates over statistical tactics and procedures arise.

## NEYMAN–PEARSON THEORY

For appropriate domains of experience let us now assume that all possible observations and data points can be represented as random variables with clearly specified probability distributions. That is to say, for all possible observations of a given kind there is a set of random variables $x_1, x_2, \ldots$ corresponding to the possible observations with a probability distribution $f(x)$ and a distribution function $F(x)$.[1] Then from our knowl-

[1] For normally distributed variables

$$f(x) = \frac{1}{\sigma \sqrt{2\pi}} e^{-x^2/2\sigma^2}, \qquad x = X - \mu,$$

and

$$F(x) = \int_{-\infty}^{x} f(x) \, dx.$$

For the discontinuous binomial variable

$$f(x) = {}_nC_x p^x q^{n-x}$$

and

$$F(x_n) = \sum_{x=0}^{n} {}_nC_x p^x q^{n-x}, \text{ for } x = 0,1, \ldots, n.$$

A condition essential to defining a probability distribution is that $F(x)$ over the entire range of its possible random variables be 1.

edge of these two functions it is possible to ascertain the probability that the value of the random variable falls within any specified class, or within any two of the allowable limits of the function.

Let us now assume two such functions as being the appropriate statistical model for some universe of potential observations. Identify this universe by the parameter $\mu_0$. We will call this the null hypothesis. Then it is a matter of convention for us to select a point $x_k$ such that it divides the probability distribution into the distinct classes $\sim w$ and $w$. Call $w$ the critical region for the hypothesis $\mu_0$, such that $P(x \in w \mid \mu_0)$ is the probability that any observation will give a value falling within the critical region given that the hypothesis $\mu_0$ is true. Let us now adopt a decision rule:

> Reject the hypothesis $\mu_0$ whenever an observation $x$ is such as to fall in the region $w$, as determined with respect to $\mu_0$.

Then given that the hypothesis $\mu_0$ is true, $P(x \in w \mid \mu_0)$ is the probability of rejecting the true hypothesis, and $P(x \in \sim w \mid \mu_0)$ is the probability of accepting the true hypothesis.

In brief, this outlines the substance of a significance test of the null hypothesis, wherein the arbitrary determination of $w$ establishes the probability of rejecting the true hypothesis, (i.e., the "significance level" or "size" of the test). One postulates his hypothesis $\mu_0$, establishes his critical region, and then on the value of $x$ corresponding to his observation he decides as to whether or not he should reject his hypothesis. The decision to reject is straightforward and has not occasioned any substantial disagreement among statistical partisans. But failure to reject is more problematic. According to R. A. Fisher (1956) failure to reject is not equivalent to outright acceptance; rather it is a matter of being noncommittal or indecisive as concerns $\mu_0$. According to Neyman and Pearson, failure to reject $\mu_0$ is equivalent to acceptance, with its corresponding possibility of error of a second kind.

To evaluate this error we must now postulate an hypothesis $\mu_1$ as an alternative to $\mu_0$. Included in the complete specification of this alternative hypothesis is its corresponding probability density and distribution function. Our decision rule is based on the critical region $w$ as established with respect to $\mu_0$. By the appropriate adjustments we can establish the probabilities of the event space for $w$ and $\sim w$ with respect to $\mu_1$ (cf. N 14.1). Hence the inclusive picture can now be represented by the familiar fourfold table of decision. In testing the hypothesis $\mu_0$ against the alternative hypothesis $\mu_1$, we have four possible outcomes: (1) we may correctly accept $\mu_0$; (2) we may incorrectly reject $\mu_0$; this is the Type I error; (3) we may incorrectly accept $\mu_0$; this is the Type II error; and (4) we may correctly reject $\mu_0$; this is the "power of the test." This is the familiar rubric of decision theory.

Several problems immediately arise. It should be observed now that, other things being equal, an optimal procedure would be one in which we could keep the probabilities of correct decision of both kinds as high as possible while keeping the probabilities of errors of both kinds as low as possible. Other things are not often equal, however; at the outset our standard statistical procedures specify our taking some conventional significance level (Type I error), say 0.05 or 0.01, without regard to the probability of committing a Type II error. Furthermore this disregard of the possibility of incorrect acceptance of $\mu_0$ is all the more imposing if by some means we should estimate that the prior probability of $\mu_1$ is

**Table 14.1**

| DECISION | WORLD SITUATION | |
|---|---|---|
| | $\mu_0$ | $\mu_1$ |
| $x \in w$, Reject $\mu_0$, (Accept $\mu_1$) | $P(x \in w \mid \mu_0)$ <br><br> Type I error ("size of test") | $P(x \in w \mid \mu_1)$ <br><br> "power" |
| $x \in \sim w$ Accept $\mu_0$, (Reject $\mu_1$) | $(P(x \in \sim w \mid \mu_0)$ <br><br> correct acceptance | $P(x \in \sim w \mid \mu_1)$ <br><br> Type II error |

higher than that of $\mu_0$. Secondly, the range of possible hypotheses over the parameter space is itself large, perhaps infinite; therefore, rather than a single alternative $\mu_1$, we should have a set of alternatives $\{\mu_i\}$ each member of which yields a "power" value in accordance with its distribution function.

Neyman addresses himself to the latter of these problems, while the decision theory of Wald (1950) concerns the former, at least so far as concerns the consequences of errors of both types.

## Power

The power of the test is the probability of a correct rejection of the primary hypothesis, and is calculable whenever we may fully specify the parameters of some alternative hypothesis. For practical purposes, we may sometimes wish the power of a test (i.e., of an inference) to be high; or, if we are primarily concerned with minimizing Type I error, we may be relatively indifferent to the possibilities of Type II error. Without regard to consequences of our errors, there is, however, a general criterion by which we should choose among possible tests of our hypotheses. We should whenever possible choose that test from a set of tests which yields the highest power for some given set of conditions.

The concept of a test needs some explanation. Let $x_1$, $x_2$, . . . , $x_n$ designate a set of observations from some event space. Then any decision procedure utilizing $\{x\}$ constitutes a test of the relevant hypothesis, $\mu_0$. Let us now open the class $\{x\}$ to that of a potential observation so that all or part of the members may be utilized in any way that constitutes a test of the hypothesis. Thus alternative tests are possible as concerns the hypothesis $\mu_0$. These may differ as to the number of variates, $x$, which enter into the test, the "size" of the test, the statistical variables constructed on $x$, and so on. Thus, for example, tests may differ as to the size of the sample, as to the "size" of the critical region, as to whether the mean or the median of a set of basic observations is utilized, and so on. From the set of possible tests of $\mu_0$, one should, according to the power principle, select that test with the greatest power.

The most powerful test of all would be that test that utilizes all the potential observations in the universe. However, since this is impossible for unlimited populations, one must reasonably restrict the size of his sample. One could also maximize his power if he agreed never to accept $\mu_0$, that is if he made the region $\sim w$ coincide with the null class. But this, too, would be an unreasonable basis for testing, since $\mu_0$ would always be rejected. Resolution of the problem now turns upon selecting from the set of all possible tests that test that is uniformly more powerful than any alternative test under a given set of conditions. Thus, for example, for a set of normally distributed variates, and for a given "size" of the test, the test based on the larger sample of variates is uniformly more powerful than one based on the smaller sample of variates. By uniformly more powerful test is meant that its power is greater than that of some other test over the whole range of alternative hypotheses $\{\mu_i\}$.

In general, then, we seek the test of $\mu_0$ such that for the given "size" of the test, $\alpha = 0.05$ or some other significance level, the power of the test is a maximum. Since power is then proportional to size of a sample of observations one would then take as large a sample as it is feasible to take. And by restricting the size of the sample we would select that test which from the property of its probability density would yield the greater power (cf. N14.2).

Although the Neyman–Pearson theory of decision is elegant in its instructional simplicity (i.e., accept or reject) there are difficulties to be faced. We may be able to establish the conditions for selecting best critical regions and most powerful tests (cf. N14.2), but the theorems do not instruct us on how to balance types of errors and risks. Traditional procedure is that we select some critical region of "size" 0.05 or 0.01, or even 0.001 and then for a given alternative hypothesis determine the power. The probabilities of the two kinds of error are for any given sample procedure inversely related. Consequently small "size" means we are placing emphasis upon protecting $\mu_0$ and relatively less emphasis upon $\mu_1$ which would serve as the replacement hypothesis in the event $\mu_0$ were rejected. Since in general $\mu_0$ stipulates the null hypothesis in our traditional significance tests, we are oriented more toward conserving that hypothesis than accepting some replacement hypothesis, which may very well represent a shift toward a new scientific development. Thus if we anticipate some treatment effect as between an experimental and a control group, we become oriented more toward conserving the hypothesis of no difference than toward seeking its replacement in accordance with some postulated effect. Under such circumstances it seems strange that we would adhere undeviatingly to standard significance levels (cf. N14.3).

We can make our concern over a reasonable balance of error types somewhat more general. Let us assume that, with the limitations imposed upon us by the costs of taking observations, our traditional test procedures are conservative with respect to $\mu_0$. However $\mu_1$, as the scientifically significant alternative, may have consequences of substantial value, or utility. The mere fact that the world of $\mu_1$ has greater utility than the world of $\mu_0$ would indicate that we might be willing to run a greater risk of rejecting $\mu_0$, when, in fact, it is true, in order to enhance the power for accepting $\mu_1$ when it is true. It would seem inappropriate, therefore, for us not to take into consideration the losses and gains (the loss functions) of our decisions and attendant errors. There is, however, another important factor to consider. We do not often come to our investigations as naive nonpartisans. Frequently we bring with us biases and other presentiments concerning hypotheses to be tested. In fact it is only in the most routinely exploratory of investigations that we are ever likely to be ignorant or indifferent to the prior plausibility of certain subsets of hypotheses. Thus personal belief serves to weigh one hypothesis against an alternative. Furthermore, a hypothesis that can be derived from a coherent scientific theory or set of principles is likely to receive higher prior weighting than some alternative hypothesis that does not enjoy such support. Under such circumstances we should want to use this prior weighting in assessing the relative significance of error types. Very likely we should wish to protect against rejecting a hypothesis which by prior judgment we hold very likely to be true.

In both of the above considerations, prior judgment and evaluation play important roles. In the one case we attend to gains and losses associated with our correct and incorrect decisions. In the other case we incline to assign weights to the truth possibilities of our hypotheses prior to our taking evidence. Traditionalists after Neyman–Pearson follow Wald (1950) in seeking minimax solutions based on risk and loss. Bayesians, on the other hand, seek optimal resolutions of decision by taking into consideration both the assessments of loss and the probability of hypotheses prior to taking evidence.

## Minimax Principle

In general the optimum decision procedure under the Neyman–Pearson rubric is that in which we may expect to minimize the maximum possible loss. Let us define a decision function of the random variable $x$ by $\delta(x)$ such that any $x$ leads to $d_0$ or $d_1$ indicating whether $\mu_0$ or $\mu_1$ is accepted (with the corresponding rejection of their respective alternatives). Let the true parameter be designated by $\theta$, where $\theta = (\mu_0, \mu_1)$ as the case may be. The decision matrix can then be dichotomized as to whether $\mu_0$ or $\mu_1$ is the true value of $\theta$. Thus $\{(d_0, \mu_0), (d_1, \mu_0)\}$ represents the decisions when $\mu_0$ is true and $\{(d_0, \mu_1), (d_1, \mu_1)\}$ represents the decisions when $\mu_1$ is true. Since no prior probabilities concerning $\theta$ are involved, the truth of $\mu_0$ or $\mu_1$ is assumed as a state of the world, and subsequent evaluation is to be made on the assumption that one or another world state obtains.

Let us now consider the costs of decision which are assessed on the basis of gains and losses accompanying correct and incorrect decisions. Since any gain can be considered a negative loss, we may generalize all cost as a loss function. Suppose now an assessment skill sufficient to assign a loss to every possible decision. Then in general, for any decision $(d_i, \mu_j)$ we have the loss function $L(d_i; \mu_j)$, or the loss associated with decision $d_i$ where $\mu_j$ is the true parameter, $\theta$. Our expected loss is then the simple mathematical expectation as associated with a loss and the probability of the decision. Thus for $\theta = \mu_0$ our expected loss is

$$E_{\mu_0} [L(d_i; \mu_0)] = L(d_0; \mu_0) \ P(d_0 \mid \mu_0) + L(d_1; \mu_0) \ P(d_1 \mid \mu_0) \qquad (1)$$

and for $\theta = \mu_1$ our expected loss is

$$E_{\mu_1} [L(d_i; \mu_1)] = L(d_0; \mu_1) \ P(d_0 \mid \mu_1) + L(d_1; \mu_1) \ P(d_1 \mid \mu_1). \qquad (2)$$

As an example of our decision procedure let us now consider two hypotheses associated with normally distributed variates such that $\mu_1 - \mu_0 = + 1\sigma_u$ (as shown, for example, in N14.1). Assume the following cost and decision matrices, with the decision rule $D_a$, "if $z_i \geq 1.65$, reject $\mu_0$."

| (Loss, $L(d_i; \mu_j)$ ) WORLD | | | (Decision probabilities, $P(d_i \mid \mu_j)$ ) WORLD | | |
|---|---|---|---|---|---|
| DECISION | $\mu_0$ | $\mu_1$ | DECISION | $\mu_0$ | $\mu_1$ |
| $d_0$ | −10 | 10 | $d_0$ | 0.95 | 0.74 |
| $d_1$ | 10 | −10 | $d_1$ | 0.05 | 0.26 |

Our test is simply the standard normal test of "size" 0.05 with $w$ in the right-hand tail of the distribution $f(0,1)$. By applying (1) and (2) we will find

$$E_{\mu_0} = -9.5 + 0.5 = -9.0,$$
$$E_{\mu_1} = 7.4 - 2.6 = 4.8.$$

The maximum loss for decision rule $D_a$ is therefore 4.8 (since a negative loss is an actual gain).

Suppose now another decision rule such as to increase the "size" of the test. Consider $z_k = (\mu_1 - \mu_0)/2$ and the rule $D_b$: "if $z_i \geq z_k$ reject $\mu_0$, where $z_i$ is the normal deviate based on the sample data. Since $z_k$ here is $+0.5$ we obtain

WORLD

|       | $\mu_0$ | $\mu_1$ |
|-------|---------|---------|
| $d_0$ | 0.69    | 0.31    |
| $d_1$ | 0.31    | 0.69    |

with the following expected losses.

$$E_{\mu_0} = -3.8, \qquad E_{\mu_1} = -3.8$$

We now have the following table of expected losses with respect to $D_a$ and $D_b$.

LOSS

|       | $\theta = \mu_0$ | $\theta = \mu_1$ |
|-------|------------------|------------------|
| $D_a$ | −9.0             | 4.8              |
| $D_b$ | −3.8             | −3.8             |

Therefore, between these two-decision rules, $D_b$ is the minimax strategy.

Although there is a large class of problems for which minimax solutions exist, minimax strategies generally are either too difficult or too cumbersome to apply in problems of scientific inference. Two implications of the present example can be pointed out, however. First, under the conditions of a symmetric loss matrix, in which the losses associated with the decision categories for the two hypotheses are equal, it can be shown that our rule $D_b$, in which the "size" of the test is equal to the probability of a Type II error, is the minimax rule among the set of all alternative tests differing as to size. Generally, then, if we are indifferent as to the costs of making one or another type of error and one or another type of correct decision, we should select a decision rule that equalizes the two types of risk.[2] Moreover we can see that for a loss matrix not possessing the sym-

[2] This is known as the equal probability test. See Arrow, 1960.

metric property, we should modify our decision rule toward diminishing the type of risk which carries the relatively greater loss. Second, it is easy to visualize conditions in which the minimax principle would seem overly pessimistic or downright irrational. Suppose a loss matrix such that

|  | LOSS $\theta = \mu_0$ | $\theta = \mu_1$ |
|---|---|---|
| $D_a$ | −9.5 | 7.4 |
| $D_b$ | −6.9 | 3.1 |

(Such is the case with our present decision rules and $L(d_0; \mu_0) = -10$, $L(d_0; \mu_1) = 10$, and the other losses equal to zero.) Again $D_b$ may be the minimax rule. But if a much higher prior probability were to be assigned to $\mu_0$ than to $\mu_1$, then our expectation of gain would be greater for rule $D_a$ than for $D_b$ (as may be verified by Bayesian procedures). Although one decision rule may include the possibility of relatively large loss, it may remain the better rule if it is very unlikely that the hypothesis with which the loss is associated is true.

Minimax strategies are therefore based upon indifference to the prior probabilities of hypotheses. In those situations, few as they may be, where assessment of prior probabilities are possible, then a Bayesian strategy and a likelihood test may yield the higher expected gain. If the world situation is such that it is unlikely that the investigator will ever assume the maximum possible loss, then the minimax criterion seems unwarrantedly conservative. That is why many theoreticians prefer some variant of Bayesian procedures to a rigidly applied minimax rule (cf. Lehmann, 1958, Ch. 1; Robbins, 1963) (cf. N14.4).

### Confidence Intervals

Thus far we have considered testing one hypothesis against an alternative or a limited set of alternatives (cf. N14.5). What is to be our procedure if we have no well-specified simple or composite hypothesis to test but only wish to establish the limits for all hypotheses that we would find acceptable by virtue of the systematic application of a rejection rule? Our question is pretty well answered by the way we have phrased it here. If we know what hypotheses are supported by any given evidence, we have then established all hypotheses that on the basis of our assumed probability distribution yield a decision to accept, as differentiated from all those hypotheses that conjointly with the evidence yield a decision to reject. Procedures for establishing such limits of hypotheses are readily available and are familiar to all students of statistical methods. Generally speaking, we compute some statistic from a set of observations, make some conjecture concerning the nature of the probability density of such statistics, and then establish an upper and lower bound for acceptable hypotheses.

For the most part there is agreement as to these procedures, or at least as to the limits themselves, in all such cases where the central limit theorem of normality applies. Contention arises only in the interpretation of the intervals. When one writer says of some such limits that ". . . we have 95% *confidence* that the true mean is in the interval such and such" (Fraser, 1958, p. 123), we are not sure whether the 95% refers to a probability value relating to our confidence, as such, to the true mean, or to a resumé of our inductive behavior. Perhaps Fraser, in the statement above, is being studiously neutral as concerns a well-publicized difference of opinion between Neyman and Pearson and R. A. Fisher. According to Neyman and Pearson we should base our interpretation on inductive behavior. Adopting the decision rule that we do and following it through many inferences then any given confidence statement indicates our long-run expectations for including the parameter within the limits. Limits which in fact do include the parameter are correct, limits which in fact do not include the parameter are incorrect. Then our confidence statement indicates what in the long run we can expect our percentage of correct inclusions to be, providing our statistical model is appropriate.

If we let $u$ equal the upper limit of hypotheses and $l$ equal the lower limit and $\theta$ the parameter, then many writers, including Neyman (1952), are prone to express the limits by a term of the form

$$l \leq \theta \leq u.$$

And from there it is an easy matter to suggest that the confidence value $1 - \alpha$ expresses the probability that $\theta$ is within these limits. Such a manner of speaking (as Neyman calls it, *lapsus linguae*) is not too objectionable if one (e.g., Fraser, 1958, p. 277) interprets it explicitly as meaning probability of inclusion in the Neyman–Pearson sense. R. A. Fisher, on the other hand, rejects such an interpretation. By "$P(l \leq \theta \leq u) = 1 - \alpha$," he means just what the function reads, our expression of confidence is the probability that $\theta$ is within a set of limits. This type of probability, in which the properties of random variables are apparently assigned to parameters themselves, is known as fiducial probability. In some cases inferences based on fiducial probability lead to the same results as do conventional confidence intervals which reduce to a systematic application of the significance test. It is tempting to say therefore that fiducial probability and the Neyman–Pearson confidence interval differ only as manners of speaking differ, but there are cases where the fiducial argument gives different results from those of Neyman and Pearson (cf. N14.6).

# BAYESIAN PROCEDURES

From our discussion of decision procedures we found that considerable sophistication is introduced into the problem of decision making when we can adopt statistical models concerning different types of error. The decision function is further refined when we can associate estimates of gains and losses with the outcomes of our decision matrix. Minimax strategies are thereby possible and protect against our assuming an over-all loss exceeding a determinate amount. However, the minimax approach is overly conservative. Optimal decision functions are available only when we can compute an over-all expectation that entails a weighting as well as a specification of the possibilities of decision.

There have already been several occasions to refer to Bayes' theorem. What distinguishes it in the present context is the fact that in those cases where it is applicable we can assign a probability to some hypothesis on the basis of some evidence. Since prior estimate of the probability of the hypothesis is required independently of the evidence, the applicability of the theorem to problems of inference is often suspect. But where some prior estimate is defensible, then the evidence yields a posterior probability that enables us to say something rather specific about the evidential support of the hypotheses. For example, suppose after the evidence is taken we compute and find

$$P(H_0 \mid E) > P(H_0).$$

Then obviously the evidence increases the credibility of the hypothesis. Our betting odds, as well as our "beliefs" and our "expectations," should then reflect this evidential support.

What is more to the point, however, is that Bayesian procedures enable us: (1) to make specific assertions about the posterior probability of hypothesis without reference to unsampled probability spaces and long-run frequencies (as required by our interpretations of the Neyman–Pearson critical regions and decision functions); (2) to establish confidence intervals (intervals of credibility) which are determined solely by the evidence and our prior considerations about the parameter space (i.e., independent of the long-run interpretation of inductive behavior); and (3) to derive optimal decision solutions which will maximize our gain or minimize our loss according to whether the world situation is favorable or unfavorable.

## Bayes' Theorem

As we have seen earlier, Bayes' theorem, in its most elementary application, is a simple development of the product rule.

$$P(H \mid E) = \frac{P(H)\ P(E \mid H)}{P(E)} \tag{3}$$

We note that the ratio of the posterior to the prior probability, i.e., $[P(H \mid E)/P(H)]$, is equal to the ratio of the likelihood of the evidence $P(E \mid H)$, to the over-all probability of the evidence $P(E)$. Since the probability of the evidence is determined over the range of all possible hypothetical conjunctions (i.e., $P(E) = P(E \cap H_1) + \cdots + P(E \cap H_k)$) for $k$ mutually exclusive hypotheses in the parameter space), it is apparent that the likelihood statistic is to play an important role in assessing the evidential support for a given hypothesis, or as between alternative hypotheses.

In general, then, for a discrete finite parameter space, Bayes' theorem is as follows:

$$P(H_j \mid E) = \frac{P(H_j) \, P(E \mid H_j)}{\sum\limits_{i=1}^{k} P(H_i) \, P(E \mid H_i)}, \qquad (4)$$

and for two alternative hypotheses that exhaust the parameter space of the set $\{H_i\}$

$$\frac{P(H_0 \mid E)}{P(H_1 \mid E)} = \frac{P(H_0) \, P(E \mid H_0)}{P(H_1) \, P(E \mid H_1)}. \qquad (5)$$

Thus the ratio of the two posterior probabilities is proportional to the ratio of their respective likelihoods. Furthermore if by some rationale we wish to assume $P(H_0) = P(H_1) = 0.5$, then a simple test of $H_0$ versus $H_1$ would be to select that hypothesis with the greatest likelihood. That is to say, as between two equally likely prior hypotheses, that hypothesis is best supported by the evidence that yields the higher likelihood, $P(E \mid H_i)$.

The likelihood principle is one which is intuitively rather easy to grasp. But unless we have means for weighting this likelihood function, as in (5) above, such functions are not always helpful. A major difficulty arises therefore in our making estimates of the probability of hypotheses prior to any evidence being taken.

In this context two classes of application of Bayesian inference are to be noted. One concerns fairly restricted parameter spaces where our knowledge of the world is sufficient for us to establish reasonable prior probabilities in a straightforward manner. Here our estimates are subject to little doubt, but the situations themselves are restricted and often scientifically uninteresting. The other class of applications concerns a larger range of hypotheses. Here the techniques of estimating prior probability often entail assumptions of rationality such as we meet in formal treatments of subjective probability.

Textbook examples of the application of Bayesian inference frequently involve urns and marbles, where the prior probability is that of selecting any one of $K$ urns, and the likelihood is the probability of selecting a sample of a given composition from the given urn. Then if the prior probabilities and likelihoods for all urns are completely specifiable, it is possible to compute the posterior probabilities for selection of the urns as contingent upon the sample evidence. In recent years the Bayesian has not been hesitant to venture forth from the world of urns and marbles.

Consider one example that was brought to the attention of the writer. In a seed-cleaning plant that processes grass seed, the fine seed are subjected to several screenings and blowings in order to get a product pure enough for certification. As each batch of seed is run through a screening it is sacked, tagged, and stored for future rerunning. Suppose now that a disgruntled employee pulls off all the tags and shifts the bags around so as utterly to confuse the lot assignments: we end up with a random mixture of sacks all looking pretty much alike except for the purity of their contents. Now let us assume that the foreman can make fairly reliable estimates of the number of sacks in the warehouse which are finished and ready for certification, the number that have one run remaining, and so on, down to the number that have been run but once. Suppose he can also make an estimate of the percentage purity of seed after any given stage (call this the hypothesis for each stage of running). Then by analyzing samples of seed from each sack and applying Bayes' theorem, he can assign posterior probabilities to the hypothesis that any given sack is at any given stage in the cleaning process.

One of the simplest applications of Bayes' theorem in behavioral sciences concerns the evaluations of diagnostic tests. If medical statistics enable us to establish the base rate for some given syndrome and if we have information on diagnostic tests sufficient to establish likelihoods, then it is possible to assess the posterior probabilities. For a number of years the electroencephalogram (EEG) was used in diagnosing epilepsy. Let $H$ be the hypothesis, epilepsy, and $\sim H$ the complement, freedom from epilepsy. Let $E$ be the occurrence of dysrhythmia in the EEG and $\sim E$ the normal complement. Estimates from Lennox (1941) give the following.

$$
\begin{array}{ll}
P(H) = 0.005 & P(\sim E \mid H) = 0.05 \\
P(\sim H) = 0.995 & P(E \mid \sim H) = 0.10 \\
P(E \mid H) = 0.95 & P(\sim E \mid \sim H) = 0.90
\end{array}
$$

Bayes' theorem then enables us to compute the following.

$$
\begin{array}{ll}
P(H \mid E) = 0.046 & P(\sim H \mid \sim E) = 0.9997 \\
P(\sim H \mid E) = 0.954 & P(H \mid \sim E) = 0.0003
\end{array}
$$

It is a source of some concern to diagnosticians that $P(\sim H \mid \sim E)$ is substantially greater than $P(H \mid E)$, i.e., that tests are good as exonerative devices but poor as positive diagnostics. But this is generally the case in diagnosis where we take $E \equiv H$ and where the likelihoods associated with erroneous prediction, i.e., $P(E \mid \sim H)$ and $P(\sim E \mid H)$, are substantially greater than zero.

The more interesting case arises when the diagnostic test itself gives a continuum of response, such that by manipulating the "cutting score" we may alter the likelihoods concerning positive and negative diagnosis. The problem then is to manipulate the cutting score until we maximize the numbers of hits (i.e., correct diagnoses both positive and negative). Solutions to such problems are readily available (e.g., Cureton, 1957; Guttmann, 1941); however, the problem is complicated by the fact that maximizing the number of hits may not be optimal diagnosis. There may be greater utility in correct positive diagnosis than in correct negative diagnosis. Consequently we may wish to shift the cutting score so as to pick up more valid positives, even if in so doing we should increase the rate of false positive diagnosis. The issues here involve loss functions and assignment of risk, and the proper place to consider them is in the discussion of Bayesian decision functions.

If Bayesian procedures are to have general utility, they must be applicable to those problems in scientific inference where our knowledge of the universe to be sampled is limited and the parameter space is continuous and infinitely dense. Here we are not dealing with simple dichotomous parameter spaces such as "syndrome" and "no syndrome," nor a world in which all possibility is neatly partitioned into an array of urns, but rather a world of open possibility in which one and only one hypothesis identifies the true parameter. In this context Bayesians have proposed three tactics for dealing with the assignment of prior probabilities. One, we can simply develop a coherent set of subjective estimates over the entire range of hypotheses, as prescribed by personalistic probability. Two, we can adopt simplifying assumptions as concerns the uniformity or equal likeliness of subsets of hypotheses in the parameter space. And three, we can use what information is available prior to taking our additional test evidence in order to establish an empirically based estimate of the prior probabilities.

Of these tactics the first is the least satisfactory. Each of two individuals may possess a set of mutually consistent and coherent estimates of prior probability over the parameter space. Yet the two may disagree over their respective probability estimates concerning individual hypotheses. On limited evidence our two people will then disagree as to the posterior probabilities which they would calculate on the evidence. Only when extensive evidence is taken can we expect our people of divergent prior estimates to come to reasonable agreement (Blackwell and Dubins, 1962). The problem here is not one merely of developing a consistent set of personal probabilities, but of developing a set of opinions which are consistent with some rationale of expectation as has proved useful or reasonable on the basis of past experience. In a sense, then, prior probabilities are not prior to any experience. The challenge is to utilize poorly codified experience and our presumptions as reasonably as we can in making assignments of probability prior to our taking *additional* evidence. Mere opinion, however consistent, is not enough; we must justify one set of estimates over another on the basis of experience or privileged intutition. Our estimates should establish that the betting odds we are willing to give will not result in long-term loss.

Bayesians, of course, seldom defend our making estimates of prior probability independently of any experience. In cases of ignorance, principles of symmetry, exchangeability, indifference, and so on, are invoked to support a partition of the parameter space into equally likely hypotheses. Suppose, for example, we are to make an inference concerning the true probability of the toss of a coin's being heads. Rather than applying our assumption of indifference to the outcome of the toss (thereby favoring the hypothesis $H : p = 0.5$), we say there is a plausible stretch of hypotheses over which we assume the probability density for hypotheses in the parameter space is uniform. Thus suppose we take discrete values of *p,* from 0.45 to 0.55, i.e., $H : p = (0.45, 0.46, \ldots , 0.55)$. To each of these we assign equal probability. Then on the basis of an actual sample of $n$ tosses of the coin, we can compute a posterior probability for each of the hypotheses (parameters) within the parameter space. In order to apply this tactic it is necessary to consider that the prior probability density of the parameter space behaves "gently" with respect to the region favored by the data (Edwards, Lindeman, and Savage, 1963). That is to say, (1) some region which we delimit as the parameter space is highly favored by the data; (2) the prior density within this space is fairly uniform; (3) most of the posterior probability is to be found within this region. Naturally then if the data do not in fact support these assumptions, we must seek a redefinition of the region over which we take our parameter space.

Our third tactic is that of using extant evidence for estimating our prior probabilities. Where apparently applicable, this tactic seems the least presumptive of all. In the case of diagnostics, for example, we utilize an extensive survey of our population to estimate what proportion of the population exhibits a given syndrome, and then on the basis of some diagnostic response characteristic of the syndrome and no-syndrome populations we may compute the posterior probabilities to be considered in diagnosis (Meehl and Rosen, 1955). Such procedures are by now well established; however, we should not overlook the fact that the prior probabilities are not really prior at all, but are taken on the presumption of empirical laws of large numbers and the principle of convergence, which for the most part are non-Bayesian. More systematic estimates of the prior densities are in effect achieved by the so-called "empirical Bayes approach" (Robbins, 1956; Robbins and Samuel). Here a parameter $\theta_i$

is associated with each sample in the series $x_1, x_2, \ldots, x_{n-1}, x_n$. Thus in effect the posterior probability determined on the $n$th observation utilizes a prior probability that is a function of $(x_1, x_2, \ldots, x_{n-1})$ (cf. N14.8).

## Interval Estimation

Bayesian procedures permit the direct calculation of confidence intervals. Although in certain problems of estimation such as that for the normal probability density the Bayesian intervals of credibility coincide with the classical Neyman–Pearson intervals, the credibility itself is not to be interpreted in terms of inductive behavior and long-run frequency of successful inclusion of parameters. Credibility refers to the inclusion of whatever percentage of the posterior probability is to be included in the "confidence" interval. Since the sum of the posterior probabilities on the evidence is necessarily 1, then determination of the "shortest" credibility interval entails our establishing the smallest range of hypotheses such that the sum of the posterior probabilities over that range is equal to the credibility value. The shortest credibility interval then indicates to us a proposition of the form

$$P(H_i \vee \cdots \vee H_j \vee \cdots \vee H_k \mid E) = \sum_{j=1}^{k} P(H_j \mid E) = C,$$

where the term on the right is equal to our degree of credibility, and where no other $\Sigma P(H \mid E) = C$ will sum over a smaller range of hypotheses.

# BAYESIAN DECISION PROCEDURES

Although posterior probabilities may be interesting in their own right as supportive of belief, they are subject to the ambiguities of the classical confidence interval. The data are supportive of many hypotheses, and if the range of hypotheses is large the decision situation as concerns any small range of hypotheses may itself be ambiguous. However, the primary advantage of Bayesian procedures is their optimal decision properties. Where prior probabilities (or weightings) are known and where losses and gains are known, then Bayesian solutions are at least as good as any other solutions in statistical decision theory.

Let us first consider the simple decision problem in which we test the null hypothesis against some single alternative. Then, according to the classical Neyman–Pearson situation, we should choose a decision rule that minimizes maximum error (such as in the equal probability test), or where losses and gains are assessable we should choose that rule that minimizes maximum loss. The difficulty with these procedures is that we cannot compute our long-run over-all expectations. In fact if the hypothesis with which we associate maximum possible loss itself possesses low prior probability, then our concern for a maximum loss that we are likely never to assume is unnecessarily pessimistic. In Bayesian decision the situation is quite different. We can compute over-all expectation for any decision rule we may wish to adopt.

The concept of expectation reduces to weighted loss or gain. As in classical decision let us assume some decision rule and some critical region such that if the observation falls within the critical region we reject the null hypothesis; otherwise we accept. Then, as before, the possible likelihoods of decision are those given in Table 14.1. Let us abbreviate the decision function such that

$P(d_0 \mid \mu_0)$ = probability of accepting $\mu_0$ when $\mu_0$ is true,
$P(d_0 \mid \mu_1)$ = probability of accepting $\mu_0$ when $\mu_1$ is true,
$P(d_1 \mid \mu_0)$ = probability of rejecting $\mu_0$ when $\mu_0$ is true,
$P(d_1 \mid \mu_1)$ = probability of rejecting $\mu_0$ when $\mu_1$ is true.

(Rejection of $\mu_0$ is to be interpreted as acceptance of $\mu_1$.) Assume now that with every likelihood we can assign some loss (with gain being a negative loss). Thus with each decision we associate some loss $L_{i,j}$, where $i$ indicates the decision and $j$ indicates the hypothesis. Our expected loss over the entire decision space is then

$$E(L,d) = L_{0,0}\, P(d_0 \mid \mu_0)\, P(\mu_0) + L_{0,1}\, P(d_0 \mid \mu_1)\, P(\mu_1) \qquad (6)$$
$$+ L_{1,0}\, P(d_1 \mid \mu_0)\, P(\mu_0) + L_{1,1}\, P(d_1 \mid \mu_1)\, P(\mu_1).$$

Thus, for any decision rule enabling us to establish the likelihoods of the decision matrix and for the appropriate loss matrix, we may compute the expectation.

An optimal decision rule is one which, for the parameter space $\{\mu_0,\mu_1\}$, minimizes the expected loss (or if we were to assign positive values to gain, to maximize expected gain). Since the losses $L_{i,j}$ and the prior probabilities $P(\mu_j)$ in equation (6) can be regarded constants, the problem of optimal decision reduces to one of selecting a critical region such that the likelihoods $P(d_i \mid \mu_j)$ associated with that region minimize $E(L,d)$.

Solutions to optimal decision rules are not simple ones since they involve differentiating equations of type (6) with respect to the likelihoods (i.e., probability densities for $\mu_0$ and $\mu_1$) (cf. N14.7). However, it is possible to point out some features of our expected-loss function as expressed in (6). If our prior probabilities are assumed to be equal ($P(\mu_0) = P(\mu_1) = 0.5$), and if our loss table has zero values throughout, or is otherwise symmetrical, then the optimal decision rule reduces to the equal probability rule. That is, we select a critical region such that $P(d_1 \mid \mu_0) = P(d_0 \mid \mu_1)$. Furthermore for symmetrical loss tables we should in general modify our decision rule in accordance with the prior probabilities. Thus if $P(\mu_0) > P(\mu_1)$ we should select a decision rule such that $P(d_1 \mid \mu_0) < P(d_0 \mid \mu_1)$. On the other hand if our prior probabilities are assumed to be equal and our loss table is nonsymmetrical, then we should modify our decision rules so as to decrease the likelihood associated with the larger loss[3] (cf. N14.8).

# CRITIQUE OF OPTIMIZATION PROCEDURES

There is little question but that the Bayesian procedures are to be preferred to any other when prior probabilities and costs can be assessed. But whether Bayesian procedures are to supplant all other decision policies, or to render the Neyman–Pearson theory of statistical decision obsolescent (Anscombe, 1961; Lindley, 1961; Edwards, Lindman, and Savage, 1963) is questionable. We need only reiterate the question that occurred to the Reverend Thomas Bayes himself: How do we assay the prior probabilities?

There are problems of inference where Bayesian procedures are clearly applicable. For example, if for a set of hypotheses $H_1, H_2, \ldots, H_k$ no one is deemed more probable than the other, then a rational Bayesian policy dictates that, costs being equal, we should choose the hypothesis with the greatest likelihood. In business situations both prior probabilities and costs are easily determined, and Bayesian procedures of optimization are clearly applicable (see, for example, Schlaifer, 1959). And in diagnostics wherein large numbers permit reliable estimates of base rates, optimal cutting scores can be determined by similar procedures (Meehl and Rosen, 1955; Cureton, 1957; Alf, Turner, and Dorfman, 1965). But, these applications aside, what of problems of scientific inference? The "compleat Bayesian" must answer two questions: one, how does one assay the prior probabilities? and two, how does one make a fair assessment of the costs?

Let us consider two levels of scientific inference. At the lower level we have our empirical studies in which we take a sample of observations in order to make an inference concerning a parameter about which we have no preconceptions. If we force the parameter space into the mold of an indifferent partition then, of course, Bayesian rules of inference are applicable. One of the most sophisticated supports of this kind of infer-

---

[3] It is of interest to bring these general principles to focus upon traditional $\alpha$-level significance tests. Should one consider the null hypothesis more probable than the alternative, then, as is customary, $\alpha = P(d_1 \mid \mu_0)$ should be smaller than $\beta = P(d_0 \mid \mu_1)$. However, should the alternative be regarded the more probable, and should the loss matrix be symmetrical, then our rejection rule is too conservative. Since the issue is complicated by both the prior probabilities and the loss functions, no general recommendation can be made as to the proper balance between $\alpha$- and $\beta$-risk. However, it does seem fair to say that rigid adherence to standard $\alpha$-levels, such as 0.01 or 0.05, is not to be condoned.

ence is to be found in the works of Harold Jeffreys (1919, 1939, 1957). Furthermore, if we allow empirical estimates of prior probabilities as in empirical Bayesian procedures (Robbins, 1963) or if we accept the reliability of base rates, or if we define an indifference range for the parameter space on the basis of some kind of prior information (Jeffreys, 1939, 1957; Edwards, Lindman, and Savage, 1963), then posterior probabilities are calculable on the evidence. Such applications, however, are often based on a rather primitive level of scientific sophistication. At a more advanced level of sophistication, the investigator operates within the hypothetico-deductive framework in which, if he is more than indifferently involved with his theory, he is likely to show a strong preference for one over another theory. Suppose our investigator considers three viable theories, $T_1$, $T_2$, and $T_3$, each of which generates a hypothesis. Since he has a strong preference for one over another theory, the three hypotheses, $H_1$, $H_2$, and $H_3$, which are presumed for the purpose of simplification to exhaust the parameter space, are not regarded as equally probable. He himself may, of course, develop a consistent set of prior probabilities within the rubric of subjective belief. But another partisan investigator may have a different consistent set of prior probabilities, and following prescribed decision policies, may arrive at a different decision from that of his colleague. Simple Bayesian decisions [see (5) above] are based on a prior weighting of likelihoods. There are no rules for prescribing that all investigators, irrespective of their biases, should arrive at or adopt the same consistent set of prior weightings. Unfortunately for the Bayesians, the situation is not ameliorated by our appealing to those situations wherein inter-investigator reliability of subjective judgment is established by reference to frequentist or classical estimates of probability. Nor are our misgivings completely nullified by the realization that the likelihood factor upon which a Bayesian decision is made is, for large samples of evidence, relatively robust (i.e., the decision function is insensitive to error, variability, or differences of opinion with respect to the prior probabilities of hypotheses) (cf. N14.9).

Still, it must be acknowledged that the failure to make valid estimates of prior probabilities is not fatal to Bayesian procedures for scientific inference. A more serious problem arises in our assessing costs, our losses and gains, for the decision matrix when such are required for optimal decisions. Again the problems are simplified when we are dealing with business decisions, problems in military strategy, problems in diagnosis. The costs are often easily computable. But how do we assess the losses and gains of decision concerning scientific hypotheses that themselves are derived from theories. For a person who is involved in elaborating the applications of some model of behavior, the losses would indeed be high for him were he to reject his hypothesis when it is true. His whole scientific life may have been given to the elaboration of this model. Another investigator, less personally involved in this particular theory and its model, may arrive at a quite different cost matrix. There have perhaps been but few crucial confrontations at the theoretical frontiers of science. But how, for example, could the Ptolemaists and the Copernicans have come to an agreement as to the costs of decision in crucial tests of their theories. How could Newton and Huygens have gotten together on the costs of decision concerning the nature of light. If $H_0$ and $H_1$ are complementary hypotheses in the dichotomous test situation, and one hypothesis, $H_0$, is held by one partisan and the other hypothesis, $H_1$, is held by the other partisan, then it might be argued that the only fair cost matrix is a symmetrical one, with equal losses and gains assignable to the two hypotheses. Moreover, if it were contended that among partisans all hypotheses should have equal prior probabilities, then minimization of the risk function (cf. N14.8), and the subsequent optimal decision would reduce to a simple likelihood test.

Optimal decision procedures are indeed sophisticated ones. Their formal structure is impressive. What is distressing is the lack of any rigorous procedure for eliminating differences of opinion concerning the weighting factors of the risk function. The risk function [Equation (9), N14.8], which is to be minimized for optimal decision, involves three classes of factors: (1) prior probabilities; (2) costs; (3) likelihoods. In matters of scientific inference, only the latter class is free of subjective judgment. To the extent that optimal decision involves factors of class (1) or class (2) they become subjective. In general, then, minimax procedures involve the subjective judgment of costs.[4] Bayesian procedures are twice subjective. They involve both costs and prior probabilities. Only likelihoods are free of subjective judgment, and simple likelihood tests of hypotheses are very easy to apply.

Now something of a quandary arises for the scientific empiricist. How subjective should he be in matters of decision? The likelihood test is the most simple, the most objective. Yet it appears to be indifferent to the state of knowledge in a given science at a given time. If prior knowledge has any value, it ought to enter into the matter of decision. At the other extreme, Bayesian procedures, as we have seen, are those in which likelihoods are twice weighted. Decision becomes less and less contingent upon the data themselves. There is no way out of this quandary, this indecision about the proper degree of subjectivity in the application of decision theory. Doubtless, however, some subjectivity is essential to our decision-making. We are reminded that for the scientific empiricist, neither in conceptualization nor in decision is it so much a matter of his objectivity as it is of his bringing about conformal judgments in what amounts to his subjective commitments.

---

[4] Note that minimax solutions for dichotomous decisions involve selecting a critical region such that the maximum value of *either* $R(d;\theta_0)$ or $R(d;\theta_1)$ [see formulas (7) and (8) N14.8] is a minimum over the set of all possible critical regions.

# NOTES

### NOTE 14.1

In the text we have not distinguished between random variables with a discontinuous distribution and those with a continuous distribution. Consider first a discontinuous distribution in which the random variable can take only the discrete integer values between 0 and $n$. A fine partition of our event space is such that we can assign probabilities to each of the possible values of our random variable. Consider now the binomial model of our random variable, which is perhaps the most widely applicable of discrete distributions in all of applied statistics. Let our event be constituted of $n$-elements in which each element either does or does not possess some property as ascertained by observation. Then any event is signified by $x$, with $x$ taking values from 0 to $n$ as determined by the number of elements in the event complex which manifest the given property. The probability distribution is then given by

$$x_i \; : \quad 0 \qquad 1 \quad \cdots \quad r \quad \cdots \quad n$$
$$P(x_i) : {}_nC_0 p^0 q^n \; {}_nC_1 p^1 q^{n-1} \cdots {}_nC_r p^r q^{n-r} \cdots {}_nC_n p^n q^0$$

where ${}_nC_r = n!/r!\,(n-r)!$, $p$ is the probability that any element possesses the given property, and $q$ is its complement. The probability distribution for the binomial variable is then

$$P(x_r) = {}_nC_r p^r q^{n-r}$$

which gives us the probability of any $x = r$, whatever the value of $r$. The distribution function $F(x_k)$ is the cumulative probability over all $x$ from 0 to $k$ and is given by

$$F(x_k) = \sum_{r=0}^{k} {}_nC_r p^r q^{n-r}.$$

Now let us consider $k$ such that $F(x_k)$ accumulates all but a small proportion of events such that any event $x \geq k$ is considered improbable. The value $k$ then identifies our critical region with $x = (k, k+1, \ldots, n)$ constituting the class $\{w\}$ and all $x < k$ constituting the class $\{\sim w\}$. Then for some hypothesis $\mu_0 : p$ our decision rule will be: if $x \geq k$ reject $\mu_0$, otherwise accept. Our probability of rejecting $\mu_0 : p$ when that hypothesis is true will be the "size" of the test as indicated by

$$P(x \geq k \mid p) = \sum_{r=k}^{n} {}_nC_r p^r q^{n-r},$$

where $k$ is selected according to some suitable significance level. The probability of a correct acceptance is thus the complement of this value.

Let us now designate the hypotheses to be tested as $\mu_0 : p_0$ and some given alternative $\mu_1 : p_1$. Then for the decision functions we have

$$x_i \quad : \quad 0, \qquad 1 \quad \cdots \quad k \quad \cdots \quad n$$
$$P_0\,(x_i) \ : \ {}_nC_0p_0^0q_0^n, \ {}_nC_1p_0^1q_0^{n-1}, \ \cdots \ {}_nC_kp_0^kq_0^{n-k}, \ \cdots \ {}_nC_np_0^nq_0^0, \ : \text{for } \mu_0$$
$$P_1\,(x_i) \ : \ {}_nC_0p_1^0q_1^n, \ {}_nC_1p_1^1q_1^{n-1}, \ \cdots \ {}_nC_kp_1^kq_1^{n-k}, \ \cdots \ {}_nC_np_1^nq_1^0, \ : \text{for } \mu_1$$

Thus if $x = k$ is the critical value such that $\{w\}$ includes all $x \geq k$,

$$P(x \geq k \mid p_0) = \sum_{r=k}^{n} {}_nC_r p_0^r q_0^{n-r} \ ; \ P(\text{Type I error}),$$

$$P(x \geq k \mid p_1) = \sum_{r=k}^{n} {}_nC_r p_1^r q^{n-r} \ ; \ \text{power of test}.$$

Suppose, as an example, the hypothesis to be tested is $p_0 = 0.50$ against the alternative $p_1 = 0.60$ with $n$, the number of elements constituting the sample, being 20. Suppose further that we arbitrarily take the size of our test, $\alpha$, to be 0.05. Reference to tables of binomial functions indicates that if we take $k = 14$, then

$$P(x \geq 14 \mid p_0 = 0.5; n = 20) \approx 0.05.$$

Correspondingly, for $p_1 = 0.60$

$$P(x \geq 14 \mid p_1 = 0.6; n = 20) \approx 0.25.$$

This indicates the power of the test for $k = 14$. We can, of course, increase the power of the test by taking $k$ less than 14. But then we must increase the "size" of our test, with its corresponding enhancement of Type I error. The two types of error are thus inversely related; for a given $n$, we can diminish the magnitude of one error only by increasing the other. However, a fundamental theorem of our decision procedure (e.g., Neyman; 1952, p. 261) indicates that for any pair $(\mu_0, \mu_1)$ we cannot enhance the power of our test, for whatever critical region $w$, such that the probability of Type II error is less than the probability of a Type I error. Under some circumstances we find that an optimal determination of $k$ is such that the probabilities of the two types of error are identical.

As a paradigm of the argument for continuously distributed variables consider two unit normal distributions with the functions $f(0, 1)$ and $g(1, 1)$ and each with the probability density of the form

$$y = \frac{1}{\sqrt{2\pi}}\, e^{-z^2/2}$$

In Figure 14.1 $\mu_0 = 0$, and the alternative $\mu_1 = 1$. The rejection rule is if $z_i \geq z_k$ reject $\mu_0$ for $\mu_1$; otherwise accept. One can adjust the critical region $w$ so as to reduce the "size" of the test, but he does so only by diminishing the power; and vice versa. In the statistical literature '$\beta$' is taken by some writers to designate the probability of Type II error; by others to designate the complement, power. Here it designates the error term.

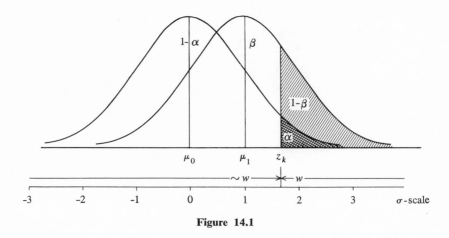

**Figure 14.1**

## NOTE 14.2

In general the defense of the Neyman-Pearson decision procedure rests in our finding a *best critical region* that maximizes the power of a test of one hypothesis against its simple alternative. A *best critical region* is a critical region $w_0$ defined with respect to $\mu_0$ which satisfies the following conditions:

(1)   For some $E$, constructible from some set of random variables,
$$P(E \in w_0 \mid \mu_0) = \alpha;$$

and

(2)   $P(E \in w_0 \mid \mu_1) \geq P(E \in w_j \mid \mu_1)$, with $w_j$ being some other critical region of size not exceeding $\alpha$.

Conceivably a critical region of size $\alpha$ can be taken any place over the range of values of our distribution identified by $\mu_0$, providing $P(E \in w \mid \mu_0) = \alpha$. But a best critical region is that region $w_0$ out of all *possible* $w_i$ of the same size which maximizes the value $P(E \in w \mid \mu_1)$.

The fundamental lemma of Neyman and Pearson establishes the conditions for indicating most powerful tests (i.e., for ascertaining best critical regions). Let $\mu_0$ indicate one hypothesis with its probability density specified; let $\mu_1$ be the simple alternative hypothesis; then the lemma states:

A most powerful test of $\mu_0$ against the alternative $\mu_1$ obtains if there is a region $w$ of size $\alpha$ and a constant $k$ such that

$$\frac{P(E \in w \mid \mu_1)}{P(E \in w \mid \mu_0)} \geq k \tag{3}$$

and

$$\frac{P(E \in \sim w \mid \mu_1)}{P(E \in \sim w \mid \mu_0)} \leq k. \tag{4}$$

Proof of this theorem is beyond the scope of the present discussion. However, one should note that all probabilities expressed in this theorem are likelihoods of the evidence being or not being included in the critical region. Thus if any region $w$ can be selected such that the ratio of the liklihoods of inclusion in $w$ is equal to or exceeds $k$ [as in (3)], *and* such that the ratio of the likelihoods of exclusion from $w$ is equal to or less than $k$ [as in (4)], then $w$ is a best critical region for a most powerful test. An implication of this theorem for tests using symmetrical distributions such as the normal distribution is that the critical region, of whatever size, should be taken in that extremity of the sampling distribution for $\mu_0$ which lies in the direction of $\mu_1$.

Where costs (losses and gains) are not involved or where they are equated for different types of risk, a reasonable assumption might be to select a decision procedure and a critical region such that, as between $\mu_0$ and $\mu_1$, select that hypothesis which on the evidence yields the greater likelihood.

Both (3) and (4) above are likelihood ratios and establish the kinship of the Neyman–Pearson and likelihood ratio test procedures. Discussions and proofs of the power properties of tests are mathematically difficult. However relatively simple accounts can be found in Neyman (1950) and Fraser (1958). A technical discussion is to be found in Lehmann's *Testing Statistical Hypotheses,* a work that presents a sophisticated analysis and defense of Neyman–Pearson test procedures.

## NOTE 14.3

Issues concerning null hypothesis testing have been debated in the psychological literature (Rozeboom, 1960; Grant, 1962; Binder, 1963). In its most general interpretation the null hypothesis is any simple hypothesis expressing the value of some parameter or any composite hypothesis expressing a set of possible values for the parameter, each of which is less than (or greater than) some specified value. Now what should be the testing and inference strategy? In general the Popperian thesis of disconfirmation holds in statistical inference. Rejection of a hypothesis is less subject to doubt than is acceptance. Therefore, research problems designed to verify differences in treatments as between experimental and control groups are subject to affirmation on the grounds of data sufficient to reject the null hypothesis. But what of problems wherein a theory leads to a clearly specified hypothesis such that support of a theory is contingent upon *acceptance* rather than rejection of the hypothesis. Several alternatives may be open, such as supporting the hypothesis by regression or by trend analyses, in which cases support again would come by way of a rejection test (Grant, 1962). However, one cannot muster unequivocal support for his hypothesis by tests of goodness of fit, or by other acceptance tests. Under such circumstances, other alternatives are available. One is to take a set of observations sufficiently large so that the confidence interval for all acceptable hypotheses is so limited that all hypotheses within the limits are by any practical judgments of difference considered to be homogeneous. Then, if the null hypothesis falls within the confidence interval of "practically homogeneous" hypotheses, acceptance over that entire set of hypotheses amounts to selecting hypotheses that in no practical sense differ from the null hypothesis. Narrowing the confidence interval for any given confidence level is achieved by taking large samples, since, in general, sampling variability is inversely a function of sample size. If sampling size is to be restricted for practical reasons, other alternatives than the preceding one must be found.

The simplest of these alternatives is merely to increase the critical region for rejection, thereby restricting the region of acceptance, increasing the size of the test, and, of course, increasing its power. One such suggestion has been made by Neyman (1942). Since traditional significance levels tend to be stringent, why not relax on Type I error and more nearly balance the two types? Although one now increases the risk of rejecting the null hypothesis when it is true, he has a more homogeneous set of hypotheses to accept. And if the null hypothesis is a member of that set, then it may become the focal hypothesis in the relatively homogeneous set. Perhaps one should not play lightly with our error traditions. Costs should be considered. However, it should be noted that if we can make indifference assumptions about the costs of decision *and* the prior probabilities of hypotheses, then an optimal Bayesian solution would be such that the critical region would be one wherein the probabilities of the two types of error would be identical.

(Another possibility which the present writer has suggested is that against the null hypothesis one selects a "just practically different" hypothesis such that it becomes a matter of indifference to the investigator if he accepts or rejects it when it, the j.p.d. hypothesis, is true. This test is more conservative than the preceding one, and can devolve into an argument over sample size. Generally, in the context of this test, one might argue that for hypotheses derived from well-established theories only small samples are required; for new theories and radical hypotheses large samples are required.)

If one seeks optimal rather than merely optical decision rules, then he should resort to Bayesian procedures which alone combine costs and prior probabilities in the risk function. Moreover, we might find it possible to use likelihood tests that would enable us to accept the null hypotheses over other possible hypotheses. But whether assessments of loss and subjective probability are possible in scientific inference is subject to debate (Fisher, 1959; Binder, 1964).

## NOTE 14.4

To other requirements of statistical tests (e.g., unbiasedness and sufficiency) Abraham Wald added that of *admissibility*. When loss–gain risk functions are taken into consideration, our primary criterion for selecting among alternative tests and strategies is that of optimality, i.e. of maximizing our expected gain. Without reliable estimates of the prior probabilities of hypotheses, however, unique solutions to the decision problem frequently cannot be determined. However, one can seek to eliminate some tests, among all possible tests, which clearly may be regarded unsatisfactory. For example, if a decision strategy $D_1$ yielded higher loss for all possible world hypotheses than did an alternative $D_2$, then $D_2$ would dominate over $D_1$ and $D_1$ would be regarded an *inadmissible* test.

It is frequently the case that from a set of tests $\{D_i\}$ there is some subset such that no one test clearly dominates over, or is dominated by, any other test. For example, a Bayes strategy is any strategy that in accordance with the prior probabilities of the possible hypotheses is such that the rule $D_b$ enables one to minimize the expected loss associated with incorrect decision. Then all such Bayes strategies (corresponding to assignments of positive prior probabilities) are admissible, and any admissible strategy could be reduced to a Bayes strategy for some set of prior probabilities.

## NOTE 14.5

A distinction is to be made between simple hypotheses and composite hypotheses. A hypothesis is *simple* if it completely specifies a probability distribution; otherwise it is *composite*. Thus, for example, the hypothesis $H : \mu = \mu_0$ is simple; the hypothesis $H : \mu > \mu_0$ is composite since it expresses the possibility of an infinite set of hypotheses, any one of which is greater than $\mu_0$. In the significance test we may test the composite hypothesis $H_0 : \mu \leq \mu_0$ against the simple hypothesis $H_1 : \mu = \mu_1$. Then it is possible to assert that the probability of a Type I error is at most no greater than $\alpha$. The long-run interpretation of this probability would be as follows:

Call all hypotheses in the set $\{\mu \leq \mu_0\}$ the parameter space $\Omega_0$; then for all hypotheses selected from this space and for all significance tests utilizing the critical region $w$ as defined on $\mu_0$ the probability of rejecting $H_0$ does not exceed $\alpha$.

## NOTE 14.6

Since neither Neyman nor Fisher were reluctant polemicists, the controversy has been well publicized. Speaking of Neyman, Fisher writes:

He seems to claim that the statement (a) '$\theta$ has a probability of 5 percent of exceeding $T$' is different from (b) '$T$ has a probability of 5 percent of falling short of $\theta$.' Since language is meant to be used, I believe it is essential that such statements, whether expressed in words or symbols, should be recognized as equivalent, even when $\theta$ is a parameter, defined as an objective character of the real world, entering into our specification of our hypothetical population, whilst $T$ is directly calculable from its observations (1955, p. 70).

A case where the fiducial argument leads to the same limits as confidence limits is one using "Student's" $t$-distribution as the probability density. Here the statistic has Students distribution

$$ t = \frac{\bar{x} - \mu}{s_x / \sqrt{n}}, \tag{1} $$

which itself is a function of $n - 1$, the degrees of freedom which can be assigned to the variance $s_x^2$. By virtue of tables or actual integration of the $t$-distribution we can establish

$$P(- t_{a/2} < t < + t_{1-a/2}) = 1 - \alpha, \tag{2}$$

where $+ t_{1-a/2}$ and $- t_{a/2}$ are limits and $1 - \alpha$ the confidence that the random variable $t$ falls in such limits.

Treating $\mu$ as a hypothesis, and $t$ as a pivotal quantity, we may use (1) and (2) to write

$$P\left\{ \bar{x} - t_{a/2} \frac{s_x}{\sqrt{n}} < \mu < \bar{x} + t_{1-a/2} \frac{s_x}{\sqrt{n}} \right\} = 1 - \alpha. \tag{3}$$

This is an expression of the confidence limits and is subject to Neyman's interpretation in terms of inductive behavior.

However, in a similar context, $\mu$ may be considered a variable so that from (1) we obtain

$$\mu = \bar{x} - ts_x/\sqrt{n}. \tag{4}$$

Since $x$ and $s_x$ are now assumed to be constants, then the fiducial distribution of $\mu$ has the distribution of $t$, and the fiducial limits for $\mu$ coincide exactly with (3).

Generally a satisfactory mathematical formalism has not been worked out for the fiducial argument. There are occasions where the two methods of establishing limits differ as to numerical results (cf. Neyman, 1952, pp. 229–254); but for the Behrens–Fisher problem, at least, the fiducial argument gives a solution superior to that of confidence intervals. (Cf. Fraser, 1958, pp. 289–291.)

Differences between these partisans of statistical theory are not confined to matters of limits and confidence. Some of Fisher's sharpest criticism is reserved for the Neyman–Pearson–Wald schemata of statistical decision (Fisher, 1955, 1959). He makes the following charges.

(1)    The model of repeated sampling from the same universe, such as Neyman's conception of "inductive behavior" visualizes, is unreal in matters of scientific investigation. Although we sample a given universe, there is to be sure a multiplicity of populations to which a given sample belongs. "Acceptance" relates to a class of hypotheses all supportable by the sample data. Thus we should avoid emphasizing significance tests that give privileged acceptance to one over another hypothesis.

(2)    " 'Errors of the second kind,' although apparently only a harmless piece of technical jargon, is useful as indicating the type of mental confusion in which it was coined." (1955, p. 73). The null hypothesis is never accepted outright to the exclusion of other hypotheses but only as a tentative conjecture that experimental results as yet do not warrant its rejection. One should look at the analysis of the experimental situation and arrive at provisional conjectures rather than assigning probabilities in the artificial dichotomization of error.

(3)   Insistence upon "inductive behavior" as against "inductive reasoning" is a matter of verbal preference and results in unnecessary restrictions being placed on the interpretation of probability and inference.

(4)   The scientific investigator "introduces no cost functions for faulty decisions . . ." (1959, p. 103). His inferences are provisional and are made in the context of experimental design and the state of scientific knowledge. Rather than computerized acceptance decisions based on objective sampling situations, significance tests are based on highly tentative speculations about the world. We seek support of hypotheses without the decisive decision that simplifies the world of commerce.

> . . . the Natural Sciences can only be successfully conducted by responsible and independent thinkers applying their mind and their imaginations to the detailed interpretation of verifiable observations. The idea that this responsibility can be delegated to a giant computer programmed with Decision Functions belongs to the phantasy of circles rather remote from scientific research (1959, p. 101).

## NOTE 14.7

If for our two sample hypotheses $\mu_0$ and $\mu_1$ we have the probability densities $f_0(x : \mu_0, \sigma_0)$ and $f_1(x : \mu_1, \sigma_1)$, then we seek the critical region over the range of $x$ such that the decision function $d(x)$ minimizes expected loss. Consider now two such normal probability densities with $\mu_1 > \mu_0$ and $\sigma_0 = \sigma_1$, such that the overlapping densities appear as in Figure 14.2.

Granted a table of loss functions, then the task is to select a critical value $k$ and the decision function $d(x)$ such that the expected loss is a minimum. Generally then we minimize the expectation

$$E[L_{i,j}d(x)] = L_{0,0} \int_{-\infty}^{k} f_0(x)\, dx\ P(\mu_0) + L_{0,1} \int_{-\infty}^{k} f_1(x)\, dx\ P(\mu_1) \tag{1}$$

$$+ L_{1,0} \int_{k}^{\infty} f_0(x)\, dx\ P(\mu_0) + L_{1,1} \int_{k}^{\infty} f_1(x)\, dx\ P(\mu_1).$$

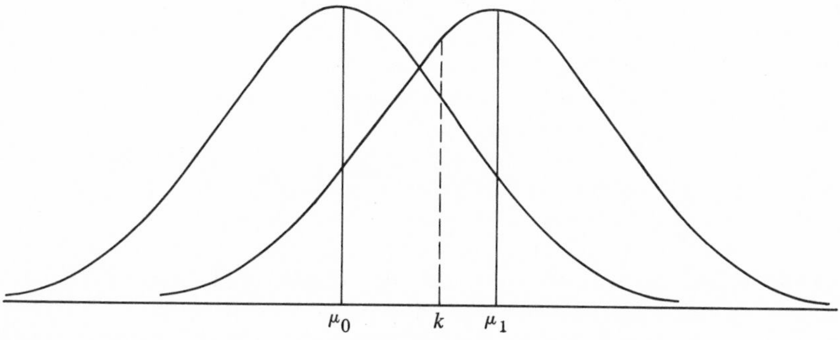

**Figure 14.2**

For typical problems in determining optimal cutting scores, Alf (Alf, Turner, and Dorfman, 1965) has worked out the following solutions.

(1)    For $\mu_1 > \mu_0$; $\sigma_0 = \sigma_1$; $P(\mu_0) = P(\mu_1)$

$$z_k = \frac{\log \left( \dfrac{L_{0,0} + L_{1,0}}{L_{1,1} + L_{0,1}} \right)}{\dfrac{\mu_1 - \mu_0}{\sigma}} + \frac{\mu_1 - \mu_0}{2\sigma}, \tag{2}$$

where $z_k$ is a standard score computed on $\mu_0$.

If the loss matrix is symmetrical then the log of the ratio of the losses becomes zero, and our optimal $z_k$ yields the "equal probability test,"

$$z = \tfrac{1}{2} \frac{\mu_1 - \mu_0}{\sigma}. \tag{3}$$

(2)    For $\mu_1 > \mu_0$; $\sigma_0 = \sigma_1$; $P(\mu_0) \neq P(\mu_1)$

$$z_k = \frac{\log_e \left( \dfrac{P(\mu_0)\,(L_{0,0} + L_{1,0})}{P(\mu_1)\,(L_{1,1} + L_{0,1})} \right)}{\dfrac{\mu_1 - \mu_0}{\sigma}} + \frac{\mu_1 - \mu_0}{2\sigma}. \tag{4}$$

Should the loss matrix be symmetrical our problem reduces to one of maximizing the number of correct decisions. Thus we would choose $z_k$ such that

$$z_k = \frac{\log \dfrac{P(\mu_0)}{P(\mu_1)}}{\dfrac{\mu_1 - \mu_0}{\sigma}} + \frac{\mu_1 - \mu_0}{2\sigma}. \tag{5}$$

If we regard $(\mu_0 - \mu_1)/\sigma$ as the standard difference between our two hypotheses, then in order to maximize correct inferences, the reference for the equal probability test is to be corrected by the ratio between the log of the odds in favor of $\mu_1$ and the standard difference between hypotheses.

(3)    For $\mu_1 > \mu_0$; $\sigma_0 \neq \sigma_1$; $P(\mu_0) \neq P(\mu_1)$

$$z_k = \frac{-\dfrac{\sigma_0(\mu_1 - \mu_0)}{\sigma_1^2} \pm \sqrt{\dfrac{\sigma_0^2(\mu_1 - \mu_0)^2}{\sigma_1^4} + \left(1 - \dfrac{\sigma_0^2}{\sigma_1^2}\right)\left[\dfrac{(\mu_1 - \mu_0)^2}{\sigma_1^2} + 2\log_e \dfrac{P(\mu_0)(L_{0,0} + L_{1,0})\sigma_1}{P(\mu_1)(L_{1,1} + L_{0,1})\sigma_0}\right]}}{1 - \dfrac{\sigma_0^2}{\sigma_1^2}} \tag{6}$$

Equation (6) is derived from a quadratic equation and offers the standard solution to the roots of the equation. It should be noted then that when $\sigma_1 = \sigma_0$, the equation from which (6) is derived reduces to (4), whereas (6) itself would give an indeterminate solution for $z_k$.

In principle, then, optimal solution should be available for any problem with sufficient information concerning the prior probabilities, densities, and loss functions. Short of omniscience or an uncanny predictive intuition, then Bayesian solutions to decision should be the best we could hope for.

As an aside we might find that Bayesian solutions give support to Pascal's wager. Should one decide for God? Pascal writes:

> Let us weigh the gain and the loss in wagering that God is. Let us estimate these two chances. If you gain, you gain all, if you lose you lose nothing. Wager then without hesitation that He is (1958, p. 67).

As good skeptics, let us assume that $P(G) \ll P(\sim G)$, but let us also assume that eternal felicity is an infinite gain. Assume that $x$ from which $z$ is computed is the evidential continuum on a hedonic scale. Then providing we take preschool liberties with infinite values, we may determine a critical decision value, a cutting score, such that whatever the evidence—no matter what the count is over our joys and sorrows—we will decide for God. Such is the Bayesian support of Pascal's wager. However, an important corollary, which Pascal appears to have overlooked, is that it should make no difference as to which God we skeptics should choose to believe in (Turner, 1966).

## NOTE 14.8

A more general treatment of the optimal decision problem is that of considering prior probabilities simply as the weights we assign to the various likelihoods of equation (6) Note 14.7, regardless how such weights are arrived at. Then for any problem for which equation (6) applies optimal decision policies can be determined. And in those cases where the weights are legitimate expressions of the prior probabilities of hypotheses, then (6) becomes the means for arriving at optimal Bayesian strategies.

According to classical decision procedures a risk function is the product of losses and likelihoods. Thus for the dichotomous test situation with $\theta = \theta_0, \theta_1$

$$R(d;\theta_0) = L_{0,0} \, P(d_0 \,|\, \theta_0) + L_{1,0} \, P(d_1 \,|\, \theta_0) \tag{7}$$

is the risk of the decision function $d(x)$ when $\theta = \theta_0$. And

$$R(d;\theta_1) = L_{0,1} \, P(d_0 \,|\, \theta_1) + L_{1,1} \, P(d_1 \,|\, \theta_1) \tag{8}$$

is the risk of the decision function $d(x)$ when $\theta = \theta_1$.

Since (7) and (8) are conditional upon $\theta$, we must introduce weightings in order to derive an over-all expected loss as in (6). Thus a weighted average of the two risks, (7) and (8) is given by

$$R(d;\xi) = \xi \, R(d;\theta_0) + (1 - \xi) \, R(d;\theta_1) \tag{9}$$

where $\theta \leq \xi \leq 1$ is the weighting factor assuming the status of a prior probability in Bayesian procedures. The task of optimization is then to determine a decision function $d(x)$ such that $R(d;\xi)$ for that function is at least as small as it would be for any other decision function. For the dichotomous (nonrandomized) decision function this reduces to the rule

$$d(x) = \begin{cases} \theta = \theta_1 & \text{if } \xi \, R(d;\theta_0) < (1 - \xi) \, R(d;\theta_1), \\ \theta = \theta_0 & \text{otherwise.} \end{cases} \quad (10)$$

That is to say we choose our decision rule $d(x)$ such that we reject $H : \theta = \theta_0$ only if the weighted risk involved when $\theta_0$ is true is less than the weighted risk when its complement $\theta_1$ is true.

Actual determination of an optimal decision rule, $d(x)$, is beyond the scope of the present discussion; but it is easy to verify that for symmetrical cost matrices, and $\xi = (1 - \xi)$ the optimal test is the equal probability test.

Robbins (1963) gives an interesting interpretation and extension of this decision problem; first, by assigning to $\xi$ the role of a weighting factor (which may or may not have a Bayesian interpretation as the prior probability of a hypothesis) and second, by giving $\xi$ a frequency interpretation in "a sequence of decision problems."

Let

$$\begin{cases} \theta_1, \theta_2, \ldots, \theta_n \; ; \text{ for all } \theta_i = \theta_0, \theta_1 \\ x_1, x_2, \ldots, x_n \end{cases}$$

be a finite sequence of parameters and observable random variables with $x_i$ associated with $\theta_i$ and each $x_i$ leading to a decision as to $\theta_i = \theta_0, \theta_1$. Thus for each decision in the above sequence there would be a computable risk as in equation (9). And the average expected loss in the set of $n$ decisions is the average of the $n$ determinations of $R(d; \xi)$. In the series of $n$ tests some proportion $\bar{\theta}_n$ of the parameters will in fact be $\theta_1$'s. We then develop a new decision rule analogous to (10), only substituting the quantity

$$\bar{\theta}_n = \frac{1}{n} \sum_{i=1}^{n} \theta_i = (0,1) \quad (11)$$

for $\xi$ in rule (10). For any given decision, say the $n$th decision, this entails our computing $\bar{\theta}_{n-1}$ for the $n - 1$ previous applications of the decision procedure. Robbins establishes not only that such decision procedures would give results formally similar to the one obtained when (9) and (10) are known, but also that in the absence of any knowledge of (11) (which would require more information than is usually available to us), an unbiased estimate of $\bar{\theta}_{n-1}$ is obtainable from a relatively simple function based on the fact of a given value of $x$ in the series $x_1, x_2, \ldots, x_{n-1}$ falling into one or another class of the set $\{S, \sim S\}$. We first establish the function

$$g(x) = \begin{cases} 1 \text{ if } x \in S \\ 0 \text{ if } x \in \sim S \end{cases} \quad (12)$$

as in the usual decision procedure. With this we define the function

$$h(x) = \frac{g(x) - P(x \in S \mid \theta = \theta_0)}{P(x \in S \mid \theta = \theta_1) - P(x \in S \mid \theta = \theta_0)}. \quad (13)$$

Suppose now we need to make a decision after the paradigm expressed in (10). Let $\{x_1, x_2, \ldots, x_n\}$ be the set of observations upon which the estimate of $\xi$ is to be made. Then using the fact that $h(x)$ is an unbiased estimate of $\theta$ ($\theta = \theta_0, \theta_1$), we compute

$$\psi(x) = \frac{1}{n} \sum_{i=1}^{n} h(x_i)$$

wherein the expectation of $\psi(x)$ is the proportion of times $\theta = \theta_1$,

$$E\,[\psi(x)] = \bar{\theta}_i.$$

Thus the expression for $\psi(x)$, a function computable from the data, is an empirical estimate of $\xi$.

In effect each $x$ in the set $\{x_1, x_2, \ldots, x_n\}$ yields a decision. Of these, $(x_1, x_2, \ldots, x_{n-1})$ yield an estimate of $\xi$, to be incorporated into a rule analogous to (10) wherein $x_n$ now yields either of the two decision values: $d_0 : \theta = \theta_0$ or $d_1 : \theta = \theta_1$.

Since estimation of $\xi$ is now based on empirical sampling, and thus is subject to error, Robbins does not wish to maintain that the above decision procedures are optimal (as for example when $\xi$ is known independently of estimation procedures). However, such a procedure does permit one to utilize an optimization paradigm when the weighting factor can only be estimated from a finite set of observations. Thus empirical Bayesian procedures are possible when more direct assessment of the prior probability $\xi$ is not within reason.

## NOTE 14.9

One should not overlook the predominance of the likelihood principle in simple Bayesian inference. For the dichotomous situation

$$\frac{P(H_0 \mid E)}{P(H_1 \mid E)} = \frac{P(H_0)}{P(H_1)} \frac{P(E \mid H_0)}{P(E \mid H_1)} \tag{5}$$

we would decide $H_0$ if the ratio of the posterior probabilities were greater than 1. The ratio of the prior probabilities is a constant and on any provisional grounds of indifference should be very nearly 1. In such cases the likelihood ratio is the significant detector of which hypothesis is to be chosen. But even when the assumption of indifference is suspect or where there is substantial disagreement as to the ratio of the prior probabilities, in the long run of extensive sampling the likelihood ratio should predominate. The argument is fully supported mathematically (Savage, 1962). However, it can be plausibly pointed up in the following way. Even allowing for substantial differences in prior probabilities, the likelihood ratio will in the long run emerge as the decisive function. For if one or another hypothesis is presumed to be correct, and they are discrepant, then by virtue of the principle of convergence for large numbers we would expect that $P(E \mid H_i \gg P(E \mid H_j)$ and that the likelihood ratio would approach infinity or zero as $n$, the number of observations, approaches infinity.

For a discussion of Bayes' theorem and the likelihood principle see L. J. Savage (1962). For a more philosophical defense of the likelihood principle see Hacking (1964). This latter article is for the most part the summary of an argument of a book on the *Foundations of Statistics* (1965). Note that Hacking regards likelihoods, $P(E \mid H)$, as the "likelihood of the hypothesis." Thus the likelihood of the hypothesis is to be regarded as equivalent to the probability of the evidence given the hypothesis.

# CHAPTER 15

# The Problem of Induction

AS AN EPILOGUE to this section and to this book, we turn to the problem of induction. How is synthetic knowledge possible? How do we justify our inductive inferences? A survey of the vast literature on the justification of induction would seem to indicate that this is a knotty problem. Yet surprisingly there are a number of writers who would maintain that the so-called problem of justifying induction is not a problem at all (e.g., Black, 1949, 1954) or that it is really a linguistic problem in which the analysis of the muddle of meaning will clarify its answer (e.g., Strawson, 1952; von Wright, 1957).

Tempting as both these suggestions may be, we shall have to consider our questions as meaningful ones, at least to the extent of our providing a defense of the assertion that there is reasonable support for the propositions of science. Traditionally, critical philosophy has been called upon to elucidate meaning and the support of statements; it has been called upon to distinguish sense from nonsense on the basis of rigorously applied criteria of meaning. 'Support,' 'justification,' 'explanation,' and 'reasons for' are all cognates in the family of expressions which signify our confidence in the assertions of science.

If a statement is a logical one, that is, if it expresses a theorem in a formal system, then it is found reasonable. It is justified; it is supported by the fact of its being the consequence of a set of initial postulates and a set of operational rules within that system. A proof constitutes the justification of the theorem. If our statement is an empirical statement, then its justification rests in its being a true account of the affairs it asserts. Thus factual statements are themselves the justification of empirical statements. And any factual statement is meaningful or justifiable in the context of experience in which it is uttered. However, if our statement is now regarded as that of an inductive inference whose possible extension exceeds the immediate data, then justification is not a simple matter of ostensification. And we are, indeed, confronted with the problem of Hume.

Consider predictions. All predictions involve future events and cannot be justified wholly on the basis of a finite set of observations. According to Hume, our predictive expectations cannot be justified on purely logical grounds, for both the prediction and its negation are meaningful statements of possible events; and they cannot be justified on grounds that they have worked in the past, since our seeking to justify that the past carries into the future is the problem at hand. There is no purely logical justification of induction since both members of a set of contradictory hypotheses about the future are meaningful in an empiricistic theory of meaning. And any pragmatic justification of induction is suspect by virtue of its assuming as its own means of support the very hypothesis we are seeking to justify.

Since the time of Hume such arguments have seemed to foreclose the issue. There is no "satisfactory" justification of induction. Yet what is judged to be satisfactory is itself a matter of convention. If we seek deductive support and only deductive support of our hypotheses, then there is no complete support of inductive hypotheses which, though they may be logically valid, can only be true by virtue of empirical states of affairs. On the other hand, if we seek support of our procedures of inference on grounds that they seem to have worked in the past and ought therefore to work in the future, this *is* support of the procedures of inductive inference—providing, of course, we are willing to accept as elucidatory the very thing we feel compelled to justify. To argue that the circularity of this latter tactic is indefensible, as many critics of induction have argued, is understandable. Yet the argument can be a rather preemptory one, for psychologically, at least, this tactic provides a satisfactory answer at the specific level of interrogation upon which we may have entered.

In Part III of this book we have been concerned with problems of statistical inference and decision. Our discussion of justification will concentrate on these. It should be noted, however, that throughout this book we have been concerned with the justification of assertions; for example, the data assertions, assertions of hypotheses, assertions of theoretical terms, of theories and models, and so on. Thus the problem of justification is not new to us. Furthermore, justification and support are by no means so conclusive that once a justification is presented it is once and forever accepted by the confrerie as well established. Even for the nonconventionalist what is acceptable justification has an element of convention to it (cf. N15.1). And as often as not we may find that laments over the impossibility of justifying induction stem as much from the collective inability to codify justification as they do from some profound epistemological principle.

As a result, justification is as much a psychological notion as it is a purely logical one. That is, there are cognitive levels of justification just as there are cognitive levels of explanation. What satisfies us at one level, and what is thereby justified or supported, may not satisfy us at another level. As was pointed out in the chapter on explanations, what the child may accept as plausible explanation at one time ceases to be satisfactory at another. Just as the causal analyst in antiquity ended up in the nebulous descent into "first cause," so does the contemporary "justificationist" end up in the regressive pursuit of support where ultimately no one argument and no hypothesis is pervasively defensible.

The argument of the present writer is that justifications of induction are meaningful. Such justifications propose meaningful questions at given levels of interrogation, and they propose meaningful answers at those given interrogative levels. The rub is that those answers invariably suggest new questions, and new demands for justification. But that is not, of itself, to say that answering questions is either meaningless or fruitless. Simply stated, the predicament of justifying induction is that there is no end to the questions that arise in the regressive quest for justification.

## IS THERE A PROBLEM OF JUSTIFICATION?

Before turning to the paradigm for the justification of statistical induction, it will be well to respond to those who deny there is any problem of justification. Max Black sets the tenor of the critique when he writes:

> The supposed "problem" has been so framed as to block at the outset any attempt at solution. But if this is so, to persist in trying to solve it would be like continuing to try to square the circle. The philosophy of induction has many unsolved problems; but the so-called "problem" of justifying induction is not one of them (1954, p. 159).

Here he is responding to several aspects of the problem. In an earlier paper, he addresses himself specifically to the issue of formal justification (Black, 1949). He rejects the suggestion that the problem is a relevant one on the familiar grounds that skeptics insist that the criterion of justification, its meaning, be the same for inductive inference as it is for deductive inference. A conclusion, an inference, is said to be justified if it follows from a set of postulates and logical rules. The validity of a purely logical proposition can be established wholly within the syntactical system. The "validity," or rather the truth status of an inductive hypothesis, is contingent upon experience. An inductive inference as formulated within some formal theory, such as that of probability, may be a valid theorem within the theoretical calculus, but the truth status of that hypothesis is ascertained only by a set of observations. A prediction may be formally correct, but empirically false. To insist, therefore, that inductive inferences be justified in the same manner as deductive inference is justified is to confuse the two types of inference. There is no problem of justifying induction. It is a pseudo-formulation which rests upon our imposing inappropriate criteria of justification on a type of inference that by its very nature is uncertain.

Doubtless this line of criticism is useful in pointing to the difference between reasoning which yields apodictic conclusions and that which does not. To the extent that a person would insist that all inference be of an apodictic kind, or that it meet the same deductivist standards of proof, he is, of course, in error. Part of his confusion undoubtedly rests in his seeking support in a descending chain of explications, only to become perturbed that there is no conclusive support, no Q.E.D., to all the questions he thinks it appropriate to ask. There is, moreover, the implication that the person who despairs over justification is attempting to suppress the distinction between analytic and synthetic arguments, at least to the extent of his wanting to know that a synthetic proposition is true in the same way that he knows that an analytic proposition is true.

Now the substance of this argument is that the question of justifying induction is a meaningless one since the kind of answer that is, in some confused way, intended is impossible to give. One cannot give purely deductive justifications of inductive arguments. This, of course, is very much to the point. However, this muddle does not rule out the possibility of our formulating questions and answers that, if only in some conventional (psychological?) sense, do constitute support of our inductive argument. The fact is that we have supported inductive arguments throughout the history of human thought, and in a rather distinctive manner since the advent of experimental science. Our support of the most sophisticated of inductive arguments may be in part deductive support (of which there is no present question) and in part evidential support. The problem of justifying induction is the problem of formulating criteria of evidential support.

A second line of critique is that based more explicitly on philosophical analysis. Like many other problems in the compendia of philosophy, that of justifying induction derives from imprecise usage in the ordinary language. We have no clear conception of what we are asking when we ask for a justification. The argument of Black and others as presented above alludes to one aspect of the muddle. Strawson (1952) carries the argument further. Not only is it inappropriate to request that induction be shown to be really a kind of deduction or "that one kind of reasoning be shown to be another different kind," but our attempts to justify induction often conflate two quite different questions. One question concerns the success of particular applications of an inductive procedure which incorporates general rules in the inferential chain. Our justification then rests upon our successfully testing that such general rules are useful. A second question concerns whether the method of induction, and not just the general law or rule of inference which the method incorporates, is itself a justifiable method for making inferences concerning potential evidence. According to Strawson the answer to the latter questions involves *a priori* assumptions concerning the character of the world. To the one question we give our answers in terms of pragmatic support, itself an inductive answer. To the other, we give an answer that presupposes that induction will be the only method by which we can make predictions of the potential evidence.

It is well to keep the distinction between these two types of questions in mind. I do not, however, think they are fatal to the interrogations that inductivists may wish to make in support of inference. Nor do I think it correct to assert that the two questions call for radically different kinds of support. At one level the "inductivist" (here the person justifying inductive inference) may justify his prediction by showing that his inference from general rule to hypothesis about a particular event is supported by the evidence. He shows that the inference procedure is useful. At another level he may show that the method itself, e.g., that of adopting complex statistical theories, with their assumptions concerning probability densities, is successful. No doubt at the first level of statistical inference we make some *a priori* assumption that inductive method is a justifiable method of inference; but if the assumption is challenged, as it would be in the second question of justification, then it in turn becomes a problem for inductive assessment. The fact that every inductive inference involves presuppositions, which themselves are not subject to test by the designated evidence, is not fatal to the possibility of inductive inference. Nor is it fatal to our efforts to justify inductive inference. Such, I think, becomes apparent in the examination of statistical induction.

## JUSTIFYING STATISTICAL INDUCTION

Let us now consider the paradigm of statistical induction. The content and machinery of inference is composed of (1) evidence, (2) statements about the evidence, (3) a statistical theory of random variables, and (4) evidential predictions. We need not overly concern ourselves with semantic problems. It is taken for granted that there is a dictionary for translating statements in the theoretical language of random variables into statements in the evidential language, and that, moreover, the truth of a statement in the evidential language is itself determined by the evidence. We have therefore the following schema.

(1)  $E_1, \ldots, E_m$           events in the physical world
(2)  $e_1, \ldots, e_m$           statements about such events
(3)  $x_1, \ldots, x_n, \ldots$      random variables in the formal system

(4)  $G(x;\theta_1, \ldots, \theta_k)$       statistical theory incorporating parameters, probability distributions, and rules of inference

(5)  $P_1, \ldots, P_j$       statements about applicability of statistical theory

(6)  $e_1, \ldots, e_N, \ldots$       statements about actual and potential evidence

(7)  $E_1, \ldots, E_N, \ldots$       evidence, actual and potential

A problem in statistical inference then involves taking a sample of data involving (1) and (2), applying a statistical theory involving (3), (4), and (5), and arriving at an inductive hypothesis involving (2), (3), (4), (5), and (6). As is usually the case, the hypothesis involves a statement in the theoretical language signifying a plausible range of values  for one or more of the parameters, $\theta_1, \ldots, \theta_k$, in (4). Since these parameters are presumed to have significance in the evidential language (e.g., true means, true proportions, true variances, and so on, which are logical constructions in the evidential language), then evidential support of inference is achieved through the reference to a dictionary as between the language of random variables, (3) and (4), and the evidential language. Under (5) we specify the applicability of the statistical theory. That is, we assert that conditions of random sampling and good fit exist as between the evidence and the random variables. We assert that the formal model of the theory is a good model of the evidence.

In the most general form our statistical paradigm is of the form, if $p$ then $q$. The antecedent, however, is a complex proposition involving evidential statements, the statistical theory and its formal data, and statements of the assumptions. Let us then separate the evidential components of the proposition from the presumptive components. We then have "if $e$ and $g$, then $h$," where $h$ is the inductive inference. What, now, is the nature of justifying the inductive inference? We may proceed initially by showing that all such applications of the paradigm do in fact lead to true inferences. Laying aside the question-begging issue of our adopting an inductive strategy for supporting inductive inference, we set about establishing that our procedures of inference are in fact successful. How do we do this? First, let us note what kinds of propositions are denoted by '$h$.' Let us assume them to be statements of confidence intervals; namely, that "the parameter $\theta_j$ is to be found within some prescribed limits," which we assert with a confidence of $1 - \alpha$. How may we establish that this has been a successful inference? Not by actual observation, since a strict determination of $\theta_j$ would involve infinite sampling. Not even by increasing the size of our sample by a finite amount, for that would involve only our narrowing the set of our limits for $\theta_j$ without necessarily increasing our confidence—or vice versa. The problem of justifying the new inference would, of course, remain. Furthermore we note that according to our interpretation of inference as inductive behavior, the statement of limits and confidence is meaningful only for the long run of inferences of a similar kind. A probabilistic hypothesis $(0 < P < 1)$ can neither be confirmed nor disconfirmed by a single application of the rule.

Direct confirmation of a "successful" inference is impossible; we must adopt a second tactic. Rather than attempting to confirm the inference, let us attempt to show that the inference is a reasonable one on the grounds that the presumptive propositions as expressed in $g$ above are reasonable ones. Here $g$ asserts (3), (4), and (5) of our schema which together with the evidence certainly justify the inference. That is to say, if for "if $e$ and $g$ then $h$" $e$ is equivalent to statements in class (2) and $g$ is equivalent to (3), (4), and (5), then certainly $e$ and $g$ entail the inference of $h$. Our justification is thus a simple deductive one; it may well be an elaboration of mathematical laws of large numbers. However, this begs the question. How do we know we have an appropriate statistical model? In order to utilize our deductive support we must first determine whether the set of assumptions expressed in (5), $P_1, \ldots, P_j$ are themselves justified. Our initial problem then degenerates to one of establishing support for the assumptions $P_1, \ldots, P_j$.

Now this problem itself becomes a legitimate one for inductive inference. For example, suppose $P_1$ asserts that the evidential measure is conformal with a normal probability density. We wish to justify $P_1$. This we may attempt to do by running a test of goodness of fit. That is, for the set of evidential measures we run another test with a different statistical model (say, a chi-square test) to see if the data conform within allowable limits to the prescribed distribution.[1] If they appear to be tenable by virtue of our acceptance procedure, we deem $P_1$ supported. However, our new test also involves assumptions and a paradigm identical with our first one. (If it is a chi-square test, for example, it involves the binomial model of the discrepancies between observed and expected frequencies.) Thus from the beginning our justification proceeds (degenerates):

$$
\begin{array}{ll}
e\, g_1 \supset h & : \text{first level of support} \\
g_1\, ? & : \text{request to justify; 2nd level} \\
e\, g_2 \supset g_1 & \\
\text{and} & \\
e\, g_1\, g_2 \supset h & : \text{second level of support} \\
g_2\, ? & : \text{third level of interrogation} \\
\text{and so on.} &
\end{array}
$$

We may carry this regressive justification as far as we like. We may test

---

[1] We ignore the problems of testing for the acceptance of a specific hypothesis against all possible alternatives. Our justification above is contingent upon a rule of acceptance.

for the model of expected sampling frequencies as stipulated by the binomial model, and subsequently for the conformity of sample chi-squares to the expected distribution of chi-square. Since a test for conformity is itself a test of goodness of fit, we are confronted with a new test for which it is legitimate to request justification. And so on, to an infinite regress.

Let us detail the regress. First we assume $g_1$, our initial statistical model, in order to infer $h$. Inference $h$ is justified if we can in turn justify our assuming $g_1$. Second, we test $g_1$ by a test of goodness of fit requiring our assuming $g_2$. Assumptions $g_1$ are subject to justification if we may in turn justify the assumptions $g_2$. Third, since $g_2$ itself involves postulation of a probability density, then it too is testable by a test of goodness of fit, requiring assumptions $g_3$. And so on.[2]

Thus our inductive inference $h$ is justified if assumptions $g_1$ are justifiable. Assumptions $g_1$ may be justified if assumptions $g_2$ are justifiable. Assumptions $g_2$ may be justified if assumptions $g_3$ are justifiable. And so on. Now each step in this procedure entails our taking additional data, with each step involving a replication of the data intake of the preceding step. Each step, however, is a unique test unto itself representing a unique step in the regress of justification. Thus each step presents an answer to some specific request for justification.

Doubtless this infinite regress leaves us uncomfortable, but it should not be regarded as destructive of all quests after justification. After all, the statistician often does run a test on some of his initial assumptions. Running tests of goodness of fit are not uncommon. But generally that is as far as the regress goes.[3]

Thus it is apparent that our statistician is "satisfied" at second-level testing and justification. (He is, in a word, content to find that Atlas himself is supported by the tortoise.) Should he be requested to justify the assumptions necessary to justify his justification of his critical inference, he would indeed know how to proceed. Each level of interrogation poses a unique and meaningful question. And for each question there is a specifiable procedure for obtaining an answer.

---

[2] Suppose our second test involves testing the data for goodness of fit to a normal probability density which is assumed for the initial inference. The third test would then be one to ascertain whether the probability density for the test of goodness of fit (chi-square test) is an appropriate description for tests of class two. Such a test would involve repetitions of class two chi-square tests to ascertain whether the results of such tests conform to chi-square distribution. But then a fourth test, another chi-square test, is requested to ascertain whether the assumed chi-square probability density is appropriate for describing the results of class three tests. And so on, such that at any level $n$ another chi-square test is required to justify the conformity of results of class $n-1$ tests to the chi-square distribution. At each step we must, of course, replicate the work of each preceding step sufficient times to yield an appropriate sample for the succeeding chi-square test.

[3] See Yule and Kendall, 1950, p. 476, for examples of third-level testing and justification.

The tendency to find this kind of regressive justification problematic stems from the failure to make the simple distinction between *contextual* and *ultimate* justification. For a given context, i.e. level of justification, some procedure for justification is always specifiable. However, if we demand that the context be all-inclusive so that all levels of justification be entertained simultaneously, as it were, and so that the regress be terminated by some ultimate justification, then no such justification is possible. But we need not, and should not, insist on ultimate justification. Contextual justification is both satisfying and meaningful, just as contextual explanation is. A question of justification is answerable at any given level of interrogation—answerable, that is, in the context of our making new assumptions. We may legitimately request justification of these new assumptions, but that is indeed a different question.

It should be noted now that for the regress of justification any rejection of assumptions at some given level of justification invalidates the support of assumptions at all previous levels of justification. This fact points to the distressing likelihood that in the long run of regressive support no justification will be sustained. There is not much that we can do to counter this depressing outlook except to remind ourselves that we are usually only concerned with short-run justifications, and that no inference and no assumption is ever likely to be precisely true (cf. N15.2). What is significant in this discussion is not that the justification of an inductive inference will be sustained through all descending levels of interrogation, but rather that a method exists for legitimately carrying out this interrogation (cf. N15.3).

# NOTES

## NOTE 15.1

By conventional justification I mean a justification which implicitly or explicitly sets the level of interrogation in the quest.

It is not difficult to invent examples of traps laid by the regressive request for justification. Suppose, for example, I am asked to justify the statements I make. Being a good empiricist, I propose the justification of a statement is its truth status, namely, it is justified by the truth of what it asserts. Events, conditions, data, observations justify the statement. But what I now assert, my justification, is itself a statement, a statement among statements to be justified. What now is the nature of this next level of justification. My answer is framed in terms of the relation of statements to data, events, observations, i.e., it is a bit of semantic exegesis. Now this too is by way of statement. What is it, what is the state of the world, the relation of the other statements and observations, that justifies my exegesis. My explication of this justification is itself a statement to be further justified by my stating that this statement correctly asserts a statement of the relation of statements to observation. And so to the regress. Confusing as this effort to state the regressive justification of statements may be, it is clear that the justification of statements justifying statements is at a different level of explication than my merely justifying statements.

A classic account of the problem of regressive justification is to be found in Lewis Carroll's "What the Tortoise said to Achilles." In short, from a major premise $P$, and a minor premise, $p$, we draw the conclusion $C$. How do we justify this syllogistic inference. By the rule $B$, of course, which asserts the syllogistic rule (Barbara). Very well then, rather than $P$, $p$, and $C$ we now have $P$, $p$, $B$, and $C$. But now how do we justify this sequence leading to $C$? Why by stating a new rule which asserts that if we have a major premise and if we have a minor premise and if we have a rule which explicates our utilization of the syllogism in Barbara, then we may conclude $C$. Call this the rule $R$. Now what we have is $P$, $p$, $B$, $R$ and $C$. But how do we make explicit that $P$, $p$, $B$, and $R$ justify our concluding $C$? By proposing a new rule, of course. There is no end to the justification, no end to rules about applying rules about rules about rules. . . . The Tortoise was observed to push Achilles to the one thousand and first regress, where, "in the hollow tones of despair," he emerged briefly to swap a pun with "Taught Us."

## NOTE 15.2

The difficulty of sustaining support for an inference is this. Every level of justification is sustained itself by a test involving assumptions—say, a test of goodness of fit. Each test in the regress itself involves a decision to accept or reject the fit, with its corresponding probabilities of Type I and Type II error. In order to safeguard against false acceptance we increase the risk of false rejection, possibly even to adopt an equal probability test. At any rate, in a protracted program of regressive justification, it becomes likely that even for universes in which inductive inferences are warranted some test at some level of justification will result in rejection of good fit—and hence invalidate all previous justifications.

If one responds to this deplorable state of affairs by safeguarding against committing an error of false rejection, he may indeed choose a decision rule that diminishes the probability of his rejecting as unjustified an inference which is truly justified. But in so doing he is, of course, running the risk of accepting many regressive justifications as sustained, when in fact there are true violations of the presumptive structure of support.

In addition the justification is complicated by the fact of its being contingent upon the strategy of acceptance. Generally we are content to accept an hypothesis if for the family of acceptable hypotheses to which it belongs (i.e., the confidence interval in which it is found) there are no practical differences among its members. In other words, we accept a hypothesis because, although it may have but a small Bayesian probability of being true, any discrepancy between it and the true hypothesis is likely to be small. This is suggestive of a postulate of the improbability of the null hypothesis; more blatantly we may assert "the null hypothesis (i.e., any *a priori* hypotheses) is never true." (Such a postulate would appear easily to be supported by the maximum likelihood principle and likelihood ratio tests, where the best-supported hypothesis is usually that coinciding with some statistical construction of the data.) The question then becomes one of what precision we prescribe for goodness of fit. How fine must be the support of justification? If some hypothesis, other than the *a priori* one which we wish to support, is invariably more probable on the evidence than that *a priori* hypothesis, then we might wish to consider all such hypotheses as rejectable—and hence no justification is sustained.

Now the postulate of the improbability of the truth of any *a priori* hypothesis does not prevent us from holding that the hypothesis falls within a plausible range of hypotheses, homogeneous for their lack of practicable differences. We live in penumbral rather than knife-edge worlds. The concept of the practicable difference is more to be cultivated as a working principle than is the absolute difference. Hence, the conventional element of decision. But again, what is significant is not whether any inference is absolutely justified but whether we have a method for provisionally acting as if an inference is justified.

## NOTE 15.3

The defense of induction presented here is that of statistical induction. This may appear as a rather restricted treatment of the problem of induction. Yet, so far as concerns inductive methodology in the sciences, this restriction seems warranted. At least so far as statistical inference is concerned, there exist means for evaluating assumptions implicit within the inferential paradigm, and at any level of interrogation we may wish to undertake.

In the present note somewhat broader scope is given to the discussion of justification. First, a brief summary is undertaken of the various strategies of justification. And then, a more attentive note is devoted to a few of the more recent efforts to justify induction, each of which is compatible with the commitment to scientific empiricism.

(A) *Justifications of induction.* For the most part, arguments for induction fall into the following categories (see, for example, Katz, 1962): (1) deductivistic defense, (2) principle of uniform nature, (3) principle of synthetic *a priori*, (4) empirical support, (5) pragmatic defense, and (6) intuitive support. According to (1) inductive inference is not different from deductive inference. The inductive conclusion follows logically from the premises of the argument. The difficulty, of course, is that the question of whether any deductive system (such as, for example, a probability calculus) is a reliable instrument for making inferences concerning the world is itself an inductive problem not to be reduced to a deductive schema. Proposal (2) is question-begging; the hypothesis of a uniform nature itself must be evaluated on inductive grounds. Alternative (3), the Kantian gambit of the synthetic *a priori,* has been found wanting for its imposing a straight jacket upon phenomena to which we have found phenomenology need not conform. Empirical supports of induction, alternative (4), are obviously question-begging. And the notions of intuitive support, (6), are so fuzzily conceived, or are so imbued with those questionable properties of the enduring *a priori* bias, as to be unsupportable in the face of even the most ingenuous of skepticism. This leaves alternative (5), the pragmatic defense of induction, to which we should give more than passing attention.

(B) *Pragmatic justifications of induction.* These are the justifications most likely to be incorporated in the tenets of systematic scientific empiricism. However informal, the justification of statistical induction presented in the text intones a pragmatic answer to the questions of justification. But generally, pragmatic justifications attend more to the idea of self-correctiveness and to the problems of limiting frequencies than to the test-by-test step procedures as sketched in the text. On the first two counts we note the works of Peirce (1878) and Reichenbach (1938, 1949) and on the last count specifically, the work of Braithwaite (1953).

Although the pragmatic argument has been most explicitly developed by Reichenbach, Charles Peirce was perhaps the first to set its theme. In one of his essays on induction, Peirce proposes our making an inference from sampling a cargo of grain. From twenty-seven thimbles of grain taken from different parts of the hull of the ship, we are to make an inference concerning the quality of what, for all practical counts of the individual kernels, is an infinite universe. Assuming random sampling and freedom of access to the cargo, we are able to make provisional estimates as to the quality of the cargo, i.e., as to what percentage of the cargo is of quality A.

"By saying that we draw the inference *provisionally,* I mean that we do not hold that we have reached any assigned degree of approximation as yet, but only hold that if our experience be indefinitely extended, and if every fact of whatever nature, as fast as it presents itself, be duly applied, according to the inductive method, in correcting the inferred ratio, then our approximation will become indefinitely close in the long run; that is to say, close to the experience *to come* (not merely close by the exhaustion of a finite collection) so that if experience in general is to fluctuate irregularly to and fro, in a manner to deprive the ratio sought of all definite value, we shall be able to find out approximately within what limits it fluctuates, and if, after having one definite value, it changes and assumes another, we shall be able to find that out, and in short, whatever may be the variations of this ratio in experience, experience indefinitely extended will enable us to detect them, so as to predict rightly, at last, what its ultimate value may be, if it have any ultimate value, or what the ultimate law of succession of values may be, if there be any such ultimate law, or that it ultimately fluctuates irregularly within certain limits, if it do so ultimately fluctuate. Now our inference, claiming to be no more than thus experiential and provisional, manifestly involves no postulate whatever" (1893, p. 327).

Now there are several points in this argument which are to be emphasized. One, the inductive inference includes no postulate concerning the latent character of the cargo itself. The procedure of inference is purely experiential.

Two, in the long run of sampling we may expect the experientially inferred ratio of the cargo to converge upon the true quality ratio of the cargo. Three, no matter how heterogeneous is the quality mixture of the cargo, no matter how fluctuating the ratio, the inductive inference is self-corrective. And four, if there is a stable ratio for the quality of the cargo, or if that ratio fluctuates within certain limits, then long-run sampling should detect either the stability or the instability of that ratio, as the case may be. Peirce offers no formal elaboration of his justification of induction—but, as Reichenbach (1949, p. 446) implies, it is to be assumed that he based his account on laws of large numbers.

Reichenbach's own more rigorous presentation of the argument agrees in all points, except that he makes it explicit that the justification of inductive inference must be made prior to the utilization of mathematical laws of large numbers.

Like Peirce in such arguments, Reichenbach restricts his attention to inferences concerning relative frequency. First, consider the method of anticipation and the rule of induction. They are based on the simple assumption that if one samples long enough he will in the long run learn what can be known of the population. A sample at any given point in an iterated sampling procedure yields an *empirically* determined posit. Then on the assumption that the universe has a limiting frequency we adopt the following rule of induction:

> If an initial section of $n$ elements of a sequence $x_i$ is given, resulting in the frequency $f^n$, and if, furthermore, nothing is known about the probability of the second level for the occurrence of a certain limit $p$, we posit that the frequency $f^i(i > n)$ will approach a limit $p$ within $f^n \pm \delta$ when the sequence is continued (1949, p. 446).

Although this rule of induction is compatible with mathematical laws of large numbers, support of the rule by law would be presumptive. Justification of the rule is based upon the asymptotic property of any empirical sampling procedure—the larger the sample the more the ingress into the as yet unknown world. And the closer we are to the end of the procedure.

Now a casual reading of the above quotation would appear to reveal its kinship to statements of mathematical laws of large numbers; but it would be a mistake to equate the two. Although the principle of convergence finds expression in both Reichenbach's rule of induction and, say, Bernoulli's law of large numbers, the two statements are not the same. The former states a posit, a fiducial commitment, a working hypothesis, as it were, whereas the latter is a theorem to be indubitably proved within the formal theory of probability.

In order to point up the difference of the two one needs to distinguish between what Feigl (1950) subsequently has designated justification by *validation* and justification by *vindication*. Validation belongs to formal systems of proof. An argument is valid and hence justified if it is logically true. Thus deductive arguments are justified by validation. As Hume pointed out, however, it is not possible to validate inductive conclusions; whether any inductive conclusion, valid in the sense of its being logically consistent with a set of premises, is true is itself subject to empirical verification. And since by Reichenbach's rule, verification is contingent upon convergence and the principle of limiting frequency, one needs to verify the applicability of that principle which would make verification possible. One can, however, vindicate his rule of induction if he adopts it as a premise, as a means in a means-end approach, to making anticipative posits. That is to say, if, *granting limits,* if, *granting specifiable statistical properties of the universe,* our rule of induction is sufficient for drawing true conclusions about the limiting frequency, then the rule of induction will be vindicated. Vindication thus identifies the pragmatic argument: if a rule of induction works under certain circumstances, then it is vindicated wherever such circumstances obtain. Vindication is contingent upon the circumstances; so long as there is some chance that the circumstances will hold (e.g., that events are conformal with probability models), then our rule of induction is subject to vindication. And so long as there is some chance that these very circumstances will obtain, then our rule of induction is pragmatically defensible.

In a concise statement of his argument, Reichenbach writes:

> We used the assumption of the existence of a limit of the frequency in order to prove that, if no probabilities are known, the anticipative posit is the best posit because it leads to success in a finite number of steps. With respect to the individual act of positing, however, the limit assumption does not supply any sort of information. The posit may be wrong, and we can only say that if it turns out to be wrong we are willing to correct it and to try again. But if the limit assumption is dispensable for every individual posit, it can be omitted for the method of positing as a whole. The omission is required because we have no proof for the assumption. But the absence of proof does not mean that *we know that there is no limit;* it means only that *we do not know whether there is a limit.* In that case we have as much reason to try a posit as in the case that the existence of a limit is known; for, if a limit of the frequency exists, we shall find it by the inductive method if only the acts of positing are continued sufficiently. Inductive positing in the sense of a trial-and-error method is justified so long as it is not known that the attempt is hopeless, that there is no limit of the frequency. Should we have no success, the positing was useless; but why not take our chance? (1949, p. 473)

Note again that no postulate is adopted, no hypothesis subject to verification asserted, which stipulates that a limit exists—only that if a limit exists the rule of induction is sufficient to ascertain it in a protracted sampling procedure. Reichenbach summarizes his justification of induction in a sentence:

> *The rule of induction is justified as an instrument of positing because it is a method of which we know that if it is possible to make statements about the future we shall find them by means of this method* (1949, p. 475).

He spells out the argument as follows. Let *a* be "There exists a limit of the frequency." Let *b* be "I use the rule of induction in a repeated procedure." Let *c* be "I shall find the limit of the frequency." His argument then asserts

$$a \supset (b \supset c).$$

That is to say, granting there is a limit, then our inductive procedure will lead to finding that limit. Logically $b \supset c$ is the *necessary* condition for *a*. And granting *a,* then *b* is *sufficient* for concluding *c*.

Reichenbach is careful to point out that his rule of induction does not assert a relation between an observed frequency and unobserved, unverified future events. Rather it becomes the "grounds-for-assertion relation" between the observed frequency and the statement of probability which will be a true statement of the limit after exhaustive sampling.

Critique of Reichenbach's defense of induction focuses in large measure upon the issue of alternative rules of induction. According to Reichenbach himself, the anticipative posit should pivot on the function

$$f_n + c_n$$

where $f_n$ is the frequency and $c_n$ is some arbitrary function. Consistent with his frequency treatment of probability, Reichenbach selects the function $c_n = 0$, namely, that the relative frequency is uncorrected as the anticipatory posit of the limit. There may be good reasons for assuming $c_n \neq 0$; e.g., cases appearing to warrant a classical enumeration of equally likely outcomes. However, Reichenbach asserts, without rigorous defense, that his assumption is descriptively simpler.

To be sure, it is consistent with a radical empiricism. But is it simpler? This is the critical point. The statistician's evaluation of best estimates is made on the basis of known properties of his formal systems, on the basis of *efficient, unbiased, most powerful,* and *admissible* tests and measures. Reichenbach would limit the assumptions relating empirical frequency and the properties and entities of formal deductive systems. However, if one is to make additional assumptions concerning the world, then $c_n$ may not be taken to be zero, and there may be a more direct route to convergence upon the limiting frequency. The correction factor $c_n$ may thus be the factor of intuition, clairvoyance, etc., any one of which would in effect nullify the pivotal significance of the empirical frequency, $f_n$. Reichenbach points out, however, that we can ascertain the efficacy of clairvoyance only by resorting to the protracted empirical sampling procedures which would assure convergence. But disdain of clairvoyance does not rule out the possibility that any putatively random sampling procedure may itself be biased, such that on the basis of some corrective assumption expressed in $c_n$ we would, in effect, have a corrected inference preferred to the uncorrected inference from empirical frequency. (See, for example, Kemeny, 1953.)

One needs to be reminded in all such discussions that justification is not the source of distress to the statistician that it is to philosophers. The statistician would justify induction on the grounds that his formal system (e.g., probability theory and the mathematical laws of large numbers) is an appropriate description of the universe to which inductive inference is made. Unfortunately, his assumptions prejudge the issue at hand. For the philosopher, the question is: Are the assumptions sufficient to reach true conclusions which are testable only in an empirical context?

Another pragmatic defense of induction can be found in Braithwaite's *Scientific Explanation.* Consider first the problem of statistical decision. How do we justify an inference about some hypothesis concerning *p,* the true proportion of members of a hyperspace (a universe) having some specified property. Although Braithwaite relies heavily upon Tchebycheff's theorem (see page 423) the argument can be carried out with reference only to classical significance tests. We are to test the hypothesis $H_k : p = p_k$. By virtue of the two-tail test and a rejection rule, we reject $H_k$ if the difference $|p_f - p_k|$ exceeds a certain critical value; otherwise we accept. The justification of rejection is based upon the improbability that our sampling difference, $|p_f - p_k|$, will fall in the critical region, given $p_k$ is a true hypothesis. This justification, however, involves a class of many such tests; the probability designating the possibility of error is assignable only to the collective of repeated tests. Hence, the justification of an individual decision expands into a collective undertaking in which we expect for many such tests that just the proportion $\alpha$ of such tests will lead to the false rejection of $p_k$.

But now we may ask: How do we know that $\alpha$, as spelled out in our presumptive sampling model, is the appropriate probability of false-rejection? It would appear that another statistical decision is called for and subsequently another justification. For this next level of inference we would repeat the earlier experiment $n_1$ times and observe the frequency of sampling differences falling in the critical region. Thus we set up a new test and a new critical region. But here too we are confronted with a decision which is justified only as a collective undertaking. Hence we are confronted with a new test involving $n_2$ replications of the $n_1$ replications of the original experiment. And so on.

This is not unlike the account of justification given in the text. At any level of the regress, tests can be arranged for deciding whether the assumptions necessary for the application of the previous test are themselves warrantable. There is no end to the challenges to assumptions we may raise, no end to the justifications. But the process of justification is, at least, a meaningful one.

However, in addressing himself specifically to the justification of induction, Braithwaite examines the accusation of circularity which confronts pragmatic treatments of the problem. Consider now a more general policy of inductive inference which is based on simple enumeration. In general our policy is such that we continue to expect what has happened in the past. How do we justify such a policy? If our justification is based on the assertion that it works, we run the risk of assuming the effectiveness of a policy in order to justify its effectiveness.

Now Braithwaite is concerned to show that the pragmatic justification involves no "vicious circularity." What is to be regarded as vicious is, in such matters, likely to be a personal issue. However, Braithwaite's argument is that the circularity, whatever its nature, does not incapacitate us for offering justifications of inductive policy. The argument is too involved to give in detail, but in substance it is as follows.

Let $\Pi$ be an inductive policy incorporating evidence, $E$, *and* a rule of inference by simple enumeration, $\pi$, such that belief in an hypothesis, $h$, follows from $E$ and $\pi$. How do we justify this policy? We adopt $e$, the proposition that $\Pi$ is effective. Hence $e$ becomes the justification of $\Pi$. But to say $e$ justifies $\Pi$ is not to say that $e$ is included in the premises of $\pi$. Braithwaite then maintains that support of $e$ by virtue of $\pi$ and $E$, i.e., evidence for $e$, does not involve one's committing a *petitio principii*. We could justify induction in terms of the effectiveness of $\pi$ without circularity "if the criterion of valid inference did not require reasonable [well justified] belief in the effectiveness of the policy of inference, but only required alternatively either the fact of this effectiveness or belief in this effectiveness" (1953, p. 284). That is to say, we may make use of a policy of inference without at the same time believing in the reasonableness of the policy on grounds prescribed by the policy itself.

The argument is not an easy one to follow. However, we can regard it as supportive of the proposition that justification of inductive policy does involve circularity, but it is a circularity which arises only when we confuse levels of interrogation in the regressive steps of justification.

(C)   *Some other justifications of induction.* It is obvious that the philosophical scandal of induction derives from the circularity of premise and support, of presumption and "proof." In order to show that experience is a reliable predictor of the future we make assumptions about the character of the universe to which we are predicting. The predicament is more embarrassing for the pragmatic empiricists than it is for Keynesians, Bayesians, subjectivists, and others who utilize theorems of conditional probability as vehicles of induction. Among the latter, assumption is made an explicit part of the rationale of induction, and the task of justifying induction is merely to show that inductive inference is reasonable in light of those assumptions. They, at least, are saved the embarrassments of the objectivists by candidly admitting that inductive inference is based upon prior subjective commitments.

(1)   For many of those who would prejudge the complexity and uniformity of the world, Bayes' theorem becomes the primary instrument of induction (Broad, 1920, 1928; Keynes, 1921; Jeffreys, 1939). Let $h$ be some hypothesis or generalization; $D$ the state of knowledge, data, experimental conditions prior to taking additional evidence, and $E$, the additional evidence corroborative of $h$. Then Bayes' theorem allows us to write

$$P(h \mid ED) = \frac{P(E \mid hD)}{P(E \mid D)} \, P(h \mid D).$$

Now if we treat $E$ as an evidential statement (prediction) deducible from $h$ but not from $D$ alone, the ratio term in the equation above should be greater than 1. We may then conclude

$$P(h \mid ED) > P(h \mid D)$$

that is to say, confirmation of the evidential statement $E$ increases the probability of the hypothesis over what it was prior to the confirmation. This will be the case, however, only if we can assign some prior probability to $h$ greater than zero, that is, some finite probability to our hypothesis prior to our taking the evidence. Defense of Bayesian inference now rests upon our strategies for assigning these prior probabilities.

For the early Bayesians, the strategy involved making assumptions about the complexity of the world; for contemporary subjectivists, the strategy involves only the development of a coherent set of opinions. As a member of the first group, we consider Keynes (1921) and his postulate of limited independent variety; namely, the assumption that the objects in the field, over which our generalizations extend, do not have an infinite number of independent qualities; that, in other words, their characteristics, however numerous, cohere together in groups of invariable connection, which are finite in number (1921, p. 256). If there were a limited number of entities and a limited number of properties, then it would be possible to assign prior probabilities to any generalization involving these entities and properties—e.g., "all $x$ that are $A$ are also $B$." Although these prior probabilities might reflect bias, we could conceivably randomize the distribution of properties on assumptions of indifference. Then any generalization relating properties or sets of properties would have some prior probability, however small. These assumptions, however, are too restrictive. Limited as we wish to take our time–space span, there is, in the case of scientific induction, no good support for the postulates of a limited number of entities.

The postulate of limited variety, on the other hand, states only that there are fewer properties or qualities than there are distinct entities and that the number of such properties is finite. In advancing the argument, Keynes first postulates a set of generator properties $\phi_1$, $\phi_2$, $\phi_3$, . . . , $\phi_N$ such that any set of these properties will specify a group. Now assume that the set of generator properties for group $g_a$ is not completely specified. We act on the surmise that two sets of "apparent properties" belong to the same set. Thus, if in our experience $a_r$ is taken to be one set of apparent properties and $a_s$ is to be taken as another, we may wish to establish that $a_r$ and $a_s$ belong to the same group. In practice we make inferences concerning group structure through the inclusion and exclusion which is effected by positive and negative analogy. But this would not be possible either if there were an unlimited number of properties or if there were a plurality of generators. We must postulate that the probability of $a_r$ and $a_s$ being associated in the same group is greater than zero. And this would not be possible if we extended the limits of negative analogy by postulating an unlimited number of properties to complicate group structure. No inductive inference relating $a_r$ and $a_s$ to the same group would be possible; and all generalization would be suspect, due to the possibility of negative analogy implicit in infinitely complex group determinations.

In order to defend the possibility of induction concerning group structure, we need only show that any hypothesis relating apparent properties has some initial probability. Confirmatory evidence will then enhance the probability of the hypothesis. However, the premise of prior probability can be justified only if we assume a limited number of properties; hence, the postulate of limited variety. This is the argument. What differentiates it from that of latter day Bayesians is its ontological doctrine. Postulates of limited variety are postulates about the world, about generators, and groups as distinct from fictions of the mind, conventions, or judgment.

(2)  Among the writings of the subjectivists and personalists, perhaps the most explicit defense of induction is to be found in de Finetti's essay "Foresight: Its Logical Laws, Its Subjective Sources" (originally published in 1937, but more recently up-dated and translated—see Kyburg and Smokler, 1964). An avowed subjectivist himself, de Finetti takes frequentists and other objectivists to task for not being sufficiently operational concerning the nature of the limits and "unknown probabilities" which are focal entities in their treatments of induction. There are no more grounds for predicating absolute ob-

jective probabilities than there are for predicating absolute time and space. We cannot provide strict operational procedures for revealing what such entities are. And even laws of large numbers, where applicable, are better interpreted if we make explicit the *a priori* character of certain of our probability concepts. Furthermore, as we have seen in our discussion of subjective probability, objectivists have not clearly differentiated that which is presumptive and thereby subjective from that which is purely objective. The connection between limiting frequency as an objective entity and subjective judgments remains "subjective." De Finetti believes that the clarification of probability and induction will only come through analysis of the subjective element to which these ideas and procedures of inference are anchored.

In brief, the problem of induction is not to show that there is a relation between a subjective estimate (no matter how objective the pivotal frequency) and a determinate objective limit, but only that there is a calculable difference as between the probability of an event prior to evidence being taken and the probability of the same event after evidence on preceding trials is taken into consideration. Thus to justify induction, we elaborate the relation between prior and conditional (posterior) probability.

Consider now what is perhaps the simplest case of induction, that from simple Bernoullian trials. Out of a sequence of $n$ trials, let $r$ be the number showing the property $E$ and $s = n - r$ the number of trials showing $\bar{E}$, (i.e. $\sim E$). Let $E_i$ be the $i$th trial showing the property $E$ and let $A$ be the set of outcomes on $n$ trials such that

$$A = \{E_{i_1}\, E_{i_2} \cdots E_{i_r}\, \bar{E}_{j_1}\, \bar{E}_{j_2} \cdots \bar{E}_{j_s}\}.$$

(The notation of subscripts is somewhat unique to de Finetti but it facilitates the discussion of the notion of exchangeability soon to be introduced.) Here, $A$ is simply the set of $n$ trials, $r$ of which show the property $E$ and $s$ of which do not. One would think then that on the basis of the simple frequency principle the best posit for the probability of $E$ on trial $n + 1$ would be $r/n$; i.e.,

$$P(E_{n+1} \mid A) \cong r/n. \tag{1}$$

However, such a best posit holds only for restricted cases. More generally we should express this probability as a conditional probability such that

$$P(E_{n+1} \mid A) = \frac{P(A \cdot E_{n+1})}{P(A)}. \tag{2}$$

Equation (2) should not be treated as a computational formula; but since we are concerned with probability as a matter of subjective judgment, we may surmise that $P(E_{n+1} \mid A)$ and $P(E_{n+1})$ are not necessarily equal. If we regard $P(E_{n+1})$ as a prior estimate of the probability of $E$ on trial $n + 1$, we refer to $P(E_{n+1} \mid A)$ as the corrected probability contingent upon the evidence as specified in $A$. Both of these probabilities are essentially subjective. They enable us only to compare a corrected judgment contingent upon evidence with an uncorrected one independent of the evidence of preceding trials.

Now in order to show that our corrected estimate above is an application of the principle of induction we predicate that the conditional estimate is independent of the particular $n$ trials we select. In a word we are to defend induction on the basis of the principle of *exchangeability*—a principle, incidentally, which belongs to the larger class of postulates of uniformity. In a word, this principle states that $P(A)$ is independent of the order of the $r$ occurrences of $E$ and the $s$ occurrences of $\bar{E}$ which constitute $A$. Although this may appear to be a rather mild and innocuous assumption for anyone trained in classical probability theory, it proves for de Finetti to have profound significance. For example, it enables him to defend his corrective judgments of probability without his resorting to semantically questionable references to unknown objective probabilities.

More explicitly, what does the principle of exchangeability assert? Since de Finetti is a subjectivist, it is meaningful for him to assign probabilities to the occurrence of $E$ on any given trial in the sample set of $n$-trials. And since the constitution of $A$ is by the principle of exchangeability to be designated as independent of the order of the occurrences of $E$ and $\bar{E}$, $P(A)$ is to be regarded as the average of the probabilities of all sequences of $r$ $E$'s and $s$ $\bar{E}$'s. Although it is conceivable that the probabilities of these sequences will be a function of the order, the case for induction is made on the premise of exchangeable orders. From classical enumeration there are $_nC_r$ possible sequences of $r$ $E$'s and $s$ $\bar{E}$'s. If the sum of the probabilities of these $_nC_r$ sequences is $w^{(n)}_r$ then

$$P(A) = \frac{w^{(n)}_r}{_nC_r}, \tag{3}$$

and by the principle of exchangeability, $P(A)$ is the probability we can assign to any one of the $_nC_r$ sequences.

Now it may appear that the premise of exchangeability is rather a familiar one, like the assumption of independence in classical computations or like the place principle in von Mises' frequency treatment of probability. There are similarities, to be sure, but the exploitation of this principle enables de Finetti to calculate the conditional probability (2) without making reference to objective probabilities of independent events or to any random sampling procedures that are definable alone in terms of selection among physical occurrences. The $P(A)$ is known by virtue of determining the average probability (3); and since $A \cdot E$ is simply another set of occurrences, now with $r + 1$ $E$'s and $s$ $\bar{E}$'s, application of the principle of exchangeability yields

$$P(A \cdot E) = \frac{w^{(n+1)}_{r+1}}{_{n+1}C_{r+1}} \tag{4}$$

and then, by virtue of (2), (3), and (4),

$$P(E \mid A) = \frac{r + 1}{n + 1} \cdot \frac{w^{(n+1)}_{r+1}}{w^{(n)}_r}.$$

The average, $P(A)$, is calculated on the basis of the initial probabilities we wish to assign to the occurrence of $E$ on any given trial. In his defense of induction, de Finetti only wishes to show that there is a rationale for correcting any subjective estimate, $P(E)$, on the basis of the evidence as constituted in $A$. But both $P(E)$ and $P(E \mid A)$ are subjective probabilities, hence the principle of induction relates two subjective estimates, and *not* an estimate and an objective limit or a frequency subsisting in a real world.

De Finetti is able to accommodate the results of laws of large numbers within inductive inference, but it is clear to him that his "solution" of the problem of induction rests in his avoiding the semantic pitfalls inherent within the language of long-run objective limits and infinite sampling. Still it is a conservative doctrine withal, for if we translate exchangeability into expectation it is much the same expectation we would have were we to be convinced of the hypothesis of uniform nature.

*Bibliographic addendum:*

(a)   Additional statements and defenses of the pragmatic justification of induction can be found in Feigl (1934, 1950, 1961), Kneale (1949), Salmon (1957, 1961, 1963). Critical revisions are to be found in Kemeny (1953) and Katz (1962). What amounts to rejections of Reichenbach's pragmatic argument are to be found in the criticism of Lenz (1958, 1960), Russell (1948), Goodman (1955).

(b)   Expositions of Keynes' principle of limited independent variety are to be found in Russell (1948) and J. O. Wisdom (1952). Besides Keynes own statement of the principle (1921, Ch. XXII), there is discussion of a similar principle, that of "natural kinds," in Broad (1918, 1920). Criticism of Keynes' general theory of inductive inference is offered by Nicod (1930) and von Wright (1952).

(c)   A good exposition of statistical induction and the nature of its justification is to be found in Churchman's *Theory of Experimental Inference*. An attempt to validate (as against vindicate) inductive inference is to be found in Williams' *The Ground of Induction*. Von Wright's *The Logical Problem of Induction* undertakes to show that the question of justifying induction is in some senses a meaningful one and in some senses a meaningless one. Russell's own defense of inductive method in the sciences is to be found in *Human Knowledge*. For the most part it builds upon postulates of uniformity and limited variety. Therefore it is compatible with Bayesian defenses of induction, based as they are on predicating antecedent probabilities.

(D)   Our treatment of induction and its justification has been a restricted one. For example, no coverage has been given Carnap's important works on inductive logic (e.g., 1950). Nor have we taken cognizance of the problems and paradoxes of confirmation theory. The selection of topics has been confined primarily to inductive inference as applied in the empirical sciences.

As an example of exegesis on non-statistical induction we may note an important essay of Nelson Goodman, "The New Riddle of Induction" (in *Fact, Fiction, and Forecast*, 1955). For Goodman the problem of induction as Hume saw it has been satisfactorily analyzed, solved, or dissolved as the case may be. Rather . . . "The problem of induction is not a problem of demonstration but a problem of defining the difference between valid and invalid predictions" (1955, p. 68). The constructive task of confirmation theory is that of defining the conditions for valid inductive inference, of clearly specifying those conditions in which it is appropriate to apply well-formalized principles of inductive inference. According to some earlier work of Hempel, the problem of confirmation is to establish the relation between an evidential statement, say $E$, and a general statement (hypothesis) $H$. Simple as the relation of confirmation might appear, it leads to embarrassments. As Goodman finds, not only may $E$ support $H$ where $H$ is some general law, but $E$ may also support $H$ where $H$ is some accidental generalization. For example if $E$ is the event: "John Jones is six feet tall and John Jones is dying," not only does $E$ tend to confirm the general proposition "all men are mortal" but also quite accidentally the proposition "all men are six feet tall." And it is easy to show that two events, $E_1$ and $E_2$, which may confirm the same lawlike generalization, may also confirm quite contradictory accidental generalizations. In order to avoid both paradoxes and embarrassments of confirmation, it is necessary to distinguish support of lawlike generalizations from that of accidental generalizations. But how may we do this?

It should be quite obvious that we cannot make the distinction on any *a priori* grounds. One needs to know of a given set of particulars that such particulars have an open-ended but partially enumerated set of properties such that the particulars of the set can be identified and examined for appropriate lawlike generalizations which add to the fund of properties. Consider the proposition "All metals conduct electricity." This is a lawlike generalization supported, say, by the event "This specimen of copper conducts electricity." Let us be explicit as to how we show the lawlike character of the initial proposition. There is some set of particulars with a set of properties which define the particulars as metals. Designate this set of properties $P_m$. Designate the new property to be assigned by virtue of the lawlike generalization $P_n$. Then we have the generalization

$$(x) \; P_m x \supset P_n x.$$

But note here that our search for lawlike generalizations is not characterized by our searching simultaneously for a set of properties which will define the class of particulars *plus* an additional property which extends the set of properties of those particulars. We have some prior knowledge which enables us initially to define the class $\{(x)P_m x\}$; i.e., the class of all particulars which have the properties of metals designated by $P_m$.

Now it is just this prior knowledge, Goodman asserts, which has to be "smuggled in" to the lawlike generalization. We require the information that the set of properties $P_m$ binds a set of particulars so as to make its members amenable to further generalization. That is, we have already assumed a generalization for the set $\{(x)P_m x\}$ in order to make our definition of lawlike generalization possible. But now how do we know whether $P_m$ itself constitutes a lawlike set of properties or merely an accidental set? We must now justify our procedure by specifying some new set of properties, $P_l$, such that

$$(x) \; P_l x \supset P_m x.$$

And our initial lawlike generalization would for the inductionist be more appropriately expressed

$$(x) \quad P_l x \supset P_m x$$
$$(x) \quad P_m x \supset P_n x$$
$$\overline{(x) \quad P_l x \supset P_n x}$$

However the regress is underway. We may pursue the same status interrogation with respect to $P_l$, thereby searching for the set of properties $P_k$; for the status of $P_k$ we require $P_j$, and so on.

Our original proposition is "all metals conduct electricity." In order to make sure that our confirmation is justifiable confirmation, we must make sure that our proposition is lawlike. We then proceed to enumerate a set of properties common to many particulars but which, prior to our seeking observational confirmation, do not include the property of conductance. These, for example, might be properties assigned by a relatively naive phenomenological chemistry (e.g., lustre, heat conductance, fusion, etc.). But how do we know that the cluster of these properties is itself not accidental? We then proceed by showing that all substances having some set of atomic and molecular properties have the phenomenological set of properties which we assign to metals. Then to justify the set of atomic properties as being lawlike rather than accidental we must carry the interrogation further into subatomic analysis. (What may be of interest in this example is the prospect of their being technological and possibly logical barriers to carrying our regress further. If contemporary quantum theory precludes the introduction of underlying or hidden variables, then the basis for distinction between lawlike and accidental properties would need somehow to be implicit within the formal system of quantum physics.)

Another aspect of Goodman's argument considers predictive projection. We are used to lawlike generalizations such as

"all emeralds are green";

but what of the predicate "grue" which means green up to time $t$ but blue thereafter. Although worlds that violate principles of consistency, invariance, and uniformity might indeed play havoc with science and prediction, their possibility does not, it seems to me, dissuade us from adopting inductive strategies as the best possible under the circumstances. (cf. Salmon, 1963.)

Nevertheless, the argument here appears to be a troublesome one. "Grue" belongs to the domain of qualitative predicates and its notion is perhaps something more than a bit of philosophical whimsy. Any student of perception would know what predicate the term "blay" would seem to signify, namely, "blue up to the point of retinal satiation (adaptation) then gray. . . ." This is the appropriate predicate to apply under conditions of continuous focus upon a blue color patch. Predicates such as "grue" and "blay" therefore need not be suggestive of some cosmological demon who conspires to complicate the problems of induction and prediction.

One can usually rule out such predicates by appeals to principles of exchangeability and linguistic invariance (Salmon, 1961). In such a case, a pragmatic vindication of an inference rule would be supportable in those cases where invariance and exchangeability applied. (Salmon, 1963; Levi, 1965). However, in the case of predicates such as "blay," appropriate as we find them to be in the science of visual perception, these premises are known not to apply. Here, one needs also to know something about how the context of the events resulting in the appropriateness of "blay" is constituted. For example, we must know that the subject was maintaining a continuous focus upon a blue stimulus patch for a given period of time and that the fading of bluishness and the emergence of grayishness is observed to occur in the given period of time. By incorporating the sequential context into the premises of the inductive procedures, we are able to write general laws including the predicate "blay," and in a way, it seems to me, that does not preclude our appeal to pragmatic vindication.

Examples of induction which necessitate "individuation," i.e., the explicit description or enumeration of the data sequence, do indeed complicate the support of induction (see, for example, Hacking, 1965; Levi, 1965); but primarily what the premise of individuation (that one must know where in the sampling sequence he is to make his estimate) results in, is the displacement of the premise of exchangeability from one to another level. There is some domain of experience such that the order of the phenomena which are confirmatory of "blay-type" laws is inconsequential to the inferences made from such laws. That is to say the ordering of the sampling of instances confirmatory of the blay-type laws is irrelevant to the formulation of those laws.

Should one now argue that blay-type laws themselves are time-capricious in the way specified by the grue-type predicates, then this displaces the premise of exchangeability to yet another level. Thus, our efforts to assign properties to Goodman's grue-type predicates require our proceeding as we do in all other types of induction. Time-capricious properties do indeed complicate the character of inductive generalizations, but they do not, it seems to me, offer any insuperable difficulties to our attempts to *vindicate* inductive procedures.

# REFERENCES

ADJUKIEWICZ, K. The scientific world perspective. (original 1935) In H. Feigl and W. Sellars (editors), *Readings in philosophical analysis.* New York: Appleton-Century-Crofts, 1949.

ALLPORT, F. H. *Social psychology.* Boston: Houghton-Mifflin, 1924.

ALLPORT, G. W. *Personality, a psychological interpretation.* New York: Henry Holt, 1937.

ALLPORT, G. W. Personalistic psychology as a science: a reply. *Psychol. Rev.,* 1946, **53,** 132–135.

ANSCOMBE, F. J. Bayesian statistics. *Amer. Stat.,* 1961, **15,** 21–24.

APOSTEL, L. Toward a formal study of models in the non-formal sciences. *Synthese,* 1960, **12,** 125–161. Also in H. Freudenthal (editor), *The concept and role of the model in mathematics and natural and social sciences.* Dordrecht: D. Reidel, 1961.

ARBUTHNOT, J. An argument for Divine Providence taken from the constant regularity observed in the births of both sexes. *Philos. Trans. Roy. Soc.,* 1710, **27,** 186–190.

ARROW, K. J. Decision theory and the choice of a level of significance for the *t*-test. In I. Olkin and others (editors), *Contributions to probability and statistics.* Stanford: Stanford University Press, 1960.

ASHBY, W. R. *Design for a brain.* London: Chapman & Hall, 1952.

ASHBY, W. R. Induction, prediction, and decision-making in cybernetic systems. In H. E. Kyburg (editor), *Induction: some current issues.* Middletown: Wesleyan University Press, 1963.

ATKINSON, R. C. *See* Suppes and Atkinson, 1960.

ATTNEAVE, F. *Applications of information theory in psychology.* New York: Holt-Dryden, 1959.

ATTNEAVE, F. Perception and related areas. In S. Koch (editor), *Psychology, a study of a science,* Vol. 4. New York: McGraw-Hill, 1962.

AUSTIN, J. L. Other minds. *Proc. Arist. Soc. Suppl.,* 1946, **20,** 148–157. Also in J. L. Austin, *Philosophical papers.* Oxford: Clarendon Press, 1961.

AYER, A. J. Demonstration of the impossibility of metaphysics. *Mind,* 1934, **43,** 335–345.

AYER, A. J. The criterion of truth. *Analysis,* 1935, **3,** 28–32.

AYER, A. J. *The foundations of empirical knowledge.* London: Macmillan, 1940.

493

AYER, A. J. Other minds. *Proc. Arist. Soc. Suppl.,* 1946, **20,** 188–197.

AYER, A. J. *Language, truth and logic.* New York: Dover, original 1936; revised 1946.

AYER, A. J. The terminology of sense-data. (original 1947) In *Philosophical essays.* London: Macmillan, 1959.

AYER, A. J. *Philosophical essays.* London: Macmillan, 1954.

AYER, A. J. *The problem of knowledge.* Harmondsworth: Penguin Books, 1956.

AYER, A. J. (editor). *The revolution in philosophy.* London: Macmillan, 1956.

AYER, A. J. *The foundations of empirical knowledge.* London: Macmillan. 1958.

AYER, A. J. (editor). *Logical positivism.* Glencoe: Free Press, 1959.

BACON, F. *Novum organum.* (original 1621) Oxford: Oxford University Press, 1889.

BARKER, S. F. *Induction and hypothesis.* Ithaca: Cornell University Press, 1957.

BARRY, G. *See* Fitch and Barry, 1950.

BEAMENT, J. W. L. (editor). *Models and analogues in biology.* Cambridge: Cambridge University Press, 1960.

BECK, W. W. Constructs and inferred entities. *Philos. Sci.,* 1950, **17,** 74–86.

BECKER, G. M. Objective measures of subjective probability. *Psychol. Rev.,* 1962, **69,** 136–148.

BERENDA, C. W. Is clinical psychology a science? *Amer. Psychol.,* 1957, **12,** 725–729.

BERGMANN, G. The logic of psychological concepts. *Philos. Sci.,* 1951, **18,** 93–110.

BERGMANN, G. Theoretical psychology. *Annu. Rev. Psychol.,* 1953, **4,** 435–458.

BERGMANN, G. Reduction. In J. T. Wilson and others. *Current trends in psychology and the other behavioral sciences.* Pittsburgh: University of Pittsburgh Press, 1954.

BERGMANN, G. *Philosophy of science.* Madison: University of Wisconsin Press, 1957.

BERGMANN, G. *Meaning and essence.* Madison: University of Wisconsin Press, 1960.

BERGMANN, G. Physics and ontology. *Philos. Sci.,* 1961, **28,** 1–14.

BERGMANN, G. and SPENCE, K. W. Operationism and theory in psychology. *Psychol. Rev.,* 1941, **48,** 1–14.

BERGMANN, G. and SPENCE, K. W. The logic of psychophysical measurement. *Psychol. Rev.,* 1944, **51,** 1–24.

BERGMANN, G. The logic of psychological concepts. *Philos. Sci.,* 1951, **18,** 93–110.

BERGSON, H. *Creative evolution.* (translated by A. Mitchell) New York: Henry Holt, 1911.

BERGSON, H. *An introduction to metaphysics.* London: Macmillan, 1913.

BERKELEY, G. *The analyst.* (original 1734) In A. C. Fraser (editor), *Berkeley's works.* London: Oxford University Press, 1871.

BERKELEY, G. Philosophical commentaries. In A. A. Luce and T. E. Jessop (editors), *Berkeley's works.* London: Nelson, 1948.

BERKELEY, G. *The principles of human knowledge.* (original 1710) La Salle: Open Court, 1946.

BERKELEY, G. *Selections.* (M. W. Calkins, editor) New York: Scribners, 1929.

BERKELEY, G. *Three dialogues between Hylas and Philonous.* (original 1713) La Salle: Open Court, 1947.

BERKELEY, G. *Works of George Berkeley.* (A. A. Luce and T. Jessop, editors) London: Nelson, 1948.

BERLIN, I. Verifiability in principle. *Proc. Arist. Soc.,* 1939, **39,** 225–248.

BERLYNE, D. E. *Conflict, arousal, and curiosity.* New York: McGraw-Hill, 1960.

BEVERIDGE, W. I. B. *The art of scientific investigation.* London: Heinemann, 1950.

BILLS, A. G. Blocking: a new principle in mental fatigue. *Amer. J. Psychol.,* 1931, **43,** 230–245.

BINDER, A. Further consideration on testing the null hypothesis and the strategy and tactics of investigating theoretical models. *Psychol. Rev.* 1963, **70,** 107–115.

BINDER, A. Statistical theory. *Annu. Rev. Psychol.,* 1964, **15,** 277–310.

BIRKHOFF, G. D. and LEWIS, D. C. Stability in causal systems. *Philos. Sci.,* 1935, **2,** 304–333.

BIRNBAUM, A. On the foundations of statistical inference. *J. Amer. Stat. Assoc.,* 1962, **57,** 269–306.

BLACK, M. Principle of verifiability. *Analysis,* 1934, **2,** 1–6.

BLACK, M. *Language and philosophy.* Ithaca: Cornell University Press, 1949.

BLACK, M. (editor) *Philosophical analysis.* Ithaca: Cornell University Press, 1950.

BLACK, M. *Problems of analysis.* London: Routledge, 1954.

BLACK, M. *Models and metaphors.* Ithaca: Cornell University Press, 1962.

BLACKWELL, D. and DUBINS, L. Merging opinions with increasing information. *Annal. Math. Stat.,* 1962, **33,** 882–886.

BLACKWELL, D. and GIRSHICK, M. A. *Theory of games and statistical decisions.* New York: Wiley, 1954.

BLANSHARD, B. The philosophy of analysis. *Proc. Brit. Acad.,* 1952, **38,** 39–69.

BLANSHARD, B. *Reason and analysis.* London: G. Allen, 1962.

BLUMBERG, A. E. *See* Feigl and Blumberg, 1931.

BODE, B. N. Psychology as a science of behavior. *Psychol. Rev.,* 1914, **21,** 41–61.

BOHR, N. Discussion with Einstein. In P. A. Schilpp (editor), *Albert Einstein, philosopher-scientist.* New York: Tudor, 1949. (Reprinted New York: Harper Torchbook, Harper & Row, 1959.)

BOHR, N. On the notions of causality and complementarity. *Science,* 1950, **111,** 51–54.

BOOLE, G. *An investigation of the laws of thought.* New York: Dover, 1854.

BORING, E. G. *The physical dimensions of consciousness.* New York: Appleton-Century, 1933.

BORING, E. G. Temporal perception and operationism. *Amer. J. Psychol.,* 1936, **48,** 519–522.

BORING, E. G. A history of introspection. *Psychol. Bull.,* 1953, **50,** 169–189.

BORING, E. G. *A history of experimental psychology.* New York: Appleton-Century-Crofts, 1929; (2nd edition) 1956.

BOWDER, H. H. Presuppositions of a behavioristic psychology. *Psychol. Rev.,* 1918, **25,** 171–190.

BRADLEY, F. H. *Appearance and reality.* London: Sonneschein, 1893.

BRAGG, W. H. and BRAGG, W. L. *X-rays and crystal structure.* London: G. Bell, 1925.

BRAIN, W. R. *Mind, perception, and science.* Oxford: Blackwell, 1951.

BRAIN, W. R. Physiological basis of consciousness. *Brain,* 1958, **81,** 426–455.

BRAITHWAITE, R. B. Propositions about material objects. *Proc. Arist. Soc.,* **38,** 269–290.

BRAITHWAITE, R. B. *Scientific explanation.* Cambridge: Cambridge University Press, 1953.

BRAITHWAITE, R. B. Models in empirical science. In E. Nagel, P. Suppes, and A. Tarski (editors), *Logic, methodology, and philosophy of science.* Stanford: Stanford University Press, 1962.

BRIDGMAN, P. W. *The logic of modern physics.* New York: Macmillan, 1927.

BRIDGMAN, P. W. Some general principles of operational values. *Psychol. Rev.,* 1945, **52,** 246–249.

BRIDGMAN, P. W. Remarks on the present state of operationism. *Sci. Mon.,* 1954, **79,** 224–226.

BROAD, C. D. The relation between induction and probability. *Mind,* 1918, **27,** 389–404; 1920, **29,** 11–45.

BROAD, C. D. *Mind and its place in nature.* London: Kegan Paul, 1925.

BROAD, C. D. The principles of problematic induction. *Proc. Arist. Soc.,* 1928, **28,** 1–46.

BROAD, C. D. Critical notice; *Probability and induction* (Kneale). *Mind,* 1950, **59,** 94–115.

BROADBENT, D. *Perception and communication.* New York: Pergammon Press, 1958.

BRODBECK, MAY. Explanation, prediction and 'imperfect' knowledge. In H. Feigl and G. Maxwell (editors), *Minnesota studies in the philosophy of science,* Vol. III. Minneapolis: University of Minnesota Press, 1962.

BRODBECK, MAY. Meaning and action. *Philos. Sci.,* 1963, **30,** 309–324.

BRONOWSKI, J. The logic of mind. *Amer. Sci.,* 1966, **54,** 1–14.

BRUNSWIK, E. Distal focussing of perception: size-constancy in a representative sample of situations. *Psychol. Monogr.,* 1944, **56,** No. 254.

BUCK, R. C. Reflexive predictions. *Philos. Sci.,* 1963, **30,** 359–369.

BUNGE, M. A general black box theory. *Philos. Sci.,* 1963, **30,** 346–358.

BUNGE, M. Phenomenological theories. In M. Bunge (editor), *The critical approach to science and philosophy.* Glencoe: Free Press, 1964.

BURT, C. The concept of consciousness. *Br. J. Psychol.,* 1962, **53,** 229–242.

BURTT, E. A. *The metaphysical foundations of modern science.* (revised edition) New York: Humanities Press, 1932. (Reprinted Garden City: Anchor Books, Doubleday, 1955.)

BUSH, R. R. and MOSTELLER, F. *Stochastic models for learning.* New York: Wiley, 1955.

BUTTERWORTH, H. *The origins of modern science.* (original 1949) New York: Macmillan, 1960.


CALKINS, MARY W. The truly psychological behaviorism. *Psychol. Rev.,* 1921, **28,** 1–18.

CAMPBELL, N. R. *Physics, the elements.* Cambridge: Cambridge University Press, 1920. Also published as *Foundations of science.* New York: Dover, 1957.

CAMPBELL, N. R. *What is science?* (original 1921) New York: Dover, 1952.

CARNAP, R. *Der logische Aufbau der Welt.* Berlin: Weltkreis-Verlag, 1928.

CARNAP, R. *Philosophy and logical syntax.* London: Kegan Paul, 1935.

CARNAP, R. Testability and meaning: I, II. *Philos. Sci.,* 1936, **3,** 419–471; 1937, **4,** 1–40.

CARNAP, R. *The logical syntax of language.* London: Kegan Paul, 1937.

CARNAP, R. *Introduction to semantics.* Cambridge: Harvard University Press, 1946.

CARNAP, R. *Meaning and necessity.* Chicago: University of Chicago Press, 1947.

CARNAP, R. Truth and confirmation. In H. Feigl and W. Sellars (editors), *Readings in philosophical analysis.* New York: Appleton-Century-Crofts, 1949.

CARNAP, R. *Logical foundations of probability.* Chicago: University of Chicago Press, 1950.

CARNAP, R. The methodological character of theoretical concepts. In H. Feigl and M. Scriven (editors), *Minnesota studies in the philosophy of science,* Vol. I. Minneapolis: University of Minnesota Press, 1956.

CARROLL, L. What the tortoise said to Achilles. In Lewis Carroll, *Complete works.* Glasgow: Nonesuch Press, 1939.

CECCATO, S. Contra Dingler, pro Dingler. *Methodos,* 1952, **4,** 266–290.

CHISHOLM, R. M. The contrary-to-fact conditional. *Mind,* 1946, **55.** Also in H. Feigl and W. Sellars (editors), *Readings in philosophical analysis.* New York: Appleton-Century-Crofts, 1949.

CHISHOLM, R. M. (editor), *Realism and the background of phenomenology.* Glencoe: Free Press, 1960.

CHURCH, A. A note on the Entscheidungs-problem. *J. symbol. Log.,* 1936, **1,** 40–41; 101–102.

CHURCHMAN, C. W. *Theory of experimental inference.* New York: Macmillan, 1948.

CLAGETT, M. *Greek science in antiquity.* New York: Abelard-Schuman, 1955.

CLAGETT, M. *The science of mechanics in the middle ages.* London: Madison, 1959.

498    REFERENCES

CLOPPER, C. J. and PEARSON, E. S. The use of confidence of fiducial limits illustrated in the case of the binomial. *Biometrika,* 1934, **26,** 404–413.

COBURN, R. C. Braithwaite's inductive justification of induction. *Philos. Sci.,* 1961, **28,** 65–71.

COMTE, A. The positive philosophy of Comte. (free translation by H. Martineau) London: G. Bell, 1896.

COMBS, W. W. *See* Snygg and Combs, 1949, 1959.

COTTON, J. W. On making predictions from Hull's theory. *Psychol. Rev.,* 1955, **62,** 303–314.

COURANT, R. *Differential and integral calculus,* Vol. I. (translated by J. E. McShane) London: Blackie, 1937.

COUSIN, D. R. Carnap's theory of truth. *Mind,* 1950, **59,** 1–22.

CRAIG, W. Replacement of auxiliary expressions. *Philos. Rev.,* 1956, **65,** 38–55.

CRAIK, K. J. W. *The nature of explanation.* Cambridge: Cambridge University Press, 1943.

CROMBIE, A. C. *Medieval and early modern science.* (2 vols.) Garden City: Doubleday, 1959.

CRONBACH, L. J. and MEEHL, P. E. Construct validity in psychological tests. *Psychol. Bull.,* 1955, **53,** 281–302.

CRUTCHFIELD, R. S. *See* Krech and Crutchfield, 1947.

CURETON, E. E. Recipe for a cookbook. *Psychol. Bull.,* 1957, **54,** 494–497.


DAVIDSON, D., SUPPES, P., and SIEGEL, S. *Decision making: an experimental approach.* Stanford: Stanford University Press, 1957.

DAVIS, M. *Computability and unsolvability.* New York: McGraw-Hill, 1958.

DE FINETTI, B. Foresight: its logical laws, its subjective sources. In H. E. Kyburg and H. E. Smokler (editors) *Studies in subjective probability.* New York: Wiley, 1964.

DELAFRESNAYE, J. F. (editor), *Brain mechanisms and consciousness.* Oxford: Blackwell, 1954.

DELAFRESNAYE, J. F. (editor), *Brain mechanisms and learning.* Oxford: Blackwell, 1961.

DESCARTES, R. *Discourse on method.* (original 1637; translated by J. Veitch) La Salle: Open Court, 1946.

DESUA, F. C. Metamathematics: a non-technical exposition. *Amer. Sci.,* 1954, **42,** 488–495.

DEUTSCH, J. A. *The structural basis of behavior.* Chicago: University of Chicago Press, 1960.

DIRAC, P. A. M. *The principles of quantum mechanics* (3rd edition). London: Oxford University Press, 1947.

DISERENS, C. M. Psychological objectivism. *Psychol. Rev.,* 1925, **32,** 121–152.

DUBINS, L. *See* Blackwell and Dubins, 1962.

DUFFY, E. *Activation and behavior.* New York: Wiley, 1962.

DUHEM, P. *The aim and structure of physical theory* (1914, 2nd edition, translated by P. P. Weiner). Princeton: Princeton University Press, 1954. Also New York: Atheneum, 1962.

DUNLAP, K. The case against introspectionism. *Psychol. Rev.*, 1912, **19**, 404–413.

DUNOÜY, L. *Human destiny.* New York: Longmans, London: 1947.

ECCLES, J. L. *The neurological basis of mind.* London: Oxford University Press, 1953.

EDDINGTON, A. *Space, time, and gravitation.* Cambridge: Cambridge University Press, 1920.

EDDINGTON, A. *The nature of the physical world.* Cambridge: Cambridge University Press, 1928.

EDDINGTON, A. *The philosophy of physical science.* Cambridge: Cambridge University Press, 1939.

EDWARDS, W. The theory of decision making. *Psychol. Bull.*, 1954, **51**, 380–417.

EDWARDS, W. Subjective probabilities inferred from decisions. *Psychol. Rev.*, 1962, **69**, 109–135.

EDWARDS, W., LINDMAN, H., and SAVAGE, L. J. Bayesian statistical inference for psychological research. *Psychol. Rev.*, 1963, **70**, 193–242.

EINSTEIN, A. *The origin of the general theory of relativity.* Glasgow: Jackson Wylie, 1933.

ESTES, W. K. The statistical approach to learning theory. In S. Koch (editor), *Psychology: a study of a science*, Vol. 2. New York: McGraw-Hill, 1959.

ESTES, W. K. Toward a statistical learning theory. *Psychol. Rev.*, 1950, **57**, 94–107.

ESTES, W. K., MacCORQUODALE, K., MEEHL, P. E., MUELLER, C. G., JR., SCHOENFELD, W. N., and VERPLANCK, W. S., *Modern learning theory.* New York: Appleton-Century-Crofts, 1954.

ESTES, W. K. and SUPPES, P. C. Foundations of linear models. In R. R. Bush and W. K. Estes (editors), *Studies in mathematical learning theory.* Stanford: Stanford University Press, 1959.

EVANS, J. L. On meaning and verification. *Mind*, 1953, **62**, 1–19.

EWING, A. C. *Kant's critique of pure reason.* London: Methuen, 1938.


FARBER, M. *See* Sellars, McGill, and Farber, 1949.

FARRINGTON, B. *Greek science, I, II.* Harmondsworth: Penguin Books, 1949.

FEIGL, H. The logical character of the principle of induction. *Philos. Sci.*, 1934, **1**, 20–29. Also in H. Feigl and W. Sellars (editors), *Readings in philosophical analysis.* New York: Appleton-Century-Crofts, 1949.

FEIGL, H. Logical empiricism. In D. D. Runes (editor), *Twentieth century philosophy.* New York: Philosophical Library, 1943. Reprinted in H. Feigl and W. Sellars (editors), *Readings in philosophical analysis.* New York: Appleton-Century-Crofts, 1949.

FEIGL, H. Operationism and scientific method. *Psychol. Rev.*, 1945, **52**, 250–259.

FEIGL, H. Some remarks on the meaning of scientific explanation. In H. Feigl and W. Sellars (editors), *Readings in philosophical analysis.* New York: Appleton-Century-Crofts, 1949.

FEIGL, H. De Principiis non est disputandum? In M. Black (editor), *Philosophical analysis*. Ithaca: Cornell University Press, 1950.

FEIGL, H. Existential hypotheses. *Philos. Sci.,* 1950, **17**, 35–62.

FEIGL, H. Principles and problems of theory construction in psychology. In W. Dennis (editor), *Current trends in psychological theory*. Pittsburgh: University of Pittsburgh Press, 1951.

FEIGL, H. The mind-body problem in the development of logical empiricism. *Rev. Int. Philosophie,* 1950. In H. Feigl and M. Brodbeck (editors), *Readings in the philosophy of science*. New York: Appleton-Century-Crofts, 1953.

FEIGL, H. Unity of science and unitary science. (original 1939) In H. Feigl and M. Brodbeck (editors), *Readings in the philosophy of science*. New York: Appleton-Century-Crofts, 1953.

FEIGL, H. The 'mental' and the 'physical'. In H. Feigl and G. Maxwell (editors), *Minnesota studies in the philosophy of science,* Vol. II. Minneapolis: University of Minnesota Press, 1958.

FEIGL, H. Philosophical embarrassments of psychology. *Amer. Psychol.,* 1959, **14**, 115–128.

FEIGL, H. On the vindication of induction. *Philos. Sci.,* 1961, **28**, 212–216.

FEIGL, H. Reduction of psychology to neurophysiology. Paper read to AAAS meetings, Denver, December, 1961.

FEIGL, H. and BLUMBERG, A. E. Logical positivism. *J. Philos.,* 1931, **28**, 281–296.

FEIGL, H. and MAXWELL, G. (editors), *Current issues in the philosophy of science*. New York: Holt, Rinehart and Winston, 1961.

FELLER, W. *An introduction to probability theory and its applications,* Vol. 1 (1st edition). New York: Wiley, 1950.

FEYERABEND, P. K. On the quantum theory of measurement. In S. Körner (editor), *Observation and interpretation in the philosophy of physics*. New York: Dover, 1957.

FEYERABEND, P. K. An attempt at a realistic interpretation of experience. *Proc. Arist. Soc.,* 1958, **58**, 141–170.

FEYERABEND, P. K. Complementarity. *Proc. Arist. Soc. Suppl.,* 1958, **32**, 75–104.

FEYERABEND, P. K. Niels Bohr's interpretation of the quantum theory. In H. Feigl and G. Maxwell (editors), *Current issues in the philosophy of science*. New York: Holt, Rinehart and Winston, 1961.

FEYERABEND, P. K. Explanation, reduction and empiricism. In H. Feigl and G. Maxwell (editors) *Minnesota studies in the philosophy of science,* Vol. III. Minneapolis: University of Minnesota Press, 1962.

FEYERABEND, P. K. Problems of microphysics. In R. G. Colodny (editor), *Frontiers of science and philosophy*. Pittsburgh: University of Pittsburgh Press, 1962.

FEYERABEND, P. K. Realism and instrumentalism. In M. Bunge (editor), *The critical approach to science and philosophy*. Glencoe: Free Press, 1964.

FINDLAY, J. Goedelian sentences: a non-numerical approach. *Mind,* 1942, **51**, 259–265.

FISHER, R. A. Statistical methods and scientific induction. *J. Roy. Stat. Soc., Ser. B.,* 1955, **17**, 69–78.

FISHER, R. A. *Statistical methods and scientific inference*. Edinburgh: Oliver & Boyd, 1956, 1959.

FITCH, F. B. and BARRY, G. Towards a formalization of Hull's behavior theory. *Philos. Sci.*, 1950, **17**, 260–265.

FLEW, A. G. N. (editor), *Logic and language: first series*. Oxford: Blackwell, 1951.

FLEW, A. G. N. (editor), *Logic and language: second series*. Oxford: Blackwell, 1953.

FRANK, P. *Philosophy of science*. New York: Prentice-Hall, 1957.

FRANK, P. *Modern science and its philosophy*. Cambridge: Harvard University Press, 1941. Reprinted New York: Collier Books, 1961.

FRASER, D. A. S. *Statistics, an introduction*. New York: Wiley, 1958.

FREGE, G. *The foundations of arithmetic*. (translated by Austin; revised edition, original 1884). Oxford: Blackwell, 1953. Also New York: Harper Torchbooks, Harper & Row, 1960.

FREUDENTHAL, H. (editor), *The concept and the role of model in mathematics and natural and social sciences*. Dordrecht: D. Reidel, 1961.

GAITO, J. and ZAVALA, A. Neurochemistry and learning. *Psychol. Bull.*, 1964, **61**, 45–62.

GALANTER, E. *See* Miller, Galanter, and Pribram, 1960.

GALLISTEL, C. R. Electrical self-stimulation and its theoretical implications. *Psychol. Bull.*, 1964, **61**, 23–34.

GARNER, W. R. A technique and a scale for loudness measurement. *J. acoust. Soc. Amer.*, 1954, **26**, 73–88.

GELLNER, E. *Words and things*. London: Gollancz, 1959.

GEORGE, F. H. Logical constructs and psychological theory. *Psychol. Rev.*, 1953, **60**, 1–6.

GEORGE, F. H. Inductive machines and the problem of learning. *Cybernetica*, 1959, **2**, 109–126.

GEORGE, F. H. Models in cybernetics. In J. W. L. Beament (editor), *Models and analogues in biology*. Cambridge: Cambridge University Press, 1960.

GEORGE, F. H. *The brain as a computer*. New York: Pergammon Press, 1961.

GIBSON, J. *Locke's theory of knowledge*. Cambridge: Cambridge University Press, 1917.

GIBSON, J. J. The concept of stimulus in psychology. *Amer. Psychol.*, 1960, **15**, 694–703.

GINSBERG, A. Hypothetical constructs and intervening variables. *Psychol. Rev.*, 1954, **61**, 119–131.

GIRSHICK, M. A. *See* Blackwell and Girshick, 1954.

GNEDENKO, B. V. and KHINCHIN, A. YA. *An elementary introduction to the theory of probability*. (translated by W. R. Stahl) San Francisco: Freeman, 1961.

GÖDEL, K. *On formally undecidable propositions of Principia Mathematica and related systems*. (translated by B. Meltzer; introduction by R. B. Braithwaite; original 1931) London: Oliver Boyd, 1962.

GOOD, I. J. Kinds of probability. *Science*, 1959, **129**, 443–447.

GOODFIELD, J. *See* Toulmin and Goodfield, 1961.

GOODMAN, N. The problem of counterfactual conditionals. *J. Philos.*, 1947, **44**, 113–128.

GOODMAN, N. *The structure of appearance.* Cambridge: Harvard University Press, 1951.

GOODMAN, N. *Fact, fiction and forecast.* Cambridge: Harvard University Press, 1955.

GOUDGE, T. A. Causal explanation in natural history. *Br. J. Philos. Sci.*, 1958, **9**, 194–202.

GRANT, D. A. Testing the null hypothesis and the strategy and tactics of investigating theoretical models. *Psychol. Rev.*, 1962, **69**, 54–61.

GREGORY, R. L. On physical model explanations in psychology. *Br. J. Philos. Sci.*, 1953, **4**, 192–197.

GREGORY, R. L. The brain as an engineering problem. In W. H. Thorpe and O. L. Zangwill (editors), *Current problems in animal behavior.* Cambridge: Cambridge University Press, 1961.

GUTHRIE, E. R. *The psychology of learning.* New York: Harper, 1935.

GUTHRIE, E. R. Association by contiguity. In S. Koch (editor), *Psychology: a study of a science,* Vol. 2. New York: McGraw-Hill, 1959.

GUTTMAN, L. An outline of the statistical theory of prediction. In P. Horst (editor) *The prediction of personal adjustment.* New York: Social Science Research Council, 1941 (Bull. 48).


HACKING, I. On the foundations of statistics. *Br. J. Philos. Sci.*, 1964, **15**, 1–26.

HACKING, I. Salmon's vindication of induction. *J. Philos.*, 1965, **62**, 260–266.

HACKING, I. *The foundations of statistics.* Cambridge: Cambridge University Press, 1965.

HADAMARD, J. *The psychology of invention in the mathematical field.* London: Oxford University Press, 1945.

HALL, A. R. *The scientific revolution: 1500–1800.* London: Longmans, 1954.

HANSON, N. R. Professor Ryle's Mind. *Philos. Quart.*, 1952, **2**, 246–248.

HANSON, N. R. *Patterns of discovery.* Cambridge: Cambridge University Press, 1958.

HANSON, N. R. Five cautions for the Copenhagen interpretation's critics. *Philos. Sci.*, 1959, **26**, 325–337.

HANSON, N. R. On the symmetry between explanation and prediction. *Philos. Rev.*, 1959, **68**, 349–358.

HANSON, N. R. The Copenhagen interpretation of quantum theory. *Amer. J. Physics*, 1959, **27**, 1–19. Abridged in A. Danto and S. Morgenbesser, (editors), *Philosophy of science.* New York: Meridian Books, 1960.

HANSON, N. R. The dematerialization of matter. *Philos. Sci.* 1962, **29**, 27–38.

HANSON, N. R. *The concept of the positron.* Cambridge: Cambridge University Press, 1963.

HAWKINS, D. Existential and epistemic probability. *Philos. Sci.*, 1943, **10**, 255–261.

HAWKINS, D. Design for a mind. *Daedelus*, 1962, **61**, 560–577.

HAWKINS, D. *The language of nature.* San Francisco: Freeman, 1964.

HAYEK, F. A. *The sensory order.* London: Routledge, 1952.

KRECH, D. Notes toward a psychological theory. *J. Person.,* 1949, **19,** 66–87.

KRECH, D. Dynamic systems as open neurological systems. *Psychol. Rev.,* 1950, **57,** 345–361.

KRECH, D. Dynamic systems, psychological fields and hypothetical constructs. *Psychol. Rev.,* 1950, **57,** 783–790.

KRECH, D. and CRUTCHFIELD, R. S. *Theory and problems of social psychology.* New York: McGraw-Hill, 1947.

KRECH, D., CRUTCHFIELD, R. S. and BALLACHEY, E. L. *Individual and society.* New York: McGraw-Hill, 1962.

KUENZLI, A. *The phenomenological problem.* New York: Harper & Row, 1959.

KYRURG, H. E. and SMOKLER, H. E. (editors). *Studies in subjective probability.* New York: Wiley, 1964.


LACHMAN, R. The model in theory construction. *Psychol. Rev.,* 1960, **67,** 113–129.

LANDAUER, T. K. Two hypotheses concerning the biochemical basis of memory. *Psychol. Rev.,* 1964, **71,** 167–179.

LANGFELD, H. S. A response interpretation of consciousness. *Psychol. Rev.,* 1931, **38,** 87–108.

LAPLACE, P. S. *A philosophical essay on probabilities.* (translated by F. W. Truscott and F. L. Emory; original 1796) New York: Dover, 1951.

LASHLEY, K. S. The behavioristic interpretation of consciousness, I, II. *Psychol. Rev.,* 1923, **30,** 237–272; 329–353.

LEHMAN, E. L. Significance level and power. *Annal. Math. Stat.,* 1958, **29,** 1167–1176.

LEHMAN, E. L. *Testing statistical hypotheses.* New York: Wiley, 1959.

LENNOX, W. G. *Science and seizures.* New York: Harper, 1941.

LENZ, J. W. Problems of a practicalist's justification of induction. *Philos. Studies,* 1958, **9,** 4–8.

LENZ, J. W. The pragmatic justification of induction. In E. H. Madden (editor), *The structure of scientific thought.* Boston: Houghton Mifflin, 1960.

LEVI, I. Hacking Salmon on induction. *J. Philos.,* 1965, **62,** 481–487.

LEWIN, K. *A dynamic theory of personality.* New York: McGraw-Hill, 1935.

LEWIN, K. *Principles of topological psychology.* New York: McGraw-Hill, 1936.

LEWIS, C. I. A pragmatic conception of the *a priori. J. Philos.,* 1923. In H. Feigl and W. Sellars (editors), *Readings in philosophical analysis.* New York: Appleton-Century-Crofts, 1949.

LEWIS, C. I. *Mind and the world order.* (original 1929) New York: Dover, 1956.

LEWIS, C. I. Experience and meaning. *Philos. Rev.,* 1934. Also in H. Feigl and W. Sellars (editors), *Readings in philosophical analysis.* New York: Appleton-Century-Crofts, 1949.

LEWIS, D. C. *See* Birkhoff and Lewis, 1935.

LINDLEY, D. V. The use of prior probability distributions in statistical inferences and decisions. In *Proceedings of the fourth Berkeley symposium on mathematics and probability,* Vol. 1. Berkeley: University California Press, 1961.

LINDMAN, H. *See* Edwards, Lindman, and Savage, 1963.

LINDZEY, G. Hypothetical constructs, conventional constructs and the use of physiological data in psychological theory. *Psychiatry,* 1953, **16**, 27–33.

LOCKE, J. *An essay concerning human understanding.* (original 1960; abridged and edited by A. S. Pringle-Pattison) Oxford: Clarendon Press, 1924.

LORENTE DE No', R. Cerebral cortex: architecture. In J. F. Fulton, *Physiology of the nervous system.* (3rd edition) New York: Oxford University Press, 1949.

LUCAS, J. R. Mind, machines, and Gödel. *Philosophy,* 1961, **36**, 112–127.

LUCE, R. D. *Individual choice behavior.* New York: Wiley, 1959.

LUCE, R. D. and SUPPES, P. Preference, utility, and subjective probability. In R. D. Luce, R. R. Bush, and E. Galanter (editors), *Handbook of mathematical psychology,* Vol. III. New York: Wiley, 1965.


MACCORQUODALE, K. and MEEHL, P. E. On a distinction between hypothetical constructs and intervening variables. *Psychol. Rev.,* 1948, **55**, 95–107.

MACCORQUODALE, K. and MEEHL, P. E. Preliminary suggestions as to formalization of expectancy theory. *Psychol. Rev.,* 1953, **60**, 50–63.

MACCORQUODALE, K. and MEEHL, P. E. Edward C. Tolman. In W. K. Estes and others, *Modern learning theory.* New York: Appleton-Century-Crofts, 1954.

MCCULLOCH, W. S. and PITTS, W. A logical calculus of ideas immanent in nervous activity. *Bull. Math. Biophys.,* 1943, **5**, 111–133.

MCCULLOCH, W. S. *See* Pitts and McCulloch, 1947.

MCDOUGALL, W. *Introduction to social psychology.* London: Methuen, 1908.

MCDOUGALL, W. Men or robots? In C. Murchison (editor), *Psychologies of 1925.* Worcester: Clark University Press, 1928.

MCDOUGALL, W. *See* Watson and McDougall, 1928.

MCGEOCH, J. A. The vertical dimensions of mind. *Psychol. Rev.,* 1936, **43**, 107–129.

MCGEOCH, J. A. A critique of operational definition. *Psychol. Bull.,* 1937, **34**, 703–704.

MCGILL, V. J. *See* Sellars, R. W., McGill, and Farber, 1949.

MACKAY, D. M. The epistemological problem of automata. In C. W. Shannon and J. McCarthy (editors), *Automata Studies.* Princeton: Princeton University Press, 1956.

MACLEOD, R. B. The phenomenological approach to social psychology. *Psychol. Rev.,* 1947, **54**, 193–210.

MACH, E. *The science of mechanics.* (translated by T. J. McCormack; original 1883) LaSalle: Open Court, 1960.

MACH, E. *Space and geometry.* La Salle: Open Court, 1906.

MACH, E. *The analysis of sensations.* (original 1897) La Salle: Open Court, 1914.

MADDEN, E. H. *The structure of scientific thought*. Boston: Houghton Mifflin, 1960.

MADDEN, E. H. Definition and reduction. *Philos. Sci.,* 1961, **28**, 390–405.

MALCOLM, N. Moore and ordinary language. In P. A. Schilpp (editor), *The philosophy of G. E. Moore*. New York: Tudor, 1952.

MALCOLM, N. Wittgenstein's *Philosophical investigations*. *Philos. Quart.,* 1954, **63**, 530–559.

MALCOLM, N. *Ludwig Wittgenstein: a memoir*. London: Oxford University Press, 1958.

MARGENAU, H. *The nature of physical reality*. New York: McGraw-Hill, 1950.

MARHENKE, P. Phenomenalism. In M. Black (editor), *Philosophical analysis*. Ithaca: Cornell University Press, 1950.

MARSHALL, W. H. and TALBOT, S. A. Recent evidence for neural mechanisms in vision leading to a general theory of visual acuity. In H. Klüver (editor), *Visual mechanisms*. Lancaster: Cattell, 1942.

MARX, M. H. Intervening variable or hypothetical construct? *Psychol. Rev.,* 1951, **58**, 235–247.

MARX, M. The general nature of theory construction. In M. Marx (editor), *Psychological theory*. New York: Macmillan, 1951. Revised in M. Marx (editor), *Theories in contemporary psychology*. New York: Macmillan, 1963.

MAUDSLEY, H. *The physiology and pathology of the mind*. London: Macmillan, 1867.

MAXWELL, G. The ontological status of theoretical entities. In H. Feigl and G. Maxwell (editors), *Minnesota studies in the philosophy of science,* Vol. III. Minneapolis: University of Minnesota Press, 1962.

MAXWELL, G. Theories, frameworks, and ontology. *Philos. Sci.,* 1962, **29**, 132–138.

MAYO, B. The existence of theoretical entities. *Penguin Science News,* 1954, **32**, 7–18.

MAZE, J. R. Do intervening variables intervene? *Psychol. Rev.,* 1954, **61**, 226–231.

MEEHL, P. E. On the circularity of the Law of Effect. *Psychol. Bull.,* 1950, **47**, 52–75.

MEEHL, P. E. *Clinical versus statistical prediction*. Minneapolis: University of Minnesota Press, 1954.

MEEHL, P. E. and ROSEN, A. Antecedent probability and the efficiency of psychometric signs, patterns, or cutting scores. *Psychol. Bull.,* 1955, **52**, 194–216.

MEEHL, P. E. *See* MacCorquodale and Meehl, 1948; 1953; 1954.

MEEHL, P. E. *See* Cronbach and Meehl, 1955.

MEISSNER, W. W. Non-constructual aspects of psychological constructs. *Psychol. Rev.,* 1958, **65**, 143–150.

MERLEAU-PONTY, M. *The structure of behavior*. (translated by A. L. Fisher; original 1942) Boston: Beacon Press, 1963.

MERLEAU-PONTY, M. *Phenomenology of perception*. (translated by C. Smith) London: Routledge, 1963.

MERTON, R. K. *Social theory and social structure*. Glencoe: Free Press, 1957.

MICHOTTE, A. E. *The perception of causality.* New York: Basic Books, 1963.

MILL, J. S. *An examination of Sir William Hamilton's philosophy.* London: Longmans, 1878.

MILL, J. S. *A system of logic.* London: Longmans, 1884.

MILLER, G. A., GALANTER, E. and PRIBRAM, K. H. *Plans and the structure of behavior.* New York: Henry Holt, 1960.

MILNER, P. M. The cell assembly: Mark II. *Psychol. Rev.* 1957, **64,** 242–252.

MISES, R. VON. *Probability, statistics and truth.* (revised edition) New York: Macmillan, 1957.

MONTGOMERY, K. C. An experimental investigation of reactive inhibition and conditioned inhibition. *J. exp. Psychol.,* 1951, **41,** 39–51.

MOORE, G. E. The refutation of idealism. In *Philosophical studies.* London: Kegan Paul, 1922.

MOORE, G. E. *Philosophical studies.* London: Kegan Paul, 1922.

MOORE, G. E. *In defense of common sense.* In J. H. Muirhead (editor), *Contemporary British philosophy.* London: G. Allen, 1925.

MOORE, G. E. Proof of an external world. *Proc. Br. Acad.,* 1939, **25,** 273–300.

MOORE, G. E. Russell's theory of descriptions. In *Philosophical papers.* London: G. Allen, 1959.

MORGAN, C. L. Physiological theory of drive. In S. Koch (editor), *Psychology: a study of a science,* Vol. 1. New York: McGraw-Hill, 1959.

MORRELL, F. Electrophysiological contributions to the neural basis of learning. *Physiol. Rev.,* 1961, **41,** 442–494.

MOSTELLER, F. *See* Bush and Mosteller, 1955.

MUENZINGER, K. F. Vicarious trial and error at a choice point, I: a general survey of its relation to learning. *J. genet. Psychol.,* 1938, **53,** 75–86.

MUENZINGER, K. F. *Psychology: the science of behavior.* New York: Harper & Row, 1942.

MURPHY, G. *See* Schafer and Murphy, 1943.


NAGEL, E. The meaning of reduction in the natural sciences. In R. C. Stauffer (editor), *Science and civilization.* Madison: University of Wisconsin Press, 1949.

NAGEL, E. Some issues in the logic of historical analysis. *Sci. Mon.,* 1952, **74,** 162–169. Also in H. Feigl and M. Brodbeck (editors), *Readings in the philosophy of science.* New York: Appleton-Century-Crofts, 1953.

NAGEL, E. *The structure of science.* New York: Harcourt, Brace & World, 1961.

NAGEL, E. and NEWMAN, J. R. *Gödel's proof.* New York: New York University Press, 1958.

NAGEL, E. and NEWMAN, J. R. Putnam's review of *Gödel's proof. Philos. Sci.,* 1961, **28,** 209–211.

NEUGEBAUER, O. *The exact sciences of antiquity* (revised edition). Providence: Brown University Press, 1957. Reprinted New York: Harper Torchbooks, Harper & Row, 1962.

NEUMANN, J. VON. The general and logical theory of automata. In L. A. Jeffress (editor), *Cerebral mechanisms in behavior.* New York: Wiley,

1951. Reprinted in J. R. Newman (editor), *The world of mathematics*, Vol. 4. New York: Simon and Schuster, 1956.

NEUMANN, J. VON. *Foundations of quantum mechanics.* (original 1932) Princeton: Princeton University Press, 1955.

NEURATH, O. Sociology and physicalism. (original 1931) In A. J. Ayer (editor), *Logical positivism.* Glencoe: Free Press, 1959.

NEWMAN, J. R. *See* Nagel and Newman, 1958; 1961.

NEYMAN, J. L'estimation statistique traiteé comme un problème classique de probabilité. *Actualites scientifiques et industrielles*, 1938, 739, 54–57.

NEYMAN, J. Basic ideas and theory of testing statistical hypotheses. *J. Roy. Stat. Soc.*, 1942, **105**, 292–327.

NEYMAN, J. *First course in probability and statistics.* New York: Henry Holt, 1950.

NEYMAN, J. *Lectures and conferences on mathematical statistics and probability.* Washington: U. S. Department of Agriculture, 1952.

NEYMAN, J. and SCOTT, E. L. The distribution of galaxies. *Scientific American*, 1956, **195**, 187–200.

NICOD, J. The logical problem of induction. In J. Nicod *Foundations of geometry and induction.* (translated by P. Wiener) London: Routledge, 1930.


O'NEILL, W. M. Hypothetical terms and relations in psychological theorizing. *Br. J. Psychol.*, 1953, **44**, 211–220.

OPARIN, A. I. *The origin of life.* (translated by S. Mogulis) New York: Macmillan, 1938.

OPPENHEIM, P. *See* Hempel and Oppenheim, 1948.

OPPENHEIM, P. *See* Kemeny and Oppenheim, 1956.

OSGOOD, C. E. and HEYER, A. W. A new interpretation of figural after-effects. *Psychol. Rev.*, 1951, **59**, 98–118.


PAP, A. *The a priori in physical theory.* New York: Kings Crown Press, 1946.

PAP, A. *Elements of analytic philosophy.* New York: Macmillan, 1949.

PAP, A. *An introduction to the philosophy of science.* Glencoe: Free Press, 1962.

PAP, A. and EDWARDS, P. *A modern introduction to philosophy.* Glencoe: Free Press, 1957.

PARZEN, E. *Modern probability theory and its applications.* New York: Wiley, 1960.

PASCAL, B. *Pascal's Pensées.* New York: Dutton, 1958.

PASSMORE, J. *One hundred years of philosophy.* London: Duckworth, 1957.

PEARSON, E. S. *See* Clopper and Pearson, 1934.

PEARSON, K. *The grammar of science.* (original 1892) London: Dent, 1937.

PEIRCE, C. S. How to make our ideas clear. (original 1878) In J. Buchler (editor), *The philosophy of Peirce.* London: Routledge, 1940.

PEIRCE, C. S. On the doctrine of chances, with later reflections. (original 1878) In J. Buchler (editor), *The philosophy of Peirce.* London: Routledge, 1940.

PEIRCE, C. S. The doctrine of necessity examined. (original 1892) In J. Buchler (editor), *The philosophy of Peirce*. London: Routledge, 1940.

PEPPER, S. Emergence. *J. Philos.*, 1926, **23**, 241–245.

PEPPER, S. *World hypotheses*. Berkeley: University California Press, 1948.

PETERS, R. S. *The concept of motivation*. London: Routledge, 1958.

PITCHER, G. *The philosophy of Wittgenstein*. Englewood Cliffs: Prentice-Hall, 1964.

PITTS, W. and McCULLOCH, W. S. How we know universals: the perception of auditory and visual forms. *Bull. Math. Biophys.*, 1947, **9**, 127–147.

PITTS, W. *See* McCulloch and Pitts, 1943.

PLACE, U. T. Is consciousness a brain process? *Br. J. Psychol.*, 1956, **47**, 44–50.

POINCARÉ, H. *Science and hypothesis*. (translated by W. J. G., original 1905) New York: Dover, 1952.

POINCARÉ, H. *The value of science*. (translated by G. B. Halstead; original 1913) New York: Dover, 1958. Also published in Poincaré, *The foundations of science*. Lancaster: The Science Press, 1913.

POINCARÉ, H. *Science and method*. (translated by F. Maitland, orig. 1914) New York: Dover, 1952.

POPPER, K. R. *The poverty of historicism*. London: Routledge, 1957.

POPPER, K. R. *The logic of scientific discovery*. (original *Logik der Forschung*, Vienna: Springer, 1935.) London: Hutchinson, 1959. Also New York: Wiley, 1961.

POPPER, K. R. The propensity interpretation of the calculus of probability, and the quantum theory. In S. Körner (editor), *Observation and interpretation in the philosophy of physics*. New York: Dover, 1957.

POSTMAN, L. The history and present status of the Law of Effect. *Psychol. Bull.*, 1947, **44**, 489–563.

PRATT, C. C. *The logic of modern psychology*. New York: Macmillan, 1939.

PRIBRAM, K. H. Toward a science of neurophysiology (method and data). In *Current trends in psychology and the behavioral sciences*. Pittsburgh: University Pittsburgh Press, 1954.

PRIBRAM, K. H. A review of theory in physiological psychology. *Annu. Rev. Psychol.*, 1960, 11, 1–40.

PRIBRAM, K. H. *See* Miller, Galanter, and Pribram, 1960.

PRICE, H. H. *Perception*. London: Methuen, 1950.

PRINCE, M. Fundamental errors of the behaviorists. In C. Murchison (editor), *Psychologies of 1925*. Worcester: Clark University Press, 1928.

PUTNAM, H. Review of Nagel and Newman: *Gödel's proof*. *Philos. Sci.*, 1960, **27**, 205–207.

PUTNAM, H. Minds and machines. In S. Hook (editor), *Dimensions of mind*. New York: New York University Press, 1960. Reprinted New York: Collier Books, 1961.


QUINE, W. O. Two dogmas of empiricism. In W. Quine, *From a logical point of view*. Cambridge: Harvard University Press, 1953.

QUINE, W. O. *Methods of logic*. New York: Henry Holt, 1950.

RAMSEY, F. P. *The foundations of mathematics.* London: Kegan Paul, 1931.

RAMSEY, F. P. Truth and probability. (orig. 1926) In F. P. Ramsey, *The foundations of mathematics.* London: Kegan Paul, 1931.

RESCHER, N. On explanation and prediction. *Br. J. Philos. Sci.,* 1958, **8,** 281–290.

RESCHER, N. Fundamental problems in the theory of scientific explanation. In B. Baumrin (editor), *Philosophy of science: the Delaware Seminar,* Vol. 2. New York: Wiley, 1963.

REICHENBACH, H. *Experience and prediction.* Chicago: University of Chicago Press, 1938.

REICHENBACH, H. On the justification of induction. *J. Philos.,* 1940, **37,** 97–103. Also in H. Feigl and W. Sellars (editors), *Readings in philosophical analysis.* New York: Appleton-Century-Crofts, 1949.

REICHENBACH, H. *Theory of probability.* (2nd edition) Berkeley: University of California Press, 1949.

REID, T. *Inquiry into the human mind.* Edinburgh: Bell and Bradfute, 1810.

RESTLE, F. A survey and classification of learning models. In R. R. Bush and W. K. Estes (editors), *Studies in mathematical learning theory.* Stanford: Stanford University Press, 1959.

RIESEN, A. H. The development of visual perception in man and chimpanzee. *Science,* 1947, **106,** 107–108.

ROBBINS, H. A new approach to a classical decision problem. In H. E. Kyburg and E. Nagel (editors), *Induction: some current issues.* Middletown: Wesleyan University Press, 1963.

ROBBINS, H. and SAMUEL, E. Testing statistical hypotheses—the "compound" approach. In R. E. Machol and P. Gray (editors), *Recent developments in information and decision processes.* New York: Macmillan, 1962.

ROSEN, A. *See* Meehl and Rosen, 1955.

ROSENBLATT, F. The perceptron. *Psychol. Rev.,* 1958, **65,** 386–408.

ROSENBLEUTH, A. and WIENER, N. The role of models in science. *Philos. Sci.,* 1945, **12,** 316–321.

ROSSER, B. An informal exposition of proofs of Gödel's and Church's theorems. *J. symbol. Log.,* 1939, **4,** 53–60.

ROTH, L. *Descartes' discourse on method.* London: Oxford University Press, 1937.

ROZEBOOM, W. W. Mediation variables in scientific theory. *Psychol. Rev.,* 1956, **63,** 249–264.

ROZEBOOM, W. W. The fallacy of the null hypothesis significance test. *Psychol. Bull.,* 1960, **57,** 416–428.

ROZEBOOM, W. W. Ontological induction and the logical typology of scientific variables. *Philos. Sci.,* 1961, **28,** 337–377.

RUSSELL, B. *A critical exposition of the philosophy of Leibniz.* (orig. 1900; 2nd edition 1937) London: G. Allen, 1937.

RUSSELL, B. *Problems of philosophy.* London: Oxford University Press, 1912.

RUSSELL, B. *Mysticism and logic.* London: G. Allen, 1917.

RUSSELL, B. The philosophy of logical atomism. *Monist.,* 1918. In R. C. Marsh (editor), *Logic and knowledge.* London: G. Allen, 1956.

RUSSELL, B. *Our knowledge of the external world.* (revised edition) London: G. Allen, 1926.

RUSSELL, B. *History of western philosophy.* London: G. Allen, 1946.

RUSSELL, B. *Human knowledge: its scope and limits.* London: G. Allen, 1948.

RUSSELL, B. The cult of 'common usage'. *Br. J. Philos. Sci.,* 1953, **3**, 303–307.

RUSSELL, B. *Portraits from memory.* London: G. Allen, 1956.

RUSSELL, B. *Logic and knowledge.* (edited by R. C. Marsh) London: G. Allen, 1956.

RUSSELL, B. *See* Whitehead and Russell, 1913.

RYLE, G. *Philosophical arguments.* London: Oxford University Press, 1945.

RYLE, G. *The concept of mind.* London: Hutchinson, 1949.


SALMON, W. C. Should we attempt to justify induction? *Philos. Studies,* 1957, **8**, 33–48.

SALMON, W. C. Vindication of induction. In H. Feigl and G. Maxwell (editors), *Current issues in the philosophy of science.* New York: Holt, Rinehart and Winston, 1961.

SALMON, W. C. On vindicating induction. In H. E. Kyburg and E. Nagel (editors), *Induction: some current issues.* Middletown: Wesleyan University Press, 1963.

SAMBURSKY, S. *The physical world of the Greeks.* (translated by M. Dagut) London: Routledge, 1956.

SAMUEL, E. *See* Robbins and Samuel, 1962.

SANTILLANA, G. DE. *The origins of scientific thought.* Chicago: University of Chicago Press, 1961. Reprinted New York: Mentor Books, New American Library.

SARBIN, T. R. The logic of prediction in psychology. *Psychol. Rev.,* 1944, **51**, 210–228.

SARTON, G. *A history of science,* 2 vols. Cambridge: Harvard University Press, 1952.

SAVAGE, L. J. *The foundations of statistics.* New York: Wiley, 1954.

SAVAGE, L. J. *The foundations of statistical inference.* London: Methuen, 1962.

SAVAGE, L. J. The foundations of statistics reconsidered. In H. E. Kyburg and H. E. Smokler (editors), *Studies in subjective probability.* New York: Wiley, 1964.

SAVAGE, L. J. *See* Edwards, Lindman, and Savage, 1965.

SAW, R. L. *The vindication of metaphysics.* London: Macmillan, 1951.

SCHAFER, R. and MURPHY, G. The role of autism in figure-ground relationships. *J. exp. Psychol.,* 1943, **32**, 335–343.

SCHEFFLER, I. Explanation, prediction, and abstraction. *Br. J. Philos. Sci.,* 1957, **7**, 293–315. Also in A. Adorno and S. Morgenbesser (editors), *Philosophy of science.* New York: Meridian Books, 1960.

SCHLAIFER, R. *Probability and statistics for business decisions.* New York: McGraw-Hill, 1959.

SCHLICK, M. Is there a factual *a priori.* (original 1930) In H. Feigl and W. Sellars (editors), *Readings in philosophical analysis.* New York: Appleton-Century-Crofts, 1949.

SCHLICK, M. Positivism and realism. (original 1932) In A. J. Ayer (editor), *Logical positivism*. Glencoe: Free Press, 1959.

SCHLICK, M. Facts and propositions. *Analysis,* 1935, **2,** 65–70.

SCHLICK, M. Meaning and verification. *Philos. Rev.,* 1936, **45,** 339–369. Also in H. Feigl and W. Sellars (editors), *Readings in philosophical analysis.* New York: Appleton-Century-Crofts, 1949.

SCHLICK, M. Are natural laws conventions? (original 1938) In H. Feigl and M. Brodbeck (editors), *Readings in the philosophy of science.* New York: Appleton-Century-Crofts, 1953.

SCHMIDT, F. O. (editor), *Macromolecular specificity and biological memory.* Cambridge: M.I.T. Press, 1962.

SCHREINER, OLIVE. *The story of an African farm.* (original 1883) New York: Modern Library, 1927.

SCHRÖDINGER, E. *What is life?* Cambridge: Cambridge University Press, 1944. Reprinted Garden City: Anchor Books, Doubleday, 1956.

SCOTT, L. *See* Neyman and Scott, 1956.

SCRIVEN, M. A study of radical behaviorism. In H. Feigl and M. Scriven (editors), *Minnesota studies in the philosophy of science,* Vol. I. Minneapolis: University of Minnesota Press, 1956.

SCRIVEN, M. Definition, explanation, and theories. In H. Feigl, G. Maxwell, and M. Scriven (editors), *Minnesota studies in the philosophy of science,* Vol. II. Minneapolis: University of Minnesota Press, 1958.

SCRIVEN, M. The compleat robot. In S. Hook (editor), *Dimensions of mind.* New York: New York University Press, 1960. Reprinted New York: Collier Books, 1961.

SCRIVEN, M. Explanations, predictions, and laws. In H. Feigl and G. Maxwell (editors), *Minnesota studies in the philosophy of science,* Vol. III. Minneapolis: University Minnesota Press, 1962.

SCRIVEN, M. Limits of scientific explanation. In B. A. Baumrin (editor), *Philosophy of science: the Delaware Seminar,* Vol. II. New York: Wiley, 1963.

SELLARS, R. W., McGILL, V. J., and FARBER, M. *Philosophy for the future.* New York: Macmillan, 1949.

SELLARS, W. Empiricism and the philosophy of mind. In H. Feigl and M. Scriven (editors), *Minnesota studies in the philosophy of science,* Vol. I. Minneapolis: University of Minnesota Press, 1956.

SELLARS, W. The language of theories. In H. Feigl and G. Maxwell (editors), *Current issues in the philosophy of science.* New York: Holt, Rinehart and Winston, 1961.

SELLS, R. L. *See* Weidner and Sells, 1960.

SENDEN, M. VON. *Space and sight.* (translated by P. Heath; original 1932) Glencoe: Free Press, 1960.

SEWARD, J. P. The constancy of the I–V: a critique of intervening variables. *Psychol. Rev.,* 1955, **62,** 155–168.

SHANNON, C. E. and WEAVER, W. *The mathematical theory of communication.* Urbana: University Illinois Press, 1949.

SHANNON, C. E. Presentation of a maze solving machine. In H. von Foerster (editor), *Cybernetics. Transactions of the eight conference of Josiah Macy Jr. foundation, 1951.*

SHOLL, D. A. *The organization of the cerebral cortex.* London: Methuen, 1956.

SIEGEL, S. *See* Davidson, Suppes and Siegel, 1957.

SKAGGS, E. B. Personalistic psychology as a science. *Psychol. Rev.,* 1945, **52,** 234–240.

SKINNER, B. F. The generic nature of the concepts of stimulus and response. *J. gen. Psychol.,* 1935, **12,** 40–65.

SKINNER, B. F. *The behavior of organisms: an experimental approach.* New York: Appleton-Century-Crofts, 1938.

SKINNER, B. F. Card guessing experiments. *Amer. Sci.,* 1948, **36,** 456–458.

SKINNER, B. F. Are theories of learning necessary? *Psychol. Rev.,* 1950, **57,** 193–216.

SKINNER, B. F. *Science and human behavior.* New York: Macmillan, 1953.

SMART, J. J. C. The reality of theoretical entities. *Austral. J. Philos.,* 1956, **34,** 1–12.

SMART, J. J. C. Sensations and brain processes. *Philos. Rev.,* 1959, **68,** 141–156.

SMART, J. J. C. *Philosophy and scientific realism.* London: Routledge, 1963.

SNYGG, D. and COMBS, W. W. *Individual behavior.* New York: Harper & Row, 1949; revised edition, 1959.

SPENCE, K. W. *See* Bergmann and Spence, 1941.

SPENCE, K. W. *See* Bergmann and Spence, 1944.

SPENCE, K. W. *Behavior theory and conditioning.* New Haven: Yale University Press, 1956.

SPERRY, R. W. Neurology and the mind-body problem. *Amer. Sci.,* 1952, **40,** 291–312.

SPIEGELBERG, H. *The phenomenological movement.* 2 Vols. The Hague: Martinus Nijhoff, 1960.

SPINOZA, B. *Ethics* (translated by A. Boyle) London: Dent, 1910.

STACE, W. T. Metaphysics and meaning. *Mind,* 1935, **44,** 417–438.

STEBBING, L. S. The a priori. *Proc. Arist. Soc. Suppl.,* 1933, **12,** 178–197.

STEBBING, L. S. *A modern introduction to logic.* (6th edition) London: Methuen, 1948.

STEVENS, S. S. The operational basis of psychology. *Amer. J. Psychol.,* 1935, **47,** 323–330.

STEVENS, S. S. The operational definition of psychological concepts. *Psychol. Rev.,* 1935, **42,** 517–527.

STEVENS, S. S. Psychology and the science of science. *Psychol. Bull.,* 1939, **36,** 221–263.

STEVENS, S. S. Mathematics, measurement, and psychophysics. In S. S. Stevens (editor), *Handbook of experimental psychology.* New York: Wiley, 1951.

STEVENS, S. S. The direct estimate of loudness. *Amer. J. Psychol.,* 1956, **69,** 1–25.

STEVENS, S. S. Measurement, psychophysics, and utility. In C. W. Churchman and P. Ratoosh, (editors), *Measurement: definition and theories*. New York: Wiley, 1959.

STOUT, G. F. Phenomenalism. *Proc. Arist. Soc.*, 1938, **39**, 1–18.

STRATTON, G. M. Vision without inversion of the retinal image. *Psychol. Rev.*, 1897, **4**, 341–360, 463–481.

STRAWSON, P. F. *Introduction to logical theory*. London: Methuen, 1952.

SUPPES, P. *Introduction to logic*. Princeton: Van Nostrand, 1957.

SUPPES, P. *Axiomatic set theory*. Princeton: Van Nostrand, 1960.

SUPPES, P. A comparison of the meaning of models in mathematics and the empirical sciences. *Synthese*, 1960, **12**, 287–300. Also in H. Freudenthal (editor), *The concept and the role of model in mathematics and natural and social sciences*. Dordrecht: D. Reidel, 1961.

SUPPES, P. Models of data. In E. Nagel, P. Suppes, and A. Tarski (editors), *Logic, methodology and philosophy of science*. Stanford: Stanford University Press, 1962.

SUPPES, P. and ATKINSON, R. C. *Markov learning models for multipersonal interactions*. Stanford: Stanford University Press, 1960.

SUPPES, P. *See* Davidson, Suppes, and Siegel, 1957.

SUPPES, P. *See* Estes and Suppes, 1959.

SUPPES, P. *See* Luce and Suppes, 1965.


TARSKI, A. *Introduction to logic*. New York: Oxford University Press, 1941, 1946.

TARSKI, A. The semantic conception of truth. *Philos. Phenom. Res.*, 1944, **4**, 341–375. Also in H. Feigl and W. Sellars (editors), *Readings in philosophical analysis*. New York: Appleton-Century-Crofts, 1949.

TARSKI, A. *Logic, semantics and metamathematics*. Oxford: Clarendon Press, 1956.

TAYLOR, J. G. *The behavioral basis of perception*. New Haven: Yale University Press, 1962.

THOMAS, G. J. Neurophysiology of learning. *Annu. Rev. Psychol.*, 1962, **13**, 71–106.

THORNDIKE, E. L. and HERRICK, C. J. The origin of behavioristic theory and method. *J. animal Beh.*, 1915, **5**, 462–470.

TINBERGEN, N. *The study of instinct*. London: Oxford University Press, 1951.

TITCHENER, E. B. On "Psychology as the behaviorist views it." *Proc. Amer. Philos. Soc.*, 1914, **53**, 1–17.

TOLMAN, E. C. A new formula for behaviorism. *Psychol. Rev.*, 1922, **29**, 44–53.

TOLMAN, E. C. A behavioristic account of emotion. *Psychol. Rev.*, 1923, **50**, 217–227.

TOLMAN, E. C. *Purposive behavior in animals and man*. New York: Appleton-Century, 1932.

TOLMAN, E. C. Theories of learning. In F. A. Moss (editor), *Comparative psychology*. New York: Prentice-Hall, 1934.

TOLMAN, E. C. Operational behaviorism and current trends in psychology. *Proc. 25th Ann. Celebr. Inaug. Gr. Stud., Univ. So. Calif.,* 1936, 89–103. Also in M. Marx (editor), *Psychological theory.* New York: Macmillan, 1951.

TOLMAN, E. C. An operational analysis of demands. *Erkenntnis,* 1937, **6,** 383–392.

TOLMAN, E. C. Prediction of vicarious trial and error by means of the schematic sow-bug. *Psychol. Rev.,* 1939, **46,** 318–336.

TOLMAN, E. C. Cognitive maps in rats and men. *Psychol. Rev.,* 1948, **55,** 189–208.

TOLMAN, E. C. Principles of purposive behaviorism. In S. Koch (editor), *Psychology: a study of a science,* Vol. 2. New York: McGraw-Hill, 1959.

TOULMIN, S. *The philosophy of science.* London: Hutchinson, 1953.

TOULMIN, S. and GOODFIELD, J. *The fabric of the heavens.* London: Hutchinson, 1961.

TREISMAN, M. Psychological explanation: the 'private data' hypothesis. *Br. J. Philos. Sci.,* 1962, **13,** 130–143.

TURING, A. M. On computable numbers, with an application to the Entscheidung's problem. *Proc. London Math. Soc.,* 1937, **42,** 230–265; 1937, **43,** 544–546. Reprinted in M. Davis (editor), *The undecidable.* Hewlett, N.Y.: Raven Press, 1965.

TURING, A. M. Computing machinery and intelligence. *Mind,* 1950, **59,** 433–460. Reprinted as "Can a machine think?" in J. R. Newman (editor), *The world of mathematics,* Vol. 4. New York: Simon and Schuster, 1956.

URMSON, J. O. *Philosophical analysis.* London: Oxford University Press, 1956.

UTTLEY, A. M. The classification of signals in the nervous system. *EEG Clin. Neurophysiol.,* 1954, **6,** 479–494.

UTTLEY, A. M. The conditional probability of neural connexions. *Proc. Roy. Soc.,* 1955, **B144,** 229.

UTTLEY, A. M. Conditional probability machines and conditioned reflexes. *Automata Studies,* 253–275. Princeton: Princeton University Press, 1956.

VENN, J. *The logic of chance.* (original 1866) New York: Chelsea (4th edition), 1962.

VERPLANCK, W. S. Burrhus F. Skinner. In W. K. Estes and others, *Modern learning theory.* New York: Appleton-Century-Crofts, 1954.

VOEKS, V. W. Formalization and clarification of a theory of learning. *J. Psychol.,* 1950, **30,** 341–362.

WAISMANN, F. Verifiability. In A. G. N. Flew (editor), *Logic and language: first series.* Oxford: Blackwell, 1952.

WALD, A. *Statistical decision functions.* New York: Wiley, 1950.

WALKER, K. K. A critique of phenomenological theory. *Austr. J. Psychol.,* 1957, **9,** 97–104.

WALTER, W. G. *The living brain.* London: Duckworth, 1953.

WARNOCK, G. J. *English philosophy since 1900.* London: Oxford University Press, 1958.

WASHBURN, M. Introspection as an objective method. *Psychol. Rev.,* 1922, **29,** 89–112.

WATSON, J. B. Psychology as the behaviorist views it. *Psychol. Rev.,* 1913, **20,** 158–177.

WATSON, J. B. *Behavior: an introduction to comparative psychology.* New York: Henry Holt, 1914.

WATSON, J. B. *Psychology from the standpoint of a behaviorist.* Philadelphia: Lippincott, 1919, 1929(3).

WATSON, J. B. *Behaviorism.* New York: Norton, 1925, 1929.

WATSON, J. B. and McDOUGALL, W. *The battle of behaviorism.* London: Kegan Paul, 1928.

WATSON, W. H. *On understanding physics.* Cambridge: Cambridge University Press, 1938.

WEATHERBURN, C. E. *A first course in mathematical statistics.* (2nd edition) Cambridge: Cambridge University Press, 1957.

WEAVER, W. *See* Shannon and Weaver, 1949.

WEIDNER, R. T. and SELLS, R. L. *Elementary modern physics.* Boston: Allyn and Bacon, 1960.

WEINBERG, J. R. *An examination of logical positivism.* London: Kegan Paul, 1936.

WEISS, A. P. Relation between structural and behavioral psychology. *Psychol. Rev.,* 1917, **24,** 301–316.

WEISS, A. P. Relation between functional and behavior psychology. *Psychol. Rev.,* 1917, **24,** 353–368.

WEISS, A. P. One set of postulates for a behavioristic psychology. *Psychol. Rev.,* 1925, **32,** 83–87.

WEISS, L. *Statistical decision theory.* New York: McGraw-Hill, 1961.

WHITEHEAD, A. N. and RUSSELL, B. *Principia Mathematica,* 3 vols. Cambridge: Cambridge University Press, 1913.

WHITELEY, C. H. *An introduction to metaphysics.* London: Methuen, 1949.

WHORF, B. L. *Language, truth, and reality.* (J. B. Carroll, editor) New York: Wiley, 1956.

WIENER, N. *Cybernetics.* New York: Wiley, 1948.

WIENER, N. *See* Rosenbleuth and Wiener, 1945.

WILLIAMS, D. and others. A symposium on probability: parts I, II, III. *Philos. Phenom. Res.,* 1945, **5,** 449–532; 1946, **6,** 11–86; 590–622.

WILLIAMS, D. *The ground of induction.* Cambridge: Harvard University Press, 1947.

WINCH, P. *The idea of a social science.* London: Routledge, 1958.

WINDELBAND, W. *An introduction to philosophy.* (translated by J. McCabe) London: Unwin, 1921.

WISDOM, JOHN. Logical constructions: I–V. *Mind,* 1931, **40,** 188–216 (I); 460–475 (II); 1932, **41,** 441–464 (III); 1933, **42,** 43–66 (IV); 186–202 (V).

WISDOM, JOHN. *Other Minds.* Oxford: Blackwell, 1952.

WISDOM, JOHN. Metaphysics and verification. *Philosophy and psychoanalysis.* Oxford: Blackwell, 1953.

WISDOM, JOHN. *Philosophy and psychoanalysis.* Oxford: Blackwell, 1953.

WISDOM, J. O. *Foundations of inference in natural science.* London: Methuen, 1952.

WISDOM, J. O. Esotericism. *Philosophy,* 1959, **34,** 338–354.

WITTGENSTEIN, L. *Tractatus logico-philosophicus.* London: Routledge, 1922.

WITTGENSTEIN, L. *Philosophical investigations.* (translated by G. E. M. Anscombe) Oxford: Blackwell, 1953.

WOLFF, R. P. *Kant's theory of mental activity.* Cambridge: Harvard University Press, 1963.

WOODGER, J. H. *Biological principles.* London: Kegan Paul, 1929.

WOODGER, J. H. *Axiomatic method in biology.* Cambridge: Cambridge University Press, 1937.

WOODGER, J. H. *Language and biology.* Cambridge: Cambridge University Press, 1952.

WOODWORTH, R. S. *Psychology.* New York: Henry Holt, 1922 (1st edition); 1929 (2nd edition); 1935 (3rd edition); 1940 (4th edition); 1947 (5th edition); 1949 (6th edition). (1949 edition with D. Marquis.)

WOODWORTH, R. S. *Contemporary schools of psychology.* New York: Ronald Press, 1931.

WRIGHT, G. H. VON. *The logical problem of induction.* (2nd edition) New York: Macmillan, 1957.

WRIGHT, G. H. VON. Remarks on the epistemology of subjective probability. In E. Nagel, P. Suppes, and A. Tarski (editors), *Logic, methodology and philosophy of science.* Stanford: Stanford University Press, 1962.

WRINCH, D. *See* Jeffreys and Wrinch, 1919.


YAMAGUCHI, H. G. Superthreshold reaction potential (*sEr*) as a function of experimental extinction (N). *J. exp. Psychol.,* 1951, **41,** 391–400.

YOLTON, J. W. Philosophy and scientific explanation. *J. Philos.,* 1958, **55,** 133–143.

YOLTON, J. W. Explanation. *Br. J. Philos. Sci.,* 1959, **10,** 194–208.

YULE, G. U. and KENDALL, M. G. *An introduction to the theory of statistics.* (14th edition) London: Griffin, 1950.


ZABEEH, F. *Hume, precursor of modern empiricism.* The Hague: Martinus Nijhoff, 1960.

ZAVALA, A. *See* Gaito and Zavala, 1964.

ZEAMAN, D. An application of *sEr* quantification procedure. *Psychol. Rev.,* 1949, **56,** 341–350.

ZIPF, G. K. *The psycho-biology of language: an introduction to dynamic philosophy.* Boston: Houghton Mifflin, 1935.

ZIPF, G. K. *Human behavior and the principle of least effort; an introduction to human ecology.* Cambridge: Addison-Wesley, 1949.

# NAME INDEX

# SUBJECT INDEX